The Biochemistry of
Fruits and their Products

Volume 1

FOOD SCIENCE AND TECHNOLOGY

A SERIES OF MONOGRAPHS

Editorial Board

The Biochemistry of
Fruits and their Products

Edited by
A. C. HULME
A.R.C. Food Research Institute, Norwich, England

VOLUME 1
1970

ACADEMIC PRESS London and New York

ACADEMIC PRESS INC. (LONDON) LTD
Berkeley Square House
Berkeley Square
London, W1X 6BA

U.S. Edition published by

ACADEMIC PRESS INC.
111 Fifth Avenue
New York, New York 10003

Library of Congress Catalog Card Number: 77–117145
SBN: 12–361201–2

Printed in Great Britain by
Butler and Tanner Ltd, Frome and London

Contributors to Volume I

E. G. BOLLARD, Plant Diseases Division, Department of Scientific and Industrial Research, Auckland, New Zealand.

L. F. BURROUGHS, University of Bristol, Department of Agriculture and Horticulture, Research Station, Long Ashton, Bristol, England.

R. L. CLEMENTS, Institute of Nutrition, Ohio State University, Columbus, Ohio, U.S.A.

DAVID R. DILLEY, Department of Horticulture, Michigan State University, East Lansing, Michigan, U.S.A.

L. J. GOAD, Department of Biochemistry, University of Liverpool, Liverpool, England.

T. W. GOODWIN, Department of Biochemistry, University of Liverpool, Liverpool, England.

E. HANSEN, Department of Horticulture, Oregon State University, Corvallis, Oregon, U.S.A.

F. A. ISHERWOOD, A.R.C. Food Research Institute, Norwich, England.

W. B. McGLASSON, C.S.I.R.O., Division of Food Preservation, New South Wales, Australia.

L. W. MAPSON, A.R.C. Food Research Institute, Norwich, England.

P. MAZLIAK, Faculté des Sciences, Sorbonne, Paris, France.

D. F. MEIGH, A.R.C. Food Research Institute, Norwich, England.

J. P. NITSCH, Laboratoire de Physiologie Pluricellulaire, C.N.R.S., 91 Gif-sur-Yvette, France.

H. E. NURSTEN, The Procter Department of Food and Leather Science, The University, Leeds, England.

W. PILNIK, Department of Food Science, State Agricultural University, Wageningen, The Netherlands.

M. J. C. RHODES, A.R.C. Food Research Institute, Norwich, England.

R. ULRICH, Faculté des Sciences, Sorbonne, Paris, France.

J. VAN BUREN, New York State Agricultural Experiment Station (Cornell University), Geneva, New York, U.S.A.

A. G. J. VORAGEN, Department of Food Science, State Agricultural University, Wageningen, The Netherlands.

G. C. WHITING, University of Bristol, Department of Agriculture and Horticulture, Research Station, Long Ashton, Bristol, England.

B. G. WILKINSON, East Malling Research Station, Maidstone, England.

Preface

In a strictly botanical sense, "fruits"—the fertilized and developed ovaries of plants—cover a wide range of commodities from grain, through pulses to fleshy fruits. In this book, the word "fruit" is used in the strictly commercial sense so that even among the cucurbitaceae melons are dealt with but not marrows or squashes which are generally regarded commercially as vegetables. It was found impossible to cover all the fruits of commerce, and the most important from an economic standpoint have been chosen. The mango has been taken to represent tropical fruits since it is widely grown and consumed in its country of origin; other tropical fruits are coming more and more into the Western scene but they still form a small proportion of the total world fruit consumption.

Fruit becomes of particular interest to the industry as it approaches maturity, and the object of this book is primarily to deal with that aspect of the ontogeny of the fruit variously described as maturation, post-harvest physiology, senescence and storage rather than with the growth processes. Inevitably, however, the one cannot be adequately covered without some reference to the other. Concentration on maturation processes is no hardship for biochemists—some of the most exciting researches into senescence have, in recent years, centred around the biochemistry of maturing fruits.

Except in a few specific instances, little is known of the detailed biochemistry of fruit processing, while commercial practice in processing is well documented for many of the major fruits. Preservation by treatment with sugar remains one of the most important commercial methods, and this will be dealt with in a special book in the present series. The state of the "live" fruit before it is processed is of vital importance to the quality of the processed article, so that no apology is needed, even to the fruit technologist, for devoting most of this book to the raw material of processing.

The biochemistry of maturation and post-harvest behaviour has its roots in the early attempts made to extend the life of fresh fruits for the beleaguered populations in the First World War. The successes and failures of these practical experiments in storage led the various authorities involved to call in the scientist to provide a more logical basis for improving promising methods, and to attempt to eliminate the failures. The physiologists came first and established certain gross generalities of temperature and environment which could be related to storage behaviour. Out of this grew, in England, the use of "gas storage"—later called controlled atmosphere storage—for apples and pears. This also led to the establishment of critical control of temperature during the ripening and storage of such fruits as the banana and the tomato. Little further progress was possible so long as the details of intermediary metabolism were unknown. At this point the biochemist became involved, but in those early days he was handicapped, as were all plant biochemists, by the lack of suitable techniques. In fact, the fruit biochemist was particularly handicapped by the intractability of his material—high acidity, and, in many cases, the high content of phenolic compounds—which rendered difficult a study of enzyme-mediated processes.

The great advances, perhaps the most important of which was the development of chromatography in all its forms, in techniques available to the biochemist which took place during the Second World War and the years following, opened up the field to systematic study. In the past twenty years an ever-increasing stream of scientific papers on fruit biochemistry and physiology (the two cannot usefully be separated) has poured from laboratories all over the world, especially the United Kingdom, America and Australasia. Apart from review articles, no major books on the subject have appeared since the early ones, for example, "The Apple" by Smock, and "The Banana" by von Loeseke, and these, perforce, contain little biochemistry. It is felt that progress has been so rapid in the last two decades that the time is now ripe for a gathering together, in an integrated form, by experts actively working in the field, of the accumulated data on fruit biochemistry scattered throughout many of the world's scientific journals.

The fruit biochemist and physiologist will be most directly interested in this book, where he will find under one cover details of the principal constituents of fruits and their relations with one another, the results of investigations into the biochemical events occurring during critical stages in the maturation and senescence of different types of fruits and the similarities and differences they exhibit, the origins of colour and flavour, etc. Specific factors of a hormonal type, such as the effect of ethylene on the biochemical sequences of ripening, are of particular interest at the present time.

The book will also be of interest to plant biochemists generally, for the development and ripening of many fruits provides an insight into particular aspects of ageing which can be investigated over considerable periods under controlled conditions. The present volume deals mainly with the chemistry of the groups of compounds found in fruits with special reference to their specific role in the fruit metabolism. In Volume 2, the biochemistry and physiology of the more important fruits will be dealt with individually, together with aspects of commercial processing such as dehydration, freezing and juice production.

Finally, as the scope of fruit processing widens, those working in this field, whether in the laboratory or in the factory, will be greatly helped by a book to which they can refer for the latest information on the biochemical aspects of their raw material. Fruit growers themselves are becoming increasingly aware of the complexity of the factors affecting the quality of their crops, and the more enlightened of them are clamouring to learn more of the background to their successes and failures.

NORWICH   A. C. HULME
MAY, 1970

Acknowledgements

The Editor wishes to thank contributors for their patience and readiness to answer queries and to accept without complaint cuts and additions to their original manuscripts. It would be impossible to name all the people who have helped the production of this book by their suggestions and advice—the correspondence involved has been enormous—and he asks them to accept this general acknowledgement of their invaluable assistance. He would, however, like to thank especially Dr George Stewart for suggesting that the book should be written and for the enormous increase in the Editor's knowledge of fruits which the editing of the book has brought about.

Thanks are also due to Academic Press for the patience they have exercised over the various delays in getting the material to press and for the painstaking way in which they have redrawn many of the figures.

Finally, the Editor wishes to express his thanks to Drs Rhodes and Galliard and Mr Harkett for assistance with checking of proofs.

Contents

Part I   Constituents of Fruits

1. Sugars
G. C. WHITING

2. Hexosans, Pentosans and Gums
F. A. ISHERWOOD

3. Pectic Substances and other Uronides
W. PILNIK AND A. G. J. VORAGEN

4. Organic Acids
R. ULRICH

5. Amino Acids
L. F. Burroughs

6. Proteins
Elmer Hansen

7. Protein Patterns in Fruits
R. L. Clements

8. Enzymes
David R. Dilley

9. Lipids
P. Mazliak

Abbreviations

Å	Angstrom unit
ACP	acyl carrier protein
ADH	alcohol dehydrogenase
AIS	alcohol insoluble solids
AMP, ADP, ATP	adenosine-5'-mono, di-, and tri-phosphate
B9 (Alar)	N-dimethylaminosuccinamic acid
CA storage	controlled atmosphere storage ("gas" storage)
CCC	(2-chloroethyl)-trimethylammonium chloride
CH	cycloheximide
CMP, CDP, CTP	cytidine-5'-mono, di-, and tri-phosphate
CoA	co-enzyme A
2:4-D	2:4-dichlorophenoxyacetic acid
DAHP	3-deoxy-D-arabino-heptulosonic-7-phosphate
DEAE cellulose	diethylaminoethyl cellulose
DHA	dehydro-L-ascorbic acid
DIECA	diethyldithiocarbamate
DMSO	dimethylsulphoxide
DNA	deoxyribonucleic acid
DNP	2:4-dinitrophenol
$\overline{DP}$	degree of polymerization
DPT	diphosphothiamine
Dr.wt.	dry weight
EDTA	ethylenediaminetetraacetic acid
EMP	Embden-Meyerhof-Parnas pathway
Ethrel	2 chloroethylphosphonic acid
FAD	flavin-adenine dinucleotide
FMN	flavin mononucleotide
F-6-P	fructose-6-phosphate
F-1, 6-diP	fructose-1,6-diphosphate
Fr.wt.	fresh weight
GA_1–GA_9	gibberellic acids
GDP	guanosine-5'-diphosphate
GLC	gas-liquid chromatography
G-6-P	glucose-6-phosphate
HMP	hexose monophosphate pathway
IAA	indolyl-3-acetic acid
MAK	methylated albumen on Kieselguhr
MD	malate dehydrogenase

MDHA	mono-dehydroascorbic acid
ME	malic enzyme (NADP-malate dehydrogenase)
NAD, $NADH_2$	oxidized and reduced nicotinamide adenine dinucleotide
NADP, $NADPH_2$	oxidized and reduced nicotinamide adenine dinucleotide phosphate
NOA	naphthyl-2-oxy-acetic acid
OAA	oxalacetic acid
PATE	pectic acid-*trans*-eliminase
PD	pyruvate decarboxylase
PE	pectin esterase
PEP	phosphoenolpyruvate
PG	polygalacturonase
PGA	phosphoglyceric acid
PK	pyruvate kinase
PMG	polymethylgalacturonase
P/O ratio	ratio of micromoles inorganic phosphate esterified/microatoms oxygen absorbed
p.p.m.	parts per million
PPP	pentose phosphate pathway
PTE	pectin-*trans*-eliminase
PVP	polyvinylpyrrolidone
RNA	ribonucleic acid
m-RNA	messenger-RNA
t-RNA	transfer-RNA
RQ	respiratory quotient (CO_2 production/O_2 absorption)
SD	succinate dehydrogenase
2,4,5-T	2,4,5-trichlorophenoxyacetic acid
TCA cycle	Krebs tricarboxylic acid cycle
TLC	thin-layer chromatography
TMS	trimethylsilyl
TPP	thiamine pyrophosphate
TTC	triphenyltetrazolium chloride
UMP, UDP, UTP	uridine-5'-mono-, di-, and tri-phosphate
UDPG	uridine diphosphoglucose

Contents of Volume 2

To R. G. Tomkins in gratitude for many years
of encouragement and support

Part I

Constituents of Fruits

Chapter 1

Sugars

G. C. WHITING

Department of Agriculture and Horticulture, University af Bristol, England

I. INTRODUCTION

Fruits have long been valued by man for their attractive flavour, appearance and texture; in more recent years their vitamin content has become recognized as an important feature. In all these properties sugars, either in the free state or as derivatives, play an important role. Flavour is fundamentally the balance between sugar and acid and, in addition, specific flavour constituents are often glycosides; the attractive colours of many fruits are due to sugar derivatives of anthocyanidins; texture is governed by structural polysaccharides; and finally ascorbic acid (vitamin C) commonly considered to be a sugar derivative is found widely and sometimes abundantly in fruits.

In this chapter monosaccharides, their derivatives and oligosaccharides (defined as oligomers with a chain length of up to six sugar units) are described. Ascorbic acid (Chapter 13) and sugars which occur only in combination with phenolics (Chapter 6) are omitted.

II. SUGARS FOUND IN FRUITS

It is apparent from the flavours of different fruits that their sugar contents vary widely. At one end of the range the juice of the lime may contain no more than traces of sugar (Swisher and Higby, 1961); at the other extreme 61% of the fresh weight of the date consists of sugar (Biale, 1960). In most fruits the main storage material is sugar but in the avocado it consists of fat, and only 0·4% of sugar is present at normal harvest (Biale, 1960). Sugar contents of fruits of a particular species may vary considerably with the variety, soil and climatic conditions during their life on the plant. In addition, climacteric fruits in particular may show considerable changes in sugar content between harvesting and eating ripeness. The average total sugar contents together with minimum and maximum values for a number of commercial fruits are shown in Table I. Many of the earlier determinations and indeed many recent ones have been done by measuring total reducing sugars after inversion. The values in Table I are of this type, and as sugars other than glucose, fructose and sucrose are rarely present in more than very small amounts the values are close to the sum of these three sugars in terms of invert sugar. Most of the determinations were done on ripe fruit, but Biale's (1960) values are for fruit at normal harvest.

TABLE I. Sugar contents of fruits

| Fruit and variety | No. of samples | Sugars as per cent fresh weight[a] | | | Reference |
		Total sugars	Maximum value	Minimum value	
Apple, dessert	113	11·57	16·60	6·01	Money and Christian (1950)
Apple, culinary	75	9·64	13·05	5·34	Money and Christian (1950)
Apple, cider (juice)		12·5	21·0	8·5	Charley (1949a)
Apple, crab	9	12·66	14·10	11·60	Osborn (1964)
Apricot	92	6·05	11·85	1·57	Money and Christian (1950)
Avocado		0·4			Biale (1960)
Banana	62	18·0	21·7	11·4	Money (1958)
Blackberry, cultivated	46	4·49	10·42	2·41	Money and Christian (1950)
Blackberry, wild	24	5·01	7·60	1·70	Money and Christian (1950)
Blueberry	8	10·68			Eheart and Mason (1967)
Cherry, black	26	12·40	17·30	7·69	Money and Christian (1950)
Cherry, Morello	7	9·81	13·00	7·44	
Cherry, red	36	9·41	15·30	6·38	
Cherry, white	30	11·03	14·05	7·30	
Cranberry	4	4·31			Eheart and Mason (1967)
Currant, black	96	6·27	10·64	1·58	Money and Christian (1950)

Fruit and variety	No. of samples	Sugars as per cent fresh weight[a]			Reference
		Total sugars	Maximum value	Minimum value	
Currant, red	48	5·10	8·32	0·60	Money and Christian (1950)
Date		61·0			Biale (1960)
Dewberry	4	5·05			Eheart and Mason (1967)
Elderberry	2	7·81	7·86	7·75	Osborn (1964)
Feijoa		6·6			Biale (1960)
Fig, Kadota	3	15·9	18·2	13·1	Osborn (1964)
Gooseberry	118	4·58	10·25	1·98 ⎫	
Grape	25	14·81	18·91	9·58 ⎬	Money and Christian
Grapefruit	78	6·74	9·96	3·30 ⎭	(1950)
Guava	6	5·71	10·00	3·30	Osborn (1964)
Lemon	62	2·19	3·56	0·92	Money and Christian (1950)
Lime (juice)	13	0·72	1·74	0·00	Swisher and Higby (1961)
Loganberry	33	4·27	7·28	1·11	Money and Christian (1950)
Mango		14·0			Biale (1960)
Melon, cantaloupe	15	6·92		⎫	
Melon, honeydew	4	7·49		⎬	Eheart and Mason
Nectarine	8	7·91		⎭	(1967)
Olive	4	2·22	2·76	1·07	Sandret (1958)
Orange, bitter	36	5·49	9·43	3·85	Money and Christian (1950)
Orange, sweet	92	7·88	11·98	3·96	Money and Christian (1950)
Papaya		9·0			Biale, 1960
Passion fruit		10·0	13·3	7·4	Pruthi (1963)
Peach	13	8·45	11·70	6·32	Money and Christian (1950)
Pear	61	9·95	13·15	6·51	Money and Christian (1950)
Pear, perry, juice		11·90	14·98	10·56	Charley (1949b)
Persimmon		16·0			Biale (1960)
Pineapple	59	12·3	18·4	7·5	Money (1958)
Plum, green and yellow	36	7·59	13·32	2·91 ⎫	
Plum, red	122	7·40	13·40	2·28 ⎪	
Plum, blue	136	7·79	13·24	2·88 ⎬	Money and Christian
Plum, damson	22	8·51	13·84	5·58 ⎪	(1950)
Plum, greengage	86	8·49	14·47	4·05 ⎭	
Plum, Italian prune	5	9·94	13·7	8·07	Osborn (1964)
Quince	4	8·10	9·96	6·50	Osborn (1964)
Raspberry	372	4·46	8·67	1·74 ⎫	
Strawberry	533	5·65	9·81	2·81 ⎪	Money and Christian
Tangerine	10	9·15	11·36	6·94 ⎪	(1950)
Tomato	16	2·80	4·26	1·76 ⎭	

[a] Per cent fresh weight of edible portion

Values of Money (1958) and Money and Christian (1950) reproduced by permission

The average total sugar contents of many fruits lie in the region of 5–10%. Fruits preserved by drying (date, fig, raisin grape), those used in the production of alcoholic drinks (grape, cider apple, perry pear) and a few tropical fruits (pineapple, banana) contain higher amounts.

A. Monosaccharides

The numerous determinations of Strachan *et al.* (1951) on fruits grown in British Columbia give the ranges of reducing sugars present. The analyses were done in such a way as to avoid sucrose inversion, and their results together with those of other workers are shown in Table II. Since sucrose, a non-reducing sugar, is almost invariably the major oligosaccharide, the values for reducing sugars are a fairly accurate measure of total monosaccharides.

TABLE II. Reducing and non-reducing sugars of fruits

Fruit	No. of samples	Average sugar content as per cent of fresh weight[a]		Reference
		Reducing sugars	Sucrose	
Apple	53	8·37 (6·33–10·67)	3·06 (1·28–6·64)	Strachan *et al.* (1951)
Apricot	25	1·87 (1·17–2·71)	5·60 (2·73–7·67)	Strachan *et al.* (1951)
Blueberry	8	8·21	2·36	Eheart and Mason (1967)
Cherry	27	13·03 (9·26–17·56)	0·10 (0·00–0·63)	Strachan *et al.* (1951)
Dewberry	4	4·09	0·92	Eheart and Mason (1967)
Fig	4	14·90	1·05	Eheart and Mason (1967)
Grapefruit (juice)	3	4·13 (3·44–5·0)	2·19 (1·34–3·0)	Burdick (1961)
Lemon (juice)		1·67 (0·78–2·63)	0·18 (0·03–0·63)	Swisher and Higby (1961)
Lime (juice)		0·72 (0·0–1·74)[b]	0·14 (0·02–0·26)	Swisher and Higby (1961)
Mango	4	3·50	7·36	Eheart and Mason (1967)
Nectarine	8	2·50	5·14	Eheart and Mason (1967)
Orange (juice)		2·6–5·8	1·9–5·1	Veldhuis (1961)
Papaya	4	7·18	0·42	Eheart and Mason (1967)
Passion fruit		4·6 (3·6–8·3)	3·2 (2·3–7·9)	Pruthi (1963)
Peach	46	2·45 (1·96–3·17)	6·35 (4·94–7·93)⎫	
Pear	25	7·89 (6·27–10·01)	1·84 (1·03–4·73)⎬ Strachan *et al.* (1951)
Plum, Italian prune	7	4·65 (3·59–5·39)	5·39 (3·59–7·71)⎭	
Tangerine	4	2·49	3·80	Eheart and Mason (1967)

     [a] Results expressed as per cent by weight (as invert sugar) of fresh edible portion
     [b] Total sugars (as invert sugar)

The results of Strachan *et al.* (1951) were obtained over three seasons. The ranges in sugar content for certain varieties of apple were sometimes almost as great as the average range for all varieties.

These results are further discussed in Section IIB.1.

1. *Hexoses*

Prior to the introduction of the paper chromatographic technique, separation and identification of individual sugars in mixtures and their quantitative determination was tedious and difficult. However, adequate chemical methods were available for the determination of the main reducing sugars, glucose and fructose. Widdowson and McCance (1935) determined glucose,

TABLE III. Glucose, fructose and sucrose contents of fruits[a]

Fruit	Sugar content as per cent by weight of edible portion		
	Glucose	Fructose	Sucrose
Apple, dessert	1·72	6·08	3·62
Apple, culinary	1·82	5·01	2·40
Apricot	1·93	0·37	4·35
Banana	5·82	3·78	6·58
Blackberry	3·24	2·88	0·24
Cherry, dessert	4·70	7·24	0·0
Cherry, culinary	5·50	6·11	0·0
Cranberry	2·66	0·74	0·14
Currant, black	2·35	3·67	0·62
Currant, red	2·28	1·93	0·15
Currant, white	3·03	2·56	0·0
Date	32·00	23·70	8·20
Fig, green	5·54	4·00	0·0
Gooseberry	4·40	4·10	0·71
Grape, black	8·20	7·28	0·0
Grape, white	8·12	8·01	0·0
Grapefruit	1·95	1·24	2·14
Lemon (juice)	0·52	0·92	0·18
Loganberry	1·94	1·26	0·23
Melon, Cantaloupe	1·16	0·83	3·26
Melon, yellow	2·09	1·52	1·43
Mulberry	4·44	3·64	0·0
Orange (juice)	2·36	2·38	4·70
Peach	1·47	0·93	6·66
Pear, dessert	2·44	7·00	0·98
Pear, culinary	2·18	6·00	1·12
Pineapple	2·32	1·42	7·89
Plum, dessert	4·00	1·34	4·26
Plum, culinary	3·50	1·27	1·45
Plum, damson	5·22	3·42	0·96
Plum, greengage	5·00	2·60	4·16
Pomegranate (juice)	5·46	6·14	0·0
Raspberry	2·26	2·39	0·96
Strawberry	2·59	2·32	1·30
Tomato	1·63	1·17	0·0

[a] Reproduced with permission from Widdowson and McCance (1935)

fructose, sucrose and starch in a wide variety of fruits both grown locally and imported. Four to six samples of each fruit were obtained and determinations were done on the mixed samples. The values obtained for glucose, fructose and sucrose in 35 fruits are given in Table III.

In most fruits the glucose concentration exceeds that of fructose, occasionally the former is double the latter, while in cranberry, apricot and plum it is three to five times greater. Grape, blackberry, gooseberry, raspberry, strawberry, blueberry (Barker *et al.* 1963) and orange contain similar amounts of glucose and fructose. In the olive, fructose comprises 39–67% of reducing sugars (Sandret, 1958). Apples and pears are the main fruits in which fructose is present in amounts up to three times greater than glucose; in cider apples the relative proportion may be even greater as glucose comprises only 9–26·5% and fructose 91–73·5% of the reducing sugars (Charley, 1949a).

Hexoses other than glucose and fructose are rarely found in fruits and then usually in trace amounts only. The paper chromatographic technique has been applied to very many fruits, and most reports of sugars other than glucose, fructose and sucrose are qualitative only. The observations of different workers are sometimes not in agreement. This is not surprising in view of the masking effect of high concentrations of glucose and fructose. A varietal effect has been observed in some fruits for particular trace sugars (Wali and Hassan, 1965).

Mannose has been detected in the apple (Guichard, 1954), peach and orange (Genevois *et al.*, 1955), olive (Sandret, 1958), and in one pear variety (Wali and Hassan, 1965). Ash and Reynolds (1955a) however did not detect mannose in either the apple or the peach. Ash and Reynolds (1955a) reported the presence of galactose in pears and possibly in apples and peaches. Kliewer (1965b) was able to detect galactose in grapes which had a low glucose concentration. Galactose is present in olives (Sandret, 1958) and in the sapodilla (fruit of the Achras sapota) to the extent of 5·4% of the total sugars (Venkataraman and Reithel, 1958).

2. *Pentoses*

Arabinose has been detected in a number of fruits by Wali and Hassan (1965) including apple, quince, fig, pomegranate, lime, grapefruit, tangerine and in some varieties of grape, date, mango and guava. Other workers who have identified arabinose are Genevois *et al.* (1955) in the fig, Misra and Seshadri (1968) in guava and Guichard (1954) in the grape. Kliewer (1965b) detected no pentoses in a range of grape varieties. Xylose is well authenticated in fruits of the family Rosaceae, namely strawberry (Williams *et al.*, 1952), cherry, peach and strawberry (Genevois *et al.*, 1955), apricot, peach, pear and apple (Ash and Reynolds, 1955a), plum (0·1% of juice by weight), damson and quince (Hay and Pridham, 1953). Later, Hough and Pridham (1959) showed that the xylose present in Victoria plum was the D(+) isomer. Whiting and Coggins (1960a) found this isomer in cider apple juice in an average concentration of 0·05% (Whiting, 1961). Xylose has been found in olives (Sandret, 1958).

3. C_7, C_8 and C_9 sugars

The first longer-chain sugar to be found in fruits was D-manno-heptulose (perseulose) in the avocado (Laforge, 1917); a yield of 1·4% was obtained from the variety Trapp. Later work showed a considerable range of concentrations in Florida varieties varying from 0·2 to 5% of the wet weight of fruit pulp (Richtmyer, 1962). The avocado has been intensively studied as a source of longer-chain sugars; two other seven-carbon sugars have been isolated from avocado, namely D-talo-heptulose (Charlson and Richtmyer, 1960) and D-glycero-D-galacto-heptose (Sephton and Richtmyer, 1963a). In addition, two octuloses and two nonuloses have been isolated and identified, namely D-glycero-D-manno-octulose (Charlson and Richtmyer, 1960), D-glycero-L-galacto-octulose (Sephton and Richtmyer, 1963a), D-erythro-L-gluco-nonulose (Sephton and Richtmyer, 1963b) and D-erythro-L-galacto-nonulose (Sephton and Richtmyer, 1966). The first-mentioned octulose was obtained in a yield of 1 g from 27 kg of fruit pulp although the amount present varied with the variety.

Paper chromatographic examination has revealed the presence of heptuloses in Cantaloupe melon, Kadota fig, orange, strawberry, tomato and in the peel of grapefruit and orange (Williams *et al.*, 1952). Subsequently, two heptuloses present in the fir were identified as D-manno- and D-altro-heptulose (Bevenue *et al.*, 1961). These two heptuloses and one unknown heptulose, together with D-glycero-D-manno- and one unknown octulose, have been detected in fermented grape juice and it seems likely that all were present in the grape before fermentation (Esau and Amerine, 1966).

B. Oligosaccharides

1. *Disaccharides*

Sucrose is the main disaccharide present in fruits. Its concentration in fruits is often determined by the difference between the reducing sugar content before and after inversion. The ranges of sucrose concentration and average sucrose concentrations for a range of fruits are shown in Tables II and III. Although sucrose is the main sugar of translocation, only in a few fruits does its concentration exceed that of the total reducing sugars; these fruits include apricot, nectarine, peach, Italian prune, mango, Cantaloupe melon, pineapple and tangerine, while in the orange the two concentrations are similar. Some fruits contain extremely small amounts of sucrose, notably blueberry (Barker *et al.*, 1963), cherry, lime and lemon, white currant, green fig, grape, mulberry, pomegranate and tomato (Tables II and III). In the olive, sucrose comprises 9–33% of the total sugars (Sandret, 1958). The sucrose content of grapes varies with the species and variety; American varieties of *Vitis vinifera* contain 0·019–0·18% while Russian varieties have 0·2–1·5%; mature berries of *V. labrusca* and *V. rotundifolia* show a range of 0·2–5·0% (Kliewer, 1965b).

Disaccharides other than sucrose have rarely been reported; the sapodilla contains lactose and maltose which contribute 0·1% and 0·5% respectively of the total sugars (Venkataraman and Reithel, 1958). Kliewer (1965b) detected trace amounts of maltose and melibiose in the grape. Maltose constitutes 0·2% of the fresh weight of the banana (Poland *et al.*, 1937) and has been reported in the guava (Misra and Seshadri, 1968).

Using the paper chromatographic technique, Wali and Hassan (1965) could not detect sucrose in lime, grape (some varieties) or in pomegranate (some varieties); olives contained trace amounts. No maltose was found in any of the 18 species of fruit examined.

2. *Tri- and higher oligosaccharides*

Although many oligosaccharides occur in fruits, usually in small amounts, they have only occasionally been characterized. Both raffinose (α-D-galacto-pyranosyl-(1 → 6)-α-D-glucopyranosyl-(1 → 2) β-D-fructofuranoside) and stachrose (α-D-galactopyranosyl-(1 → 6)-α-D-galactopyranosyl-(1 → 6)-α-D-glucopyranosyl-(1 → 2)-β-D-fructofuranoside) have been detected in grapes, the former constituting 0·015 to 0·34% of fresh weight according to the variety (Kliewer, 1965b). Kliewer (1966) also showed the presence of the related manninotriose (α-D-galactopyranosyl-(1 → 6)-α-D-galactopyranosyl-(1 → 6)-α-D-glucopyranoside). Traces of raffinose have been detected in plums (Hough and Pridham, 1959), but it was not detected in any of the 18 species of fruit investigated by Wali and Hassan (1965). Sapodilla contains 6·4% of total sugars as uncharacterized oligosaccharides (Venkataraman and Reithel, 1958). Ripening bananas contain a trisaccharide thought to be 6G-β-fructosyl-sucrose (6-kestose) (Henderson *et al.*, 1959) but it has been suggested that a mixture of this trisaccharide with 1F-β-fructosyl-sucrose (1-kestose) may be present (Bacon, 1959). Fructose-containing oligosaccharides were reported in the apricot, peach, pear and apple by Ash and Reynolds (1955a). Apricots were found to contain a trisaccharide consisting of one glucose and two fructose residues; of the other oligosaccharides present, each in a concentration of less than 0·003% of the fresh weight, one contained glucose only, another consisted of fructose and a hexitol, and the remainder of fructose and glucose units (Ash and Reynolds, 1955b).

C. Sugar Derivatives

1. *Sugar acids*

D-Galacturonic acid is rarely found in the free state in sound fruit, but like D-xylose it does occur in some fruits of the family Rosaceae. In the juice of sound apples, Harris (1948) found 13–54 μg/ml depending upon the variety. Cider apples have been found to contain trace amounts, and where microbial attack has occurred galacturonic acid is accompanied by di-, tri- and higher oligogalacturonic acids (Whiting and Coggins, 1960b). It is possible that fruit which appears to be sound may be infected with small numbers of micro-organisms, sufficient to produce, from pectin breakdown, the trace amounts sometimes detected. McClendon *et al.* (1959) found traces in apples and tomatoes, 12 and 140 μg/g fresh weight respectively. Fresh sound strawberry juice contains 36–56 μg/g (Mills, 1953) and grape juice 0·1 g/litre (Schormuller and Clauss, 1966). Ash and Reynolds (1954) found that peaches and pears ripened at 20°C contained up to 350 μg/g fresh weight of galacturonic acid, but none was found in green or tree-ripened peaches or pears, nor in apples or apricots whether ripened at 20°C or tree-ripened.

D-Gluconic acid is found in traces in apples (Winkler, 1953) and cider apples (Whiting and Coggins, 1960b); grape juice contains amounts of less than 0·1 g/litre (Schormuller and Clauss, 1966).

Galactaric acid (mucic acid) has been isolated from ripe peaches and pears (100 mg from 2 kg of fruit) and probably occurs in apricots, black-berries and passion fruit (Anet and Reynolds, 1954). It has also been identi-fied in cider apples (Whiting and Coggins, 1960b) and in grapes, but only in those infected with *Botrytis* (Schormuller and Clauss, 1966).

D-Glucuronic acid has been stated to occur together with D-galacturonic acid in grape juices (Blouin and Peynaud, 1963 and Kliewer, 1966) but their presence may be the result of microbiological attack (Schormuller and Clauss, 1966). Glucuronic acid has been identified in detached strawberry fruit (Markakis and Embs, 1964). Although D-glucuronic acid is rare in the free state it is found as a constituent of many polysaccharides, e.g. plum fruit gum in which its 4-*O*-methyl derivative also occurs (Hough and Pridham, 1959).

L-Ascorbic acid together with dehydroascorbic acid is found in a wide range of fruits and is discussed in Chapter 13.

2. *Polyols*

(a) *Straight chain polyols.* There are few reports of the presence of the shorter chain members of this group in plant tissues. The olive is noteworthy in that it contains free glycerol (Sandret, 1958). Lewis and Smith (1967) believe that a search for free pentitols may well show them to be more wide-spread than is now apparent. Ribitol probably occurs universally in fruits in the form of its derivatives riboflavin, flavin mononucleotide and flavin adenine dinucleotide. Of the hexitols D-glucitol (sorbitol) is found in many fruits, notably those of the family Rosaceae (Strain, 1937). Strain found 0·2% in the loquat; contents in other fruits of this family are, apple 300–800 mg/100 ml of juice (Minsker, 1962); cherry pulp 14–82 g/litre with an average of 27·2 g/litre (Haeseler and Misselhorn, 1966); Conference pear 2–3% (Kidd *et al.*, 1940); perry-pear juice 1% to more than 5% w/v (Whiting, 1961); Victoria plum 5% of the dry weight (Rees, 1958); Kelsey plum 2·8% of the fresh weight (Donen, 1939). Ash and Reynolds (1955a) found D-glucitol in apricot, peach, pear and apple; in the last two-mentioned fruits its concentration approximated to that of sucrose. Reif (1934) detected sorbitol in apple, pear, quince, cherry, plum, peach, apricot, raisin, currant, sultana and dried date. Trace amounts (0–5·5 mg/100 ml) may occur in grape juice (Minsker, 1962). Although D-mannitol is found in many plant tissues it rarely occurs in fruits; seeds of melon contain 0·066% (Higgins and Dunker, 1945); unripe olives may contain more mannitol than total sugars, but the proportion is as low as 23% at ripeness, a decrease from 3·8 to 0·34% of fresh weight (Sandret, 1958).

The longer chain polyols D-glycero-D-galacto-heptitol (perseitol) and D-erythro-D-galacto-octitol have been isolated from the avocado. The former was obtained in 0·4% yield from the variety Trapp but the content varies with the variety (Montgomery and Hudson, 1939). The octitol was isolated with a yield of 1·2 g from 27 kg of ripe fruit (Charlson and Richtmyer, 1960).

(b) *Cyclic polyols.* Of this group of compounds, only myo-inositol (formerly known as meso-inositol) has been found in fruits. It is probably ubiquitous in plant tissues (Angyal and Anderson, 1959), and often occurs as its hexaphosphoric acid ester (phytate) in seeds. Although myo-inositol has frequently been tentatively identified by paper chromatographic means in fruits, e.g. in apricot, peach, pear and apple (Ash and Reynolds, 1955a), it has rarely been identified chemically; one such identification is in apricot (Ash and Reynolds, 1955b). Microbiological assay has been used for some fruits, particularly juices, as shown in Table IV.

TABLE IV. Myo-inositol content of fruits

Fruit	Content in mg/100 g of juice or edible portion	Reference
Orange (juice)	128–170	Krehl and Cowgill (1950)
Tangerine (juice)	135	Krehl and Cowgill (1950)
Grapefruit (juice)	88–112	Krehl and Cowgill (1950)
Lemon (juice)	56–76	Swisher and Higby (1961)
Apple (edible portion)	24	Esselen *et al.* (1947)

3. *Sugar phosphates*

These esters, active intermediates in sugar metabolism, are usually present in mature tissues in low concentrations only. Enzymatic methods have made possible their determination provided the extraction procedures employed rapidly inactivate phosphatases. D-Glucose-6-phosphate (G-6-P) is the ester found in the largest amounts, several times greater than that of D-fructose-6-phosphate (F-6-P); fructose-1,6-diphosphate (F-1,6-diP) is usually found in even lower concentrations. Contents of sugar phosphates have been determined only in a few fruits, mostly by Barker and his collaborators. Typical values for apple (Bramley's Seedling) are as follows: G-6-P 2·2, F-6-P 0·5 and F-1,6-diP 0·1 μmoles/100 g fresh weight (Barker and Khan, 1968).

4. *Glycosides*

Glycosides are derivatives of the cyclic forms of sugars in which the hydroxyl group attached to C-1 condenses with an alcohol or phenol group of another molecule. Oligo- and polysaccharides are, of course, built up by formation of such glycosidic linkages, but the term glycoside is normally used to describe compounds in which a sugar molecule is linked to a non-sugar molecule; the latter is the aglycone.

A very important class of glycosides, the phenolic glycosides, occur widely in fruits and many contain sugars not otherwise found in plant tissues. These are described in Chapter 6.

Cyanogenetic glycosides, in particular glycosides of mandelonitrile, the cyanohydrin of benzaldehyde, are found in a number of fruits. Amygdalin, D(-)-mandelonitrile-β-gentiobioside occurs in the seeds of apple, apricot, plum, peach, cherry, quince and damson (Hickinbottom *et al.*, 1956). Sambunigrin, L(+)-mandelonitrile-glucoside is a constituent of immature elderberries to which it imparts a bitter flavour (Baumann, 1958).

One sterol glycoside has been identified in fruits, β-sitosteryl-D-glucoside obtained in a yield of 0·0037% from the juice of Florida Valencia orange (Swift, 1952) and of 0·0058% from commercial dried grapefruit pulp (Ma and Schaffer, 1953).

The term glycoside extends to compounds in which N instead of O links the sugar residue and the aglycone. The N-D-ribosides and N-D-2-deoxyribosides of the purine and pyrimidine bases (nucleosides) are of fundamental importance as their diphosphate esters, the nucleotides.

5. *Sugar nucleotides*

In the sugar nucleotides, an ester linkage is formed between a sugar or sugar derivative and the terminal phosphate residue of a nucleoside-5'-diphosphate. The range of nucleosides found in plant sugar nucleotides includes uridine, guanosine, cytidine, adenosine, thymidine and 2-deoxyuridine; the commonest sugars found as nucleotide derivatives are glucose and galactose (Neufeld and Hassid, 1963). As these substances play an important part in sugar interconversions and synthesis of polysaccharides, they are no doubt widespread in fruits but only in trace amounts.

6. *Other sugar derivatives*

L-Rhamnose (6-deoxy-L-mannose) is a frequent constituent of glycosides but is rarely found free. It has been reported after fermentation of grape juice (Esau and Amerine, 1966) but may have been released by glycosidase action. 2-Deoxy-D-ribose was reported in the same wine.

D-Glucosamine (2-amino-2-deoxy-D-glucose) has been identified in grape juice; Deibner (1964) found 29·2 mg N per litre of juice of the variety Cinsault to be present as hexosamine. Both glucosamine and galactosamine have been obtained from plant tissues as their uridine diphosphate-N-acetyl derivatives but as yet these have not been found in fruits. Unripe guava fruits contain 0·1% of an unusual sugar ester which completely disappears as the fruits ripen. The two *cis* hydroxyl groups attached to C's 3 and 4 of the sugar molecule, L-arabinose, are esterified by the two carboxyl groups of hexa-hydroxydiphenic acid (Misra and Seshadri, 1968).

Olives contain two unusual sugar derivatives. The first is an ester of sucrose with oleuropeic acid (a monoterpenoid-carboxylic acid) and the second, oleur-opein, the bitter principle, which is a complex β-glucoside (Panizzi *et al.*, 1965).

III. CHANGES IN SUGARS DURING LIFE OF THE FRUIT

A. Changes During Growth

During the early stages of fruit growth the developing ovules are nurtured in part at least by the ovary and its ancillary parts, sepals, bracts and the receptacle. These are normally green and capable of photosynthesis. While the fruit is small these organs play an important part in its nutrition, but as the fruit grows, although the outer layer of cells may photosynthesize until maturity, the main source of nutrition is the leaf. Cell division in the young fruit may be complete in as little as three to four weeks for the apple, or may proceed up to maturity* as in the avocado. Cell extension continues up to maturity in all fruits (Biale, 1964).

The main sugar transported from the leaves to the fruits is sucrose, but other sugars or their derivatives are important for translocation in some plants; these include sugars of the raffinose family (Trip *et al.*, 1965), heptu-lose in the avocado (Davenport and Ellis, 1959) and D-glucitol (Lewis and Smith, 1967). In the apple it has been shown that ^{14}C labelled D-glucitol is

_____
* In this chapter maturity signifies normal harvest condition.

translocated from the leaves at a greater rate than sucrose, and the labelling rapidly appears in sugars, aminoacids and phloridzin (Williams *et al.*, 1967). While part of the sugar translocated to the young fruit is used for synthesis to pectic substances and other cell-wall materials, part is converted to the usual storage product, starch.

1. *Starch*

Starch is commonly found in the outermost cells of the fruit probably as the product of photosynthesis of these cells. Many young fruits, e.g. apple, pear, tomato, citrus fruits, mango and banana contain starch; in some fruits an initial increase in concentration is followed by a decrease while in others the concentration may increase up to maturity. Among the latter, climacteric fruits are prominent, e.g. banana (Biale, 1964), mango (Biale, 1960) and passion fruit (Pruthi, 1963), but in the plum, another climacteric fruit, very little starch is present from the immature to the mature stage where it may be completely absent (Rees, 1958).

2. *Sucrose*

No consistent patterns emerge from changes in sucrose concentration during growth and maturation with respect to the distinction between climacteric and non-climacteric fruits. Some climacteric fruits, e.g. apricot, peach (Deshpande and Salunkhe, 1964), mango (Biale, 1960) and passion fruit (Pruthi, 1963) show a high sucrose content at maturity. But while in apricot and peach sucrose increases in concentration during maturation, in passion fruit it shows a slight decrease. Other climacteric fruits, however, show very little or no sucrose during growth and maturation, e.g. tomato (Dalal *et al.*, 1965), while plum has none at the immature stage but shows a rapidly increasing content from the yellow to ripe stage (Rees, 1958). Apple and pear show an increasing sucrose concentration up to normal harvest (Hulme, 1958).

Among non-climacteric fruits, immature oranges have fairly high sucrose concentration but during maturation this decreases slightly (Sawyer, 1963). A similar trend occurs in grapefruit (Hilgeman and Smith, 1940). The sucrose content of pineapple increases rapidly during the last two months of maturation to a high value (Singleton and Gortner, 1965). In the cherry, sucrose is absent throughout growth and maturation (Constantinides and Bedford, 1964). Throughout the whole life of the grape both sucrose and raffinose concentrations are very low but reach their maxima at maturity (Kliewer, 1965b).

3. *Reducing sugars*

Reducing sugars often increase steadily throughout growth and maturation in both climacteric, e.g. tomato (Dalal *et al.*, 1965), passion fruit (Pruthi,

1963) and in non-climacteric fruit e.g. cherry (Constantinides and Bedford, 1964) and grape (Kliewer, 1965a). In cherry the proportion of glucose to fructose remains at 1·1 to 1·0 throughout maturation. Unripe grapes contain slightly more glucose than fructose but at over-ripeness the proportions are reversed. In certain climacteric fruits considerable changes in relative proportions may occur. In apples and pears, the glucose exceeds the fructose concentration during the early weeks of growth, then the glucose concentration remains constant and the fructose concentration increases up to and just after normal harvest (Hulme, 1958).

4. *Sugar derivatives*

D-Glucitol shows a steady concentration of 5% on a dry weight basis throughout growth and maturation in Victoria plum (Rees, 1958), but in the Kelsey plum, after an initial accumulation of 1% of the fresh weight, no further accumulation occurs until stone growth is complete and the reducing sugar concentration has become constant (Donen, 1939). Perseitol in the avocado reaches its maximum content at normal harvest (Davenport and Ellis, 1959). Free galacturonic acid remains at a steady concentration from the unripe to the ripe stage in Delicious apples, while in the tomato the concentration increases ten-fold from unripe to ripe condition (McClendon *et al.*, 1959).

B. Changes During Storage

In fruits of the non-climacteric type, harvest is normally either at ripeness or may be later. Such fruits show only slow steady changes in sugar content, hence harvest may be spread over a long period without loss of quality. Citrus fruits are of this type and the sugar content may show an initial increase on storage as a result of metabolism of cell-wall polysaccharides. In the orange, the concentrations of sugars in both the juice and the rind increase initially; subsequently the sugar content of the rind decreases. During storage of grapefruit similar changes occur (Biale, 1960).

Climacteric fruits on the other hand are picked prior to the onset of ripening and ripeness is attained only during, or just after, the climacteric rise in respiration. Changes in fruit colour and texture occur at the climacteric notably in the banana, mango and avocado. Almost complete hydrolysis of starch occurs in the banana and mango during ripening. In the former, approximately equal concentrations of glucose and fructose, together with a little sucrose, appear. After prolonged storage all three sugars decrease (Biale, 1960). The mango, on the other hand, shows a large increase in sucrose concentration, and a smaller proportion of reducing sugars as starch is hydrolysed. Later in storage, sucrose tends to disappear to be replaced by an equal amount of reducing sugars (Biale, 1960).

Initial hydrolysis of starch with the concomitant appearance of sucrose is seen in apples and pears; in apples, however, the increase in sucrose content is much greater than could be accounted for by hydrolysis of starch. Reducing sugars also increase initially and then decrease in apples, while in pears reducing sugars show less change (Hulme, 1958). The sucrose content of apricots and peaches shows little change on storage; reducing sugars in apricot decrease while in peach a decrease is followed by an increase (Deshpande and Salunkhe, 1964).

D-Glucitol in both plums (Donen, 1939) and pears is rapidly metabolized on storage; in pears, loss of D-glucitol is accompanied by an increase in fructose content (Kidd et al., 1940). In the apple, however, it seems likely that during low temperature storage fructose is reduced to D-glucitol (Fidler and North, 1968).

The 7-C compounds D-manno-heptulose and perseitol in avocado are both metabolized almost completely on storage (Davenport and Ellis, 1959).

Galacturonic acid increases very considerably from ripeness to over-ripeness in apple (McClendon et al., 1959), but tomatoes during storage show a small decrease in this constituent (Borenstein et al., 1955).

Sugar phosphates show variations in some fruits between the immature state and the climacteric state. The contents of the main sugar phosphates in three immature fruits are shown in Table V.

TABLE V. Sugar phosphate contents of immature fruits[a]

	Content in μ moles per 100 g fresh weight		
	Banana (green)	Tomato (green)	Apple (immature)
Glucose-6-phosphate	7·0	8·0	8·0
Fructose-6-phosphate	1·5	1·5	1·0
Fructose-1,6-diphosphate	0·05	0·03	0·11–0·17

[a] Reproduced with permission from Barker et al. (1962)

During the climacteric phase of banana the fructose-1,6-diphosphate content increased twenty times, while glucose-6-phosphate and fructose-6-phosphate increased only two or three times (Barker and Solomos, 1962). Apples, however, showed no such rise and pre-climacteric and climacteric fruits showed similar glucose-6-phosphate and fructose-1,6-diphosphate contents (Barker, 1968).

IV. METABOLISM

A. Embden-Meyerhof-Parnas and Hexose Monophosphate Pathways

Sucrose in most fruits is the carbohydrate source for biosynthesis and for the provision of energy. The two major pathways involved in both functions are the glycolytic Embden-Meyerhof-Parnas (EMP) and the oxidative Hexose Monophosphate (HMP) pathways. The former yields pyruvic acid which after oxidative decarboxylation to acetyl co-enzyme A is further metabolized by the citric acid cycle; these steps in pyruvic acid breakdown have been shown in the tomato by Doyle and Wang (1960). Large amounts of energy are made available and cycle intermediates may be utilized for biosynthesis. The HMP pathway may be used either for complete oxidation of sugars with formation of high energy phosphate or for the provision of biosynthetic intermediates. The early steps in the metabolism of sucrose are shown in Fig. 1.

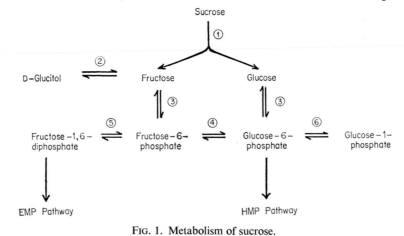

FIG. 1. Metabolism of sucrose.
(1) Invertase; (2) D-Glucitol dehydrogenase; (3) Hexokinase; (4) Glucose phosphate isomerase; (5) Phosphofructokinase; (6) Phosphoglucomutase.

Sucrose is hydrolysed by the commonly-occurring enzyme invertase (β-fructofuranosidase) to β-D-fructofuranose and α-D-glucopyranose. The furanose form of fructose changes to the pyranose form, the usual form of free fructose, before phosphorylation to fructose-6-phosphate. Fructose may also be formed from sorbitol, probably by the action of a NAD-dependent dehydrogenase, which has hitherto received little attention in plant tissues (Lewis and Smith, 1967). Fructose-6-phosphate is in equilibrium with glucose-6-phosphate, which is in turn in equilibrium with glucose-1-phosphate. The last-mentioned ester as we shall see later (Section IVB) is a key compound in sugar interconversions and syntheses; it may be formed also by the action of phosphorylase on starch. Glucose-6-phosphate is the first member of the chain of phosphate esters in the HMP pathway.

Fructose-6-phosphate after the virtually irreversible phosphorylation by phosphofructokinase to fructose-1,6-diphosphate (Wood, 1966) is metabolized by the EMP pathway. It is however possible that the latter compound may be hydrolysed to fructose-6-phosphate by the action of fructose diphosphatase, an enzyme which has been isolated from spinach leaves (Racker and Schroeder, 1958). This enzyme may be one means of controlling the amount of sugar phosphate metabolized by the EMP pathway.

1. *Embden–Meyerhof–Parnas pathway*

The sequence of events in this pathway is well-known and it is not proposed to detail them here. The main point of interest is one regarding the use of ^{14}C-labelled sugars in order to determine the relative proportions metabolized by the EMP and HMP routes. The calculation is complicated by the action in the former of triose phosphate isomerase. This enzyme interconverts glyceraldehyde-3-phosphate and dihydroxy-acetone phosphate. As a result, the ^{14}C-labelling of the triose phosphate derived from C's 1, 2 and 3 of glucose (and of fructose-1,6-diphosphate) randomizes with that from C's 6, 5 and 4 respectively as shown in Fig. 2.

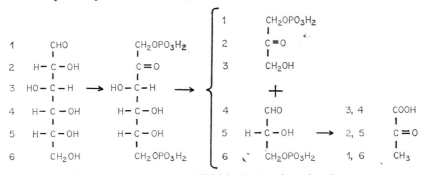

FIG. 2. Randomization of ^{14}C-labelling in triose phosphate.

In the EMP pathway therefore, CO_2 is released first from C's 3 and 4 of the original glucose. Subsequently, from reactions of the citric acid cycle, CO_2 is released from C's 2, 5, 1 and 6.

2. *The Hexose Monophosphate pathway*

This pathway oxidizes glucose-6-phosphate to 6-phosphogluconate which is oxidatively decarboxylated to ribulose-5-phosphate. Subsequent steps are shown in Fig. 3.

One molecule of D-xylulose-5-phosphate and one molecule of D-ribose-5-phosphate, each derived from D-ribulose-5-phosphate, react together the reaction being catalysed by transketolase. The products sedoheptulose-7-phosphate and glyceraldehyde-3-phosphate in a transaldolase-catalysed reaction yield D-erythrose-4-phosphate and fructose-6-phosphate.

In the complete oxidation of hexose phosphate, a third molecule of pentose phosphate and erythrose-4-phosphate undergo reaction, also catalysed by transketolase, with formation of D-glyceraldehyde-3-phosphate and fructose-6-phosphate; oxidation of three more molecules of hexose phosphate yields a

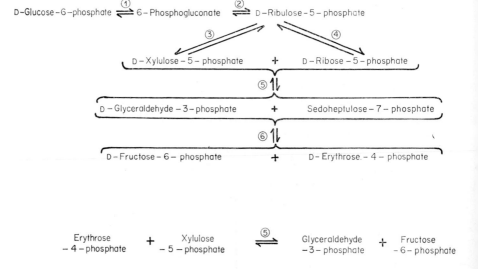

FIG. 3. Hexose Monophosphate pathway.
(1) Glucose-6-phosphate dehydrogenase; (2) 6-Phosphogluconate dehydrogenase; (3) D-Ribulose-5-phosphate-3-epimerase; (4) Ribose phosphate isomerase; (5) Transketolase; (6) Transaldolase.

second molecule of glyceraldehyde-3-phosphate, hence by triose-phosphate isomerase and aldolase action a molecule of fructose-1,6-diphosphate is formed. This synthesis involving transposition of ^{14}C labelling in hexoses from C-6 to C-1 and *vice versa* has been demonstrated in strawberry and tomato. In ripening strawberries the ^{14}C in specifically labelled glucose is redistributed in the hexose phosphate pool in such a way that 15% of the label rapidly appears in the other triose moiety of the sugar (Loewus and Jang, 1958). In the tomato, 20% of the ^{14}C at C-6 of gluconate is transposed to C-1 of glucose (Wang *et al.*, 1962). The net result is that six molecules of hexose phosphate yield five molecules of fructose phosphate, 12 $NADPH_2$ and 6 CO_2 (all from C-1 of the hexose). Alternatively, intermediates may be channelled to biosynthetic pathways, e.g. erythrose-4-phosphate to yield a precursor of shikimate for aromatic metabolism.

3. *Relative contributions of EMP and HMP pathways in fruits*

It is now generally accepted that both the major pathways play important roles in sugar metabolism, and it is of importance to determine their relative contributions during the whole life of the fruit. Three methods of attack have been used to try and solve this problem and these will be discussed.

(a) *Activities of enzymes associated with different pathways.* A number of fruits, particularly those of the climacteric type, have been used for this purpose. Tager and Biale (1957) found that both fructose-1,6-diphosphate aldolase and pyruvic acid decarboxylase showed very low activity in pre-climacteric bananas, but during the climacteric phase their activities increased greatly. They concluded that during the climacteric a shift occurred from the HMP to the EMP pathway. This work was criticized by Young (1965) who considered that their assays of enzymatic activity in the pre-climacteric fruit were low due to enzyme inactivation. A leuco-anthocyanin present in the latex cells of pre-climacteric tissue diffused readily on maceration and became adsorbed to cell-débris; in this state protein was bound and enzyme inactivation resulted. In post-climacteric tissue, however, the leuco-anthocyanin was non-diffusible and on maceration no enzyme inactivation occurred. Young was able to prevent adsorption of leuco-anthocyanins in macerated preclimacteric tissue, and enzyme inactivation was prevented. He then found that aldolase activity was the same in pre- and post-climacteric bananas, while the activities of hexokinase, phosphofructokinase and the dehydrogenases for glyceraldehyde phosphate, glucose-6-phosphate and 6-phosphogluconate were unchanged or decreased on ripening. It was therefore difficult to draw any conclusions concerning the relative importance of the two pathways as ripening occurred.

Hartmann (1966) using pears, observed that glucose-6-phosphate dehydrogenase activity diminished rapidly by 50% during maturation but remained substantial at senescence. Aldolase activity on the other hand was feeble at the start of maturation but increased parallel to respiration up to the climacteric peak and later decreased. Pyruvate decarboxylase showed a large increase up to the climacteric. It was concluded that the HMP pathway was active in pre-climacteric fruit but that glycolysis was important at the climacteric.

(b) *Use of enzyme inhibitors.* Iodoacetate and fluoride have been widely used in studies of sugar breakdown. Hartmann (1966) found that inhibition of the respiration of pear pulp caused by fluoride increased from 20% to 60% as the fruit passed from the pre-climacteric to the climacteric phase. This observation was in keeping with his conclusion from enzyme activities that a shift from the HMP to the EMP pathway took place at this time. It was pointed out, however, that fluoride is an inhibitor not only of enolase but also of succinate dehydrogenase.

(c) *Use of ^{14}C-labelled sugars.* This technique due to Bloom and Stetten (1953) is based on determinations of labelled $^{14}CO_2$ when two equal amounts of tissue metabolize equal amounts of glucose-1-^{14}C and glucose-6-^{14}C respectively. The initial CO_2 from the HMP pathway is entirely from C-1; that from the EMP pathway comes initially from C-3 and C-4 equally, later from C-2 and C-5 equally, and finally from C-1 and C-6 again equally. When yield of $^{14}CO_2$ from glucose-6-^{14}C/yield of $^{14}CO_2$ from glucose-1-^{14}C is unity, the glycolytic (EMP) is the pathway; when the ratio is less than unity the HMP pathway is active.

Hartmann (1966) applied this technique to apples and pears which had been stored at 0°C and then brought to 15°C. Labelled glucose was administered to the fruits and the ratio of $^{14}CO_2$ from ^{14}C-1/$^{14}CO_2$ from ^{14}C-6 was measured over two to three weeks. For pears the ratio decreased from 4·6 to 0·9 and for apples from 4·5 to 2·8 suggesting that the HMP pathway was being replaced by glycolysis. Barbour *et al.* (1958), using Bloom and Stetten's technique, demonstrated that an appreciable proportion of glucose was catabolized by the HMP pathway in tomato, lime and orange. Subsequently, after verification of a number of working assumptions (Doyle and Wang, 1960), Wang *et al.* (1962) elaborated the technique. The incorporation of ribose-1-^{14}C, gluconate-2-^{14}C and gluconate-6-^{14}C into the glucose of intact tomato fruit was studied. None of these compounds can be converted directly to glucose, and assuming that their phosphate esters behave like the corresponding intermediates of the HMP pathway it was possible to allow for the CO_2 formed from C-6 and C-3 and 4 of glucose after re-cycling. It was calculated that the EMP pathway accounted for 73% of glucose catabolized and the HMP pathway for 27%. The latter route was considered mainly to be a means of providing essential metabolic intermediates; excess hexose phosphate was catabolized via fructose-6-phosphate, fructose-1,6-diphosphate and the EMP pathway. Ramsey and Wang (1962) administered labelled glucose to mature green, medium ripe and full ripe tomatoes. A steadily increasing difference between the $^{14}CO_2$ from glucose-1-^{14}C and glucose-6-^{14}C indicated the increasing role of the HMP pathway.

The amounts of hexose phosphate metabolized by the two main pathways may be influenced by a number of factors. For example, the HMP pathway may be affected by the rate at which $NADPH_2$ is utilized or oxidized. Also particular enzymes of one pathway may be inhibited by intermediates of another pathway, for example glucose-6-phosphate isomerase is inhibited by 6-phosphogluconate (Parr, 1956). The inter-relations of sugars and acids are of considerable importance. While pyruvic acid formed in the EMP pathway can be utilized in biosynthesis of other acids the reverse process may occur. Drawert and Steffan (1966) investigated metabolism of ripening grapes using labelled sugars and acids. In the dark there was preferential formation of acids by fixation of CO_2, but labelled malic, acetic and glutamic acids all yielded some labelling in sugars. The same technique showed the conversion of acids into sugars during ripening of grapes.

4. *Other pathways of sugar metabolism*

While it is possible that other pathways may play some part in sugar catabolism, they are probably only of minor importance. A route known as the D-glucuronate-D-xylulose cycle is found in mammalian tissues: it does not involve phosphorylation of hexose. In a tentative scheme for plant tissues, D-glucose is directly oxidized to D-glucuronate, which is reduced to L-gulonate; oxidative decarboxylation then yields L-xylulose which gives D-xylulose via xylitol (Loewus *et al.*, 1958). The non-oxidative part of the HMP pathway completes the cycle. It seems more probable that the earlier steps go via uridine diphosphate (UDP) derivatives; in addition the type of change via xylitol is unknown in higher plants (Lewis and Smith, 1967). It is possible, however, that some steps in the cycle may be operative and yield precursors of L-ascorbic acid. In their work on tomato fruit Wang *et al.* (1962), found that a small fraction of the C-6 of glucuronate could yield CO_2, but they considered that probably less than 5% of glucose is catabolized by this route.

B. Interconversion of Monosaccharides and their Derivatives

In most fruits, sugars other than glucose, fructose and sucrose, are rarely found in the free state in more than very small amounts. A number of mechanisms occur for interconversions of sugars. Occasionally free sugars are involved but much more usually reactions proceed via phosphate esters or sugar-nucleotides.

1. *Simple sugars*

D-Xylose and D-ribose may be converted to D-xylulose and D-ribulose respectively by isomerases or perhaps by one and the same isomerase present in higher plant tissues (Pubols *et al.*, 1963). No direct kinases are known in these tissues for D-xylose and D-ribose. A kinase has however been described for D-xylulose and D-ribulose which probably yields their respective 5-phosphates (Zahnley and Axelrod, 1965). Other kinases found in higher plants, in addition to those related to the EMP and HMP pathways, have been described by Neufeld *et al.*; they yield the corresponding l-phosphates of the following: L-arabinose and D-galactose (1960), D-glucuronic acid (1959) and D-galacturonic acid (1961).

An unusual enzyme, probably a flavoprotein, is found in the juice sacs of young oranges and in a number of other citrus fruits. It catalyses the oxidation of D-glucose, D-galactose, D-mannose, 2-deoxy-D-glucose, D-xylose, cellobiose, lactose and maltose to the corresponding aldonic acid (Bean *et al.*, 1961).

D-Glucuronic and D-galacturonic acids are oxidized by mung bean seedlings to D-glucaric and galactaric acids respectively; at the same time D-glucuronic acid is partly converted to gluconic acid by an unknown mechanism (Kessler *et al.*, 1961). Ripening strawberries reduce the carbonyl group of D-glucuronolactone with the formation of L-gulonic acid (Loewus and Kelly, 1959).

2. *Sugar phosphates*

A number of isomerases and epimerases interconvert sugar phosphates for further metabolism by the EMP and HMP pathways. Those detected in higher plants include glucose phosphate isomerase (glucose-6-phosphate ⇌ fructose-6-phosphate) (Ramasarma and Giri, 1956), ribose phosphate isomerase (D-ribose-5-phosphate ⇌ D-ribulose-5-phosphate) (Srere *et al.*, 1955) and ribulose-5-phosphate-3-epimerase (D-xylulose-5-phosphate ⇌ D-ribulose-5-phosphate) (Hurwitz and Horecker, 1956).

Ribose-5-phosphate is a particularly important intermediate formed in the HMP pathway. Sable (1966) has suggested two non-oxidative schemes by means of which enzymes of this pathway form three molecules of ribose-5-phosphate from two molecules of hexose phosphate and one molecule of glyceraldehyde-3-phosphate. The interconversions D-fructose-6-phosphate ⇌ D-mannose-6-phosphate ⇌ D-mannose-1-phosphate are important as leading to the formation of guanosine-diphosphate-D-mannose for mannan biosynthesis (Ginsburg, 1964).

Longer-chain sugars may be formed directly by the HMP pathway (sedoheptulose) or by the action of aldolase, transaldolase or transketolase. Sephton and Richtmyer (1963a) obtained D-glycero-L-galacto-octulose from dihydroxyacetone phosphate and D-xylose in the presence of aldolase. They suggest that D-erythro-L-gluco- and D-erythro-L-galacto- nonuloses having the D-manno- and D-gluco- instead of the D-xylo- configurations in the corresponding portions in their molecules could be formed from dihydroxyacetone phosphate and the appropriate sugar (1966).

D-Glucosamine (2-amino-2-deoxy-D-glucose) is formed initially as its 6-phosphate ester by amination of D-fructose-6-phosphate with glutamine or asparagine as donor. In extracts of mung bean seedlings, acetyl-CoA reacts with the 6-phosphate to form the *N*-acetyl derivative. Mutase then brings about conversion to the 1-phosphate which with uridine triphosphate (UTP) and pyrophosphorylase forms UDP-*N*-acetyl-D-glucosamine (Mayer *et al.*, 1968).

An important conversion which occurs via phosphate esters is that of D-glucose to myo-inositol. The direct cyclization of glucose-6-phosphate to myo-inositol-l-phosphate was first demonstrated in yeast cells (Chen and Charalampous, 1965). Owing to the different conventions for numbering sugars and cyclitols, C-6 of glucose becomes C-1 of myo-inositol. Loewus (1963) showed that the same direct cyclization occurred in detached parsley leaves. The fact that further metabolism of myo-inositol may take place was shown by Loewus (1965). Administration of ^{14}C-labelled or tritiated myo-inositol to stalks of detached ripening strawberries resulted in oxidative cleavage between C-1 and C-6 giving D-glucuronic acid with the C atoms numbered as in the original glucose molecule. Before the further metabolism of D-glucuronic acid is described, it is convenient to outline the part played by sugar nucleotides in sugar interconversions.

3. *Sugar nucleotides*

Great advances both in our understanding of sugar inter-conversions and in oligo- and polysaccharide biosynthesis have stemmed from the discovery of uridine diphosphate-D-glucose by Cardini *et al.* (1950). This substance was first described as a co-factor in the conversion of D-galactose-1-phosphate to D-glucose-1-phosphate by a cell-free preparation from bakers' yeast. Subsequently Leloir (1951) showed that an enzyme present in *Saccharomyces fragilis* was able to interconvert uridine diphosphate-D-glucose (UDP-D-glucose) and uridine diphosphate-D-galactose. UDP-D-glucose was found to be formed from α-D-glucose-1-phosphate and uridine triphosphate by the action of an enzyme present in dialysed yeast macerate juice, namely uridyl transferase or UDP-D-glucose pyrophosphorylase (Munch-Petersen *et al.*, 1953). The reaction proceeds thus: UTP + D-glucose-1-phosphate $\rightleftharpoons$ UDP-D-glucose + inorganic pyrophosphate. This reaction is normally irreversible as the pyrophosphate formed is hydrolysed to orthophosphate in a strongly exergonic reaction: pyrophosphate + $H_2O \rightarrow$ 2-orthophosphate. A whole range of nucleotide-sugars are now known to be formed in plant tissues from the 1-phosphate esters of, for example, glucose, galactose, mannose, xylose, arabinose, galacturonic and glucuronic acids and the appropriate nucleoside triphosphate, e.g. uridine, deoxyuridine, adenosine, guanosine, thymidine and cytidine triphosphates (Barber, 1965). In addition, uridine diphosphate-D-fructose has been reported in plant tissues (Gonzalez and Pontis, 1963).

The nucleotide-sugars undergo a number of transformations the more important of which are as follows:

(i) Epimerization. The interconversion of UDP-D-glucose and UDP-D-galactose described above has been observed in the mung bean (Bourne *et al.*, 1965). It occurs also in other plants together with the following analogous reactions demonstrated by Feingold *et al.* (1960).

UDP-D-xylose $\rightleftharpoons$ UDP-L-arabinose.

UDP-D-glucuronic acid $\rightleftharpoons$ UDP-D-galacturonic acid.

(ii) Epimerization and reduction of UDP-D-glucose by an enzyme preparation from tobacco leaf together with reduced pyridine nucleotide yields UDP-L-rhamnose (Barber, 1963).

(iii) Oxidation of UDP-D-glucose, mediated by nicotinamide adenine dinucleotide together with an enzyme present in pea-seedlings, gives UDP-D-glucuronic acid (Strominger and Mapson, 1957).

(iv) Decarboxylation of UDP-D-glucuronic acid to UDP-D-xylose has been shown in mung bean extracts by Feingold *et al.* (1960). UDP-D-xylose is epimerized to UDP-L-arabinose; this is the method of formation of the latter as no enzyme is known to bring about decarboxylation of UDP-D-galacturonic acid to UDP-L-arabinose.

4. *Pathways to nucleotide-sugars*

From the work described above it is seen the UDP-D-glucuronic acid may be formed from D-glucose by two routes as shown in Fig. 4.

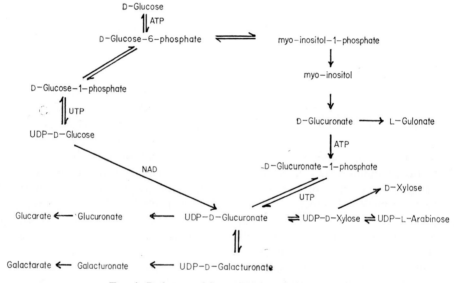

FIG. 4. Pathways of Sugar-Nucleotide formation.

This scheme is strongly supported by the work of Loewus (1965) mentioned in Section IVB 2. Labelled myo-inositol administered to detached ripening strawberries gave the greatest amount of labelling in the cell-wall polysaccharides, as shown in the D-galacturonyl, D-xylosyl and L-arabinosyl residues. D-Xylose and L-gulonate were also labelled and D-glucuronate was strongly labelled. Administration of D-glucuronate to the detached fruits gave a similar pattern of labelled compounds. It seems extremely probable that these added substrates were used for biosynthetic and not for respiratory purposes. This view is supported by the fact that when D-glucuronate, both universally labelled and labelled at C-6, was given to young wheat coleoptiles, label was rapidly incorporated into cell-wall polyuronides and xylans from the U-labelled glucuronate, but the whole of the labelled CO_2 was derived from C-6 (Slater and Beevers, 1958).

5. *Metabolism of glycosides*

Sugar nucleotides are the glycosyl donors in the formation of glycosides. The routes for biosynthesis of the phenolic glycosides are now well documented, but only more recently has the route for biosynthesis of the cyanogenetic glycosides become clearer. The precursors of the agylcone have been shown to be amino acids, the α and β C atoms and the N atom of which are retained intact (Uribe and Carr, 1966). There is now evidence that the steps are as follows: α-amino acid $\rightarrow$ aldoxime $\rightarrow$ nitrile $\rightarrow$ α-hydroxynitrile. The last-mentioned compound is then glucosylated with UDP-D-glucose (Hahlbrock *et al.*, 1968). The suggested scheme for amygdalin formation which requires a second UDP-D-glucose molecule is shown in Fig. 5.

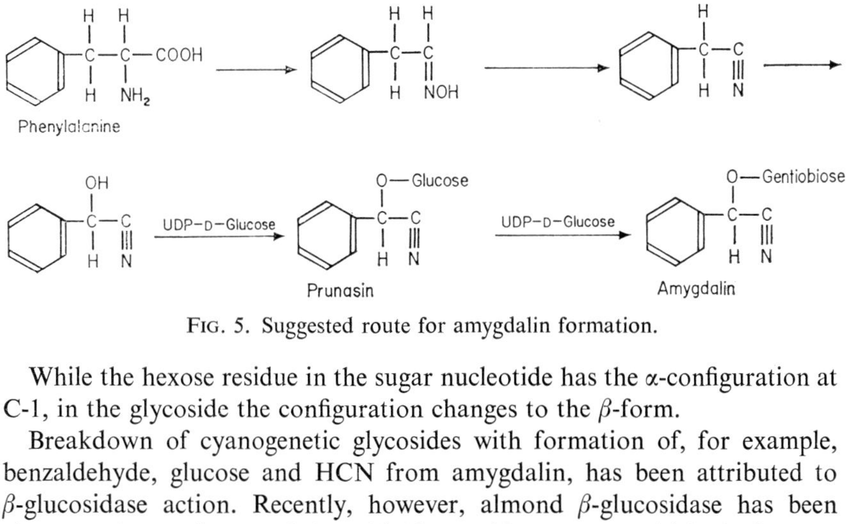

FIG. 5. Suggested route for amygdalin formation.

While the hexose residue in the sugar nucleotide has the α-configuration at C-1, in the glycoside the configuration changes to the β-form.

Breakdown of cyanogenetic glycosides with formation of, for example, benzaldehyde, glucose and HCN from amygdalin, has been attributed to β-glucosidase action. Recently, however, almond β-glucosidase has been shown to be a mixture of three highly specific enzymes which act in turn, namely amygdalin hydrolase, prunasin hydrolase and hydroxynitrile lyase (Haisman *et al.*, 1967).

C. Biosynthesis of Oligo- and Polysaccharides

In this section a brief account of the biosynthesis of oligo- and polysaccharides is given together with a mention of their breakdown. It must be remembered that in living plant tissues a dynamic equilibrium exists between cell-wall polysaccharides and the simple sugars of the cytoplasm and vacuole. Such an equilibrium has been demonstrated in growing seedlings by Nevins *et al.* (1968); no doubt it occurs also in fruits. Jermyn and Isherwood (1956), as a result of their work on changes in the constituents of pear cell-wall polysaccharides, suggested that polysaccharide synthesis and breakdown to monosaccharides were in dynamic equilibrium.

1. *Biosynthesis of oligosaccharides*

(a) *Sucrose.* Although sucrose is transported to the fruit during growth on the tree, it may be synthesized during storage (Section IIIB). Two methods have been suggested, both involving UDP-D-glucose. In the first (Cardini *et al.*, 1955), sucrose synthetase catalyses the reaction.

UDP-D-glucose + D-fructose ⇌ sucrose + UDP.

The second method (Leloir and Cardini, 1955) proceeds in two stages, first formation of sucrose phosphate, then its irreversible hydrolysis by a phosphatase.

UDP-D-glucose + D-fructose-6-phosphate ⇌ sucrose phosphate + UDP.

Sucrose phosphate → sucrose + inorganic phosphate. The second, two-stage biosynthesis, would appear more probable as the fructose moiety of sucrose is in the furanose form, but free fructose is mainly in the pyranose form, while fructose-6-phosphate is stable in the furanose form. Bean (1960) showed that in oranges and lemons, sucrose was most likely formed from sugars by reaction between UDP-D-glucose and fructose-phosphate followed by phosphatase hydrolysis of the sucrose phosphate.

It is possible that sucrose synthetase may act in the reverse direction to form UDP-D-glucose from sucrose for biosynthetic purposes. Milner and Avigad (1965) showed that not only uridine diphosphate but also other nucleoside diphosphates, namely, thymidine, adenosine, cytidine and guanosine diphosphates, may act as glucosyl acceptors in sucrose breakdown.

(b) *Raffinose, Stachyose.* Biosynthesis of raffinose has been shown to take place in an extract from *Vicia faba* seeds by transfer of the D-galactosyl residue of uridine diphosphate-D-galactose to sucrose (Bourne *et al.*, 1965). Although UDP-D-galactose may be formed from UTP and galactose-1-phosphate, it probably arises by epimerization of UDP-D-glucose.

UDP-D-galactose + sucrose ⇌ raffinose + UDP.

The higher members of the raffinose family of oligosaccharides appear to be built up by transfer of α-D-galactopyranosyl units from galactinol, *O*-α-D-galactopyranosyl-(1 → 1)-myo-inositol, rather than directly from UDP-D-galactose. Stachyose therefore is synthesized as follows:

UDP-D-galactose + myo-inositol ⇌ galactinol + UDP.

Galactinol + raffinose ⇌ stachyose + myo-inositol.

Kinetic studies suggest that, *in vivo*, galactinol may also act as galactosyl donor to sucrose with the formation of raffinose (Tanner and Kandler, 1968).

The raffinose family of oligosaccharides are hydrolysed by both invertase (β-fructofuranosidase) and α-glycosidases. Invertase removes the terminal fructofuranosyl unit, while α-glycosidase removes a galactopyranosyl unit at the other end of the chain. It seems likely that the origin of manninotroise and melibiose in fruits is the result of invertase action on stachyose and raffinose respectively.

(c) *Other oligosaccharides.* Fructose-containing oligosaccharides not belonging to the raffinose family may be synthesized by UDP-D-fructose acting as fructosyl donor. Lactose, maltose and other oligosaccharides are probably formed from the appropriate sugar acceptor and sugar nucleotide donor.

2. *Biosynthesis of polysaccharides*

Sugar nucleotides are all-important in the biosynthesis of polysaccharides. One sugar may form a range of different nucleotide derivatives but one may be specific for synthesis of a particular polysaccharide. For example, guanosine diphosphate-D-glucose is a specific glucosyl donor for cellulose formation, while ADP- and UDP-D-glucose act as starch precursors *in vitro* (Barber, 1965).

One interesting suggestion is that made by Loewus (1964, 1965) to the effect that methyl ethers of myo-inositol are the precursors of the methyl sugar derivatives of certain cell-wall polysaccharides, e.g. 2-*O*-methyl-D-glucose, 4-*O*-methyl-D-glucuronate and methyl-D-galacturonate. Methyl-D-galacturonate, the main unit of pectin, may arise as follows: myo-inositol → 1-*O*-methyl-myo-inositol → 6-*O*-methyl-D-glucuronate → 6-*O*-methyl-D-glucuronate nucleotide → 6-*O*-methyl-D-galacturonate nucleotide → pectin.

REFERENCES

Anet, E. F. L. J. and Reynolds, T. M. (1954). *Nature, Lond.* **174,** 930.

Angyal, S. J. and Anderson, L. (1959). *Adv. Carbohyd. Chem.* **14,** 135–212.

Ash, A. S. F. and Reynolds, T. M. (1954). *Aust. J. biol. Sci.* **7,** 435–43.

Ash, A. S. F. and Reynolds, T. M. (1955a). *Aust. J. Chem.* **8,** 276–9.

Ash, A. S. F. and Reynolds, T. M. (1955b). *Aust. J. Chem.* **8,** 444–50.

Bacon, J. S. D. (1959). *Biochem. J.* **73,** 507–14.

Barber, G. A. (1963). *Archs Biochem. Biophys.* **103,** 276–82.

Barber, G. A. (1965). *In* "Biosynthetic Pathways in Higher Plants" (J. B. Pridham and T. Swain, eds), pp. 117–21. Academic Press, London and New York.

Barbour, R. D., Buhler, D. R. and Wang, C. H. (1958). *Pl. Physiol., Lancaster* **33,** 396–400.

Barker, J. (1968). *New Phytol.* **67,** 213–17.

Barker, J. and Khan, M. A. A. (1968). *New Phytol.* **67,** 205–12.

Barker, J. and Solomos, T. (1962). *Nature, Lond.* **196,** 189.

Barker, J., Isherwood, F. A., Jakes, R., Solomos, T. and Younis, M. E. (1962). *Nature, Lond.* **196,** 1115.

Barker, W. G., Wood, F. A. and Collins, W. B. (1963). *Nature, Lond.* **198,** 810–11.

Baumann, J. (1958). *Flüssiges Obst* **25,** X/24-X/25.

Bean, R. C. (1960). *Pl. Physiol., Lancaster* **35,** 429–34.

Bean, R. C., Porter, G. G. and Steinberg, B. M. (1961). *J. biol. Chem.* **236,** 1235–40.

Bevenue, A., White, L. M., Secor, G. E. and Williams, K. T. (1961). *J. Ass. off. agric. Chem.* **44,** 265–6.

Biale, J. B. (1960). *Adv. Fd Res.* **10,** 293–354.

Biale, J. B. (1964). *Science, N.Y.* **146,** 880–8.

Bloom, B. and Stetten, D. (1953). *J. Am. chem. Soc.* **75,** 5446.

Blouin, J. and Peynaud, E. (1963). *C.r. Lébd Séanc. Acad. Sci., Paris* **256,** 4774–5.

Borenstein, B., Stier, E. F. and Ball, C. O. (1955). *J. Agric. Fd Chem.* **3,** 1041–4.

Bourne, E. J., Walter, M. W. and Pridham, J. B. (1965). *Biochem. J.* **97,** 802–6.

Burdick, E. M. (1961). *In* "Fruit and Vegetable Juice Processing Technology" (D. K. Tressler and M. A. Joslyn, eds), pp. 874–902. Avi Publishing Company Inc., Westport, Connecticut.

Cardini, C. E., Caputo, O., Paladini, A. C. and Leloir, L. F. (1950). *Nature, Lond.* **165,** 191–2.

Cardini, C. E., Leloir, L. F. and Chiriboga, J. (1955). *J. biol. Chem.* **214,** 149–55.

Charley, V. L. S. (1949a). *In* "The Principles and Practice of Cider-Making", p. 34. Leonard Hill Ltd, London.

Charley, V. L. S. (1949b). *In* "The Principles and Practice of Cider-Making", p. 312. Leonard Hill Ltd, London.

Charlson, A. J. and Richtmyer, N. K. (1960). *J. Am. chem. Soc.* **82,** 3428–34.

Chen, I. W. and Charalampous, F. C. (1965). *J. biol. Chem.* **240,** 3507–12.

Constantinides, S. M. and Bedford, C. L. (1964). *J. Fd Sci.* **29,** 804–7.

Dalal, K. B., Salunkhe, D. K., Boe, A. A. and Olson, L. E. (1965). *J. Fd Sci.* **30,** 504–8.

Davenport, J. B. and Ellis, S. C. (1959). *Aust. J. biol. Sci.* **12,** 445–54.

Deibner, L. (1964). *Revue Ferment. Ind. aliment.* **19,** 201–7.

Deshpande, P. B. and Salunkhe, D. K. (1964). *Fd Technol.,* **18,** 1195–1242.

Donen, I. (1939). *Biochem. J.* **33,** 1611–20.

Doyle, W. P. and Wang, C. H. (1960). *Pl. Physiol., Lancaster* **35,** 751–6.

Drawert, F. and Steffan, H. (1966). *Vitis,* **5,** 377–84.

Eheart, J. F. and Mason, B. S. (1967). *J. Am. diet. Ass.* **50,** 130–2.

Esau, P. and Amerine, M. A. (1966). *Am. J. Enol. Vitic.* 17, 265–7.

Esselen, W. B., Fellers, C. R. and Gutowska, M. S. (1947). *Bull. Mass. agric. Exp. Sta* 440.

Feingold, D. S., Neufeld, E. F. and Hassid, W. Z. (1960). *J. biol. Chem.* 235, 910–3.

Fidler, J. C. and North, C. J. (1968). *J. hort. Sci.* **43,** 429–39.

Genevois, L., Vitte, G. and Guichard, C. (1955). *C.r. Lébd Séanc, Acad. Sci., Paris* **240,** 1150–1.

Ginsberg, V. (1964). *Adv. Enzymol.* **26,** 35.

Gonzalez, N. S. and Pontis, H. G. (1963). *Biochim. biophys. Acta* **69,** 179–81.

Guichard, C. (1954). *Revue gén. Bot.* **61,** 16–65 and 86–127.

Haeseler, G. and Misselhorn, K. (1966). *Z. Lebensmittelunters. u.-Forsch.* **129,** 71–5.

Hahlbrock, K., Tapper, B. A., Butler, G. W. and Conn, E. E. (1968). *Archs Biochem. Biophys.* **125,** 1013–16.

Haisman, D. R., Knight, D. J. and Ellis, M. J. (1967). *Phytochemistry* **6**, 1501–5.
Hardy, P. J. (1968). *Pl. Physiol. Lancaster* **43**, 224–8.
Harris, T. H. (1948). *J. Ass. off. agric. Chem.* **31**, 501–7.
Hartmann, C. (1966). *Ann. Sci. Nat. Botan. Biol. Végétale* **7**, 131–214.
Hay, J. G. and Pridham, J. B. (1953). *Nature, Lond.* **172**, 207.
Henderson, R. W., Morton, R. K. and Rawlinson, W. A. (1959). *Biochem. J.* **72**, 340–344.
Hickinbottom, W. J., Garwood, R. F. and Ansell, M. F. (1956). *In* "Chemistry of Carbon Compounds" (E. H. Rodd ed.), Vol. IIIB pp. 871–954. Elsevier, Amsterdam.
Higgins, W. M. and Dunker, M. F. W. (1945). *J. Am. chem. Soc.* **67**, 153–4.
Hilgeman, R. H. and Smith, J. G. (1940). *Proc. Am. Soc. hort. Sci.* **37**, 535–8.
Hough, L. and Pridham, J. B. (1959). *Biochem. J.* **73**, 550–9.
Hulme, A. C. (1958). *Adv. Fd Res.* **8**, 297–413.
Hurwitz, J. and Horecker, B. L. (1956). *J. biol. Chem.* **223**, 993–1008.
Jermyn, M. A. and Isherwood, F. A. (1956). *Biochem. J.* **64**, 123–32.
Kessler, G., Neufeld, E. F., Feingold, D. S. and Hassid, W. Z. (1961). *J. biol. Chem.* **236**, 308–12.
Kidd, F., West, C., Griffiths, D. G. and Potter, N. A. (1940). *Ann. Bot.* **4**, 1–30.
Kliewer, W. M. (1965a). *Am. J. Enol. Vitic.* **16**, 101–10.
Kliewer, W. M. (1965b). *Am. J. Enol. Vitic.*, **16**, 168–78.
Kliewer, W. M. (1966). *Pl. Physiol. Lancaster* **41**, 923–31.
Krehl, W. A. and Cowgill, G. R. (1950). *J. Fd Sci.* **15**, 179–91.
Laforge, F. B. (1917). *J. biol. Chem.* **28**, 511–22.
Leloir, L. F. (1951). *Archs Biochem. Biophys.* **33**, 186–90.
Leloir, L. F. and Cardini, C. E. (1955). *J. biol. Chem.* **214**, 157–65.
Lewis, D. H. and Smith, D. C. (1967). *New Phytologist* **66**, 143–84.
Loewus, F. A. (1963). *Phytochemistry* **2**, 109–28.
Loewus, F. A. (1964). *Nature, Lond.* **203**, 1175–6.
Loewus, F. A. (1965). *Fedn Proc.* **24**, 855–62.
Loewus, F. A. and Jang, R. (1958). *J. biol. Chem.* **232**, 505–19.
Loewus, F. A. and Kelly, S. (1959). *Biochem. biophys. Res. Commun.* **1**, 143–6.
Loewus, F. A., Finkle, B. J. and Jang, R. (1958). *Biochim. biophys. Acta* **30**, 629–635.
Ma, R. M. and Schaffer, P. S. (1953). *Archs Biochem. Biophys.* **47**, 419–23.
Markakis, P. and Embs, R. J. (1964). *J. Fd Sci.* **29**, 629–30.
Mayer, F. C., Bikel, I. and Hassid, W. Z. (1968). *Pl. Physiol. Lancaster* **43**, 1097–1107.
McClendon, J. H., Woodmansee, C. W. and Somers, G. F. (1959). *Pl. Physiol. Lancaster* **34**, 389–91.
Mills, P. A. (1953). *J. Ass. off. agric. Chem.* **36**, 571–7.
Milner, Y. and Avigad, G. (1965). *Nature, Lond.* **206**, 825.
Minsker, F. C. (1962). *J. Ass. off. agric. Chem.* **45**, 562–4.
Misra, K. and Seshadri, T. R. (1968). *Phytochemistry* **7**, 641–5.
Money, R. W. (1958). *J. Sci. Fd Agric.* **9**, 18–20.
Money, R. W. and Christian, W. A. (1950). *J. Sci. Fd Agric.* **1**, 8–12.
Montgomery, E. M. and Hudson, C. S. (1939). *J. Am. chem. Soc.* **61**, 1654–8.
Munch-Petersen, A., Kalckar, H. M., Cutolo, E. and Smith, E. E. B. (1953). *Nature, Lond.* **172**, 1036–7.
Neufeld, E. F. and Hassid, W. Z. (1963). *Adv. Carbohyd. Chem.* **18**, 309–56.

Neufeld, E. F., Feingold, D. S. and Hassid, W. Z. (1959). *Archs Biochem. Biophys.* **83**, 96–100.

Neufeld, E. F., Feingold, D. S. and Hassid, W. Z. (1960). *J. biol. Chem.* **235**, 906–9.

Neufeld, E. F., Feingold, D. S. and Hassid, W. Z. (1961). *J. biol. Chem.* **236**, 3102–5.

Nevins, D. J., English, P. D. and Albersheim, P. (1968). *Pl. Physiol. Lancaster* **43**, 914–22.

Osborn, R. A. (1964). *J. Ass. off. agric. Chem.* **47**, 1068–86.

Panizzi, L., Scarpati, M. L. and Trogolo, C. (1965). *Gazz. chim. ital.* **95**, 1279–92.

Parr, C. W. (1956). *Nature, Lond.* **178**, 1401.

Poland, G. L., Von Loesecke, H., Brenner, M. W., Manion, J. T. and Harris, P. L. (1937). *Fd Res.* **2**, 403–7.

Pruthi, J. S. (1963). *Adv. Fd Res.* **12**, 203–82.

Pubols, M. H., Zahnley, J. C. and Axelrod, B. (1963). *Pl. Physiol. Lancaster* **38**, 457–61.

Racker, E. and Schroeder, E. A. R. (1958). *Archs Biochem. Biophys.* **74**, 326–344.

Ramasarma, T. and Giri, K. V. (1956). *Archs Biochem. Biophys.* **62**, 91–6.

Ramsey, J. C. and Wang, C. H. (1962). *Nature, Lond.* **193**, 800–1.

Rees, D. I. (1958). *J. Sci. Fd Agric.* **9**, 404–10.

Reif, G. (1934). *Z. Unters. Lebensmittel* **68**, 179–86.

Richtmyer, N. K. (1962). *In* "Methods in Carbohydrate Chemistry" Vol. 1 (R. L. Whistler and M. L. Wolfrom, eds), pp. 173–5. Academic Press, New York and London.

Sable, H. Z. (1966). *Adv. Enzymol.* **28**, 391–460.

Sandret, F. G. (1958). *Oléagineux* **13**, 459–64.

Sawyer, R. (1963). *J. Sci. Fd Agric.* **14**, 302–10.

Schormuller, J. and Clauss, W. (1966). *Z. Lebensmittelunters. u.-Forsch.* **133**, 65–72.

Sephton, H. H. and Richtmyer, N. K. (1963a). *J. org. Chem.* **28**, 1691–4.

Sephton, H. H. and Richtmyer, N. K. (1963b). *J. org. Chem.* **28**, 2388–90.

Sephton, H. H. and Richtmyer, N. K. (1966). *Carbohyd. Res.* **2**, 289–300.

Singleton, V. L. and Gortner, W. A. (1965). *J. Fd Sci.* **30**, 19–23.

Slater, W. G. and Beevers, H. (1958). *Pl. Physiol. Lancaster* **33**, 146–51.

Srere, P. A., Cooper, J. R., Klybas, V. and Racker, E. (1955). *Archs Biochem. Biophys.* **59**, 535–8.

Strachan, C. C., Moyls, A. W., Atkinson, F. E. and Britton, J. E. (1951). Dept. of Agriculture, Ottawa, Canada. Publication 862.

Strain, H. H. (1937). *J. Am. chem. Soc.* **59**, 2264–6.

Strominger, J. L. and Mapson, L. W. (1957). *Biochem. J.* **66**, 567–72.

Swift, L. J. (1952). *J. Am. chem. Soc.* **74**, 1099–1100.

Swisher, H. E. and Higby, W. K. (1961). *In* "Fruit and Vegetable Juice Processing Technology" (D. K. Tressler and M. A. Joslyn eds) pp. 903–32. Avi Publishing Company Inc. Westport, Connecticut.

Tager, J. M. and Biale, J. B. (1957). *Physiol. Plantarum* **10**, 79–85.

Tanner, W. and Kandler, O. (1968). *Eur. J. Biochem.* **4**, 233–9.

Trip, P., Nelson, C. D. and Krotkov, G. (1965). *Pl. Physiol. Lancaster* **40**, 740–7.

Uribe, E. G. and Conn, E. E. (1966). *J. biol. Chem.* **241**, 92–4.

Veldhuis, M. K. (1961). *In* "Fruit and Vegetable Juice Processing Technology" (D. K. Tressler and M. A. Joslyn, eds), pp. 838–73. Avi Publishing Company Inc., Westport, Connecticut.

Venkataraman, R. and Reithel, F. J. (1958). *Archs Biochem. Biophys.* **75**, 443–52.

Wali, Y. A. and Hassan, Y. M. (1965). *Proc. Am. Soc. hort. Sci.* **87,** 264–9.

Wang, C. H., Doyle, W. P. and Ramsey, J. C. (1962). *Pl. Physiol., Lancaster* **37,** 1–7.

Whiting, G. C. (1961). Ann. Rept (1960), Long Ashton Res. Sta. 135–9.

Whiting, G. C. and Coggins, R. A. (1960a). *Nature, Lond.* **185,** 843–4.

Whiting, G. C. and Coggins, R. A. (1960b). *J. Sci. Fd Agric.* **11,** 337–44.

Widdowson, E. M. and McCance, R. A. (1935). *Biochem. J.* **29,** 151–6.

Williams, K. T., Potter, E. F. and Bevenue, A. (1952). *J. Ass. off. agric. Chem.* **35,** 483–6.

Williams, M. W., Martin, G. C. and Stahly, E. A. (1967). *Proc. Am. Soc. hort. Sci.* **90,** 20–4.

Winkler, W. O. (1953). J. Ass. off. agric. Chem. **36,** 577–8.

Wood, W. A. (1966). *A. Rev. Biochem.* **35,** 521–58.

Young, R. E. (1965). *Archs Biochem. Biophys.* **111,** 174–80.

Zahnley, J. C. and Axelrod, B. (1965). *Pl. Physiol. Lancaster* **40,** 372–8.

Chapter 2

Hexosans, Pentosans and Gums

F. A. ISHERWOOD

A.R.C. Food Research Institute, Norwich, England

I. INTRODUCTION

The emphasis in the present article is on those polysaccharides either in the cell wall or in the cell sap which are not specifically included in the term "pectin". However, since recent work on the structure of pectin (Barrett and Northcote, 1965) and other polysaccharides accompanying it in the cell wall has shown that it is not possible to make a sharp distinction between the two groups, some description of the pectic substances is given in order to cover the subject properly. The idea behind the original request for an article describing the non-pectic polysaccharides was based on the hypothesis that only homopolysaccharides were present and that pectic acid was the poly-uronide homopolysaccharide. The early work (Hirst and Jones, 1939) on pectin supported this hypothesis and suggested that three homopolysac-charides were present, a galactan, an arabinan and a galacturanan, but later work has not confirmed this simple picture. Attempts to separate the homo-polysaccharides from material extracted from the cell wall under milder conditions than those used by the earlier workers have been unsuccessful (McCready and Gee, 1960) and it now appears that the pectic substances are much more complex than had been supposed. The same is probably true of the other polysaccharides. Partial acid hydrolysis of various polysaccharide fractions from the cell wall has yielded oligosaccharides which contained more than one sugar (Aspinall and Fanshawe, 1961) which indicated that

33

heteropolymers were present. The galactan and the arabinan isolated in the earlier work may have been artefacts produced by the method of isolation. The preparation of arabinan from sugar beet tissue required treatment at 100°C with a large volume of calcium hydroxide and this is known to degrade the pectic acid. The isolated arabinan was soluble in 70% ethanol but arabinan could not be extracted from fresh sugar beet tissue with 70% ethanol. The present position seems to be that the polysaccharides in the cell wall are for the most part highly complex, but that during extraction by any of the usual methods degradation occurs and sub-units are produced. The degradation could be caused either by enzymic or chemical attack. This does not rule out the possibility that homopolysaccharides may be present in some cases (cf. isolation of arabinan from mustard seed by Hirst, Rees and Richardson, 1965).

In the field of polysaccharide chemistry, the most urgent need is for the development of methods for the assessment of the physical and chemical heterogenity of the various polysaccharide fractions and for the fractionation on a preparative scale of closely related molecular species (Aspinall, 1959). Even with the latest techniques an exact structure of a heteropolysaccharide from the plant cell wall has yet to be fully established. The chemist obtains a statistical picture of the polysaccharide but not a true view of the whole, and our knowledge of the three-dimensional structure is nothing like as exact as that of proteins.

An additional complication in studying the polysaccharides of the cell wall is that they can form compounds with non-carbohydrate compounds. Lignin has been reported as being present in the cellulose fraction from cranberry pulp (Bennett, 1956), and compounds of polysaccharides with lignin may well be present. Such compounds have been isolated from wood meal by extraction with a variety of reagents and there seems no doubt that the polysaccharide and the lignin are bound together by a covalent link. Similarly, polysaccharides containing amino acids, particularly the unusual one hydroxyproline, have been reported. A trichloroacetic acid—soluble mucopolysaccharide containing hydroxyproline—has been isolated from corn pericarp (Bundy et al., 1967), and such compounds may be present in fruit since the fruit pulp of Parkia biglobosa is known to contain hydroxy-proline (Lanza et al., 1962a, b). In the present article, the chemistry and biochemistry of the various isolated polysaccharides will be described, but if no detailed studies have been made of fruit polysaccharides the properties of analogous polysaccharides from other plant tissues will be described. The biosynthesis and enzymic degradation will also be outlined. The composition of the insoluble carbohydrates of some fruits in terms of their constituents is given in Table I. A more detailed analysis than this is not possible with the information available.

TABLE I. Composition of polysaccharides excluding pectic materials, typical of some fruit and fruit products

Fruit	Part of fruit examined	Fraction isolated	Sugars produced on total hydrolysis						Polysaccharide isolated	Reference
			Glucose	Galactose	Mannose	Arabinose	Xylose	Others		
Pear	Pulp, minus skin and core (Parenchyma) alcohol insoluble solid	Hemicellulose A	++	++		+	++	Rhamnose ⎫	Xylan	Jermyn and Isherwood (1956)
		B	++		++		++	⎬		
		α Cellulose	++			+	+	⎭	Cellulose	
Apple	As for pear	Hemicellulose A	++	++	++	++	++			Jowett et al. (1951)
		B	++	++		++	++			
		α Cellulose	++		++	++	+			
Cranberry	Pulp	α Cellulose	+	+		+	+			Bennett (1956)
Strawberry	Water insoluble polysaccharides		++	+	+	+	+	Rhamnose Fucose		Wade (1964)
Citron melons	Water insoluble polysaccharides		+	+	+	+	+			Boltaga and Smykova (1965)
Citrus	Alcohol insoluble solids of peel		+	+		+	+	Galacturonic acid		Ting and Deszyck (1961)
Bael (Aegle Marmelos)	Mucilaginous coating of seed and fruit			++		+		Rhamnose		Parikh et al. (1958)
Plum	Gum in fruit			+	+	+	+	Rhamnose Glucuronic acid		Hough and Pridham (1959)

Hemicellulose A Carbohydrate material extracted with N alkali
Hemicellulose B Carbohydrate material extracted with 4N alkali
α Cellulose Carbohydrate material insoluble in alkali

II. POLYSACCHARIDES OF CELL WALL OF FRUIT

A. Cellulose

The presence of this polysaccharide has usually been inferred by analogy with other plant materials. The polysaccharide has been isolated and characterized in very few cases, and the evidence for its presence depends upon the presence of a residue which is resistant to most extractants, is hydrolysed to glucose, is soluble in cuprammonium solution and gives a blue colour when the tissue is treated with iodine in potassium iodide solution followed by 60–70% sulphuric acid. However, a cellulose isolated from pear cell wall (Hirst *et al.*, 1949) has been shown to be identical with cotton cellulose. Hydrolysis with 72% sulphuric acid gave only D-glucose. Methylation in nitrogen gave a trimethyl derivative which on hydrolysis gave 2,3,6 tri-*O*-methyl D-glucose (90% of theory) and 0·6% of 2,3,4,6 tetra-*O*-methyl glucose. This corresponded to a chain length of 160 units. The chain length of the native cellulose was probably much larger because the drastic purification necessary to remove the other polysaccharides undoubtedly caused some degradation.

Most of the chemistry of cellulose has been carried out on material from the cotton plant and from wood, and the description that follows applies mostly to cellulose from these sources. The term α-cellulose occurs widely in the literature and describes the insoluble material isolated from plant tissues by the procedure designed by Cross and Bevan using 15·5% NaOH under controlled conditions. This description is unfortunate because insolubility has no necessary chemical basis and it is probably true that α-cellulose is a mixture of insoluble polysaccharides.

Purified cellulose can be prepared by mild treatment of the fibres of the cotton plant which contain 98% cellulose. Commercially, wood is the most important source of cellulose, but the isolation of the cellulose requires drastic treatment with hot alkali to remove most of the lignin, hemicellulose, gums and other components which accompany cellulose in native wood. Cellulose is the most abundant compound in plants. Chemical studies on the purified cellulose showed that a yield of 95·5% methyl α and β-D-glucosides could be obtained by methanolysis of cellulose derivatives and a yield of 90·7% of crystalline D-glucose by direct hydrolysis with 72% H_2SO_4. Enzymic hydrolysis with cellulase preparations made from the gut of the snail, *Helix pomatia*, gave 95% of D-glucose. It is clear that cellulose can be considered as a polyglucosan and that there is unlikely to be more than a small proportion of other substances present.

The position of the bonds that link the glucose molecules together to make the polymer has been determined by methylation studies in which all the free hydroxyls were substituted. On hydrolysis crystalline 2,3,6 tri-*O*-methyl

D-glucose was isolated in over 90% yield. Small amounts of 2,3,4,6 tetra-*O*-methyl D-glucose were found particularly if oxygen was not excluded during methylation. Methylation is an extremely vigorous reaction and considerable reduction in the size of the cellulose molecule may take place. The tetra-methyl sugar would normally arise from the non-reducing end group of a polysaccharide molecule. The high yield of the 2,3,6 tri-*O*-methyl sugar makes it probable that the polysaccharide is a linear (1→4) linked glucan. The alternative (1→5) linked structure is ruled out, since the polysaccharide does not show the acid lability of furanosides nor have any (1→5) linked oligo-saccharides been isolated on partial hydrolysis. The amount of the tetra-methyl sugar is a measure of the degree of polymerization ($\overline{DP}$) of the poly-saccharide and represents a minimum figure for the $\overline{DP}$ of the native poly-saccharide.

The configuration of the 1→4 linkages between the D-glucose units has been proved by the isolation of cellobiose octa-acetate by acetolysis of cellulose or cellulose triacetate. The yield obtained was about 50%. Cellobiose is a diglucosaccharide known to be β-D-(1→4) linked. Partial hydrolysis of cellulose gave a homologous series of higher saccharides, all β-D-(1→4) linked. No evidence of chain branching was found. This chemical evidence has been supported by optical rotation studies. The molecular rotation of a polymer should be a simple function of the sum of those of its components, and by use of the oligosaccharides mentioned above it was possible to com-pare the expected rotation of suitable cellulose derivatives, assuming uniform configuration of the inter-glucose bonds with the observed values. The results corresponded very well with the calculated values. Other methods have confirmed this picture. Cellulose is a linear polysaccharide (often referred to as a chain molecule) consisting of (1→4) β-D-glucopyranose units.

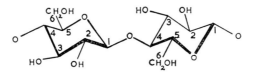

FIG. 1. β (1→4) glucopyranose glucan.

Cellulose reacts with one mole of periodate per component D-glucose unit, with scission of the C-2 to C-3 bond. No periodate-resistant residues are found which indicates that the molecule is unbranched.

In nature the chain molecules are arranged so as to form linear crystals or microfibrils. This is true of the cellulose in the plant cell wall and also when it is synthesized extra cellularly by strains of *Acetobacter*. Highly crystalline regions of the microfibrils or micelles may reach lengths of 600Å and have a diameter of 50–200Å. The length of the individual chains is probably very much longer than this. Cellulose is extremely insoluble in all ordinary solvents and it is probably true to say that any solubilization results in considerable depolymerization so that any estimates of the molecular weight by physical methods on the solution represent a minimum value. Cellulose will dissolve in solutions of cuprammonium hydroxide or cupriethylenediamine, and if oxygen is excluded these solutions can be used for the viscometric measurements of molecular weights; oxygen causes a rapid degradation of the dissolved polysaccharide. The average degree of polymerization ($\overline{DP}$) is at least 3000, and Ranby (1958) gives a maximum $\overline{DP}$ of 6000–8000 which corresponds to a chain length of 30,000–40,000Å and a molecular weight of more than a million. In the cell wall in the crystalline regions crystallographic analysis suggests (Meyer and Misch, 1937) that two extended cellulose chains pass, probably in opposite directions, through the unit cell along the longest axis and the cell itself contains one cellobiose unit from each chain. The cellobiose units are linked in one direction by hydrogen bonding and in the other by the much weaker van der Waals forces. The tensile strength of the fibre increases with increasing crystallinity, but at the same time the elasticity decreases. Aqueous solutions of salts which will break down hydrogen bonding will cause extensive swelling and may result in complete dispersion of the cellulose. The proportion of the cellulose in the crystalline and in the amorphous form is probably of considerable importance in explaining the difference in properties between the cellulose in the primary and secondary cell walls and also between the cellulose of different cells. This is relevant to the varying properties of the cell walls of fruits though it has been little studied. The general picture of the organization of the cell wall is that a number (100) of the cellulose chains possibly link together to form long thin crystallites (or elementary fibrils) shaped something like rulers. These are organized in groups of 10–20 to form microfibrils which are supposed to be flattish ribbons. These microfibrils are grouped to form macrofibrils up to $0.5 \, \mu m$ in diameter, and a large number of these macrofibrils form a fibre such as the cotton hair. This is the traditional view but may not be the only possibility. An alternative has been put forward by Manley. Examination (Manley, 1964) of microfibrils from Ramie cotton and *Valonia* has shown in general a beaded structure in negatively stained preparations, but when the beaded structure was absent sub-microfibrils of 35Å diameter were shown to be present in the microfibril (magnification 250,000 to 320,000). The recognition of these fine sub-microfibrils with their apparent periodicity of structure has prompted a suggestion that the chains of glucose units may be arranged in the form of a helix. The helix is 35Å wide and is made up of cellulose molecules running almost at right angles to the ribbon when unwound but parallel to its axis when in the helical form.

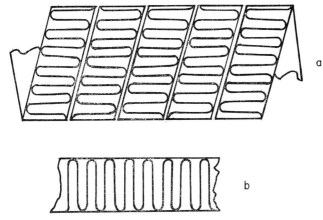

FIG. 2. Morphology of native cellulose submicrofibril. (a) Cellulose chain molecules in submicrofibril folded back and forth concertina fashion in a ribbon-like structure which is coiled into a tight helix. Two glucose residues (cellobiose units) to each fold, the direction of the main axis of which is parallel to the main axis of the helix. (b) Fragment of submicrofibril appears as an unfolded ribbon. Direction of cellobiose units at right angles to main axis of ribbon.

B. Hemicelluloses and Other Polysaccharides

The term "hemicellulose" was introduced by Schulze in 1891 and describes substances of carbohydrate nature extracted by alkali from the residue remaining after extraction of the plant tissue with hot and cold water. In more recent work, these substances are still isolated from the insoluble fraction from plant tissue by alkaline extraction, but after other extraction procedures have removed lignin and pectin. The most usual starting material for the preparation of hemicelluloses is the so called holocellulose fraction (Wise et al., 1946). Fresh plant material is disintegrated, extracted with suitable solvents to remove lipids, resins and phenols, then with water at pH 7 and finally with hot 0·5% aqueous ammonium oxalate to remove pectin. The lignin is removed by treatment with chlorite at pH 4·5 and it seems that this apparently drastic treatment has little degradative action on the polysaccharides. The white insoluble residue is called holocellulose.

Various alkaline reagents have been used to extract polysaccharides from the holocellulose but it seems that the amount removed is mainly dependent on the concentration of alkali up to 10–16%. Exclusion of oxygen is important because polysaccharides are degraded in alkaline solution in the presence of oxygen. Dimethyl sulphoxide (Hägglund et al., 1956) will extract hemicelluloses and is clearly less damaging.

Traditional thought suggested that the hemicellulose fraction originated in the cell wall. Recent evidence indicates that this may indeed be true. In some of the larger algae, the walls can be separated from the rest of the cell by gentle treatment, and if examined by the electron microscope show comparatively little structure. If extracted with alkali, a fibrous structure is revealed and the polysaccharides soluble in the alkali are similar to hemicelluloses. In the original cell walls it is probable that these were intimately associated with the fibres.

The chemistry of this group of polysaccharides is involved and it is difficult to classify them in a systematic manner. In the present article they have been grouped as follows: xylans, galactans, mannans, glucomannans and arabinogalactans.

1. *Xylans*

The hemicelluloses from citrus, tomato, apple and pear fruit contain polysaccharides which yield xylose on acid hydrolysis. In most cases the polysaccharide responsible has not been isolated and characterized. In the case of pear cell walls however (Chanda *et al.*, 1951), the polysaccharide was extracted and purified and its constitution shown to be that of a typical xylan with D-glucuronic acid residues linked directly to the xylan chain. It is therefore likely that xylans are present in the cell wall of many fruits since hydrolysis of the cell wall usually gives some xylose.

During the last decade, a large number of xylans from land plants have been examined and all have been shown to contain the same basal structure but to differ in the structural arrangement of the other sugar residues, especially the L-arabinose, the D-glucuronic acid and its 4-methylether, which are attached as side chains. The evidence for the basal structure in each of the polysaccharides is based either on the isolation of 2,3-di-*O*-methyl-D-xylose as a major product of hydrolysis of the methylated polysaccharide or on the isolation of 4-*O*-β-D-xylopyranosyl-D-xylopyranose and its polymer homologues as products of partial acid hydrolysis. 2,3-di-*O*-methyl-D-xylose could arise from methylated polysaccharides containing either $(1 \rightarrow 4)$ linked xylopyranose or $(1 \rightarrow 5)$ linked xylofuranose residues, but in view of the similarities in optical rotation and rates of hydrolysis of all the xylans with those for esparto xylan, which has been thoroughly characterized as a $(1 \rightarrow 4)$ linked xylopyranose polymer, it is probable they all have the same structure.

True xylans are rare though such a xylan has been prepared by repeated fractionation by means of the insoluble copper complex of the crude arabinoxylan fraction from esparto grass. It gives only D-xylose on hydrolysis, and it has been shown to be a chain of β-D-$(1 \rightarrow 4)$ linked D-xylopyranose units. It has a $\overline{\text{DP}}$ of about 75 and a single $(1 \rightarrow 3)$ branch point.

Differences between the various xylans arise from the presence or absence of branching in the backbone of xylose residues, variations in molecular size and in the amounts and linking of the other sugar residues to the xylan back-bone. The most common of the sugar residues are those of L-arabinofuranose (usually 1→3 linkage) and D-glucopyranosyluronic acid (usually 1→2 linkage) which are attached as single-unit side chains. Most of the polysaccharides are mixtures of closely related molecular species varying in molecular size and complexity. In the case of esparto grass, the hemicellulose fraction contains both a xylan free from other sugars and a highly branched arabinoxylan.

A summary of some of the data (Aspinall, 1959 and 1962) is given in Table II.

TABLE II. Structure of xylans

Source	Mode of linkage of other sugars to D-Xylopyranose backbone		
	L-Arabinofuranose end groups	D-Glucuronic acid end groups	Other structural features
Pear fruit cell wall	—	(1→3)	
Esparto grass	None	None	
Esparto grass	(1→3)	None	
Wheat straw	(1→3)	(1→3)	Branched xylan chain
Wheat straw	(1→3)	None	-4-D-Glu.p.1- 3
Wheat straw	None	(1→2)	
Wheat straw	(1→3)	(1→2) Me	Some branched xylan chains
Corn cobs (Maize)	(1→3)	—	-2-L-Arab.f.1-
Corn cobs (Maize)	(1→3)	(1→2) Me (1→4)	β-D-Xylo.p.(1→2)- -L-Arab.f.
Corn cobs (Maize)	(1→3)	None	-4-D-Glu.p.-1- 3

$p.$ = pyranose
$f.$ = furanose
Me indicates that D-glucuronic acid residues are present wholly or in part as the 4-methyl ether

Partly acetylated xylans have been isolated from birchwood by extraction with dimethyl sulphoxide, the acetyl being predominantly at C-3 of the D-xylopyranose units.

2. Arabinans, arabinogalactans and galactans

It has been suggested that pectic substances are complexes of three homo-polysaccharides, i.e. arabinan, galactan and galacturonan. The evidence for a separate arabinan and galactan is indirect since it is difficult to isolate a pure arabinan or galactan from the pectic complex. The arabinogalactan fraction isolated from apple fruit under very mild conditions could not be separated into two homopolysaccharides by zone electrophoresis though analytical ultra-centrifugation did suggest the presence of at least two components (Northcote, 1964). However, in the case of certain plant tissues which happen to be particularly rich sources of either arabinan or galactan, it has been possible to isolate the homopolysaccharide. The seeds of *Lupinus albus* are a rich source of galactan and a genuine galactan has been prepared from this material. Similarly a genuine arabinan has been isolated from white mustard cotyledons.

Apart from these polysaccharides the evidence for other polysaccharides based on arabinose and galactose particularly in the cell wall of fruits rests mainly on the presence of the sugars in the hydrolysis products of hemicellulose fractions extracted from the cell wall after the removal of the pectin fraction. Arabinogalactans corresponding to those isolated from the hemicellulose fraction of softwoods have not been prepared from fruit cell wall and therefore the structure of such arabinogalactans in the fruit cell wall must be deduced by analogy with those from softwood.

The galactan associated with the pectic complex prepared from *Lupinus alba* has a linear β-D-$(1\rightarrow4)$ linked molecule containing only galactopyranose residues. The $\overline{\text{DP}}$ is about 120. A similar galactan has been isolated from the seeds of *Strychnis nux-vomica*.

Two types of arabinan associated with the pectic complex appear to exist: the arabinan from white mustard which contains only arabinose and is isolated by a very mild treatment of the plant material and the arabinan from plant material like sugar beet which can only be extracted by comparatively drastic chemical methods. The latter arabinans are probably artefacts and usually contain substantial proportions of sugars other than arabinose. This is to be expected if they are formed as a result of a reaction in which the galacturan backbone of a larger molecule is split by β-elimination at some of the methyl esterified galacturonic acid units and the side chains of arabinose units released. Such side chains will be attached to fragments of the original chain. The arabinan formed in this way from sugar beet contained 5% galacturonic acid and 13·5% other sugars (Andrews *et al.*, 1959). Both types of arabinan are similar in structure, L-arabinose being the main sugar present. Structural studies indicate that the backbone of the molecule is a chain of α-L-$(1\rightarrow5)$ linked arabinofuranose residues with L-arabinofuranose residues α-L-$(1\rightarrow3)$ linked to it. The polysaccharides are highly branched and the fine structure varies a good deal with the source of the polysaccharide. The chemical evidence in general does not lead to a unique formula for the polysaccharide. The molecular weight of the arabinan from white mustard is about 6×10^3 and that produced by degradation of apple pectin 2×10^5. The latter may contain several "arabinan side chains" linked together by a fragment of the original backbone chain.

The hemicellulose fraction of softwoods contains in addition to polysaccharides based on a mannan chain (glucomannans), galactans which have L-arabinose substituent units; these are the arabinogalactans referred to earlier. The polysaccharides of this type are all highly branched and are built up mainly from (1→6) and (1→3) linked D-galactopyranose residues. The L-arabinose residues are an integral part of the structure and a considerable part is in the furanose form because gentle hydrolysis removes most of the L-arabinose. There is considerable uncertainty as to the homogeneity of these polysaccharides, especially those from larch woods, and more than one polysaccharide may be present. The polysaccharides from European larch and white spruce are typical of this group and have a basal structure composed of a backbone of β-D-(1→3) linked D-galactopyranose residues carrying side chains of two β-D-(1→6) linked D-galactopyranose residues. A considerable proportion of the L-arabinose occurs as 3-O-β-L-arabinopyranosyl-L-arabinofuranosyl groups attached to this basal structure. The structure of these arabinogalactans is quite different from that of the galactan associated with the pectic complex, for these are linked (1→3) or (1→6) whereas that from the pectic complex is (1→4).

3. *Mannans, glucomannans and galactomannans*

Hydrolysis of the cell wall of many fruits yields a mixture of sugars in which mannose is present. There is no direct evidence as to the presence in the cell wall of these fruits of polysaccharides containing mainly mannose, but it seems likely by analogy with observations on a variety of plant materials, e.g. seeds, corms and woody tissue, that such polysaccharides will be present. In coniferous woods glucomannans account for about half the hemicellulose fraction and, since in general they are less readily extracted with alkali than the xylans, can be partly separated from the xylan by taking advantage of the solubility difference. The proportion of D-glucose in these polysaccharides can range from nearly zero to about 30%. All the mannans and glucomannans from higher plants are similar in that they possess a basic structure which is made up of linear chains of mainly (1→4)-β-D-glucopyranose and β-D-mannopyranose residues. Where the disaccharide 4-O-β-D-glucopyranosyl-D-mannopyranose has been isolated as a product of partial acid hydrolysis it is clear that true glucomannans are present rather than mixtures of closely related mannans and glucans. The manner in which the D-mannose and D-glucose residues are arranged along the chain is not known. They may be present in a regular pattern or in a random distribution along the chain. The possibility of a small degree of branching and of anomalous α links cannot be excluded. The only polysaccharide of this group which appears to contain only mannose is that extracted from vegetable ivory (*Phytelephas macrocarpa*). This consists of two closely related compounds, mannan A, soluble in alkali and mannan B, which is separated from cellulose by precipitation from cuprammonium solution. Though both these polysaccharides contain over 95% of mannose there is evidence that a small proportion of D-galactose is present as non-reducing end groups. Molecular weight determinations give a $\overline{\text{DP}}$ of 17–21 and 80 respectively for mannans A and B.

Several other mannans and glucomannans contain D-galactose residues, and some glucomannans also contain small proportions of xylose residues. The galactose is definitely combined to the mannan because on partial hydrolysis (Norwegian spruce glucomannan) *O*-D-galactopyranosyl-(1→6)-*O*-β-D-mannopyranosyl-(1→4)-D-mannopyranose has been isolated. In the case of xylose, 6-*O*-α-D-xylopyranosyl-D-glucopyranose and *O*-α-D-xylo-pyranosyl-(1→6)-*O*-β-D-glucopyranosyl-(1→4)-D-glucopyranose have been isolated (by enzymic hydrolysis of jack pine glucomannan) which indicates the same is true for xylose (Aspinall, 1962). The presence of xylose is not due to incomplete removal of accompanying xylans.

4. α-Glucans

Apart from starch (amylose and amylopectin) there may be present a soluble polysaccharide which has been named phytoglycogen because of its structural similarity to the polysaccharide glycogen produced by animal tissues. It occurs in sweet corn. All these polysaccharides are based on chains of α-D-(1→4) linked glucopyranose units but with varying degrees of branching. Amylose is essentially a linear polymer while the others are highly branched, with α-D-(1→6) branch points. Plants store starch in starch granules, which vary in size from 3–100 μ in diameter and contain both amylose and amylo-pectin. Starch is often present in unripe fruit, disappearing as the fruit matures.

Amylose can be hydrolysed to yield D-glucose as the sole product in high yield. The fully methylated polysaccharide can be hydrolysed to give 2,3,6-tri-*O*-methyl-D-glucose in high yield together with a small quantity of 2,3,4,6-tetra-*O*-methyl-D-glucose. The α-D configuration is assigned to the glycoside linkages from the optical rotation and infra-red spectrum of the polysaccharide. These results indicate a linear α-D-(1→4) linked glucan. The small amount of tetra-methyl glucose arises from the non-reducing end group.

Estimates of the $\overline{\text{DP}}$ from these results gave low values (350) because some degradation occurred during the methylation procedure. Estimates based on the release of formic acid from the non-reducing end group on oxidation with periodate gave higher values (1000), and physical methods in general agree with this figure. In aqueous solution amylose readily associates which causes the polysaccharide to precipitate spontaneously ("retrogradation"). Amylose complexes very readily with certain alcohols to give highly crystalline compounds which separate from aqueous solution and provide a convenient method for separating amylose from amylopectin. Amylose gives with iodine a characteristic deep blue-coloured complex. These compounds are probably formed from a helically coiled amylose molecule with the foreign molecule inside. Amylopectin, like amylose, can be hydrolysed to give D-glucose as the only sugar. The fully methylated polysaccharide, however, yields on hydrolysis not only 2,3,6-tri-O-methyl-D-glucose but also 2,3,4,6-tetra-O-methyl-D-glucose and an equimolar amount of 2,3 di-O-methyl-D-glucose. These results suggest that the main structure is linked (1→4) with branch points linked (1→6). The tetra-methyl ether residues arise from the non-reducing ends and the dimethyl ether residues from the branch points. Partial hydrolysis of amylopectin gives a mixture of oligosaccharides from which isomaltose (6-O-α-D-glucopyranosyl-D-glucose) and panose (O-α-D-glucopyranosyl-(1→6)-O-α-D-glucopyranosyl-(1→4)-D-glucose) have been isolated. This clearly indicates the presence of α-D-(1→6) linked branch points. The proportion of tetra-methyl glucose indicates that amylopectin has short α-D-(1→4) linked chains and that a non-reducing end group occurs once in every 20–25 D-glucose units. The molecule is very large (molecular weight 10^6–10^8) and has a tree-like ramified structure. Amylopectin gives a purple red colour with iodine but does not form complexes in the same way as amylose. Retrogradation from solution is slow though it does eventually set to a gel.

5. β-Glucans

Polymers of D-glucose other than starch and cellulose have been discovered in higher plants in the last few years and it is likely that similar compounds will be found in fruit. The glucan from the mesocarp of mango fruit (Das and Rao, 1965) appears to be of this type. This neutral polysaccharide has been shown to be a glucan consisting of repeating units containing about nine (1→3) linked and nine (1→4) linked glucopyranose residues with a branch point (1→6) linked. A similar polysaccharide is reported to be associated with jack fruit pectic acid (Sen Gapta and Rao, 1963). The linear β-glucan from barley contains β-D-glucopyranose residues with (1→4) and (1→3) linkages in equal proportions. Oat β-glucan is similar but contains (1→4) and (1→3) linkages in the proportions of 2:1 or 3:1. Partial hydrolysis of this polysaccharide yielded cellobiose, (1→4) linkage, cellotriose, (1→4, 1→4) linkages, laminaribiose, (1→3) linkage and two trisaccharides containing both (1→3) and (1→4) linkages. On the basis of these results the following structure was proposed

-3-β-D-Glu.p-(1→4)-β-D-Glu.p-(1→4)-β-D-Glu.p-(1→3)-β-D-Glu.p-
(1→4)-β-D-Glu.p-1-

where Glu.p is glucopyranosyl.

Callose is a polysaccharide found on the sieve plates of the phloem of the grape vine. It is resistant to attack by periodate which indicates that most of the structure is composed of chains of (1→3) linked glucopyranosyl residues. This was confirmed by the fact that hydrolysis of the methylated polysaccharide gave 2,4,6-tri-O-methyl-D-glucose as the main product and that enzymic degradation of the polysaccharide gave a mixture of products from which laminaribiose (1→3) linked and laminaritriose (1→3, 1→3) linked, was isolated. It seems likely that callose is a β linked glucan because the optical rotation is very low.

6. Fructans

Polysaccharides containing D-fructose as the main structural unit occur as reserve materials in higher plants. Two main types are known, the *inulin* group which are linked glycosidically (2→1) and the *phlean* group which have (2→6) links. D-fructose is present in both in the furanose form. Inulin is extracted by hot water from the tubers of dahlia and Jerusalem artichoke, and can be isolated by cooling the solution. It is readily hydrolysed by dilute acid to D-fructose. Structural studies indicate that the molecule is a chain of β-D-(2→1) linked fructo-furanose residues with a $\overline{\text{DP}}$ about 35.

C. Gums

These may be normal plant products but it seems probable that mechanical injury or the presence of micro-organisms will stimulate their formation. It is possible that the function of the gum is to seal mechanical wounds and to "wall off" pockets of infection (Hough and Pridham, 1959). Experiments with plum gum showed that commercial enzyme preparations which will hydrolyse pectin and hemicelluloses, failed to degrade the gum polysaccharide. Such enzyme preparations consist of a highly reactive mixture of fungal carbohydrases, and it may be that the structure of the gum is such that the enzymes cannot degrade the appropriate polysaccharide chain because they are extensively substituted by unusual and varied sugars. The presence of the branched chain sugar apiose appears to confer a similar resistance to fungal attack on the cellulose of *Posidonia Australis* (Bell *et al.*, 1954) and this may be a general phenomenon.

Most gums contain polysaccharides of highly individual character, and generalizations concerning their constitution cannot easily be made. However, in the case of plum gum referred to above, the gums found on the fruit and elsewhere in the plant were similar although whether they were identical is difficult to establish since there are no effective general procedures for the purification of polysaccharides or for the determination of the homogeneity of purified fractions. Hydrolysis gave a mixture of sugars, D-galactose, D-mannose, L-arabinose, D-xylose, L-rhamnose, D-glucuronic acid and traces of 4-O-methyl glucuronic acid. These sugars are usually present in plant gums, but in some gums one or more of the following sugars also occur, D-galacturonic acid, L-galactose, D-glucose, D-fructose, L-fucose, 3-*O*-methyl-D-galactose and 3-*O*-methyl pentose. A proposed structure for arabic acid (the acidic polysaccharide of gum arabic) which has been investigated most thoroughly is as follows:

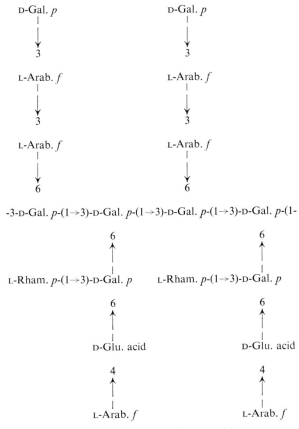

FIG. 3. Repeating unit of gum arabic

Gal. = galactose, Arab. = arabinose, Rham. = rhamnose, Glu. acid = glucuronic acid, *p* = pyranose, *f* = furanose.

Most gums show this type of ramified structure. The molecular weight of the sodium salt of arabic acid is approximately $2 \cdot 5 \times 10^5$.

III. BIOSYNTHESIS OF POLYSACCHARIDES

The discovery of uridine diphosphate D-glucose (UDP-glucose) by Leloir in 1951 (Leloir, 1951) opened up a new chapter in carbohydrate metabolism particularly with regard to complex saccharide biosynthesis. Since that time sugar nucleotides containing different sugar moieties as well as different bases have been isolated from animal tissues, plants and micro-organisms and their number has been steadily increasing. The isolation of a new sugar nucleotide immediately invites speculation as to the part it plays in the biosynthesis of an appropriate polysaccharide. In fact the isolation and identification of cytidine diphosphate-glycerol and cytidine diphosphate-ribitol preceded the isolation of the teichoic acids from *L. plantarum*. It was suggested at the time the nucleotides were discovered that they were probably involved in the formation of polymeric compounds, and this proved to be the case for they were subsequently found to be precursors of the teichoic acids.

In considering the various mechanisms by which a polysaccharide can be built up by transfer of a sugar moiety from donor to the acceptor saccharide, it is interesting to compare the thermodynamic efficiencies of the various reactions. Thus the free energy of hydrolysis ($\Delta F°$) of UDP-D-glucose (pH 7·4) is —7600 cal, α-D-glucose 1-phosphate (pH 8·5) —4800 cal, sucrose —6600 cal, glycogen (α-D-glucoside 1→4 linkage), —4300 cal, and maltose —4600 cal. From the thermodynamic point of view sugar nucleotides are superior donors to any other compound containing a glycoside linkage, and the description that follows of the biosynthesis of those polysaccharides for which the pathway is known involve sugar nucleotides. This does not exclude the possibility that some polysaccharides may be synthesized by transfer of glycosyl or fructosyl residues from a donor such as sucrose rather than from a nucleotide diphosphate sugar. Such a process occurs in various micro-organisms in the presence of high concentrations of sucrose to give the polysaccharides dextran and levan.

The most thoroughly investigated biosynthesis is that for starch. Leloir *et al.* (1961) found an enzyme associated with starch grains from beans, potatoes and corn seedlings which would catalyse the incorporation of radioactivity from UDP-D-glucose labelled with ^{14}C in the glucosyl moiety into a polysaccharide containing linkages of the α-D-(1→4) type. This was shown by degradation of the polysaccharide with β amylase to give radioactive maltose. The enzyme was closely bound to the starch granule and could not be separated from it by the methods tried. The transfer of D-glucose from adenosine diphosphate-D-glucose (ADP-D-glucose) as compared with UDP-D-glucose was ten times as fast, and since a specific enzyme that catalyses the reaction ATP + α-D-glucose-1-P→ADP-D-glucose + PPi, and ADP-D glucose have been detected in chlorella, corn and in rice grains, it seems plausible to suggest that ADP-D-glucose is the precursor of starch *in vivo*. However, the concentration of UDP-D-glucose is about 5–10 times higher than that of ADP-D-glucose in plant tissues which would make their contribution to the synthesis about equal.

Recently soluble enzymes have been prepared from sweet corn, tobacco leaves and potato tubers which will catalyse the same reactions. The specificity of these enzymes with regard to primer requirements varies with the source. That from sweet corn can only use amylopectin and glycogen, that from tobacco leaves amylopectin, glycogen, or heated starch granules, and that from potato tubers only starch granules. It seems likely that the specificity of the starch granule-bound enzyme and of the soluble enzyme will vary with the source both with regard to primer requirements and also sugar nucleotide. The general reaction catalysed by starch synthetase is:

Uridine 5^1 (α-D-glucopyranosyl pyrosphosphate) + acceptor
$\quad\quad\quad\quad\quad$ uridine 5^1 pyrophosphate + α-D-(1→4) glucosyl-acceptor.

Repetition of this process leads to the synthesis of a α-D-(1→4) glucan.

The synthesis of cellulose in plants appears to involve guanosine diphosphate-D-glucose (GDP-D-glucose) rather than UDP-D-glucose though the position is not entirely clear. An enzyme which could utilize the radioactive sugar nucleotide as substrate for the formation of a radioactive polysaccharide with chemical properties indistinguishable from those of natural cellulose was found to exist in root tissues of mung bean seedlings, peas, corn squash, string beans and in the immature seed hairs of cotton. This enzyme was capable of transferring the activated D-glucose moiety from GDP-D-glucose-^{14}C to an unknown acceptor to form the polysaccharide chain. The enzyme system showed a high specificity for GDP-D-glucose. None of the ^{14}C-labelled glucosyl nucleotides containing bases other than guanosine such as uridine adenosine, cytidine, thymidine served as substrate for the formation of cellulose.

As mentioned above, an extract from mung bean seedlings incorporated the glycosyl portion of GDP-D-glucose-^{14}C into cellulose. In the presence of GDP-D-mannose the amount of D-glucose-^{14}C incorporated into an alkali insoluble polysaccharide which was not cellulose was increased. When GDP-D-mannose-^{14}C was used as substrate, a radioactive glucomannan was synthesized. The glucomannan was characterized by the isolation of a number of oligosaccharides after treatment with partially purified β-mannase. Several of these oligosaccharides contained glucose and mannose in the ratio of 1:1, 1:2 and 1:3 or 1:4. Since ^{14}C-labelled glucose was found in the hydrolysis products it is likely that the enzyme contains an epimerase that converts GDP-D-mannose to GDP-D-glucose.

In the case of xylan the appropriate nucleotide sugar was UDP-D-xylose. A particulate preparation from asparagus shoots transferred D-xylosyl residues from UDP-D-xylose to water soluble D-xylose oligosaccharides having the same β-D-(1→4) linkages as xylan. The product, however, was an oligosaccharide containing one more unit than the acceptor. However, particulate enzyme preparations from corn shoots and immature corn cobs have been shown to incorporate D-xylose-^{14}C from UDP-D-xylose-^{14}C into a polysaccharide which appears to be a $(1\rightarrow4)$ linked xylan. The labelled polymer was indistinguishable from plant xylan. Partial degradation gave a series of labelled oligosaccharides ($\overline{\text{DP}}$ 2–7) which were chromatographically identical with authentic plant β-$(1\rightarrow4)$ xylodextrins. The same enzyme preparations will also incorporate L-arabinose from UDP-L-arabinose ^{14}C into the xylan polymer to give an arabinoxylan. Weak acid hydrolysis liberated the arabinose ^{14}C indicating that the arabinose probably had the furanose configuration.

Particulate preparations from homogenates of mung bean seedlings can catalyse the formation from UDP-D-glucose ^{14}C of an insoluble polysaccharide which is a β-D-$(1\rightarrow3)$ glucan known as callose. Partial hydrolysis with acid gave a series of labelled oligosaccharides ($\overline{\text{DP}}$ 2—8) which were chromatographically identical with those in a similar hydrolysate of the β-$(1\rightarrow3)$ linked polysaccharide laminarin. The oligosaccharides were completely hydrolysed with emulsion to D-glucose indicating that the glycosidic links were of the β type.

The biosynthesis of most of the other polysaccharides present in fruits can only be guessed at by analogy with those given above, but since research is very active in this field it is likely that these will be elucidated in the near future.

IV. ENZYMES DEGRADING PENTOSANS, HEXOSANS AND GUMS

The occurrence and properties of the enzymes in fruits has been described in Chapter 8 by D. R. Dilley and only a brief reference to them will be made in this chapter. Polysaccharide enzymes are important in two respects, the pure enzymes can be used for the determination of the fine details of the structure of polysaccharides and the part they play in the general metabolism of the fruit.

(i) *Structural analysis.* Pure enzymes are highly specific and hydrolyse only one type of inter-glycosidic linkage. The amount of material required for enzymatic studies is very small, and since the polysaccharides in the fruit are all synthesized by the action of the appropriate enzymes, it is likely that in the future when the enzymes have been isolated in a pure state and adequately characterized that structural analysis will be mainly effected by the use of such enzymes. At the present time, the main impediment to the further development of this method is the availability of pure enzymes.

For further information the reader is referred to Perlin and Reese (1963) and to Nordin and Kirkwood (1965).

(ii) *Occurrence of enzymes in fruit.* While little is known about the occurrence of enzymes degrading or synthesizing polysaccharides in fruits, it is clear by analogy with other plant tissues that a wide range of hydrolytic and glucosyl transferase enzymes must be present. It is not proposed to discuss specific examples known to be present in fruit but to indicate the range of enzymes which may well be present. It is clear that where reserve polysaccharides such as inulin and starch are present the appropriate enzymes for degrading these to smaller units must be present but usually have never been characterized; enzymes such as cellulase, xylanase, invertase, phosphorylase, α and β amylases have definitely been detected in a number of fruits.

REFERENCES

Andrews, P., Hough, L., Powell, D. B. and Woods, B. M. (1959). *J. chem. Soc.* 774.

Aspinall, G. O. (1959). Structural chemistry of hemicelluloses. *Adv. Carbohyd. Chem.* **14**, 429.

Aspinall, G. O. and Fanshawe, R. S. (1961). *J. chem. Soc.* 4020.

Aspinall, G. O. (1962). Chemistry of carbohydrates. *A. Rev. Biochem.* **31**, 79.

Barrett, A. J. and Northcote, D. H. (1965). *Biochem. J.* **94**, 617.

Bell, D. J., Isherwood, F. A. and Hardwick, N. (1954). *J. chem. Soc.* 3702.

Bennett, E. (1956). *J. Fd Sci.* **21**, 207.

Boltaga, S. V. and Smykova, N. A. (1965). *Polisakharidy Plodor i Pererabotke Sb.* 31.

Bundy, J. H., Wall, J. S., Turner, J. E., Woychick, J. H. and Dimler, R. J. (1967). *J. biol. Chem.,* **242**, 2410.

Chanda, S. K., Hirst, E. L. and Perceval, E. G. V. (1951). *J. chem. Soc.* 1240.

Das, A. and Rao, C. V. N. (1965). *Aust. J. Chem.* **18**, 845.

Hägglund, E., Lindberg, B. and McPherson, J. (1956). *Acta chem. scand.* **10**, 1160.

Hirst, E. L. and Jones, J. K. N. (1939). *J. chem. Soc.* 454.

Hirst, E. L., Isherwood, F. A., Jermyn, M. A. and Jones, J. K. N. (1949). *J. chem. Soc.* 182.

Hirst, E. L., Rees, D. A. and Richardson, N. G. (1965). *Biochem. J.* **95**, 453.

Hough, L. and Pridham, J. B. (1959). *Biochem. J.* **73**, 550.

Jermyn, M. A. and Isherwood, F. A. (1956). *Biochem. J.* **64**, 123.

Jowett, P., Arthington, W. and Hulme, A. C. (1951). D.S.I.R. Lond., Ditton Lab., I.R.M. 25.

Lanza, M., Regli, P. and Bussan, F. (1962a). *Medna trop.* **22**, 377.

Lanza, M., Regli, P. and Bussan, F. (1962b). *Medna trop.* **22**, 471.

Leloir, L. F. (1951). *Archs Biochem.* **33**, 186.

Leloir, L. F., de Fekete, M. A. R. and Cardini, C. E. (1961). *J. biol. Chem.* **236**, 636.

Manley, R. S. J. (1964). *Nature, Lond.* **204**, 1155.

McCready, R. M. and Gee, M. (1960). *J. agric. Fd Chem.* **8**, 510.

Meyer, K. H. and Misch, L. (1937). *Helv. chim. Acta* **20**, 237.

Nordin, J. H. and Kirkwood, S. (1965). *A. Rev. Pl. Physiol.* **16**, 393.

Northcote, D. H. (1964). *A. Rev. Biochem.* **33**, 51.

Parikh, V. N., Ingle, T. R. and Bhide, B. V. (1958). *J. Indian chem. Soc.* **35**, 125.

Perlin, A. S. and Reese, E. T. (1963). "Advances in enzymic hydrolysis of cellulose and related material", p. 185. Pergamon Press, New York.

Ranby, B. G. (1958). *In* "Encyclopedia of plant physiology" (Ed. Ruhland, W.), **6**, 268. Springer, Berlin.

Sen Gupta, V. K. and Rao, C. V. N. (1963). *Bull. chem. Soc. Japan* **36**, 1683.

Ting, S. V. and Deszyck, E. J. (1961). *J. Fd Sci.* **26**, 146.

Wade, P. (1964). *J. Sci. Fd Agric.* **15**, 51.

Wise, L. E., Murphy, M. and D'Addieco, A. A. (1946). *Paper Trade J.* **122**, 35.

Chapter 3

Pectic Substances and other Uronides

W. PILNIK AND A. G. J. VORAGEN

Department of Food Science, State Agricultural University,
Wageningen, The Netherlands

I. PECTIC SUBSTANCES

A. Introduction and Definitions of Terms

Pectic substances are polygalacturonides with non-uronide carbohydrates covalently bound to an unbranched chain of $1 \rightarrow 4$ linked α-galacturonic acid units. The carboxyl groups of the galacturonic acid are partly esterified with

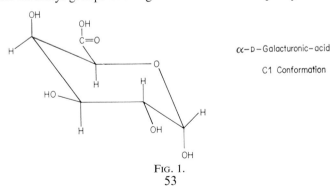

α–D–Galacturonic–acid

C1 Conformation

FIG. 1.
53

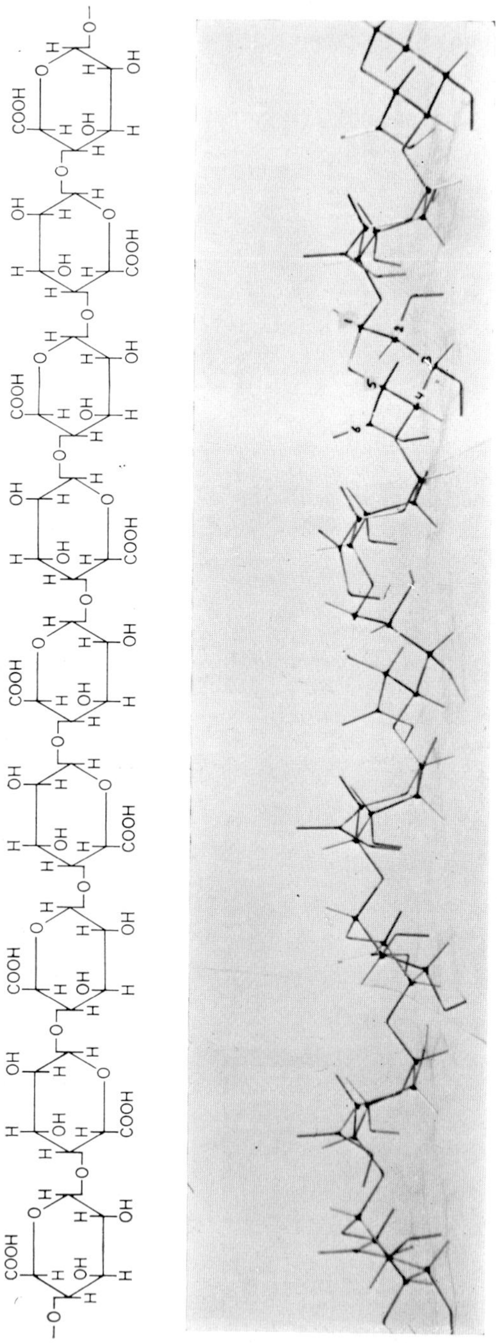

FIG. 2. Formula of polygalacturonic acid and photograph of corresponding Dreiding Model.

methanol and the free groups are more or less neutralized. Some of the hydroxyl groups on C_2 and C_3 may be acetylated. The monomer is thought to have the C1 conformation (Fig. 1). The glycosidic bonds are therefore of the axial-axial type which causes the polymer chain to have a screw axis with a tendency to coiling. Figure 2 shows the formula of polygalacturonan, and underneath it a photograph made from a maximal extended Dreiding model. Figure 3 shows the same Dreiding model coiled together.

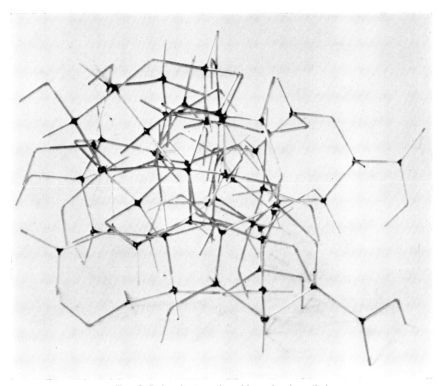

FIG. 3. Polygalacturonic acid randomly coiled.

Definition of terms: The American Chemical Society has given the following definitions (Kertesz, 1951, pp. 6–8).

Pectic substances. Pectic substances is a group designation for those complex, colloidal carbohydrate derivatives which occur in, or are prepared from, plants and contain a large proportion of anhydrogalacturonic acid units which are thought to exist in a chain-like combination. The carboxyl groups of polygalacturonic acids may be partly esterified by methyl groups and partly or completely neutralized by one or more bases.

Protopectin. The term protopectin is applied to the water-insoluble parent pectic substance which occurs in plants and which, upon restricted hydrolysis, yields pectinic acids.

Pectinic acids. The term pectinic acids is used for colloidal polygalacturonic acids containing more than a negligible proportion of methyl ester groups. Pectinic acids, under suitable conditions, are capable of forming gels (jellies) with sugar and acid or, if suitably low in methoxyl content, with certain metallic ions. The salts of pectinic acids are either normal or acid pectinates.

Pectin. The general term pectin (or pectins) designates those water-soluble pectinic acids of varying methyl ester content and degree of neutralization which are capable of forming gels with sugar and acid under suitable conditions.

Pectic acid. The term pectic acid is applied to pectic substances mostly composed of colloidal polygalacturonic acids and essentially free from methyl ester groups. The salts of pectic acid are either normal or acid pectates.

There have been many important publications on pectins. The complete knowledge of the whole field up to 1951 is reviewed and discussed in the book of Kertesz (1951). In the same year the book of Beatrice Hottenroth (1951) appeared which stresses manufacture, application and analysis. All the modern aspects of pectin chemistry, physiology, chemical and colloidal properties are covered in Doesburg's book (1965) which is essential reading for every worker on any aspect of the subject. Excellent shorter summaries are by Deuel and Solms (1954), Deuel and Stutz (1958) and, more recently, by Neukom (1967). Structural and physiological aspects have been summarized by Worth (1967). Pectin applications have been fully covered by Bender (1959) and more shortly by Joseph (1955). The industrially important gel formation properties of pectins are further discussed by Solms (1960), Owens *et al.* (1954) and, more theoretically, by Harvey (1960). Special attention to Ca-pectate gels has been paid by Baker (1948). Gelling properties of low ester pectins with Ca-ions are treated by Doesburg (1965). The newest information about industrial extractions has been published by Potter (1966) and Bulmer (1967).

The following discussion concerns only pectic substances as a natural constituent of mainly fruit and is not concerned with uses of pectin preparations as food additive.

B. Structure

It must be realized that there is no such thing as a uniform pectin or pectate molecule. With the many variations possible in molecular weight, in esterification, in acetylation, in content and type of binding of neutral sugars and in the distribution of substituents and non-uronides we can almost take it for granted that in a given preparation of pectic substances no molecule is equal to another. Furthermore, most extracted pectin preparations must be considered as artefacts, as extraction methods may change the molecule. There are, however, certain points which are of primary interest and which will type a pectin even if no complete formula is possible. The general structure of pectins of fruits does not appear to differ from that of the pectins of other plant tissue.

(a) *Chain structure.* In all the many acid, alkaline and enzymic breakdown products there have never been found any oligogalacturonic acids with a linkage other than α $(1{\rightarrow}4)$. This can be considered as proof that pectin has an unbranched chain of α-D-$(1{\rightarrow}4)$ galacturonic acid as backbone structure (Fig. 2).

(b) *Pure polygalacturonic acid chain.* In a number of pectin preparations from various sources the C1 of galacturonysylpyranose (GalpA) has been found linked to C2 of L-rhamnosyl pyranose (Rhap) which means that in these cases L-rhamnose forms part of the main chain. The following oligosaccharides have been obtained (Aspinall *et al.*, 1968) from hydrolysis of lemon pectin:

α-D-GalpA $(1{\rightarrow}2)$-L-Rha
GalpA $(1{\rightarrow}2)$-Rhap$(1{\rightarrow}4)$-GalpA$(1{\rightarrow}2)$Rha
GalpA $(1{\rightarrow}2)$Rhap$(1{\rightarrow}2)$Rha
GalpA $(1{\rightarrow}2)$-Rhap$(1{\rightarrow}4)$GalpA.

D-GalpA$(1{\rightarrow}2)$ L-Rha has also been isolated from hydrolysis products of apple pectin (Barrett and Northcote, 1965), of carnation roots pectin (Foglietti and Percheron, 1968) and of sycamore callus pectin (Stoddart *et al.*, 1967). The fact that there is usually very little rhamnose is interpreted to mean that long chains of galacturonan are linked together by rhamnose rich blocks.

(c) *Covalent linkage of neutral sugars.* The following aldobiuronic acids were identified in pectin hydrolysates:

Xylp$(1{\rightarrow}3)$GalpA (lemon; Aspinall *et al.*, 1968)
GalA$\rightarrow$Gal, GalA$\rightarrow$Xyl (apple; Barrett and Northcote, 1965)
D-GalA$\rightarrow$Fuc, DGalA$\rightarrow$2-Methyl-Xyl, D-GalA$\rightarrow$2-Methyl-Fuc, D-GalA
 $\rightarrow$Gal (Carnation root; Foglietti and Percheron, 1968)
GalA$\rightarrow$Gal, GalA$\rightarrow$Xyl (Sycamore Callus; Stoddart *et al.*, 1967).

(Xylp = Xylosylpyranose; xyl = xylose; Fuc = fucose; Gal = galactose) This leaves no doubt that many pectins have neutral sugars covalently linked to them as side chains. The presence of neutral sugars in chromatographically uniform oligouronides obtained by degradation with purified enzymes is also strong evidence of a covalent link (McCready and Gee, 1960; Hatanaka and Ozawa, 1966b). Arabinose, galactose and to a lesser extent xylose, rhamnose and glucose are, of course, frequently met in chromatographically and/or electrophoretically uniform pectins and pectates. In fact, only four cases of a pure homogalacturonan have been reported so far (Bishop, 1955—Sunflower heads; Aspinall and Cañas-Rodriguez, 1958—Sisal; Sen Gupta and Rao 1963—Jack Fruit; Bhattacharjee and Timmell, 1965—Bark of amabilis fir).

(d) *Presence of other uronides.* GpA($1\rightarrow6$)Gal and GpA($1\rightarrow4$) Fuc have been identified by Aspinall *et al.* (1968) in their lemon pectin study. This is proof that small quantities of glucuronic acid may actually be linked to pectins in a side chain.

(e) *Degree of polymerization* ($\overline{DP}$). No general figure can be given for the molecular weight of pectin preparation which depends largely on extraction conditions. Values given in the literature vary between 30,000 and 300,000. The description of the American Chemical Society mentions "colloidal" and sets a lower limit by including gel-forming capability in the definition. For plant physiological studies as well as for analytical purposes many authors take alcohol insoluble solids as a starting point and one might, therefore, base a vague definition on this. However no published data have come to our attention about the limit $\overline{DP}$ for alcohol solubility or gel-forming capability.

The pectin molecule emerges therefore as a chain structure of axial-axial α-($1\rightarrow4$) linked D-galacturonic acid units, containing blocks of L-rhamnose rich regions, with mainly arabinose, galactose and xylose as side chains. The carboxyl groups are partially methylated and the secondary hydroxyls may be acetylated.

(f) *Protopectin.* This subject has been admirably reviewed by Joslyn (1962). When protopectin insolubility is discussed on the basis of experimental facts the concept of pectin as a high polymer chain molecule with a limited heteropolysaccharic character becomes of particular importance. The high molecular weight makes extraction a diffusion phenomenon, a problem well known to, and studied by, manufacturers of commercial pectin preparations. Analytically, depolymerizing agents (enzymes, alkali, acid) are frequently used to solubilize the protopectin fraction. Joslyn and Deuel (1963) have shown how yield from apple pomace decreased when enzymic browning is allowed to build up a network of tannins and tannin-protein complexes, enmeshing the pectin molecules.

The glycosidic links to hemicellulose chains discussed above indicate how pectin can be chemically bound to other cell wall constituents. Soluble pectins of high molecular weight and with araban galactan and xylan admixed and/or covalently bound to them therefore present a model of protopectin which appears as a giant molecule, mechanically and chemically enmeshed with other cell wall substances.

C. Occurrence and Biosynthesis

Pectic substances are part of all higher plant tissues. Figure 4 (Northcote, 1958) illustrates how pectins are mainly deposited in the primary wall and the middle lamella. Meristematic and parenchymous tissue are therefore particularly rich in pectic substances. As cell wall constituents, pectic substances are part of the hemicellulose-pectin gel which fulfills functions as a structural element and as a membrane; the pectin in the middle lamella is often referred to as "intercellular cement" or as "cell adhesive". The juice of ripe fruit is rich in dissolved pectin which must be considered as solubilized protopectin dissolved partly in cell sap and partly in middle lamella liquid.

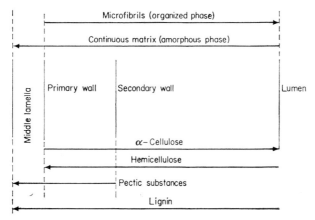

FIG. 4. Distribution of cell wall constituents (Northcote, 1958).

In ripe fruit cell walls may be partly dissolved. The average pectin content of fruit is 0·5%. For exact figures of pectin content of fruits, see Section IE 1.

Possible pathways of pectin biosynthesis have recently been discussed by Worth (1967). One possibility is via an inositol derivative, L-bornesitol, which on oxidation and epimerization becomes galacturonic acid methylester (Fig. 5). The full pathway (Loewus, 1964) would then be: D-glucose-myo-inositol-L-bornesitol-methyl-D-glucuronate-methyl-D-glucuronate nucleotide-methyl-D-galacturonate nucleotide-pectin. Supporting evidence is the description of the epimerization of uronic acid nucleotides (Feingold et al., 1960; Neufeld et al., 1957) and the incorporation of uronic acid in a chain (glycosyl transferase) (Kessler et al., 1961; Leloir et al., 1960; Loewus and Kelly, 1961). Also myo-inositol-2-^{14}C has been seen to be transformed by plants into D-galacturonic acid-5-^{14}C (Loewus and Kelly, 1963). Another pathway is seen in a series of nucleotide reactions, starting with UDP-D-glucose (Fig. 6). Contrary to the inositol oxidation scheme this pathway also accounts for the inclusion of rhamnose in the chain. On the other hand it would lead to unesterified pectic acid. However, by the isotope labelling technique, methionine has been shown to transfer its methyl group to pectic acid (Sato *et al.*, 1957; Krauss and Hassid, 1967). This reaction has been found to be catalysed by indolyacetic acid (Ordin *et al.*, 1957; Jansen *et al.*, 1960a). The nucleotide reactions are also confirmed by the group of Northcote

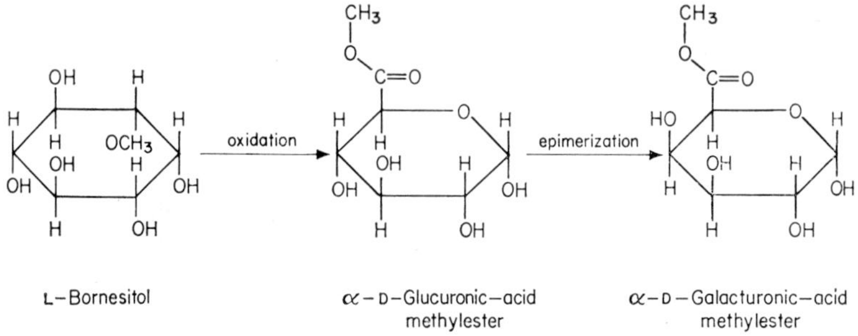

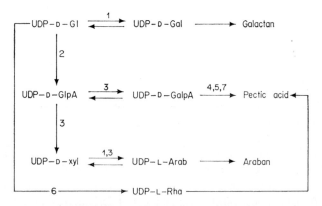

FIG. 5. Pathway for pectin biosynthesis (Loewus, 1964).

FIG. 6. Pathway for pectin biosynthesis (Worth, 1967). (1) Neufeld *et al.* (1957); (2) Smith and van Cleve (1955); (3) Feingold *et al.* (1960); (4) Kessler *et al.* (1961); (5) Loewus and Kelly (1961); (6) Barber (1962); (7) Lin *et al.* (1966).

who showed with sycamore suspension-callus tissue that the radioactivity of radioactive glucose could be found back first in the neutral polysaccharides (arabinan-galactan) then in a weakly acid pectinic acid electrophoretic fraction and finally in a strongly acid pectinic acid electrophoretic fraction. None of the radioactivity was in the methyl group. Experiments with arabinose showed the radioactivity to appear in the neutral and weakly acid fractions, but not in the strongly acidic pectinic acid (Stoddart and Northcote, 1967). Electron microscopic investigations on wheat seeds (Pickett-Heaps and

Northcote, 1966) and a technique of radioautography using light and electronic microscopy (Northcote and Pickett-Heaps 1966; cf. Section IGa) using also wheat seeds suggests that the radioactive high polymer material is formed in the Golgi apparatus and transported in Golgi vesicles through the cytoplasm to the plasmalemma which it crosses by a process of reversed pinocytosis. The vesicles are then absorbed by the cell wall. Worth (1967) points out that in different plants different pathways may exist. In guavas the appearance of pectin closely follows the biosynthesis of ascorbic acid.

D. Properties of Pectin Preparations

Pectins are soluble in water, formamide, dimethylsulfoxide, dimethylformamide and warm glycerol. In water they form viscous solutions, the viscosity depending on the molecular weight and being influenced by degree of esterification, pH and electrolyte concentration (Deuel, 1943; Deuel and Stutz, 1958). The pH of pectin solutions varies from 2·8 to 3·4 as a function of degree of esterification. As poly-electrolytes pectins have only calculated apparent dissociation constant $0·1 - 10·0 \times 10^{-4}$; monogalacturonic acid $3·25 \times 10^{-4}$ at 19°C (Speiser, 1947; Katchalski, 1954; Katchalski et al., 1954). Pectic acid and pectinic acids with very low esterification are only soluble after (partial) neutralization.

Pectins and pectates can be precipitated with water miscible organic solvents, with quaternary detergents (Scott, 1965), with water soluble basic polymers (Stutz and Deuel, 1955; Deuel et al., 1954), with proteins (Doesburg, 1965) and with polyvalent cations (Deuel and Stutz, 1958). Cation coagulation follows the Hofmeister and Schulze-Hardy rules. Pectates are also precipitated with monovalent cations (including H^+-ions). Acetyl groups decrease Ca-sensitivity (Solms and Deuel, 1951; Schweiger, 1966; Kohn and Furda, 1968) but blockwise arrangements of acid and ester groups (Stutz and Deuel, 1955) and amidation (Solms and Deuel, 1954) make pectins more Ca-sensitive. In cross-linked insoluble form pectins have ion-exchange properties with a certain selectivity for Ca and heavy metal ions (Deuel et al., 1957; Hutschneker, 1955).

Pectin solutions are optically active. The specific rotation for citrus pectin analysis was given as $+230°$ (McCready et al., 1951), but Zitko and Bishop (1965) found values increasing with purification (300° for 95·5% pure apple pectate, 277° for 92·5% pure citrus pectate and 308° for 99·2% pure sunflower pectate). $[\alpha]_D^{20}$ of monogalacturonic acid is $+51·9$. Pectin solutions are also flow birefringent (Pilnik, 1946).

Acids hydrolyse the ester and the glycosidic linkages. At low temperatures saponification prevails and at high temperatures depolymerization (Weber, 1945; Doesburg, 1965). Strong acid action degrades the molecule with formation (via the monomer) of CO_2, furfural, reductic acid and alginetine (Neukom, 1963). Alkali also acts on the ester groups which can be split off at low temperatures without depolymerization. Already at room temperature however β-elimination cleavage of glycosidic linkages is observed (Fig. 7). As this reaction occurs only next to an esterified carboxyl group, pectates are much more stable towards alkaline or neutral (at high temperatures) degradation than pectinates (Baker, 1948; Neukom and Deuel, 1958; Neukom, 1963; Doesburg, 1965). Saponification with ammonium hydroxide is accompanied by amidation (Slavikova, 1961).

Pectin is also degraded by oxidants. Mechanisms involving Red-Ox systems (Ascorbic Acid/H_2O_2/Fe'') are of special interest in this context (Doesburg, 1965; Neukom, 1967; O'Colla et al., 1962; Deuel, 1943). Concerning the influence of radiation, the reader is referred to Section IE 3.

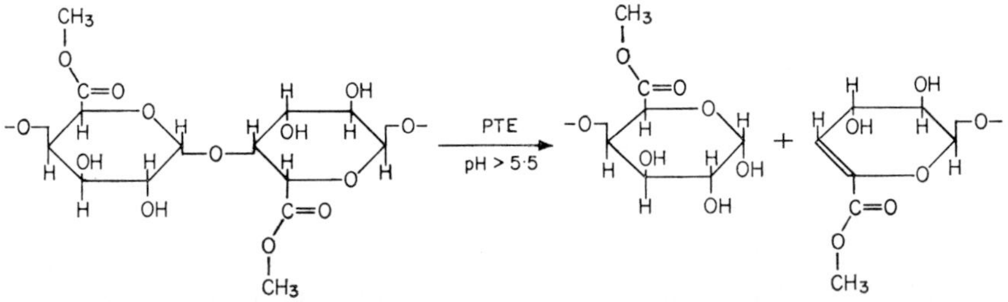

FIG. 7. Transeliminative cleavage of the glycosidic linkage by lyases or OH'-ions.

Pectins form gels under certain circumstances and this property has made them a very important food additive for the jam, jelly and marmalade as well as for the confectionery industry (Pilnik and Zwiker, 1970). It is estimated that about 10,000 tons of pectin are extracted annually from the residues of citrus and apple juice production by highly specialized factories in the U.S.A. and in Europe. Mainly two types of pectins are produced for two fundamentally different types of gels: high methoxyl pectins (60–75% esterification) for sugar-pectin-acid gels and low methoxy pectins (20–45% esterification) for "Ca-pectinate" gels. For the first type of gel it is generally accepted that gel formation occurs when pectin molecules can aggregate by H-bridges after dehydration (sugar addition) and after repression of the (strongly hydrated) dissociated carboxyl groups (acid addition). The liquid phase is then enmeshed in the three-dimensional net formed. No acid is necessary for the gelling of fully esterified pectins. Partial acetylation of the secondary hydroxyl groups prevents gel formation; one must therefore think in terms of zones of attachment rather than in terms of cross-linking points (Solms, 1960).

In such sugar-acid-pectin gels the three constituents can replace each other within certain limits. No gel will form under 55°C Brix and the upper pH limits can be seen in Fig. 8 which also shows gel strength as a function of pH for various degrees of esterification. Other factors influencing gel strength are of course molecular weight and concentration of pectin and sugar (Ehrlich, 1968). The degree of esterification also determines whether a pectin is slow or rapid to set (Pilnik, 1964; Smit and Bryant, 1968). One must however realize that the gelling temperature depends on rate of cooling, slower cooling resulting in gelling at higher temperatures (Doesburg, 1960). Setting times are

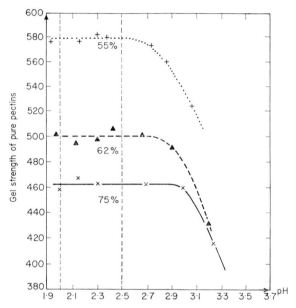

Fig. 8. Relation between gelling power of pectins with different degrees of esterification (% DE) at different pH values of test jellies (Doesburg and Grevers, 1960).

therefore best determined at constant temperatures. Using a test gel made up from water, 65% w/w sugar and buffered to pH 3·0, one finds that a rapid set pectin with a degree of esterification of about 75% will gel within 10 minutes at 85°C. Slow set pectins (degree of esterification 60–65%) will not gel at all at temperatures above 75°C and take about 20 minutes to set at 65°C. Setting rate is also increased by increased sugar and acid concentrations (Pilnik, 1964). The melting point of sugar-acid-pectin gels is much higher than their setting point; in fact most gels must be boiled to liquify them. Higher concentrations of sugar and/or pectin even allow the manufacture of jellies withstanding baking temperatures.

The reactivity of low methoxyl pectins with Ca-ions is used to make sugar free or low sugar jellies (Lopez and Li, 1968; Hills *et al.*, 1942). To obtain a gel rather than a coagulated mass a controlled reaction between pectins and Ca-ions is required (Lange *et al.*, 1965). This is obtained by adding soluble Ca-salts under boiling conditions. Gelling then occurs on cooling. The slow release of Ca-ions from insoluble salts by ion exchange also results in the formation of a regular gel structure. Other possibilities—not industrially used—are diffusion of Ca-ions into LM-pectin solutions (Wieringa, 1949; van der Lyn, 1966) or acid or enzymatic saponification of high ester pectin in the presence of Ca-ions. Although many authors still postulate a primary valence gel via Ca-bridges there is much evidence against this theory: the amount of Ca needed is always more than stoichometrically necessary but decreases with decreasing degree of esterification; "Ca-pectinate" gels are fully thermoreversible at relatively low temperatures (60°C); partial esterification of the secondary hydroxyl groups with acetic acid prevents gelling (Solms and Deuel, 1951); pectin acids containing not more free carboxyl groups than highly esterified pectins are very Ca sensitive (Solms and Deuel, 1954) and can be used for Ca-gels. One must therefore assume that gel formation is a very complex phenomenon in which, undoubtedly, secondary values between Ca and hydroxyl groups play a very important role. Contrary to high methoxyl pectin gels, the low methoxyl Ca gels have a definite setting temperature which is independent from the rate of cooling. The gels also liquify at their setting temperature. The setting temperature increases with all factors which increase gel strength (Ca, solids concentration; Janse, 1967). Commercially such pectins are used to make low calorie fruit jams and jellies or milk flans, the milk providing the necessary Ca-ions. For systems other than milk, Ca must be added, and if sorbitol is used in products destined for diabetics the Ca-chelating power of sugar alcohols must be accounted for. Milieu conditions such as solids content, buffer and neutral salts, concentration of H- and Ca-ions have a very complex and interdependent influence on gel formation which again depends on degree of esterification and the pre-history of the LM-pectin, mainly the method of de-esterification (Hills *et al.*, 1949; McCready *et al.*, 1944; Owens *et al.*, 1949; Woodmansee and Baker, 1949; Bock and Lange, 1963).

E. Pectin Changes

The physiological life of fruit processing and storage of fruit products are accompanied by changes in pectin content and pectin structure. These may involve degree of esterification, molecular weight, neutral sugar components, acetylation. These changes may be enzymic or chemical in nature. There is very little information, however, over the relation of enzyme activity and pectic changes during ripening and/or storage of fruit; such relationships have, however, been well studied for processing. Direct oxydative chemical breakdown of pectins has been ascribed to ascorbic acid but there is very little evidence of this happening.

1. *During maturation and storage of fruit*

Most authors use a fractional extraction process to describe changes in pectin structure and while this allows some general conclusions the diversity of methods used does not allow comparisons between different authors, not even for total pectin content. Aspects of this method are discussed in Section IG. Only recent work is discussed here; the reader is also referred to Joslyn (1962), Sterling (1963) and Doesburg (1965).

(a) *Apples and pears.* Tavakoli and Wiley (1968b) reported that fruit of various varieties harvested on consecutive dates decreased in firmness. Total pectin (660–810 mg%) decreased. On storage there was further loss of firmness and of total pectin. The protopectin fraction of total pectin increased before harvest and decreased after harvest. Raunhardt and Neukom (1964) determined total pectin in washed dried pomace from apples and pears picked at various dates and stored after harvest. During ripening on the tree and on storage pectin content decreased. Degree of esterification remained constant at around 70% before harvest but dropped after harvest to 60–65% (apples) and 50% (pears). Preston and Nelmes (1968) have recently examined pectin changes in apples and found a sharp drop in the proportion of galacturonic acid during the later stages of senescena.

(b) *Peaches and apricots.* Shewfelt (1965) described a storage experiment with freestone peach varieties showing decreasing firmness. Total pectin (300 mg%) did not change much but the water soluble fraction increased while the versene soluble fraction and protopectin decreased. In a Clingstone peach variety there was hardly any change of hardness, total pectin (300 mg%) and pectin composition (66% protopectin). Deshpande and Salunkhe (1964) investigated effects of maturity and storage on biochemical changes in apricots and peaches. For example, Redhaven peaches contained 1270 (hard), 800 (firm mature) and 740 (soft) mg% total pectin which decreased with maturity and upon storage.

(c) *Avocado.* Dolendo *et al.* (1966) observed decrease of protopectin (25 mg%) upon storage together with firmness while a water soluble fraction appeared. Percentage esterification of total pectin decreased from 85 to 45%.

(d) *Tomatoes.* Deshpande *et al.* (1966) found that vine ripe fruit graded for firmness had 60–100 mg% total pectin in firm, and 13–37 mg% total pectin in soft, fruit. The latter had a higher protopectin fraction. Similar results were obtained with fruit ripened after harvest. There was a significant correlation between molecular weight of the pectin (as ratio carboxyl/pectin) and firmness as well as between total mineral content and firmness.

(e) *Citrus.* Rouse *et al.* (1965) reported on the changes in water soluble, oxalate soluble and NaOH soluble (protopectin) pectin fractions of component parts of Silver Cluster grapefruit during a 10 month maturation cycle for 2 seasons. Total pectin was around 1600 mg% fresh fruit (season 1962/63) and 1300 mg% fresh fruit (season 1961/62), increasing slightly with maturity when calculated on dry weight. In peels the oxalate soluble fraction accounted for 70% and water soluble and protopectin for 15% each of total pectin. In membranes and juice sacs the fractions were much nearer to each other. There was little change with maturity. Rouse *et al.* (1964a) had also studied the same component parts of pineapple orange during a similar maturation period but used an acid extraction method (H·-exchanger). Average yields of galacturonic acid calculated on AIS were found to be 20% (peel), 29% (membrane) and 16% (juice sacs). Jelly grade averages—a measure for molecular weight—were 178 (peel), 300 (membrane) and 185 (juice sacs). Esterification averages were 53% (peel), 63% (membrane) and 57% (juice sacs). There was very little change with maturity. The same authors (1964b) obtained similar results with Silver Cluster grapefruit, the extracted pectins however were of higher molecular weight and esterification. Sinclair and Joliffe (1961) also studied the pectin of oranges.

(f) *Strawberries*. Neal (1965) considered 3 stages of maturity for 2 varieties. He found that on ripening the middle lamella of the codical parenchyma cells was separated into 2 layers, each of which remained attached to a cell wall. This effect could be imitated by the use of EDTA which had a macerating effect with a similar loss of firmness. By addition of Ca-ions the EDTA effect could be reversed. De-esterification by immersion in alkaline alcohol and addition of Ca also had a firming effect. Methylation on the other hand decreased firmness with no influence of Ca-ions. Both varieties showed water soluble pectin to increase with maturity with practically no change in the EDTA soluble fraction. Decreasing firmness is therefore attributed to methylation of pectin which inhibits the firming effect of Ca, in spite of the presence of PE in strawberries.

It would be mere speculation to draw general conclusions from these and the many other publications (Doesburg, 1965; Kertesz, 1951) in this field.

If no actual esterification analyses are made one must be wary of identifying increase of versene or oxalate soluble fractions with an increase of low methoxyl pectin. Thus Doesburg (1957) suspended apple tissue in acetate, acetate-oxalate and versene. After 3 weeks he found that 6·3, 19·3 and 82·1% respectively of the total pectin had gone into solution. The respective degrees of esterification were 92·8, 79·7 and 75%, all much higher than required for Ca-precipitation. Sioiri and Haginuma (1954) had already reported in 1954 that salts like NaCl and Na_2SO_4 were just as effective as polyphosphates in pectin extraction from apple marks. "On voit que le problème de la solubilisation des composés pectiques au cours de la maturation reste obscur" (Ulrich and Hartmann, 1967).

2. During processing and storage of fruit products

(a) *Canned and brined fruit.* Canned stone fruit becomes softer on storage. At the same time syrup viscosity increases due to the appearance of soluble pectin in the syrup. In the syrup of Blenheim apricots, Luh and Dastur (1966) found 280 mg% in the syrup of soft fruit and 350 mg% in the syrup of firm fruit after one year's storage, whereas the protopectin in the canned fruit decreased (475 mg% in soft fruit; 400 mg% in firm fruit). Pectins isolated from fresh fruit, canned fruit and syrup (stored for 6 months) all had similar and high degrees of esterification (66·8–78·3%) and acetyl content (approximately 5·5%). The syrup pectins showed the following acetyl values—firm: 3·47% (66·8% esterification); medium: 4·73% (74·4% esterification); ripe: 5·31% (78·3% esterification). Similar results were obtained for canned cling peaches (Kanujoso and Luh, 1967). Within 255 days' storage, protopectin decrease (from 579 mg%) went parallel with decrease of shear press firmness values and with increase of syrup viscosities, linked to appearance of 250 mg% pectin in the syrup. Chen and Joslyn (1967) also measured the diffusion of pectin from canned Clingstone peaches into various types of syrup and found 200 mg% pectin after one year's storage. According to Luh and Dastur (1968) 2,4-D and 2,4,5-T sprays did not affect this principal behaviour for canned Tracey and Brentwood apricots. Decreasing firmness during storage of canned Blenheim apricots were only slightly improved by addition of Calcium ions to the syrup (Mohammadzadeh-Khayat and Luh, 1968) but considerable softening occurred when oxalate was added accompanied by strong increase of syrup viscosity. After 9 months' storage, the pectin content of the syrup without addition had increased from 119 mg% to 328 mg% in one experiment.

Hsu *et al.* (1965) experimented with various blanching and holding times before processing of tomatoes and obtained the firmest fruits by adding Ca at conditions under which PE was active. From 200 mg% total pectin the oxalate soluble fraction was then 50% whereas under inactivating conditions this fraction was only 20%. A significant correlation between PE activity and firmness was established. Deshpande *et al.* (1966) found in vine ripened and post-harvest ripened tomatoes from 10 to 170 mg% pectin (cold water and hot water and EDTA soluble fractions) and a highly significant relationship with firmness. Cold water soluble and EDTA soluble fractions were also significantly related to firmness. Brined cherries (van Buren, 1967) show a strong conversion of protopectin and water soluble pectin into a calgon soluble pectin fraction (total pectin approximately 320 mg/g AIS). The firming action of Ca content in the SO_2 brine is ascribed to this conversion.

(b) *Citrus juices and concentrates.* One of the best investigated fields of pectic changes in connection with enzyme activity is the problem of cloud loss of citrus juices (Guyer *et al.*, 1956) and gellification of citrus concentrates (Wenzel *et al.*, 1951). The field has been extensively reviewed by Pilnik (1958) and Joslyn and Pilnik (1961) and, while much factual material has been published in the meantime, no new mechanisms have been presented (Primo *et al.*, 1961 ; MacDowell, 1962). Citrus juices are rich in PE which is adsorbed on pulp particles and which de-esterifies the (proto)pectin (Rouse, 1953). The pectic acid formed precipitates with the native Ca of the juice. If the juice is concentrated the clarification which occurs results in a Ca-pectate gel. Here is a clear case of creating a Ca-sensitive and therefore Ca complexing agent soluble pectin fraction, and a multiple extraction analysis gives clear indications of enzymic pectin changes. The methods used in the study and control of these phenomena have been summarized by Rouse and Atkins (1955). They also gave mean values of commercial frozen concentrated orange juices from a Florida season. Total pectin content of the concentrate was from 250–300 mg%. In high PE active concentrates (100 units) they found 40% protopectin of total pectic substances and 30% each water and oxalate soluble pectin. In low PE activity concentrates (24 units) protopectin was unchanged at 40% but there was 40% water soluble and only 20% oxalate soluble pectin. The importance of PE for undesirable quality changes has led to its use as "indicator enzyme" in the citrus industry (Pilnik and Rothschild, 1960).

(c) *Tomato juice concentrates.* Tomatoes contain PE as well as PG. Together they destroy the pectin of tomato juice, the PE transforming the high methoxyl pectin into the low methoxyl PG substrate. This pectin destruction is made use of in the production of high Brix concentrates which would not be possible with the highly viscous juices one obtains when the enzymes are inactivated immediately.

(d) *Comminuted citrus juices.* These products are finely ground whole oranges and are used as flavouring for orange squashes and drinks. The comminuting gives an optimal distribution of PE and pectin, and if these products are not pasteurized immediately they will form firm Ca-pectate gels (Charley, 1964; Huet and Ledergerber, 1964; Koch and Haase-Sajak, 1965).

(e) *Nectars* (Reintjes, 1966; Pilnik, 1969) are relatively new fruit juice products in which whole fruits and berries (pear, currants, apricots) are comminuted and made up to a beverage with sugar, water and acid. Cloud stability problems are similar to citrus juices.

F. Pharmacology

The action of pectin as a general intestinal regulator and detoxifying agent and its effectiveness in diarrhoea therapy is probably responsible for the age-old use of the apple as a household remedy ("an apple a day keeps the doctor away"). There are many pectin containing medical preparations on the market and pectin is a standard addition in commercial baby food formulae. The reason for these effects are the general adsorptive action of this high polymer substance and its metal binding capacity, but there are also claims of chemical reactions (glycosidation) with some toxins. The literature on this subject has been collected by Joseph (1963). Further pharmacological effects documented by Joseph (1963) include prolongation of drug action, wound healing and bacteriocidal activity on intestinal pathogens. Antiviral properties have also been claimed. Pectin has a haemostatic and antifibrinolytic effect (Bock et al., 1964; Deuel, 1945) and increases the sedimentation rate of erythrocytes (Deuel and Stutz, 1958; Bender, 1959). By far the most widely discussed aspect of pectin pharmacology has however been brought forward by Keys et al. (1961) with their observations on its effectiveness in reducing cholesterol levels. Many contradictory results have in the meantime been published (Groot, 1966; Bemelmans, 1967; Beresteyn, 1967; Lankveld, 1967; Norde, 1967) and no consensus of opinion is yet reached. More recently the importance of type of pectin has been recognized and significant differences in the action of low and highly esterified pectins have been seen (de Haan, 1968). This is in agreement with the results of Gilmore (1965) who found that less than 1% of a normally esterified but more than 20% of a low methoxylpectin could be recovered in animal and human faeces. This may be connected with the lower sensitivity of low methoxyl pectin for the alkaline medium of the duodenum (Section ID).

G. Methods of Investigation of Pectic Substances

Investigation of pectic substances in fruits comprises many aspects:

(a) *Histological.* For many years the Ruthenium Red method has been used to determine the position of pectin in plant tissues. This method has been recognized to be non-specific for uronides, and the only specific method available at the present time is the reaction of hydroxylamine with the ester of galacturonic acid to produce pectin hydroxamic acid which in turn can form a red complex with ferric ions (Gee et al., 1959; Kaye and Kent, 1953; McCready and Reeve, 1955). The intensity of the red colour formed is an indication of esterification but there is competition between formation of hydroxamic acid and de-esterification in the alkaline medium needed. Pectates would not show at all but Gee et al. (1959) included esterification *in situ* in their instructions. The method has also been used in connection with the electron microscope (Albersheim et al., 1960a).

A very ingenious method combines radioautography with the light and/or the electron microscope. It also allows the observation of biosynthetic pathways. Tissues grown in solutions of radioactive precursors are fixed on slides (light microscopy) or grids (electron microscopy) and covered with photographic emulsion. After days or weeks in light, sealed boxes the coated sections are developed and fixed. The labelled sites are thus sharply contrasted for microscopy (Northcote and Pickett-Heaps, 1966).

(b) *Determination of total pectin.* Methods for this determination can be divided into those using extraction methods and those determining pectic substances directly in the material. For extraction the method of McCready and McComb (1952) is widely followed. It consists of an alkaline treatment in the presence of EDTA, followed by enzymic degradation in acid medium. The extract is then supposed to contain all the uronides, and their concentration is measured with the carbazole colour reaction (cf. Section IGd). Calibration is done by comparison with decarboxylation values or with monogalacturonic acid. Decarboxylation is indeed one of the non-extractive methods used to determine total uronides. The original Lefevre–Tollens' method has been intensively studied and improved for application to mixtures with other carbohydrates which may also develop CO_2 (Doesburg, 1965). One variation, described with further improvements by Doesburg (1965), combines decarboxylation with a Zeisel demethylation thus allowing the simultaneous determination of quantity and degree of esterification. However, care must be taken of residual alcohol remaining from previous precipitations or purification steps as this will falsify the Zeisel results (Jansen et al., 1944). Another non-extractive method is the direct titration procedure of Gee et al. (1958) in which end points are sometimes difficult to obtain and which needs a correction for acetyl. These disadvantages are overcome by percolating a Ca-acetate solution through AIS in the acid form before and after saponification. Titration of the acetic acid liberated by the pectinic and pectic acid allows calculation of quantity and degree of esterification (Raunhardt and Neukom, 1964).

(c) *Fractional extraction to separate pectins, pectates and protopectin.* The desire to follow pectic changes during ripening, storage or processing has led to procedures of fractional extractions (McColloch, 1952; Rouse and Atkins, 1955) (mostly of the alchol insoluble solids) with which it is hoped to gain insight into the distribution of 3 main categories of pectic substances: high methoxyl (cold water soluble), low methoxyl or pectic acid (cold water soluble with Ca binding agents) and protopectin. As Ca binding agents oxalate, EDTA or polyphosphate are used. Protopectin is either considered as a third fraction, extractable with cold NaOH or by boiling with acid, or as the difference between total pectin and the water soluble pectin or also as the difference between total pectin and the two extracted fractions. One must realize that these extractions give at best empirical, if reproducible, results. The comment of Joslyn and Deuel (1963) really sums up the situation: "While a considerable amount of data are available on the chemical composition of extracted pectins, investigations of the rate and extent of extraction of pectins from plant tissue preparations are limited." This is reflected in the wide variations for extraction times (10 min to 24 hours) and temperatures (0°C to boiling point) which are found in the literature. McCready and McComb (1952) have also characterized the shortcomings of such multi-extraction procedures by drawing attention to the overlapping solubilities of the various pectic substances. Thus low methoxyl pectins may also be water soluble depending upon the cation composition of the fruit, and on the other hand enzyme demethylated pectins may be Ca sensitive at quite high degrees of esterification.

(d) *Determination of the concentration and properties of extracted pectins: uronide and neutral sugar content, esterification and acetylation, molecular weight.* The most widely used method to determine uronides is no doubt the carbazole method (Dische, 1950), as introduced by McCready and McComb (1952) and Rouse and Atkins (1955). It is not specific for galacturonic acid and only recently Knutson and Jeanes (1968a, b) have shown how the re-action can be used to determine the composition of uronic acid mixtures and also how it can be applied to heteropolysaccharides. Joslyn and Chen (1967) recommended a pre-purification of the pectin by Ca-precipitation. If information about degree of esterification is wanted, methanol must be de-termined in addition and this is best done by (micro)distillation after saponi-fication, oxidation to formaldehyde and determination with chromotropic acid. Very reliable values are also obtained by titration methods (Doesburg, 1965). After passage through a mixed bed ion exchanger, neutralization and saponification equivalents can be determined and this allows calculation of content and degree of esterification. If acetyl groups are present the saponi-cation equivalent is too high and must be corrected. This can be avoided by passing the saponified extract through an H·-exchanger and titrating directly the pectic acid obtained. Tibenski *et al.* (1963) precipitate with Cu-ions before and after saponification. The Cu content of the precipitates is equivalent to their carboxyl groups so that, again, calculation of quantity and degree of esterification is possible. Acetyl groups do not interfere and Cu is exactly and easily determined complexometrically. The decarboxylation procedures described under (b) can be applied to the extracts; if their volume is too great the pectic substances can be precipitated (alcohol, acetone, Cu, Ca) and the raw precipitate can be used. Acetyl can be determined by distillation after saponi-fication, most reliably after removing pectic acid by precipitation (Berglund, 1950). The hydroxamic colour reaction has also been used (McComb and McCready, 1957).

The above mentioned methods are all based on the determination of the uronide content of the pectic substances. In view of the heteropolysaccharide character of pectic substances this may not be sufficient information. Many authors therefore analyse paper chromatographical fractions of acid and/or enzyme hydrolysates (Zitko and Bishop, 1965; Hatanaka and Ozawa, 1966a, b; Barrett and Northcote, 1965; Aspinall et al., 1968; Tavakoli and Wiley, 1965). Uronides and neutral sugars in hydrolysates can also be determined gas chromatographically as trimethylsilylderivatives (Wiley et al., 1966; Tavakoli and Wiley, 1968a, b). The difficulties of this technique are mainly caused by the formation of anomers and conformers (Raunhardt, 1968). More and more such analyses are preceded by fractionation procedures like zone electrophoresis (Stoddart et al., 1967), precipitation with quaternary ammonium detergents (Stoddart et al., 1967; Scott, 1965) or with salts (Zitko and Bishop, 1965). However, the most promising method at present seems to be DEAE cellulose chromatography (Neukom and Kuendig, 1965; Heri, 1962; Smit and Bryant, 1967; Hatanaka and Ozawa, 1966a). There is good separation of neutral and acid polysaccharides. Using, for example, a NaH_2PO_4 gradient, pectins are retained more strongly with increasing uronide and decreasing methoxyl content. Pintauro (1967) succeeded in separating an almost 100% pure uronide fraction from cranberry pectic substances using DEAE-Sephadex.

Values pertaining to molecular weight can be obtained from viscosity measurements or end group determinations. Intrinsic viscosity is easily measured with Ubbelohde glass capillary viscometers but the polyelectrolyte character of pectin has to be taken into account and salt additions have to be made to depress charge effects (Vollmert, 1950; Owens et al., 1952). Deuel and Weber (1945) saponified pectins with NaOH to exclude the influence of degree of esterification; the present authors use an enzymic saponification to prevent transeliminative degradation. This phenomenon also presents the main problem when determining end groups since most of these methods are executed in an alkaline medium. Acid methods are rather tedious. Albersheim et al. (1960c) and Launer and Tomimatsu (1959) oxidized end groups with $NaClO_2$. Another possibility is to saponify pectins at low temperatures before using one of the usual end group methods (Koller, 1966).

(e) *Chemical structure of extracted pectin: determination of location (distribution) of non-uronides, methoxyl and acetyl.* The classical methods of periodate oxydation, methanolysis and acetylation are now supplemented by the study of trimethylsilylderivatives (Raunhardt, 1968). Furthermore, interesting possibilities exist for uronides by virtue of their (esterified) carboxyl group-like reduction to the primary alcohol of the ester groups alone or of all carboxyl groups after esterification with methanol or with glycols (Sen Gupta and Das, 1965).

β-Eliminative breakdown of chains, which occurs only next to esterified groups, has also been used (Stoddart et al., 1967). Oligo-uronides or aldobi- and aldotri-uronides can be separated on ion exchange columns.

There is still very little information on the distribution of substituents along the galacturonide chain. Solms and Deuel (1955) have shown that statistical or blockwise distribution of methoxyl can be recognized from the reaction velocity with PE which is known to attack only the group next to a free acid group. The same information can also be obtained by measuring Ca-ion activity in solutions of Ca-pectinate (Kohn and Furda, 1967a; Kohn et al., 1968) and by measuring stability constants for bound Ca or K/Ca selectivity coefficients (Kohn and Furda, 1967b). The stability constant of Ca-pectinate should also give information about the distribution of acetyl groups since Ca has been shown to be bound to the hydroxyl—as well as to the carboxyl group (Schweiger, 1962, 1964, 1966; Kohn and Furda, 1968). Deuel et al. (1953) showed earlier how acetylation affects cation exchange selectivity of methylene linked pectins. No other attempts have come to the authors' attention to solve the problem of the distribution of substituents or non-uronide chain links but there is no doubt that the increasing knowledge and availability of specific enzymes will create techniques to solve such problems.

(f) *Protopectin structure.* Since the admirable review of Joslyn (1962) this has been a sterile field. Again it can only be hoped that degradation by specific enzymes will bring more insight into the structure of this pectin fraction.

II. PECTIC ENZYMES

A. Definitions (Activities) and Nomenclature

There are two main groups of enzymes which affect pectic substances: saponifying and depolymerizing.

1. *Saponifying enzymes*

The saponifying enzyme is a specific pectin-methylesterase which splits the methylester group of polygalacturonic acids and which is now commonly called Pectin-Esterase or Pectin-Methyl-Esterase and abbreviated to PE. According to the International Enzyme Commission PE is a pectin-pectyl-hydrolase, number 3.1.1.11.

2. *Depolymerizing enzymes*

The depolymerizing enzymes have been classified by Demain and Phaff (1957) and Deuel & Stutz (1958) as glycosidases with specific activities pertaining to the degree of esterification of the substrate and to random or terminal cleavage. However, in 1960, Albersheim, Neukom and Deuel (Albersheim et al., 1960b) discovered transeliminative cleavage of the $\alpha\text{-}1 \rightarrow 4$-glycosidic bond in a commercial pectinase preparation (Fig. 7). This discovery was followed by a great number of publications showing a trans-elimination mechanism in pectin depolymerizing enzymes, so that a new classification became necessary, especially as it was found that these lyases could also be classified by random or terminal attack and by preference for a low or high methoxyl substrate.

This new classification was made by Neukom (1963) who subdivided all enzymes which split the α-(1→4) glycosidic bonds between galacturonic monomers in pectic substances in eight groups to which Koller (1966) assigned numbers according to the system of the International Enzyme Commission (Table I). The prefix "endo" or "exo" designates statistical or

TABLE I. Schematic classification of depolymerizing pectic enzymes
(Koller 1966)

Pectic enzymes acting mainly on pectin	
Polymethylgalacturonases (PMG)	Pectin-trans-eliminases (PTE)
1. Endo-PMG 3.2.1.41	3. Endo-PTE 4.2.2.3
2. Exo-PMG?	4. Exo-PTE?
Pectic enzymes acting mainly on pectic acid	
Polygalacturonases (PG)	Pectic acid-trans-eliminases (PATE)
5. Endo-PG 3.2.1.15	7. Endo-PATE 4.2.2.1
6. Exo-PG 3.2.1.40	8. Exo-PATE 4.2.2.2

terminal cleavage (liquefying or saccharifying). Each of these eight groups comprises enzymes which can be further subdivided according to pH optima, inhibition or activation with cations, stability and—in the case of exo-enzymes —attack on reducing or non-reducing end and degree of polymerization of end product. Names previously given to these enzymes include pectinase, polygalacturonase, depolymerase, liquefying polygalacturonase, depolymeric polygalacturonases etc. It is reasonable to assume that many of the enzymes described prior to 1960 must be recharacterized.

3. *Protopectinase and macerase*

Some investigators claim a special enzyme which solubilizes protopectin (Weurman, 1952), but no evidence has so far been presented for such an enzyme to exist. There is also a confusion of terms because other investigators consider a macerating action on plant tissue as evidence of protopectinase. However, no special enzyme is necessary to obtain maceration, which is easily achieved by "ordinary" pectic enzymes (Neukom, 1963) which degrade middle lamella pectin. One can even assume that protopectinase action in both meanings (solubilization and macerating) can be achieved by nonpectinolytic degradation of polysaccharides (cellulases and hemicellulases) which will break down the whole enmeshing structure causing solubilization of pectins as well as a macerating effect. Gremli and Neukom (1968) isolated an α-L-arabinofuranosidase from a commercial pectinase preparation and found that it macerated cucumber tissue with liberation of arabinose and galactose but not potatoes, apples and carrots. McNab et al. (1967) found that different plant tissues are differently macerated by the same enzyme preparation, surely a consequence of the different polysaccharide structure of different plants. Bateman and Miller (1966) therefore proposed the unspecific name of macerating enzymes for all cases where the specific action is unknown.

4. Oligouronidases

Glycosidases and Lyases acting on oligouronides have only recently been found in micro-organisms (Moran et al., 1968; Hasegawa and Nagel, 1968; Nagel and Hasegawa, 1968).

B. Occurrence in Fruit and General Properties

So far only PE and PG have been investigated.

1. Pectinesterase

PE has been found in:
Bananas (Hultin et al., 1966; Vas et al., 1967);
Cherries (Davignon, 1961; Al-Delaimy et al., 1966);
Cucumbers (Bell, 1951a, b);
Currants (Kieser et al., 1957: PE structure bond on insoluble pectins; Kertesz, 1951);
Papaya (Chang et al., 1965);
Pears (Weurman, 1954; Nagel and Patterson, 1967; Davignon, 1961; Vas et al., 1967);
Apples (Pollard and Kieser, 1951; Davignon, 1961);
Tomatoes (Hills and Mottern, 1947; Lee et al., 1968; Vas et al., 1967; Hobson, 1963);
Strawberries (Gizis, 1964; Leuprecht and Schaller, 1968);
Grapes (Marteau, 1967);
Citrus (Edwards and Joslyn, 1952; McDonnel et al., 1945; Jansen et al., 1960b; Rouse and Atkins, 1952, 1953, 1955; Rouse et al., 1965);
Peaches (Vas et al., 1967).

PE is adsorbed on the cell wall and can be desorbed by addition of neutral salts under slightly alkaline conditions. According to the investigations of Jansen et al. (1960b) on orange PE, this bond is an enzyme-substrate complex since the PE becomes soluble on saponification of the pectin. They also succeeded in desorbing PE at pH 3·8 by the addition of salt and a pectin solution. However, the PE binding capacity of citrus pulp (about 15 times the PE naturally present) is not specific since chymotrypsin may also be adsorbed and can be desorbed under the same conditions as PE. If cell-wall pectin is broken down enzymatically, the adsorbing capacity of the cells for both enzymes decreases.

Plant PE is almost completely specific for methylesters of polyuronides. Ethyl esters are only very slowly de-esterified (McDonnel et al., 1950) by citrus PE and glycol and glycerol esters not at all (Deuel and Stutz, 1958). The methylesters of mono-, di- and trigalacturonic acid are also not de-esterified by PE. The methylester of acetic and tartaric acid as well as the methylesters of alginate and tragacanth are resistant to PE (Deuel and Stutz, 1958). PE attacks only ester groups next to a free carboxyl group and then continues to act along the molecule. Solms and Deuel (1955) have demonstrated that PE acts more quickly on alkali presaponified pectin (statistical distribution of methoxyl groups) than on enzymatically presaponified pectin (blockwise distribution of acid and ester groups).

Kohn et al. (1968) also demonstrated the blockwise distribution of methoxyl-groups after enzymic de-esterification by measuring Ca complex stability. PE activity is inhibited by the acid groups formed. This phenomenon has also been observed for alkaline saponification and is explained by repulsion through the increasingly negatively charged colloid (Lineweaver and Ballou, 1945). The presence of neutral salt overcomes this repulsion and activates the enzyme. Simultaneous action of PG is also said to activate PE (Jansen et al., 1945).

For all fruit PE, a pH optimum between 7 and 8 has been described. Hultin and Levine (1963) have found 3 forms of PE in bananas which are differentiated by pH optima, inactivation with detergent and inactivation temperature. Microbial PEs, mostly from mould, have pH optima from 4 to 5.

Vas et al. (1967) determined the following temperature optima: citrus PE 65°C; apple PE 55°C; tomato PE 80°C. PE is in fact quite a heat stable enzyme. Pollard and Kieser (1951) found 80% residual activity in apple juice after 40 minutes at 68°C. Orange PE is only inactivated after 23 seconds at 92°C.

Mono- and divalent metallic cations are activators at low and inhibitors at high concentrations (Hultin et al., 1966), but L-ascorbinic acid and sulphite are also activators (Edwards and Joslyn, 1952). PE from higher plants is remarkably resistant to some chemicals, like formaldehyde, iodine, iodo acetic acid, cyanide and mercuric chloride (MacColloch and Kertesz, 1948). Yamasaki et al. (1967) found no effect of myristinic acid, p-chloromercuribenzoate and EDTA. Norde (1969) found no inhibition of PE in a commercial enzyme preparation by p-chloromercuribenzoate, di-isopropylfluorphosphate and urea. Polyphenolic inactivation of PE is well known (Hall, 1966). Nagel and Paterson (1967) recommend the use of polyvinylpyrrolidone to "bind" polyphenols before activity determinations in plants. Anion active detergents are also inhibitors (Kertesz, 1951; Hultin and Levine, 1963). Miller and McColloch (1959) think that fatty acids regulate PE activity in plants. Agions (Edwards and Joslyn, 1952), phosphate and nucleotides (Hultin et al., 1966) can also inactivate PE. Carbohydrates are non-competitive inhibitors (Chang et al., 1965).

2. Polygalacturonase

This enzyme is frequently found in yeasts, moulds and bacteria. Plant PG has been much less intensively investigated than microbial PG; its activity has mostly been studied *in situ* without previous extraction and/or purification. One exception is the work of Hobson (1962), who investigated the activity of sodium EDTA extracts from various fruits and vegetables.

PG has been found in:

Tomatoes (Hobson, 1962, 1964; Foda, 1957; Luh et al., 1956; Roelofsen, 1953);

Peaches (McCready and McComb, 1954);

Avocado (Hobson, 1962; McCready et al., 1955; Reymond and Phaff, 1965);

Mispel (Hobson, 1962);

Pears (Hobson, 1962; McCready and McComb, 1954; Weurman, 1953);

Ananas (Hobson, 1962).

For cherries (Yang et al., 1960) and for strawberries (Gizis, 1964; Staden and Doesburg, 1961) there is some question whether activity found is not of microbial origin. Neal (1965) found no depolymerization activity in strawberries, and the same doubt is raised for cucumbers (Bell, 1951a; Hobson, 1962), grapes (Marteau, 1967) and apples (Kertesz, 1951; Joslyn et al., 1952). There is evidence that PG activity is absent from citrus (McDonnel et al., 1945; Hobson, 1962; Joslyn and Pilnik, 1961), currants, prunes and melons (Hobson, 1962).

Tomato PG is the most thoroughly investigated fruit pectin depolymerase. It is probably a mixture of endo and exo PG (Demain and Phaff, 1957). The pH optimum lies between 3·5 and 5 but there is also an optimum at pH 2·5 (Patel and Phaff, 1958, 1960a) for degradation of acid soluble pectic acid (McCready and Seegmiller, 1954). No trace of PATE (see Table I) action could be found (Hamster, 1968).

McColloch and Kertesz (1948) thought tomato PG to have a heat stable component. Patel and Phaff (1960b) found 90% loss for purified tomato PG after 20 and 30 minutes at 60°C while Gizis (1964) found 35 minutes at 100°C necessary to inactivate strawberry PG.

Avocado PG is said to be almost identical with tomato PG (McCready *et al.*, 1955). A purified avocado PG (Reymond and Phaff, 1965) was shown to be an endo-enzyme with a pH optimum at 5·5. The pH optimum of strawberry PG lies between 4·5 and 5·5 (Gizis, 1964). The many mould PGs described usually have a pH optimum from 3 to 5, bacterial PGs are higher (Erwinia carotovora 5·2–5·4; Nasuno and Starr, 1966).

According to Deuel and Stutz (1958) the action of cations on fruit PG is not clear. The effect may be complicated by (bivalent) cation reaction with pectate substrates. Purified avocado PG (Reymond and Phaff, 1965) was inhibited by NH_4^+, K^+ and PO_4^{3-} ions but activated by metaphosphate. Inhibition of PG has been found in some fruits; for example, in pears by Weurman (1953). An inactivator of PG in grape leaves was described by Bell and Etchells (1958) as a tannin-like substance. Hobson (1964) on the other hand did not find any inhibiting action of polyphenols.

Ponomarcova (1967) found PE and PG to be present in apples, especially in the young fruits, and suggested that other workers' reports of inability to demonstrate PG activity in the fruits was due to the presence of inhibitors.

3. *Lyases (transeliminases)*

There is only one known instance of lyase activity in a higher plant (Albersheim and Killias, 1962: PTE in pea seedling). However, many microorganisms produce such enzymes and these may be important to fruit technology (Bateman and Miller, 1966). In general their pH optimum is high and they are activated by Ca^{2+}.

C. Determination of Enzyme Activity

1. *Pectin-esterase*

Qualitative pectin-esterase tests consist in mixing the enzyme with a pectin solution, adjust pH, and observe pH drop either electrometrically or with indicators. An addition of Ca¨-ions will give a Ca-pectate gel (Kertesz, 1937; Somogyi and Romani, 1964; Pilnik and Rothschild, 1960). Diffusion tests in Agar-pectin gels are also possible. Impregnation with acid will cause turbidity because of precipitation of pectic acid formed. Impregnation with a hydroxylamin-Fe reagent will only give the insoluble Fe-Hydroxamic acid complex where no PE was present (McComb and McCready, 1957). Quantitatively most authors use a titrimetric method to follow the saponifying action of PE. This method has been thoroughly investigated by Vas *et al.* (1967) and by Leuprecht and Schaller (1968). In reaction systems in which titration analyses are impossible, released methanol can be determined by distilling, oxidizing and determining formaldehyde with chromotropic acid.

2. Pectin hydrolases

PG and PMG can be differentiated by the use of the corresponding substrate, i.e. pectic acid or pectin. However, if PE is present its de-esterifying action on the pectin may prevent the correct evaluation of PMG activity. The present authors therefore use glycole esters (prepared from pectic acid and epoxide) as substrate. Pectic acid gel adsorption has been used to separate PE from the depolymerizing enzymes (Patel and Phaff, 1960a). Anyas-Weisz (1953) achieved this separation with mixed bed ion exchange. Rate of hydrolysis is determined by measuring viscosity decrease or carbonyl increase. Difficulties of end-group determination have been discussed in Section IGd. The comparison of viscosity and end-group measurements gives an indication for endo- or exo-activity. With an endo-enzyme specific viscosity is down to half when only 2 to 3% of the glycosidic linkages are split. With an exo-enzyme at least 40% of the glycosidic linkages must be hydrolysed before the half value is reached. Examination of breakdown products with paper chromatography also gives an indication of the reaction mechanism.

3. Pectin lyases

Everything said above for the hydrolases can also be applied to PATE and PTE. The appearance of unsaturated cleavage products, however, allows further and simple quantitative measurements of the double link by either measuring UV absorption at 235 mu (Albersheim *et al.*, 1960a) or using the quantitative colour development with T.B.A. reagent (Albersheim *et al.*, 1960a) or T.B.A.–periodate reagent (Weissbach and Hurwitz, 1959).

4. Mixtures of hydrolases and lyases

The quantitative measurement of appearing end-groups and formation of double links allows a calculation of relative activities, but even an added viscosity measurement will not differentiate between exo- and endo-activities. Further information is obtained by paper chromatography. Nagel and Vaughn (1961) and Edstrom and Phaff (1964) have discussed the solvents and sprays necessary to separate and develop saturated and unsaturated cleavage products. Methods for separating enzymes involve mainly the use of Ca-phosphate gels (MacMillan and Vaughn, 1964), cellulose chromatography (Hasegawa and Nagel, 1966; Nasuno and Starr, 1966) and electrophoresis (Roozen, 1967; Koller, 1966).

III. POLYURONIDES NOT PECTIN

Nomenclature of gums and mucilages becomes less stringent the better their structure becomes known. Smith and Montgomery (1959) have introduced a simplified classification into 3 groups: Acidic, Neutral and Basic.

Polyuronides would therefore belong to the first group, the acid component being uronic acid. In alginic acid we would have a "classical" polyuronide in which all the uronic acids are linked to each other by glycosidic linkages. Pectic substances already would not entirely correspond to this polyuronide character as there are rhamnose molecules even in the main chain of galacturonic acids. One may therefore take all polymer carbohydrates containing uronic acids, as polyuronides, not pectin. While many fruit trees can exude such substances (Smith and Montgomery, 1959) there is a great shortage of data concerning the fruits proper.

Büchi (1954) and Büchi and Deuel (1954) described an acid polysaccharide occurring in white grape juice or in water extractable form in grape pomace which had an equivalent weight of 1085 and a specific rotation of $+16\cdot1°$. Its components were D-galactose, D-mannose, L-arabinose, L-rhamnose and D-galacturonic acid. Partial hydrolysis gave an aldobiuronic acid which was identified as 2-α-D-galacturonopyranosido-L-rhamnopyranose which is also part of the "back bone structure" of pectin. However, no oligouronides were detected.

Tavakoli and Wiley (1965) found glucuronic acid in enzymatic degradation products of apple A.I.S. but this may well be linked to the pectin chain (cf. Section IBd).

In acid hydrolysates from quince seed mucilage (McCready and Whistler, 1959) an aldobiuronic acid was found which consists of xylose and a so far unidentified hexosyluronic acid (Smith and Montgomery, 1959).

REFERENCES

Albersheim, P., Mühlethalen, K. and Frey-Wijssling, A. (1960a). *J. biophys. biochem. Cytol.* **8**, 501–6.
Albersheim, P., Neukom, H. and Deuel, H. (1960b). *Helv. chim. Acta* **43**, 1422–6.
Albersheim, P., Neukom, H. and Deuel, H. (1960c). *Archs Biochem. Biophys.* **90**, 46–51.
Albersheim, P. and Killias, Ursula (1962). *Archs Biochem. Biophys.* **97**, 107–15.
Al-Delaimy, K. A., Borgstrom, G. and Bedford, C. L. (1966). *Q. Bull. Mich. St. Univ., U.S.A.* **49**, 164–71.
Anyas-Weiss, L. (1953). *Experientia* **9**, 1–3.
Aspinall, G. O. and Cañas-Rodrigues, A. (1958). *J. chem. Soc.* 4020–7.
Aspinall, G. O., Craig, J. W. T. and Whyte, J. Z. (1968). *Carbohydrate Res.* **7**, 442–52.
Baker, G. L. (1948). *In* "Advances in Food Research" (C. O. Chichester, E. M. Mrak and G. F. Stewart, eds), Vol. 1, pp. 395–427. Academic Press, New York and London.
Barber, G. A. (1962). *Biochem. Biophys. Res commun.* **8**, 204.
Barrett, A. and Northcote, D. (1965). *Biochem. J.* **94**, 617–27.
Bateman, D. F. and Miller, R. L. (1966). *Ann. Rev. Phytopath.* **4**, 119–46.

Bell, T. A. (1951a). *Bot. Gaz.* **113**, 216–21.
Bell, T. A. (1951b). *Archs Biochem. Biophys.* **31**, 431–41.
Bell, T. A. and Etchells, J. L. (1958). *Bot. Gaz.* **119**, 192–6.
Bemelmans, J. M. H. (1967). M.Sc. Thesis, Agricultural University, Dept. of Food Science, Wageningen, the Netherlands.
Bender, W. A. (1959). *In* "Industrial Gums" (R. L. Whistler, ed.), pp. 377–432. Academic Press, New York and London.
Beresteyn, Renske C. H. van (1967). M.Sc. Thesis, Agricultural University, Dept. of Food Science, Wageningen, the Netherlands.
Berglund, D. T. (1950). *Socker* **6**, 219–23.
Bhattacharjee, S. S. and Timmell, T. E. (1965). *Can. J. Chem.* **43**, 758–65.
Bishop, C. T. (1955). *Can. J. Chem.* **33**, 1521–9.
Bock, W. and Lange, D. (1963). *Die Nahrung*, 71–8.
Bock, W., Pose, J. and Augustat, S. (1964). *Biochem. Z.* **341**, 64–73.
Büchi, W. (1954). Diss. No. 2332, E.T.H. Zürich.
Büchi, W. and Deuel, H. (1954). *Helv. chim. Acta* **37**, 1392–8.
Bulmer, H. P. (1967). *Fd Mf.* **42**, 37–9.
Buren, J. P. van (1967). *J. Fd Sci.* **32**, 435–7.
Charley, V. L. S. (1964). *In* "Berichte der Wissenschaftlich-Technischen Kommission. Internationale Fruchtsaft-Union", **5**, 15–27.
Chang, L. W. S., Morita, L. L. and Yamamoto, N. Y. (1965). *J. Fd Sci.* **30**, 218–222.
Chen, T. S. and Joslyn, M. A. (1967). *Fd Technol.* **21**, 658–64.
Davignon, M. L. (1961). *C. R. Acad. Agr. France* **47**, 62–6.
Demain, A. L. and Phaff, H. J. (1957). *Wallerstein Labs Commun.* **20**, (69), 119–40.
Deshpande, P. B. and Salunkhe, D. K. (1964). *Fd Technol.* **18**, 1195–8.
Deshpande, P. B., Klinker, W. J., Draudt, H. N. and Desrosier, N. W. (1966). *J. Fd Sci.* **30**, 594–600.
Deuel, H. (1943). *Helv. chim. Acta* **26**, 2002–25.
Deuel, H. (1945). *Schweiz. med. Wschr.* **30**, 661–5.
Deuel, H. and Solms, J. (1954). *In* "Natural Plant Hydrocolloids", *Adv. Chem. Series* no. 11, pp. 62–7. Am. Chem. Soc., Washington, D.C., U.S.A.
Deuel, H. and Stutz, E. (1958). *Adv. Enzymol.* **20**, 341–82.
Deuel, H. and Weber, F. (1945). *Helv. chim. Acta* **28**, 1089–1110.
Deuel, H., Hutchneker, K. and Solms, J. (1953). *Z. Electrochem.* **57**, 172–3.
Deuel, H., Solms, J. and Benzler, A. (1954). *Mitt. Geb. Lebensmittelunters. u. Hyg.* **45**, 73–84.
Deuel, H., Hutchneker, K., Stutz, E. and Frederiks, J. C. (1957). *Helv. chim. Acta* **40**, 2009–14.
Dische, Z. (1950). *J. biol. Chem.* **183**, 489–94.
Doesburg, J. J. (1957). *J. Sci. Fd Agric.* **8**, 206–16.
Doesburg, J. J. (1965). "Pectic substances in fresh and preserved fruits and vegetables". pp. 24, 44. I.B.V.T. Communication No. 25. Inst. for Res. on Storage and Processing of Horticultural Produce, Wageningen, the Netherlands.
Doesburg, J. J. and Grevers, G. (1960). *J. Fd Sci.* **25**, 634–45.
Dolendo, A. L., Luh, B. S. and Pratt, H. K. (1966). *J. Fd Sci.* **31**, 332–6.
Edwards, J. W. and Joslyn, M. A. (1952). *Archs Biochem. Biophys.* **39**, 51–5.
Edstrom, R. D. and Phaff, H. J. (1964). *J. biol. Chem.* **239**, 2409–15.
Ehrlich, R. M. *Fd Product Development*, 36–42.

Feingold, D. S., Neufeld, E. F. and Hassid, W. Z. (1960). *J. biol. Chem.* **235,** 910–13.

Foda, Y. H. (1957). Ph.D. Thesis, University of Illinois, U.S.A.

Foglietti, M. J. and Percheron, F. (1968). *Carbohydrate Res.* **7,** 146–155.

Gee, Mildred, McComb, Elizabeth and McCready, R. M. (1958). *J. Fd Sci.* **23,** 72–5.

Gee, Mildred, Reeve, R. M. and McCready, R. M. (1959). *J. Agric. Fd Chem.* **7,** 34–8.

Gilmore, Norma (1965). Ph.D. Thesis, Michigan State University, U.S.A.

Gizis, E. J. (1964). Ph.D. Thesis, Oregon State University, U.S.A.

Gremli, H. and Neukom, H. (1968). *Fd Sci. Technol.* **1,** 24–5.

Groot, E. H. (1966). *Voeding* **27,** 549–54.

Guyer, R. B., Miller, W. M., Bisset, D. W. and Veldhuis, M. K. (1956). *Fd Technol.* **10,** 10–16.

Haan, H. H. de (1968). M.Sc. Thesis, Agricultural University, Dept. of Food Science, Wageningen, The Netherlands.

Hall, C. B. (1966). *Nature, Lond.* **212,** 717–18.

Hamster, R. H. (1968). M.Sc. Thesis, Agric. University, Dept. of Food Science, Wageningen, The Netherlands.

Harvey, H. G. (1960). *In* "Texture in Foods", S.C.I. Monograph no. 7, pp. 29–63. Soc. of Chem. Ind., London.

Hasegawa, S. and Nagel, C. W. (1966). *J. Fd Sci.* **31,** 834–45.

Hasegawa, S. and Nagel, C. W. (1968). *Archs Biochem. Biophys.* **124,** 513–20.

Hatanaka, Ch. and Ozawa, J. (1966a). *Ber. Ōhara Inst. landw. Biol.* **23,** 89–102.

Hatanaka, Ch. and Ozawa, J. (1966b). *Ber. Ōhara Inst. landw. Biol.* **23,** 103–9.

Heri, W. (1962). Diss. no. 3172, E.T.H. Zürich.

Hills, C. H. and Mottern, H. H. (1947). *J. biol. Chem.* **168,** 651–63.

Hills, C. H., Mottern, H. H., Nutting, G. C. and Speiser, R. (1949). *Fd Technol.* **3,** 90–4.

Hills, C. H., White, J. W. Jr. and Baker, G. L. (1942). *Proc. Inst. Fd Technol.* 47–58.

Hobson, G. E. (1962). *Nature, Lond.* **195,** 804.

Hobson, G. E. (1963). *Biochem. J.* **86,** 358–65.

Hobson, G. E. (1964). *Biochem. J.* **92,** 324–32.

Hottenroth, Beatrice (1951). "Die Pektine und Ihre Verwendung". Verlag R. Oldenbourg, Munich.

Hsu, Cecilia, Deshpande, S. N. and Desrosier, N. W. (1965). *J. Fd Sci.* **30,** 583–8.

Huet, R. and Lederberger, A. (1964). *Fruchtsaft-Ind.* **9,** 163–7.

Hultin, H. O. and Levine, A. S. (1963). *Archs Biochem. Biophys.* **101,** 396–402.

Hultin, H. O., Sun, B. and Bulger, J. (1966). *J. Fd Sci.* **31,** 320–7.

Hutschneker, K. (1955). Diss. no. 2543, E.T.H., Zürich.

Janse, Madi D. (1967). M.Sc. Thesis, Agric. University, Dept. of Food Science Wageningen, The Netherlands.

Jansen, E. F., Waisbrot, S. W. and Rietz, E. (1944). *Ind. Engng Chem. analyt. Edn* **16,** 523–4.

Jansen, E. F., MacDonnel, L. R. and Jang, R. (1945). *Archs Biochem.* **8,** 112–18.

Jansen, E. F., Jang, Rosie, Albersheim, P. and Bonner, J. (1960a). *Pl. Physiol., Lancaster* **35,** 87–97.

Jansen, E. F., Jang, Rosie and Bonner, J. (1960b). *J. Fd Sci.* **25,** 64–72.

Joseph, G. H. (1955). *In* "Use of Sugars and other Carbohydrates in the Food Industry", Adv. in Chem. Series no. 12, pp. 49–56. Am. Chem. Soc., Washington, D.C., U.S.A.

Joseph, G. H. (1963). *Citrus in Medicine* **2** (1).

Joslyn, M. A. (1962). *In* "Advances in Food Research" (C. O. Chichester, E. M. Mrak and G. F. Stewart, eds), Vol. 11, pp. 1–107. Academic Press, New York.

Joslyn, M.A. and Chen, T. S. (1967). *J. Agric. Fd Chem.* **15**, 398–402.

Joslyn, M. A. and Deuel, H. (1963). *J. Fd Sci.* **28**, 65–83.

Joslyn, M. A. and Pilnik, W. (1961). *In* "The Orange" (W. B. Sinclair, ed.), pp. 373–426. Univ. of California, U.S.A., Printing Department.

Joslyn, M. A., Mist S. and Lamberts, E. (1952). *Fd Technol.* **6**, 133–9.

Kanujoso, B. W. T. and Luh, B. S. (1967). *Fd Technol.* **21**, 457–60.

Katchalski, A. (1954). *J. Polym. Sci.* **12**, 159–82.

Katchalski, A., Shavit, N. and Eisenberg, H. (1954). *J. Polym. Sci.* **13**, 69–84.

Kaye, M. A. G. and Kent, P. W. (1953). *J. chem. Soc.* 79–83.

Kertesz, Z. I. (1937). *J. biol. Chem.* **121**, 589–98.

Kertesz, Z. I. (1951). "The Pectic Substances". Interscience, New York and London.

Kessler, G., Neufeld, E. F., Feingold, D. S. and Hassid, W. Z. (1961). *J. biol. Chem.* **236**, 308–12.

Keys, A., Grande, F. and Anderson, J. T. (1961). *Proc. Soc. exp. Biol. Med.* **106**, 555–8.

Kieser, M. E., Pollard, A. and Sissons, D. J. (1957). *Rep. agric. hort. Res. Stn. Univ. Bristol*, 134–7.

Knutson, Clarence A. and Jeanes, Allene (1968a). *Anal. Biochem.* **24**, 470–81.

Knutson, Clarence A. and Jeanes, Allene (1968b). *Anal. Biochem.* **24**, 482–90.

Koch, J. and Haase-Sajak, E. (1965). *Dt. Lebensmitt Rdsch.* **61**, 199–209.

Kohn, R. and Furda, J. (1967a). *Coll. Czech. chem. Commun. Engl. Edn* **32**, 1925–37.

Kohn, R. and Furda, J. (1967b). *Coll. Czech. chem. Commun. Engl. Edn* **32**, 4470–84.

Kohn, R. and Furda, J. (1968). *Coll. Czech. chem. Commun. Engl. Edn* **33**, 2217–25.

Kohn, R., Furda, J. and Kopec, Z. (1968). *Coll. Czech. chem. Commun. Engl. Edn* **33**, 264–9.

Koller, A. (1966). Diss. no. 3774, E.T.H. Zürich.

Krauss, H. and Hassid, W. Z. (1967). *J. biol. Chem.* **242**, 2449–53.

Lange, D., Bock, W. and Täufel, K. (1965). *Ernährungsforschung* **10**, 1–13.

Lankveld, J. M. G. (1967). M.Sc. Thesis Agricultural University, Dept. of Food Science, Wageningen, the Netherlands.

Launer, H. F. and Tomimatsu, Y. (1959). *Analyt. Chem.* **31**, 1569–74.

Lee, M. J., Miller, J. and Macmillan, J. D. (1968). *Am. chem. Soc.* 156th Nat. Meeting. Abstracts of paper Nb. Biol. 224.

Lefèvre, K. N. and Tollens, B. (1907). *Ber. dt. chem. Ges.* **40**, 4513–23.

Leloir, L. F., Cordini, C. E. and Cabib, E. (1960). "Comparative Biochemistry" Vol. 2 (Florkin, M. and Mason, H. F. Eds). pp. 97–138. Academic Press, New York and London.

Leuprecht, H. and Schaller, A. (1968). *Fruchtsaft-Ind.* **13**, 50–74.

Lin, T. Y., Elbein, A. D. and Su, J. C. (1966). *Biochem. biophys. Res. Commun.* **22**, 650–6.

Lyn, J. v. d. (1966). M.Sc. Thesis, Agricultural University, Dept. of Food Science, Wageningen, the Netherlands.

Lineweaver, H. and Ballou, G. A. (1945). *Archs Biochem.* **6**, 373–87.

Loewus, F. A. (1964). *Nature, Lond.* **203**, 1175–7.

Loewus, F. A. and Kelly, S. (1961). *Archs Biochem. Biophys.* **95**, 483–493.

Loewus, F. A. and Kelly, S. (1963). *Archs Biochem. Biophys.* **102**, 96–105.

Lopez, A. and Li-Hsieng Li (1968). *Fd Technol.* **22**, 1023–8.

Luj, B. S. and Dastur, K. D. (1966). *J. Fd Sci.* **31**, 178–83.

Luh, B. S. and Dastur, K. D. (1968). *Fd Technol.* **22,** 1481–4.

Luh, B. S., Leonard, S. J. and Phaff, H. J. (1956). *J. Fd Sci.* **21,** 448–51.

McColloch, R. J. (1952). Fruit and Vegetable Chemistry Laboratory, Pasadena, Calif. A.J.C. 337.

McColloch, R. J. and Kertesz, Z. I. (1948). *Archs Biochem.* **17,** 197–9.

McComb, Elizabeth and McCready, R. M. (1957). *Analyt. Chem.* **29,** 819–21.

McCready, R. M. and Gee, Mildred (1960). *J. Agric. Fd Chem.* **8,** 510–13.

McCready, R. M. and McComb, Elizabeth A. (1952). *Analyt. Chem.* **24,** 1986–8.

McCready, R. M. and McComb, Elizabeth A. (1954). *J. Fd Sci.* **19,** 530–5.

McCready, R. M., Owens, H. S. and Maclay, W. D. (1944). *Fd Inds* **16,** 794–6, 864–5, 906–8.

McCready, R. M. and Reeve, R. M. (1955). *J. agric. Fd Chem.* **3,** 260–2.

McCready, R. M. and Seegmiller, C. G. (1954). *Archs Biochem. Biophys.* **50,** 440–50.

McCready, R. M., Shepherd, A. D., Swenson, H. A., Erlanden, Roberta F. and Maclay, W. D. (1951). *Analyt. Chem.* **23,** 975–7.

McCready, R. M., McComb, Elizabeth A. and Jansen, E. F. (1955). *J. Fd Sci.* **20,** 186–91.

McCready, R. M. and Whistler, R. L. (1959). *In* "Industrial Gums" (R. L. Whistler ed.), pp. 443–59. Academic Press, New York and London.

McDonnel, L. R., Jansen, E. F. and Lineweaver, H. (1945). *Archs biol. Chem.* **6,** 389–401.

McDonnel, L. R., Lang, R., Jansen, E. F. and Lineweaver, H. (1950). *Archs Biochem.* **128,** 260–73.

MacDowell, L. G. (1962). *Ber. Inst. Getränkeforschung G.m.b.H.,* Mainz **1,** 49–64.

MacMillan, J. D. and Vaughn, R. H. (1964). *Biochemistry* **3,** 564–72.

McNab, J. M., Nevins, D. J. and Albersheim, P. (1967). *Phytopathology* **57,** 625–31.

Marteau, G. (1967). *Annls Nutr. Aliment.* **21** (5), 223–345.

Miller, G. J. and McColloch, R. J. (1959). *Biochem. biophys. Res. Commun.* **1,** 91–3.

Mohammadzadeh-Khayat, M. M. and Luh, B. S. (1968). *J. Fd Sci.* **33,** 493–8.

Moran, F., Nasuno, S. and Starr, M. P. (1968). *Archs Biochem. Biophys.* **125,** 734–41.

Nagel, C. W. and Hasegawa, S. (1968). *J. Fd Sci.* **33,** 378–82.

Nagel, C. W. and Patterson, M. E. (1967). *J. Fd Sci.* **32,** 294–7.

Nagel, C. W. and Vaughn, R. H. (1961). *Archs Biochem. Biophys.* **94,** 328–32.

Nasuno, S. and Starr, H. P. (1966). *J. biol. Chem.* **241,** 5298–306.

Neal, G. E. (1965). *J. Sci. Fd Agric.* **16,** 605–11.

Neufeld, E. F., Ginsburg, V., Putnam, E. W., Fanshier, D. and Hassid, W. Z. (1957). *Archs Biochem. Biophys.* **69,** 602–16.

Neukom, H. (1963). *Schweiz. Landw. Forsch.* **2,** 112–21.

Neukom, H. (1967). *Kirk-Othmer Encycl. Chem. Technol.* **14,** 636–51.

Neukom, H. and Deuel, H. (1958). *Chem. Ind.* 683.

Neukom, H. and Kuendig, W. (1965). *In* "Methods in Carbohydrate Chem." (R. L. Whistler and J. N. Bemiller, eds), Vol. 5, pp. 14–18. Academic Press, London and New York.

Norde, W. (1967). M.Sc. Thesis, Agricultural University, Dept. of Nutrition, Wageningen, the Netherlands.

Norde, W. (1969). M.Sc. Thesis, Agricultural University, Dept. of Food Science, Wageningen, the Netherlands.

Northcote, D. H. (1958). *Biol. Rev.* **33,** 53–102.

Northcote, D. H. and Pickett-Heaps, J. D. (1966). *Biochem. J.* **98,** 159–67.

O'Colla, P. S., O'Donnell, J. J. and Freley, J. M. D. (1962). *Proc. chem. Soc.* 68–9.

Ordin, L., Cleland, R. and Bonner, J. (1957). *Pl. Physiol. Lancaster* **32**, 216–20.

Owens, H. S., McCready, R. M. and Maclay, W. D. (1949). *Fd Technol.* **3**, 77–82.

Owens, H. S., McCready, R. M., Shepherd, A. D., Schultz, F. H., Pippen, E. L., Swenson, H. A., Miers, J. C., Erlandsen, R. F. and Maclay, W. D. (1952). Western Regional Research Laboratory, Albany, Calif. A.J.C. 340.

Owens, H. S., Swenson, H. A. and Schultz, T. H. (1954). *In* "Natural Plant Hydrocolloids", Adv. Chem. Series no. 11, pp. 10–15. Am. Chem. Soc., Washington, D.C.

Patel, D. S. and Phaff, H. J. (1958). *J. Fd Sci.* **23**, 693–4.

Patel, D. S. and Phaff, H. J. (1960a). *J. Fd Sci.* **25**, 37–47.

Patel, D. S. and Phaff, H. J. (1960b). *J. Fd Sci.* **25**, 47–57.

Pickett-Heaps, J. D. and Northcote, D. H. (1966). *J. exp. Botany* **17**, 20–6.

Pilnik, W. (1946). Diss. E.T.H. Zürich.

Pilnik, W. (1958). *In* "Berichte der Wissenschaftlich-Technischen Kommission Internationale Fruchtsaft Union", **1**, 203–28.

Pilnik, W. (1964). *Fruchtsaft-Ind.* **9**, 277–84.

Pilnik, W. (1969). *Flüssiges Obst.* **36**, 39–46.

Pilnik, W. and Rothschild, Gerda (1960). *Fruchtsaft-Ind.* **5**, 131–8.

Pilnik, W. and Zwiker, P. (1970). *Gordian* (in press).

Pintauro, N. D. (1967). Ph.D. Thesis, Rutgers State Univ., U.S.A.

Pollard, A. and Kieser, M. E. (1951). *J. Sci. Fd Agric.* **2**, 30–6.

Ponomarcora, N. P. (1967). *Akad. Nauk. Mold. S.S.R. Inst. Fiziol. Biochem. Res.* 1967, 33–41; *Chem. Abstracts* **68**, 75732c.

Potter, R. S. (1966). *Proc. Biochem. Soc., Calcutta* 378–84.

Preston, R. D. and Nelmes, B. J., *J. exp. Botany* **9**, 496.

Primo Yúfera, E., Koen, J. M. and Royo-Iranzo, J. (1961). *In* "Berichte der Wissenschaftlich-Technischen Kommission", Internationale Fruchtsaft-Union, **3**, 17–26.

Raunhardt, O. (1968). Diss. no. 4161, E.T.H. Zürich.

Raunhardt, O. and Neukom, H. (1964). *Mitt. Geb. Lebensmittelunters. u. Hyg.* **55**, 446–55.

Reintjes, H. J. (1966). *In* "Berichte der Wissenschaftlich-Technischen Kommission". Internationale Fruchtsaft-Union, **7**, 239–51.

Reymond, D. and Phaff, H. J. (1965). *J. Fd Sci.* **30**, 266–73.

Roelofsen, P. A. (1953). *Biochim. biophys. Acta* **10**, 410–13.

Roozen, J. P. (1967). M.Sc. Thesis, Agricultural University, Dept. of Food Science, Wageningen, the Netherlands.

Rouse, A. H. (1953). *Fd Technol.* **7**, 360–2.

Rouse, A. H. and Atkins, C. D. (1952). *Fd Technol.* **6**, 291–4.

Rouse, A. H. and Atkins, C. D. (1953). *Fd Technol.* **7**, 221–3.

Rouse, A. H. and Atkins, C. D. (1955). Techn. Bull. Univ. Florida Agric. Exper. Sta. no. 570.

Rouse, A. H., Atkins, C. D. and Moore, E. L. (1964a). *Pro. Fla. St. hort. Soc.* **77**, 271–4.

Rouse, A. H., Atkins, C. D. and Moore, E. L. (1964b). *Pro. Fla. St. hort. Soc.* **77**, 274–8.

Rouse, A. H., Atkins, C. D. and Moore, E. L. (1965). *Fd Technol.* **19**, 673–6.

Sato, C. S., Byerrum, R. U. and Ball, C. D. (1957). *J. biol. Chem.* **224**, 717–23.
Schweiger, R. G. (1962). *J. org. Chem.* **27**, 1789–91.
Schweiger, R. G. (1964). *J. org. Chem.* **29**, 2973–9.
Schweiger, R. G. (1966). Kolloid-Z.Z. Polymere **208**, 28–31.
Scott, J. E. (1965). *In* "Methods in Carbohydrate Chem." (R. L. Whistler, ed.) Vol. V, pp. 38–44. Academic Press, London and New York.
Sen-Gupta, U. K. and Das, A. (1965). *Bull chem. Soc. Japan* **38**, 1074–7.
Sen-Gupta, U. K. and Rao, C. V. N. (1963). *Bull. chem. Soc. Japan* **36**, 1683–8.
Shewfelt, A. L. (1965). *J. Fd Sci.* **30**, 573–6.
Sinclair, W. B. and Joliffe, V. A. (1961). *J. Fd Sci.* **26**, 125.
Sioiri, H. and Haginuma, S. (1954). *Rep. Fd Res. Inst., Tokyo* **9**, 89–94. Food Agency, Ministry of Agriculture and Forestry, Tokyo, Japan.
Slavičkova, Anna (1961). *Sb. Fd Technol.* **5**, 73–158.
Smit, C. J. B. and Bryant, E. F. (1967). *J. Fd Sci.* **32**, 197–9.
Smit, C. J. B. and Bryant, E. F. (1968). *J. Fd Sci.* **33**, 262–4.
Smith, F. and Cleve, J. W. van (1955). *J. Am. chem. Soc.* **77**, 3091–3096.
Smith, F. and Montgomery, R. (1959). *In* "The Chemistry of Plant Gums and Mucilages", pp. 12. Am. Chem. Soc. Monograph series. Reinhold Publ. Corp. New York.
Solms, J. (1960). *In* "Physical Functions of Hydrocolloids", *Adv. Chem. Series* no. 25, pp. 37–45. Am. Chem. Soc., Washington, D.C., U.S.A.
Solms, J. and Deuel, H. (1951). *Helv. chim. Acta* **34**, 2242–9.
Solms, J. and Deuel, H. (1954). *J. Polym. Sci.* **12**, 559–64.
Solms, J. and Deuel, H. (1955). *Helv. chim. Acta* **38**, 321–9.
Somogyi, L. and Romani, R. (1964). *Anal. Biochem.* **8**, 498–501.
Speiser, R. (1947). *J. Polym. Sci.* **2**, 281–9.
Staden, O. L. and Doesburg, J. J. (1961). Ann. Report 1961, pp. 60–2. Institute for Research on Storage and Processing of Horticultural Produce, I.B.V.T., Wageningen, the Netherlands.
Sterling, C. (1963). *In* "Recent Advances in Food Science" (J. M. Leitch and D. N. Rhodes, eds), Vol. 3, pp. 269–71. Butterworths, London.
Stoddart, R. W., Barrett, A. J. and Northcote, D. H. (1967). *Biochem. J.* **102**, 194–204.
Stoddart, R. W. and Northcote, D. H. (1967). *Biochem. J.* **105**, 45–59.
Stutz, E. and Deuel, H. (1955). *Helv. chim. Acta* **38**, 1757–63.
Tavakoli, M. and Wiley, R. C. (1965). *Proc. Am. Soc. hort. Sci.* **87**, 104–12.
Tavakoli, M. and Wiley, R. C. (1968a). *Proc. Am. Soc. hort. Sci.* **92**, 772–9.
Tavakoli, M. and Wiley, R. C. (1968b). *Proc. Am. Soc. hort. Sci.* **92**, 780–7.
Tibenski, V., Rosik, J. and Zitko, V. (1963). *Die Nahrung* **7**, 321–6.
Ulrich, R. and Hartman, C. (1967). *Ann. Nutr. Aliment.* **21**, B 161–88.
Vas, K., Nedbalek, M., Scheffer, H. and Kovacs-Proszt, G. (1967). *Fruchtsaft-Ind.* **12**, 164–84.
Vollmert, B. (1950). *Makromolek. Chem.* **5**, 110–27.
Weber, F. (1945). Mitt. Agr. Inst. E.T.H. Zürich, 9–83.
Weissbach, A. and Hurwitz, J. (1959). *J. biol. Chem.* **234**, 705–9.
Wenzel, F. W., Moore, E. L., Rouse, A. H. and Atkins, C. D. (1951). *Fd Technol.* **5**, 451–7.
Weurmann, C. (1952). Diss. Univ. Amsterdam, The Netherlands. Centraal Instituut voor Voedingsonderzoek T.N.O., Utrecht, The Netherlands, Publ. no. 147.
Weurmann, C. (1953). *Acta bot. neerl.* **2**, 107–21.

Weurmann, C. (1954). *Acta bot. neerl.* **3,** 100–7.

Wieringa, K. T. (1949). Rep. Proc. Fourth Intern. Congr. Microbiology, Copenhagen, 447.

Wiley, R. C., Tavakoli, M. and Moore, M. D. (1966). *Proc. Am. Soc. hort. Sci.* **89,** 34–9.

Willaman, J. J. and Daisson, F. R. (1924). *J. Agric. Res.* **28,** 479–88.

Woodmansee, C. W. and Baker, G. L. (1949). *Fd Technol.* **3,** 82–5.

Worth, H. G. J. (1967). *Chem. Rev.* **67,** 465–73.

Yamasaki, M., Kato, A., Chu, S. Y. and Arima, K. (1967). *Agr. Biol. Chem.* **31,** 552–60.

Yatng, H. Y., Steele, W. F. and Graham, D. J. (1960). *Fd Technol.* **14,** 644–7.

Ziko, V. and Bishop, C. T. (1965). *Can. J. Chem.* **43,** 3206–14.

Chapter 4

Organic Acids

R. ULRICH

Faculté des Sciences, Sorbonne, Paris, France

I. INTRODUCTION

The acidic properties of organic acids are due to the presence in their molecule of the carboxylic group—COOH, in the free state. Other fruit constituents may have acidic properties without possessing this group in the free state; this is especially the case for phenols and ascorbic acid in which the acidity is due to two enol groups. The long chain organic acids, the fatty acids, will be dealt with in Chapter 9, although phenolic acids will be cited in the table of acids. They will be considered in detail in Chapter 11.

Many fruits are particularly rich in organic acids which are usually dissolved in the water of the cell, either free or combined as salts, esters, glycosides, etc. Sometimes, the concentration is sufficiently high to cause crystallization (calcium oxalate in many young fruits; potassium bitartrate in grapes; see Fig. 1). Organic acids are an important source of respiratory energy in the plant cell.

Important reviews have been published on fruit acids in the past. Apart from the well-known general textbooks of Wehmer, Czapek and Klein, a modern review has been prepared by Thimann and Bonner (1950) on the metabolism of organic acids. Other recent reviews are the extensive report of Wolf (1960) on organic acids of fruits and parts of the more general papers or books of Hulme (1958c), Biale (1960), Carles (1960), Crombie (1960), Lee (general composition of fruits, 1951), and Ulrich (fruit physiology, 1952).

II. CHEMICAL NATURE AND DISTRIBUTION OF ORGANIC ACIDS IN FRUITS

A. Nature of the Acids

1. *Aliphatic monocarboxylic acids*

Formic acid, H—COOH. Volatile, widely distributed but at low concentration; observed in grapes (cf. Lee, 1951).

Acetic acid, CH_3—COOH. Volatile, widely distributed at low concentration (e.g. grapes, dates); as ester in fruit volatiles; as acetylcoenzyme A in all cells.

Butyric acid, CH_3—$(CH_2)_2$—COOH. Found by Haagen *et al.* (1949) in grapes. As ester in volatiles.

Parasorbic acid. In *Sorbus* fruits (Diemair and Franzen, 1959).

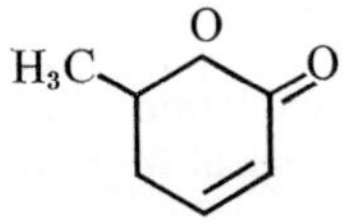

Di-oxogulonic acid, COOH—$(CO)_2$—$(CHOH)_2$—CH_2OH. Widely distributed (Chen and Schuck, 1951).

2 *Me*-2 : 3 *dihydroxy butyric acid*. In apple juice. (Whiting, 1958b).

2. *Aliphatic monocarboxylic with alcohol, ketone or aldehyde groups*

(a) Alcohols

Glycolic acid, CH_2OH—COOH. Common at low concentration (unripe grapes, apples, pears).

Lactic acid, CH_3—CHOH—COOH. May be an artefact in extracts.

Glyceric acid, CH_2OH—CHOH—COOH. As phosphoglyceric acid in green fruits as a product of photosynthesis (grapes; Ribereau and Gayon, 1968).

Mevalonic acid, CH_2OH—CH_2—$C(OH)(CH_3)$—CH_2—COOH. Traces; an intermediary step in carotenoid synthesis.

(b) Ketones

Pyruvic acid, CH_3—CO—COOH. Common at a low level; phosphoenol pyruvic acid appears in glycolysis.

(c) Aldehydes

Glyoxylic acid, CHO—COOH. In unripe grapes and apples (Haagen-Smit *et al.*, 1949).

3. *Aliphatic di- and tri-carboxylic acids*

Oxalic acid, HOOC—COOH. Uncommon as free acid; as soluble salt in banana; as insoluble calcium oxalate in numerous unripe fruits (Niethammer, 1931) (Fig. 1).

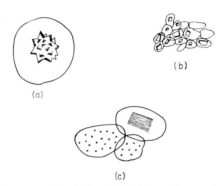

(a)

(b)

(c)

FIG. 1. Calcium oxalate crystals in fruit cells. (a) Druses in preach; (b) Single crystals in pear; (c) Raphides in banana. From Ulrich (1952).

Succinic acid, HOOC—$(CH_2)_2$—COOH. Present in very small amounts in several fruits.

Fumaric acid, HOOC—CH=CH—COOH. In green apples (Buchloh and Hane, 1962).

L-*Malic acid*, HOOC—CH_2—CHOH—COOH. Very common: apple, plum, banana, pear, etc.

D-*Malic acid*. Has been found, but its occurrence is rare.

D-*Tartaric acid*, HOOC—CHOH—CHOH—COOH. Uncommon; has been found in *Morus indica* and *Tamarindus indica* fruits; characteristic of grapes; sometimes mentioned as occurring in various fruits (raspberry, grapefruit, avocado; Lee and Jacobs, 1951).

Citramalic acid (2-methylmalic), HOOC—C(OH)(CH_3)—CH_2—COOH. In the peel of ripe apples (Hulme, 1954). In some citrus fruits (Bogin and Wallace, 1966b).

Citric acid, HOOC—CH_2—C(OH)(COOH)—CH_2—COOH. Very common in fruits. Predominate over malic acid in the banana.

Isocitric acid, HOOC—CH_2—CH(COOH)—CHOH—COOH. Traces (Mehlitz and Matzik, 1957).

Cis-*Aconitic acid*, HOOC—CH_2—C(COOH)=CH—COOH. Traces.

Oxaloacetic acid, HOOC—CH_2—CO—COOH. Traces, but very common.

α-*Oxoglutaric acid*, $HOOC—(CH_2)_2—CO—COOH$. Traces, but very common.

4. *Acids derived from sugars*

Saccharic acid, $HOOC—(CHOH)_4—COOH$. In pineapple (after Thimann and Bonner, 1950).

Mucic acid, $HOOC—(CHOH)_4—COOH$. In *Eleocarpus* fruits (Yamamoto *et al.*, from Wolf, 1960).

Galacturonic acid, $HOOC—(CHOH)_4—CHO$. In pear, peach, apricot, apple (Davignon, 1961).

Glucuronic acid, $HOOC—(CHOH)_4—CHO$. In plum, apple.

5. *Carbocyclic monocarboxylic acids*

(a) Aromatic acids

Benzoic acid, $C_6H_5—COOH$. In *Vaccinium* fruits (Griebel, 1910; Nelson, 1927).

Salicylic acid, $HO—C_6H_4—COOH$. In *Ribes*, *Fragaria*, *Rubus* fruits (Bonner, 1950).

p-Coumaric acid, $HO—C_6H_4—CH=CH—COOH$. Present as derivatives (see below).

Caffeic acid, $(HO)_2—C_6H_3—CH=CH—COOH$. Present as derivatives (see below).

Chlorogenic acid or 3,4-*cafeoylquinic acid*. Common in young apples (Hulme, 1953), pears, peaches, plums and cherries. Associated in apples with isochloro-genic and neochlorogenic acids which are probably mixtures of dicafeoyl-quinic acids, and with 4-cafeoylquinic acid.

p-Coumarylquinic acid. Common in apples and pears.

(b) Alicyclic acids

Quinic acid. Common in apple (Hulme, 1951), apricot, peach, banana, pear, . . .

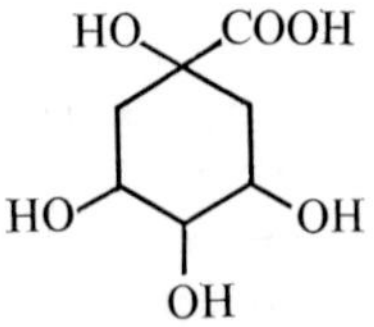

Shikimic acid. Common: gooseberry (20% of total organic acids; Whiting, 1958a), pear, apple, strawberry, banana, quince.

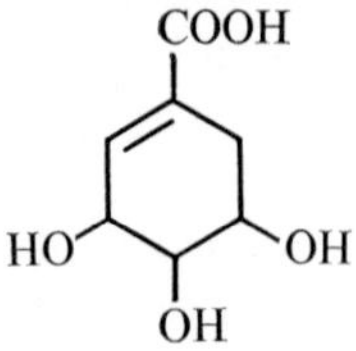

Some of the acids are evolved as esters from the tissue. Table I gives a list of esters given off by apples.

TABLE I. Organic acids evolved as esters by apples (var. Calville blanc)

Esters of formic acid		Esters of butyric acid	
Methyl formate	$\otimes$	Methyl butyrate	$\otimes$
Propyl formate	$\otimes$	Ethyl butyrate	$\times \times$
Hexyl formate	$\otimes$	Propyl butyrate	$\otimes$
Isobutyl formate	$\otimes$	Butyl butyrate	$\times$
Esters of acetic acid		Amyl butyrate	$\times$
Methyl acetate	$\otimes$	Hexyl butyrate	$\otimes$
Ethyl acetate	$\times \times$	Isopropyl butyrate	$\otimes$
Propyl acetate	$\times \times$	Isobutyl butyrate	$\otimes$
Butyl acetate	$\times \times \times \times \times$	Isoamyl butyrate	$\otimes$
Amyl acetate	$\times$	Ethyl isobutyrate	$\otimes$
Hexyl acetate	$\times \times \times$	Esters of valerianic acid	
Isobutyl acetate	$\times \times$	Ethyl valerianate	$\otimes$
Butyl (second)	$\otimes$	Butyl valerianate	$\otimes$
Isoamyl acetate	$\times \times \times$	Esters of caproic acid	
Esters of propionic acid		Methyl caproate	$\otimes$
Methyl propionate	$\otimes$	Ethyl caproate	$\times$
Ethyl propionate	$\otimes$	Butyl caproate	$\times \times$
Propyl propionate	$\otimes$	Esters of octanoic acid	
Butyl propionate	$\times \times$	Ethyl octanoate	$\otimes$
Amyl propionate	$\otimes$		
Isoamyl propionate	$\times$		

$\times$ less than 1% of the total emission; $\times \times$ 1–5%; $\times \times \times$ 5–10%; $\times \times \times \times$ 10–25%; $\times \times \times \times \times$ more than 25%; $\otimes$ traces detected with a capillary column by gas chromatography.

(From Paillard, 1968)

B. Extraction, Identification and Properties

Water or boiling ethanol are generally used for extraction of organic acids from plant tissues. The solutions obtained in this way are passed down cation exchangers which remove cations and amino acids but not free acids or neutral components. It is possible to measure the total acidity on this extract and then pass down an anion exchange resin which combines with organic anions but not with neutral substances which pass through the column. After washing, elution of acids is carried out and separation is achieved by the use of paper or column chromatography. If the material used for ion exchange is too basic, a part of the sugars may be changed into acids; in some conditions, chlorogenic acid is hydrolysed and gives quinic acid (Rentschler and Tanner, 1956).

For the isolation of acids from their salts, a cationic exchanger in the H^+ form may be used; it is easy to eliminate the resin after the reaction.

Oxo acids are very fragile and readily decarboxylate. For analysis they should be converted into 2,4-dinitrophenyl-hydrazones which may then be isolated by paper chromatography.

Acids may also be isolated from extracts by silica gel chromatography as described by Wager and Isherwood (1941), Bové and Raveux (1957), Roux and Lesaint (1959). This method was applied to oranges by Clements (1964); automatic determination is possible (Kesner and Muntwyler, 1966). Ion exchange methods applied to fruit extracts have been published by Bryant and Overell (1951), Hulme and Wooltorton (1958), and by Wyman and Palmer (1964).

Some authors have tried to apply gas chromatography to the estimation of organic acids after esterification (for example, Mazliak and Salsac, 1965; Hautala, 1966; Brunelle et al., 1967, using trimethylsilylated derivatives).

TABLE II. pK values of some organic acids[a]

Acid	pK_1	pK_2	pK_3
Acetic	4·7	——	——
Citric	3·1	4·8	6·4
Malic	3·4	5·0	——
Oxalic	1·2	4·2	——
Succinic	4·2	5·6	——
Tartaric	3·0	4·3	——

[a] From different authors, especially Sober, 1968

Results obtained in the separation of acids from the orange by silica-gel chromatography, and by gas chromatography for the methyl esters of apple acids are shown in Figs. 2a and b.

Identification of the acids is generally obtained by using paper chromatography together with information given by complementary reactions such as sublimation, colour reactions, fluorescence, etc.; for example, Kliewer, 1966; Wyman and Palmer, 1964.

In particular cases, other methods have been used: for example, biological and spectrophotometric methods for quinic shikimic and chlorogenic acids (see for example, Cookman and Sondheimer (1965), for biological methods, and Menard and Devaux (1963) or Delaporte and Macheix (1968) for spectrophotometry).

Organic acids are water soluble, especially if their carbon chain is short. They are frequently weak acids (dissociation constant about 10^{-5} at 25°C). The pK values of some common acids are given in Table II.

A list of organic acids found in fruits appears in Table III. Many of the acids are present only in traces and these have been discovered as a result of

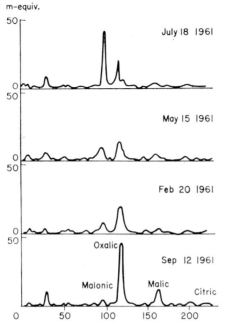

FIG. 2a. Acid chromatography on silicic acid column. Seasonal changes in flavedo acids of oranges. From Clements (1964).

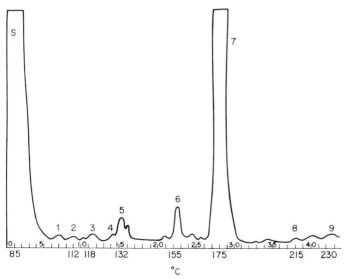

FIG. 2b. Gas chromatography of methyl esters of apple pulp. S = solvant; 1 = pyruvate; 2 = glycolate; 3 = oxalate; 4 = fumarate; 5 = succinate ; 6 = adipate; 7 = malate; 8 = citrate; 9 = isocitrate. From Mazliak and Salsac (1965).

modern methods of analysis. The most common and abundant acids of fruits are citric and malic. Some volatile and oxo acids whose analysis needs special methods, are not mentioned in the list. The presence of lactic acid in fruit extracts may be due either to the action of micro-organisms or to reaction with ion exchange resins used in the separation of the acids.

TABLE III. Acids present in fruits

Acids[a]	Apple[e]	Pear	Grapes[d]	Banana[b]	Strawberry[c]
Glycolic	+	+	+	+	tr
Lactic	+	+	+	+	
Glyceric	+	+	+	+	tr
Pyruvic	+		+	+	
Glyoxylic	+		+	+	
Oxalic	+		+	+	
Succinic	+	+	+	+	+
Fumaric	+		+		
Malic	++	++	++	++	+
Tartaric			++		
Citramalic	+	+		+	
Citric	+	+	+	+	+++
Isocitric	+		+		
Cis aconitic			+		
Oxaloacetic	+		+	+	
α-Oxoglutaric	+	+	+	+	
Galacturonic	+	+	+		
Glucuronic	+		+		
Caffeic	+		+		
Chlorogenic	+	+	+		
p-Coumarylquinic	+				
Quinic	+	+	+	+	+
Shikimic	+	+	+	+	tr

[a] In the same order as the general table
[b] In part from Wyman and Palmer (1964); more than 20 oxo acids have been separated in banana and 10 of them identified (Steward et al., 1960)
[c] After Hulme and Wooltorton (1958b) and Hane (1962)
[d] From Kliewer (1966)
[e] From Kollas (1964)

Robertson and Turner (1951) observed that in the young fruit, the proportion of malic to citric acid is low, as in leaves $\left(\dfrac{malic}{citric} = 6\right.$ in the leaf, 20 in the 50 day fruit). Later, this ratio increases to 80 at the end of fruit development on the tree. They suggest that as the fruit becomes more differentiated, its metabolic capacities change and it is able to achieve new synthesis with the raw material coming from roots and leaves.

Fruits classified on the basis of the predominating acid they contain are listed in Table IV; the figures between brackets refer to the amounts of acids calculated in milliequivalents* in 100 g of fresh fruit; these values have been taken from the review of Wolf (1960) where references to individual papers are given. Other values have been published by Thimann and Bonner (1950) and by Lee and Jacobs (1951).

TABLE IV. Fruits in terms of predominant acid of ripe fruit[a]

Predominant acid	Fruit	Amount of predominant acid	Other acids present in appreciable amounts
Malic	Apple	3–19 (80–90% of total)	Quinic in peel and young fruits
	Apricot	12 (76% of total)	Citric (12), quinic (2–3)
	Banana	4	
	Cherry	5–9	Citric, quinic, shikimic
	Grape	1·5–2	Tartaric (1·5–2·0)
	Peach	4	Citric—sometimes as high as malate
	Pear	1–2	Citric may exceed malate in some varieties
	Plum	6–11	Quinic, especially in young
Citric	Lemon	73	Malic (4), quinic
	Orange	15	Malic (3), quinic, oxalic in peel
	Currant (black)	43	Malic (6)
	Currant (red)	21–28	Malic (2–4), succinic, oxalic
	Fig	6	Malic, acetic
	Gooseberry	11–14	Malic (10–13); shikimic (1–2) corresponds to 0·3 g/100 g
	Guava	10–20	Malic
	Loganberry	30	Malic
	Pineapple	6–20	Malic (1·5–7)
	Pomegranate	7–30	Malic (uncertain)
	Raspberry	24	Malic (1)
	Strawberry	10–18	Malic (1–3), quinic (0·1), succinic (0·1)
Tartaric	Grape	1·5–2·0	Malic (1·5–2·0)

[a] Figures represent milliequivalents per 100 g fresh weight

C. Methods of Expressing Acidity

The pH of an extract is one way of expressing the acidity of fruit; for fruit juice it is generally low, for example, between 2 and 4 for lemons and tomatoes respectively. Free weak acids associated in the cell with their potassium salts constitute buffer systems, which play an important role in the cell,

* 1 milliequivalent of citric acid is 64 mg; 1 milliequivalent of malic acid is 67 mg

particularly in relation to the proteins of the cell, especially the enzymes. The buffer ratio (ΔpH/ΔNaOH) changes during fruit growth (e.g. decreasing in grapes; Amerine and Winkler, 1958).

Free acidity, or better *titratable acidity*, is measured by neutralizing fruit extracts with a strong base (N/10 soda for example). The pH increases during the neutralization and it is possible to trace a titration curve the slope of which decreases as the buffer effect of the extract increases (Fig. 3). Titratable

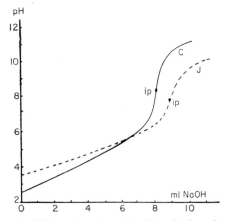

FIG. 3a. Titration curves of Valencia orange juice (J) and of a solution of pure citric acid (C). ip = inflection point. From Sinclair (1961).

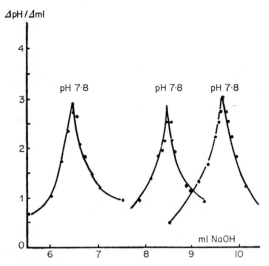

FIG. 3b. Inflection points determined by plotting the change in ratio $\dfrac{\Delta \text{pH}}{\Delta \text{ml}}$ against millilitres of NaOH added. Orange juice. From Sinclair (1961).

acidity is calculated from the quantity of base necessary to reach the pH decided on for the end point of the assay (inflection points on Fig. 3). The problem is the choice of this final pH. The aim is to measure the total neutralization of all acidic groups including phenols, amino acids and other constituents which would combine with the alkali. In practice the end point is taken at pH 8·5, by using phenolphthalein for example, as an indicator (range 8·2–9·9). Under these conditions, organic acids and only a part of phosphoric acid and phenols are involved in the final result. The titration values are generally expressed in milliequivalents of acids per unit of extract volume or of tissue fresh weight.

Figure 4 gives an example of the pattern of change in titratable acidity and

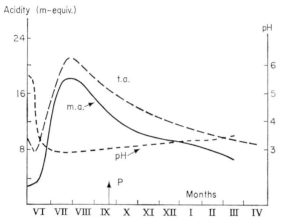

Fig. 4. Changes in pH and titratable acidity (t.a.) of apples before and after picking (P); acidity calculated for 100 g fresh weight; malic acid (m.a.) in 100 g fresh weight. From Krotkov, in Wolf (1960).

pH during ripening of fruits; some investigators have proposed that the ratio H^+/titratable acidity might be used as an index of maturity.

Total acidity represents the sum of all the acids present, free or combined with cations. Total acidity may be determined by neutralizing the extract obtained after passage through a cation exchange column.

The ratio titratable acidity/total acidity may vary considerably from fruit to fruit. From one kind of citrus fruit to another the proportion of the organic acids present as salts may vary between 3 and 15% of the total acid (Sinclair and Ramsay, 1944). In ripe bananas, titratable acidity and total malic acid (in milliequivalents) are practically identical: malic acid is almost the only acid present and it is all in the free state (Harris and Poland, 1937) in this fruit. On the other hand in green bananas, the titratable acidity is higher and other acids are present.

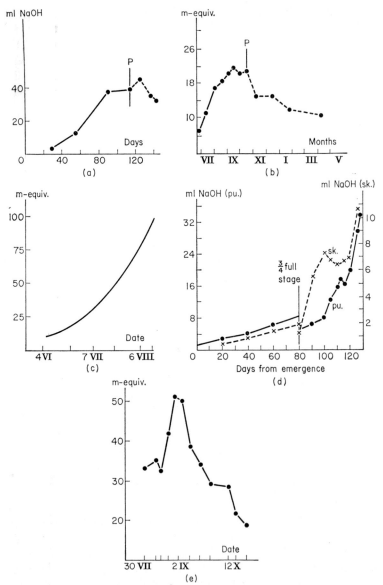

FIG. 5. Changes occurring in the titratable acidity in five species of fruits during growth and ripening (acidity calculated for one fruit). (a) Pear (from Bain, 1961); (b) Apple (from Eggenberger, 1949); (c) Peach (from Peynaud, 1950); (d) Banana (from Barnell, 1940); (e) Grapes (from Gatet, 1940). Abbreviations used: P = time of picking; sk. = skin; pu. = pulp.

During the extraction of the acids in fruits, it is important to make sure that serious errors have not occurred, such as hydrolysis during prolonged passage down ion exchange columns, esterification during extraction with boiling alcohols, destruction of oxo acids, loss of volatile acids, etc.

Acidity is sometimes expressed as the quantity of one acid assumed to be the only acid present (citric, malic) per unit of extract volume, or per unit fresh weight of the fruit. As acids are generally present in complex mixtures, it is more accurate, when expressing total or titratable acid, to express the results in milliequivalents. It is often valuable to examine the acidity not only as a concentration but in terms of individual fruits. The concentration basis shows how acidity is changing in relation to the other constituents of the fruit, while the "per fruit" basis indicates how the absolute amount of acid is changing. Figures 5 and 6, which show results for different fruits expressed in

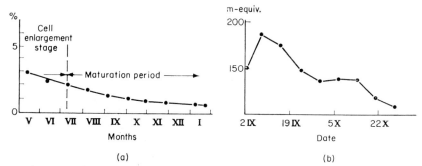

FIG. 6. Changes in the titratable acidity expressed for a unit volume of juice. (a) Orange (from Bain, 1958); (b) Grape (from Gatet, 1940).

different ways, illustrates this point. Compare, particularly, Figs 5e with 6b for the same fruit.

From a physiological point of view, since anions are involved in metabolism, titratable acidity is not very informative. Moreover we know that some acids are very important in spite of their very low concentration. The amount of each acid is, for these reasons, more important. However, from a practical point of view, titratable acidity may be useful as a reference of the stage of maturity or as objective information relating to flavour.

D. Distribution of Acids Within Fruits

Although in many fruits there is no sharp distinction between peel and pulp, differences do exist in the acid content of the outer layers and the inner, generally softer, areas of fruits. In citrus fruits the peel is poorer in total acid than the pulp. The same situation obtains in the banana up to the time of harvest (see Fig. 5d). The reverse is often the case in apples especially with regard to quinic acid; in some situations the pulp contains more acid at maturity and during storage. It is probable that most of the acid in fruit cells is in the vacuole since the pH of the cytoplasm is unlikely to be as low as would be consistent with the high acid content and low pH as the expressed juice (4 or even less). Progressive pressing of fruits yields fractions of varying acidity which indicates the presence of gradients throughout the fruit. There is, however, little information available concerning the control of the movement of acids from the vacuole through the tonoplast or through organelle membranes to the sites of metabolism.

E. Translocation of Acids from Vegetative Parts of the Plant to Fruits

There are many reasons for believing that a large part of the organic acids are translocated from leaves or roots to the fruits. Arguments in favour of this hypothesis are as follows:

(i) Acidity is higher, for example, in the centre of grape berries where the vascular tissues are more developed than in the external tissues.

(ii) Photosynthesis from which organic material originates is not very active in fruits.

(iii) After the fruits are picked, increase in organic acids is generally absent.

(iv) Fruits from partially defoliated stems are less acid than those from stems in which the leaves are still present.

Experiments with isotopically labelled materials support this argument. For example McCollum and Skok (1960) observed in tomato plant that ^{32}P given to leaves as phosphate is translocated to the fruits; ^{14}C-glucose laid down in the leaves is translocated to the young fruits but not to the ripe ones.

Evidence discussed by Nitsch (1953) suggests that, indeed, acids enter the fruit preformed, but Tomkins (1954) suggests that a part of the acids are formed in apple fruits from carbohydrates. Varma and Ramakrishnan (1956) provided evidence which they suggested showed that citrus fruit greater in diameter than 1·5 cm synthesized citric acid (also, see Section III).

It is possible that acids could come not only from leaves but from roots also. In spring, sap flowing out through the trees contains malic and citric acids (Wolf, 1938). As shown by Ribereau-Gayon (1966, 1968), citric acid may be synthesized in the roots of grapes and translocated to the aerial parts of the plant and, perhaps, partially transformed into malic acid.

F. Changes in Acids During Fruit Development and Storage

This subject is dealt with in detail in Volume 2 under individual fruits but some generalizations may be made here.

As will be seen from Fig. 7, the changes in the concentration of acids during the development of the fruit differs with the type of fruit. The grape and the apple show a peak in titratable acidity as the fruit matures whereas the banana and the pear exhibit a steady fall right up until the fruit is ripe. In absolute amounts (per fruit basis) again the apple and the grape show a peak during

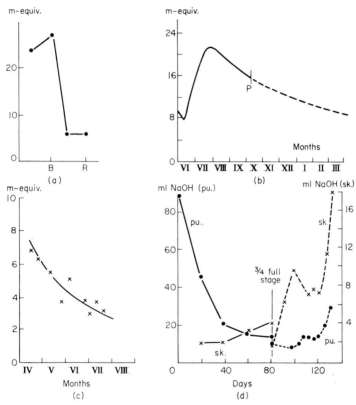

FIG. 7. Changes occurring in the titratable acidity in four species of fruits during growth and ripening. Acidity calculated for 100 g of fresh weight. (a) Grape (from Vitte and Guichard, 1955); (b) Apple (from Krotkov, in Wolf, 1960); (c) Pear (from Ulrich, 1957); (d) Banana (from Barnell, 1940). Abbreviations used: B = at the beginning of ripening; P = picking time; pu. = pulp; R = at the end of ripening; sk. = skin.

development while the banana and the pear show a steady rise to the time of harvest. In the apple during growth, the pH decreases after flowering and may be as low as 2·8. Later it rises somewhat, possibly as the result of increased cation transport from the roots (Krotkov et al., 1951). Individual acids change in different ways during the development of the fruit; examples of this are given for apples and oranges in Fig. 8.

In most fruits acid is lost during ripening after harvest, but the banana appears to be an exception as will be seen from Fig. 5d. Insoluble potassium bitartrate accumulates during ripening (Saito and Kasai, 1968). According to Wejnar (1967), black grapes absorb more of the sun's rays than green grapes and so become hotter and lose acid more rapidly.

During gas storage (controlled atmosphere storage, C.A. storage) of apples,

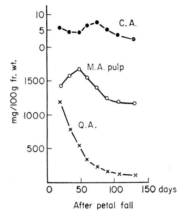

FIG. 8a. Citric (C.A.), malic (M.A.) and quinic (Q.A.) acids in the pulp of apples growing on the tree. Values calculated for 100 g fresh weight. From Hulme and Wooltorton (1957).

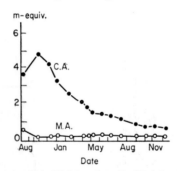

FIG. 8b. Seasonal variations in citric (C.A.) and malic (M.A.) acids in the juice of Valencia oranges. Expressed in milliequivalents per g of dry matter in the juice. Analysis after picking, without storage. From Clements (1964).

the acid content is influenced by the composition of the atmosphere (Klemm, 1967). Kollas (1964) showed that after 6 months storage at $3.5°C$ in 3% O_2 and 5% CO_2 as compared with storage in air at $0°C$ there was much less loss of acid. Most of the difference was in the malic acid fraction, although quinic and shikimic acids were higher in the C.A. stored fruit whereas citric acid was higher in the air stored samples. Kollas suggested that the decreased loss may have been due to CO_2-fixation.

Oxo acids tend to increase during low temperature storage of apples (Barker and Solomos, 1962; Wills and McGlasson, 1968).

III. METABOLISM OF ACIDS

The immediate precursors of organic acids are, in general, other organic acids or sugars; some acids appear early in photosynthesis (for example, phosphoglyceric acid). Oxo acids may arise from amino acids during trans-amination.

The main pathways for the metabolism of organic acids are in respiratory oxidations and carboxylations or decarboxylations, but specific reactions may be involved for individual acids of the fruit. We will now consider the biosynthesis of organic acids from sugars, the use of organic acids by the cell in respiration, in the Krebs cycle, in carboxylations and decarboxylations and in other metabolic processes involving acids.

A. Biosynthesis of Acids from Sugars

In young, green fruits photosynthesis may lead to the production of sugars within the fruit themselves.

If strawberries are fed with labelled fructose through the peduncle, labelled citric acid very soon appears in the fruit (Markakis and Embs, 1964).

By supplying green grapes on the plant with radioactive glucose, organic acids become labelled, particularly malic acid; with ripe fruits, the pro-duction of organic acids is very low (Ribereau-Gayon, 1966).

Detached green apples injected with U-^{14}C glucose became highly labelled in citric acid one hour later (Tishel, 1967). When green grape berries are separated from the plant and supplied through the pedicel with labelled hexoses, malic and tartaric acids may account for 25% and 10% of the total activity after 24 hours (Hardy, 1968); other authors mentioned by Hardy isolated labelled tartaric and malic acids from berries after giving $^{14}CO_2$ to leaves. Other experiments consisted of giving $^{14}CO_2$ to plants in the light and observing the changes in fruit organic acids under these conditions; however, the interpretation of the results is not simple (Kliewer, 1964; Ribereau-Gayon, 1966). In the reverse direction, it has been shown that grape berries receiving labelled tartaric acid elaborate radioactive glucose and fructose (Drawert et al., 1962). Ribereau-Gayon (1966) found that unripe grapes given radioactive malic acid on the plant in light accumulated labelled sugars. New experiments seem to be required in this field.

Another interesting problem is the synthesis of alicyclic acids from sugars. It was first studied with Escherichia Coli mutants; heptulose derivatives could be precursors arising from the combination of phosphoenolpyruvate and erythrose-phosphate. Shikimic acid is related to 5-dehydroshikimic, 5-dehydroquinic and quinic acids, and to important other metabolites (aromatic acids, cyclic amino acids, anthocyans, lignin) (see Hathway (1956), on myrobalans).

B. Utilization of Acids in Respiration

It has been known for a long time that fruit cells are able to use organic acids as a respiratory substrate. High respiratory quotient are evidence of this. The respiratory quotient (R.Q. = CO_2 production/O_2 absorption) approaching 1 when sugars are consumed, is approximately 1·33 when malic or citric acid is completely oxidized and near 1·6 for the oxidation of tartaric

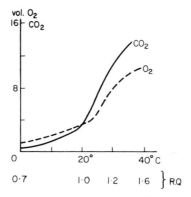

Fig. 9. Respiratory gaseous exchanges of grapes at different temperatures, expressed in volumes of CO_2 and O_2 for 100 g fresh weight in one hour. R.Q. = respiratory quotient. From Genevois, 1938. Gerber's figures.

acid. In anaerobiosis, much higher values are observed as ethanol accumulates. The classical results of Gerber (1897) are still of interest. He showed that in apples stored for six weeks, at 18°C the R.Q. was 0·93, suggesting that oxidation of sugars predominated, while at 33°C the R.Q. was 1·39 which he suggested was due to the oxidation (respiration) of malate. Figure 9 constructed by Genevois (1938) from Gerber's results on seedless grapes shows the relationship between respiration, temperature and R.Q. The ordinate shows O_2-uptake and CO_2-output. As the temperature is raised so does the R.Q. Peynaud (1946) has observed that grapes heated for 4–5 days at 35°C had a very high respiratory activity. During this time half of the malic acid disappeared, tartaric acid also was lost, but citric acid remained constant.

In picked apples, Fidler (1951) found that the evolved CO_2 and the ethanol formed corresponded to the loss as sugars plus organic acids. In plums too, determination of carbon balances in young fruits show that the production of CO_2 corresponds to the loss of sugars, sorbitol and organic acids (Donen, 1939).

The interesting discovery of Fidler (1936, 1951) that the loss of acid in apples and oranges is the same in nitrogen and in air has not yet been satisfactorily explained.

C. The Krebs Cycle in Fruits

Krebs tricarboxylic (TCA) cycle (Fig. 10) is the main channel for the oxidation of acids in living cells; it is the principal source of ATP, which represents the energy available for synthesis; moreover it supplies a series of intermediary metabolites used in many processes within the cell. Numerous experiments have shown that the TCA cycle is effective at least in part in fruit respiration (Hulme, 1958a), but some of the intermediates of the cycle important in fruits, such as malic acid, may have other origins.

The criteria necessary to establish the operation of the TCA cycle in fruits are as follows:

(i) To show the presence in tissues of the different acids of the TCA cycle.

(ii) To show that the cells are able to metabolize the different acids of the cycle when these are added to a piece of tissue or to mitochondria isolated from the fruit.

(iii) To investigate the effects of inhibitors on the enzymes of the cycle.

Some of the results obtained in the establishment of these criteria will now be examined.

1. Presence in fruits of the acids of the TCA cycle

It will be seen from Table III that all the acids of the TCA cycle are present in fruits. Some of them occur only in traces (for example, isocitric acid) while others (for example, malic acid) are present in large amounts. Where large amounts of malate and citrate are present in fruits they will, undoubtedly, accumulate in the vacuole and thus become temporarily unavailable to the sites of active metabolism.

In grapes, Kliewer (1966) found all of the acids of the cycle to be present. In the banana, pyruvic, α-oxoglutaric and oxaloacetate (OAA) acids are present and increase during ripening (Barker and Solomos, 1962); however, Wyman and Palmer (1964) failed to find isocitrate and fumarate in the banana. Since active mitochondria have been isolated from the banana (see Volume 2, Chapter 2) this has little significance.

2. Metabolism of the TCA acids when added to tissue or isolated mitochondria

Generally, mitochondria readily oxidize some of the acids (succinic, malic, citric) while others may be metabolized very slowly. This may be due to permeability difficulties, or to differences in the relative activity of the various enzymes involved (Hulme *et al.*, 1968).

Pearson and Robertson (1954) investigated the activity of apple mitochondria on the addition of various acids of the TCA cycle; they observed a

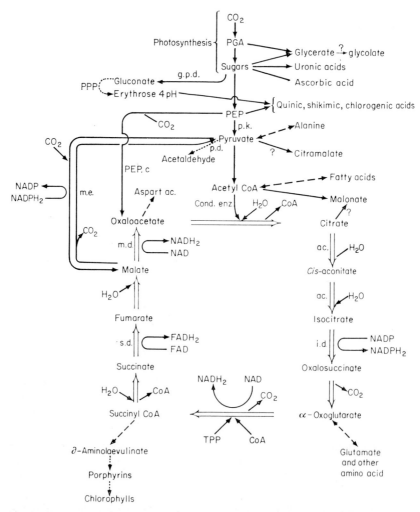

FIG. 10. Krebs cycle (⇒), with some other ways leading to organic acid synthesis (—→) or to other important constituents (—·→). Abbreviations used: ac. = aconitase; cond. enz. = condensing enzyme; g.p.d. = glucose 6-phosphate dehydrogenase; i.d. = isocitric dehydrogenase; m.d. = malate dehydrogenase; m.e. = malic enzyme; PEP.c = PEP carboxylase and carboxykinase; PGA = phosphoglyceric acid; p.d. = pyruvate decarboxylase; p.k. = pyruvate kinase; PPP = pentose-phosphate pathway; s.d. = succinic dehydrogenase; TPP = thiamine pyrophosphate.

stimulation of O_2-uptake after adding citric, malic, succinic, α-ketoglutaric or fumaric acids.

Hulme (1958a) gave labelled succinic acid to discs of apple peel and observed one hour later that all the organic acids were labelled with the exception of quinic and shikimic. When succinate, malate, α-oxoglutarate were added to peel discs from senescent apples, the respiratory activity increased, but no effect was observed with citrate of fumarate. These results are shown in Fig. 11. In the presence of succinate, apple mitochondria prepared with PVP give rise to citrate, fumarate, malate (Hulme *et al.*, 1964).

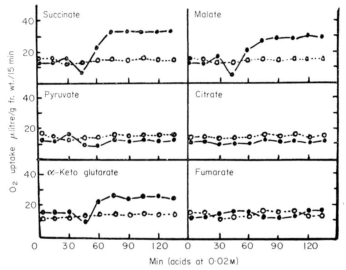

FIG. 11. The effect of the addition of various organic acids on the O_2 uptake of peel discs from senescent apples. From Hulme (1958a).

Hulme *et al.* (1967) observed an inhibition of succinate and malate oxidation by apple mitochondria due to oxaloacetate (Fig. 12); this inhibition decreased during the respiration climacteric, probably due to a coupled system metabolizing oxaloacetate; transaminase could also be involved and its activity increases during the climacteric.

Millerd *et al.* (1953) observed the oxidation of acids of the TCA cycle by cell particles from the avocado fruit. Avron and Biale (1957) later established by paper chromatography the presence of fumarate, malate and citrate when mitochondrial preparations from the avocado were incubated in the presence of malate. They also showed that the mitochondria formed citrate from added succinate and fumarate from added α-oxoglutarate. Avron and Biale also showed that for the oxidation of pyruvate by avocado mitochondria, apart from "sparker" amounts of malate, the following co-factors are required: TPP, NAD, CoA, AMP and Mg^{2+}.

Avocado mitochondria are able to oxidize succinate at all stages of development of the fruit (Lance *et al.*, 1965); with malate a block was observed in mitochondria from pre-climacteric fruits which was relieved by TPP which could stimulate oxaloacetate breakdown. This suggested to Lance *et al.* that OAA was involved as an inhibitor of malate oxidation. Other experiments with the pear (Meynhardt *et al.*, 1964) and the grape (Ribereau-Gayon, 1966)

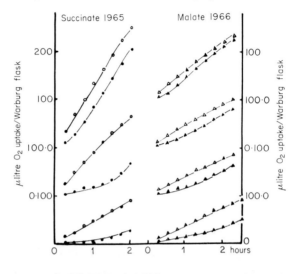

Δ O Substrate minus OAA
▲ ● Substrate in presence of OAA

FIG. 12. Recovery from inhibition by oxaloacetic acid of succinate (1965) and malate (1966) oxidation during a 2–2·5 hour period for mitochondria prepared at several stages of the climacteric. From Hulme, *et al.* (1967).

in which the fruits were supplied with some TCA cycle acids have shown that at least a part of the cycle is effective in these fruits.

3. *Proofs of the presence of the enzymes of the TCA cycle in fruits*

Malonate, which blocks succinic dehydrogenase (Fig. 10), inhibits O_2-absorption by the apple, does not lead to the accumulation of succinate (Hulme, 1958a). However, this may be due to its rapid utilization in non-oxidative processes outside the cycle since Avron and Biale (1957) have shown with avocado mitochondria that malonate inhibits their activity with accumulation of succinate. Fluoracetate also blocks the cycle by giving fluorocitrate on which aconitase (Fig. 10) has only a limited action.

Malic dehydrogenase (Fig. 10) and succinic dehydrogenase (Fig. 10) are active particularly in ripe fruits (Hulme *et al.*, 1964). In stored apples, Hartmann (1966) observed that the activity of these dehydrogenases decreases (Fig. 13). No activity of isocitric dehydrogenase (Fig. 10) was detected in fruits by Tishel (1967) but since it is now generally accepted that most fruits contain mitochondria, all the enzymes of the cycle must be present.

Some interesting data have been obtained by Bogin and Wallace (1966b) by

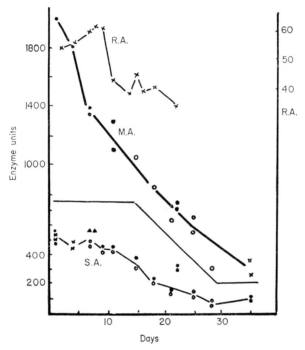

FIG. 13. Dehydrogenase activity of apple mitochondria, during ripening of fruits at 15°C (var. Calville blanc). Abbreviations used: R.A. = respiratory activity, expressed as mg of CO_2 of the whole fruit, for 100 g of fresh product per day. M.A. = malic dehydrogenase activity in μlitre of oxygen per mg of nitrogen of mitochondria, in one hour. S.A. = succinicdehydrogenase activity. From Hartmann (1966).

giving labelled pyruvate and labelled CO_2 to vesicles and mitochondrial preparations from sweet and sour lemons. The sour lemons contained much more citric acid than the sweet variety. They found that fixation of CO_2 was three times as high in the sour than in the sweet lemon preparations. NADP-dependent isocitric dehydrogenase was more active in fixing CO_2 with α-oxoglutarate in the sour lemons. Bogin and Wallace suggest that in the lemons, pyruvate enters the TCA cycle more readily through CO_2-fixation than through condensation with OAA. They also suggest that citramalate is formed from parapyruvate (OH-methyl oxoglutarate) and they showed that citramalate is an inhibitor of aconitase—a competitive inhibitor in their view. If this is so then citramalate formation could act as a feed-back regulator of the TCA cycle at the citrate-isocitrate (via aconitate) stage. Bogin and Wallace could not demonstrate the presence of the glyoxalate cycle in lemons.

D. Carboxylation and Decarboxylation

1. *Organic acid formation by carboxylation*

As mentioned in the previous section, organic acids in fruits may arise by fixation of CO_2 in the fruits themselves. A brief description of the enzymes which could be involved in this process would not be out of place here. The distribution—even the existence—of some of these enzymes in fruits has not yet been established. Further information on this topic appears in Volume 2.

(a) *Malic enzyme.* This NADP-dependent enzyme is common in fruits and it catalyses the following reaction:

$$\text{Malate} + \text{NADP} \rightleftharpoons \text{pyruvate} + \text{NADPH}_2 + \text{CO}_2 \text{ (Fig. 10)}$$

ΔF^b (left to right) under conditions close to those occurring in plant cells (Walker, 1966) is -0.24 Kcal. With high concentrations of pyruvate the reaction may be forced in the direction right to left in the above equation.

(b) *Phosphoenolpyruvate carboxykinase* (PEP carboxykinase) is very common in plants and catalyses the reaction:

$$\text{PEP} + \text{CO}_2 \overset{\text{Mn}^{2+}}{\rightleftharpoons} \text{OAA} + \text{ATP}$$

$\Delta F^b = 1.28$ Kcal. Consequently the reaction will readily go from right to left and can be concerned with the synthesis of PEP and thence to sugars.

(c) *Phosphoenolpyruvate carboxylase* (PEP carboxylase, Fig. 10) is responsible for the reaction:

$$\text{PEP} + \text{CO}_2 + \text{H}_2\text{O} \overset{\text{Mg}^{2+}}{\longrightarrow} \text{OAA} + \text{Pi}$$

$\Delta F^b = -5.7$ Kcal so that the reaction will only proceed from left to right.

(d) *Pyruvate kinase* (Fig. 10), an enzyme of glycolysis, is certain to be present in fruits as in all tissues in which glycolysis takes place. It catalyses the reaction:

$$\text{PEP} + \text{ADP} \rightarrow \text{pyruvate} + \text{ATP}$$

Since ΔF^b is 6.3 Kcal, this reaction also is irreversible.

As long ago as 1954, Allentoff *et al.* (1954) found radio activity in malic acid and certain amino acids after keeping apples in the dark in presence of $^{14}\text{CO}_2$. Huffaker and Wallace (1959) concluded from a study of CO_2-fixation by peel and vesicles from orange fruits that PEP carboxylase and PEP carboxykinase are involved. However, Clark and Wallace (1963) and Bogin and Wallace (1966a) discounted the existence of PEP carboxykinase in citrus fruits. The latter workers considered that CO_2-fixation in lemons was mainly due to PEP carboxylase and malic enzyme. As previously mentioned, they found differences between sour and sweet lemons. Clark and Wallace (1963) found that young fruits were more active in fixing CO_2 than more mature ones. Fixation of $^{14}CO_2$ as malate, citrate and aspartate was observed for whole lemons by Young and Biale (1956, 1968) who considered that the first product of the CO_2-fixation to be OAA which is then rapidly converted to citrate. This they considered to be the cause of the enhanced respiration rate which occurs when lemons are stored in an atmosphere enriched by CO_2. Malonate was also labelled but Young and Biale produced evidence which suggested that this occurred via a pathway independent of that used in the labelling of malate and citrate.

Kliewer (1964) found that the organic acids of grapes became labelled in the presence of $^{14}CO_2$, while Ribereau-Gayon showed that grapes attached to the vine and given $^{14}CO_2$ in the dark only had a low degree of fixation into malate; tartrate was unlabelled.

Another effect of CO_2 on fruit metabolism is probably due to its inhibition of succinic dehydrogenase, since Hulme (1956) found that apples stored in 10–20% CO_2 accumulated succinic acid not normally present in apples stored in air. Williams and Patterson (1964) found succinate to increase and malate to decrease in a Williams pear stored in the presence of CO_2; Flanzy (1967) observed the same situation in grapes.

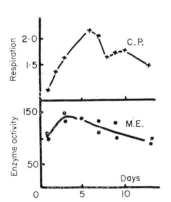 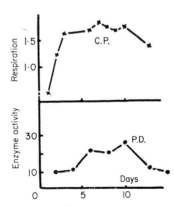

FIG. 14. CO_2 production (C.P.) and activity of decarboxylating enzymes during ripening. Williams pears at 20°C. CO_2 production expressed as ml for 100 g fresh fruit in one hour; activity of the decarboxylating enzymes expressed in μlitre CO_2 for 1 g fresh fruit in 5 minutes. Abbreviations used: M.E. = malic enzyme; P.D. = pyruvic decarboxylase. From Hartman et al. (1968).

2. *Decarboxylation of organic acids*

Two enzymes have been found in fruits which are directly concerned with the decarboxylation of malate and pyruvate outside the group of enzymes involved in the TCA cycle.

Malic enzyme, present in the apple in relatively large amounts (Dilley, 1962; Hulme *et al.*, 1963), increases in activity during the period of the respiration climacteric in the apple and pear (Hartmann *et al.*, 1968). Another decarboxylating enzyme, pyruvate decarboxylase, also increases in activity over the climacteric period in the apple, pear and banana (Tager and Biale, 1957). The results of Hartmann *et al.* (1968) are shown in Fig. 14; they found no change in the activity of the enzymes in Passe Crassane pears at 5° and 10°C at which temperatures this variety has no well defined climacteric. The combined activity of these two enzymes is:

$$\text{Malate} \rightarrow \text{pyruvate} + CO_2$$
$$ \longrightarrow \text{acetaldehyde} + CO_2$$

Hulme *et al.* (1968) have investigated changes in the activity of malic enzyme and associated processes during the climacteric in apples and during the ageing of discs of apple peel; see Volume 2, Chapter 10.

To conclude this section on organic acid metabolism of fruits, isolated observations on the metabolism of tartaric and glycollic acids may be mentioned.

The metabolism of tartrate in fruits is not known with any degree of certainty. As already mentioned, $^{14}CO_2$ is not incorporated into the acid by grapes. Ribereau-Gayon (1968) could find no evidence for the conversion of malate to tartrate in grapes, but he showed that when grapes were given glucose labelled in the C1 and in the C6 positions, the label from C1 appeared more rapidly in tartaric acid that did the carbon labelled in the 6 position. He also found that if labelled tartrate was presented to the grape no other radioactive compound appeared in the fruit at the end of 24 hours. Drawert *et al.* (1962) on the other hand found that labelled CO_2 and glucose appeared when grapes were given radioactive tartrate.

Maroc (1967) showed that if 1-^{14}C glycollate was fed to leaves and berries of the grape, label appeared in glycerate, serine and glucose.

IV. THE PHYSIOLOGICAL AND TECHNOLOGICAL IMPORTANCE OF ACIDS IN FRUITS

Organic acids have an important place in general metabolism, particularly in fruits. For example, there is the role of phosphoglyceric acid in photosynthesis, the part organic acids play in respiration, the participation of acetate in the synthesis of phenolic compounds, lipids and volatile aromas, the function of alicyclic acids in aromatic metabolism, the participation of α-oxoacids in amino acid synthesis and the neutralization of Ca^{2+} or NH_4^+ by anions, etc.

Apart from their general role in metabolism, certain acids may have more specific functions. Nitsch and Nitsch (1969) have suggested that chlorogenic acid acts synergistically with auxin, and Gortner and Kent (1953) claim that it may be an inhibitor of the oxidation of IAA. Again, Doesburg (1965) has put forward the interesting hypothesis to explain pectic changes during the ripening of fruits, namely, that organic acids remove calcium from insoluble pectic complexes and thus render them more soluble.

From a practical point of view, fruits are favoured by the consumer in relation to their flavour, and acidity plays an important role in the "flavour" of fruits; sometimes sweetness is preferred as in the pear, sometimes "acidity" as in the lemon. Little (1958) has discussed the role of acids in the context of flavour.

Attempts have been made to assess the stage of ripeness of fruits in terms of titratable acidity or the ratio of sugar to acid (grapes) or the ratio of dry matter to acidity (oranges). Although these factors are far from constant they do serve some practical purpose in the commercial assessment of fruits.

REFERENCES

Allentoff, N., Phillips, W. R. and Johnston, F. B. (1954). *J. Sci. Fd Agric.* **5**, 231–3 and 234–8.

Amerine, M. A. and Winkler, A. J. (1958). *Proc. Am. Soc. hort. Sci.* **71**, 199–206.

Anet, E. F. L. J. and Reynolds, T. M. (1955). *Austr. J. Chem.* **8**, 280–4.

Avron, M. and Biale, J. B. (1957). *Plant Physiol., Lancaster* **32**, 100–5.

Bain, J. M. (1958). *Aust. J. Bot.* **6**, 1–24.

Bain, J. M. (1961). *Aust. J. Bot.* **9**, 99–123.

Barker, J. and Solomos, T. (1962). *Nature, Lond.* **195**, 189.

Barnell, H. R. (1940). *Ann. Bot.* **4**, 39–71.

Biale, J. B. (1960). "Respiration of fruits". *In* "Handbuch der Pfanzenphysiologie", (Rukland, ed). XII/2, 536–92.

Bogin, E. and Wallace, A. (1966a). *Proc. Am. Soc. hort. Sci.* **88**, 298–307.

Bogin, E. and Wallace, A. (1966b). *Proc. Am. Soc. hort. Sci.* **89**, 182–94.

Bonner, J. (1950). "Plant Biochemistry". Academic Press, New York.

Bové, J. and Raveux, R. (1957). *Bull. Soc. chim. Fr. Docum.* 376–81.

Brunelle, R. L., Schoeneman, R. L. and Martin, G. E. (1967). *J.A.O.A.C.* **50**, 329–334.

Bryant, F. and Overell, B. T. (1951), *Nature, Lond.* **167**, 361–2.

Buchloh, G. (1957), *Gartenbauwissenschaft* **22**, 191–207, 449–79.

Buchloh, G. and Hane, M. (1962). *Gartenbauwissenschaft* **27**, 507–11.

Carles, J. (1960). "Le métabolisme des acides organiques dans l'ensemble de la plante". *In* "Handbuch der Pfanzenphysiol", (Ruhland, ed.) XII/2, 663–700.

Chen, S. D. and Schuck, C. (1951). *J. Fd Sci.* **16**, 507–9.

Clark, R. B. and Wallace, A. (1963). *Proc. Am. Soc. hort. Sci.* **83**, 322–32.

Clements, R. L. (1964). *J. Fd Sci.* **29**, 281–6.

Cookman, G. and Sondheimer, E. (1965). *Phytochemistry* **4,** 773–5.

Crombie, W. M. (1960). "Metabolism of extracyclic organic acids". *In* "Handbuch der Pfanzenphysiol". (Ruhland, ed.) XII/2, 890–933.

Davignon, L. (1961). *Revue gén. Bot.* **68,** 273–316.

Davis, M. B. and Blair, D. S. (1936). *Scient. Agric.* **17,** 105–14.

Delaporte, N. and Macheix, J. J. (1968). *Chim. analyt.* **50,** 187–98.

Diemair, W. and Franzen, K. (1959). *Z. Lebensmittelunter. u.-Forsch.* **109,** 273–378.

Dilley, D. R. (1962). *Nature, Lond.* **196,** 387–8.

Doesburg, J. J. (1965). "Pectin substances in fresh and preserved fruits and vegetables". Institute for Res. on storage and processing of hortic. produce, Wageningen.

Donen, I. (1939). *Biochem. J.* **33,** 1611–20, 1947–56.

Drawert, F., Steffan, H., Allmann, K. and Bachmann, O. (1962). *Naturwissenschaften* **49,** 159–60.

Eggenberger, W. (1949). Dissert. Zurich, p. 63.

Fidler, J. C. (1951). *J. exp. Bot.* **2,** 41–64.

Flanzy, C. (1967). *Annls Technol. agric.* **16,** 89–107.

Gatet, L. (1940). "Recherches biochimiques sur la maturation des fruits". Thèse Sciences naturelles, Bordeaux.

Genevois, L. (1938), *Rev. de Viticulture* **88,** 103, 121, 383 and 447.

Gerber, C. (1897). "Recherches sur la maturation des fruits charnus". Thèse Sciences naturelles, Paris.

Gortner, W. A. and Kent, M. (1953). *J. biol. Chem.* **204,** 593–603.

Griebel, C. (1910). *Z. Lebensmittelunters. u.-Forsch.* **19,** 241–52.

Haagen-Smit, A. J., Hirosawa, F. N. and Wang, T. H. (1949). *J. Fd Sci.* **14,** 472–80.

Hane, M. (1962). *Gartenbauwissenschaft* **27,** 453–82.

Hardy, P. J. (1968). *Plant Physiol., Lancaster* **43,** 224–28.

Harris, P. L. and Poland, G. L. (1937). *J. Fd Sci.* **2,** 135–42.

Hartmann, C. (1966). *Ann. Sc. Nat. Bot.* S.12, **7,** 131–214, and Thèse Sciences naturelles, Paris, 1966.

Hartmann, C., Lugon, M. and Valade, D. (1968). *Physiol. Véget.* **6,** 279–87.

Hathway, D. E. (1956). *Biochem. J.* **63,** 380–7.

Hautala, E. (1966). *J.A.O.A.C.* **49,** 619–21.

Huffaker, R. C. and Wallace, A. (1959). *Proc. Am. Soc. hort. Sci.* **74,** 348–57.

Hulme, A. C. (1951). *J. exp. Bot.* **2,** 298–315.

Hulme, A. C. (1953). *Biochem. J.* **53,** 337–40.

Hulme, A. C. (1954). *Bioch. biophys. Acta* **14,** 36–43.

Hulme, A. C. (1956). *Nature, Lond.* **186,** 218–19.

Hulme, A. C. (1958a). *Adv. in Hort. Sci. Proceed., XVth intern. Hortic. Congress* **1,** 77–95.

Hulme, A. C. (1958b). *Bull. Soc. fr. Physiol. vég.* **4,** 38–50.

Hulme, A. C. (1958c). *Adv. Fd Res.* **8,** 297–413.

Hulme, A. C. and Arthington, W. (1953). *J. exp. Bot.* **4,** 129–35.

Hulme, A. C. and Rhodes, M. J. C. (1968). *In* "Plant cell organelles", chapter 6 p. 99. Academic Press, London and New York.

Hulme, A. C., Jones, J. D. and Wooltorton, L. S. C. (1963). *Proc. R. Soc.* B158, 514–35.

Hulme, A. C., Jones, J. D. and Wooltorton, L. S. C. (1964). *Phytochemistry* **3,** 173–88.

Hulme, A. C., Rhodes, M. J. C., Galliard, T. and Wooltorton, L. S. C. (1968). *Plant. Physiol., Lancaster* **43**, 1154–61.

Hulme, A. C., Rhodes, M. J. C. and Wooltorton, L. S. C. (1967). *Phytochemistry* **6**, 1343–51.

Hulme, A. C. and Wooltorton, L. S. C. (1957). *J. Sci. Fd Agric.* **8**, 117–22.

Hulme, A. C. and Wooltorton, L. S. C. (1958a). *J. Sci. Fd Agric.* **9**, 150–8.

Hulme, A. C. and Wooltorton, L. S. C. (1958b). *Chemy Ind.* 659.

Kesner, L. and Muntwyler, E. (1966). *Analyt. Chem.* **38**, 1164–8.

Kidd, F., West, C., Griffiths, D. G. and Potter, N. A. (1951). *J. hort. Sci.* **26**, 169–185.

Klemm, K. (1967). *Mitt. Klostern.* **17**, 50–5.

Kliewer, W. M. (1964). *Plant Physiol., Lancaster* **39**, 869–80.

Kliewer, W. M. (1966). *Plant Physiol., Lancaster* **41**, 923–31.

Kollas, D. A. (1964). *Nature, Lond.* **204**, 758–9.

Krotkov, G., Wilson, D. G. and Street, R. W. (1951). *Can. J. Bot.* **29**, 79–90.

Lance, C., Hobson, G. E., Young, R. E. and Biale, J. B. (1965). *Plant Physiol., Lancaster* **40**, 1116–23.

Lee, F. A. and Jacobs, M. B. (1951). "Fruits and Nuts". *In* "The Chemistry and Technology of Food and Food Products". Interscience, New York, t.2, 1348–1589.

Little, N. D. (1958). "Flavor Research and Food Acceptance". Reinhold, New York.

McCollum, J. P. and Skok, J. (1960). *Proc. Am. Soc. hort. Sci.* **75**, 611–16.

Markakis, P. and Embs, R. J. (1964). *J. Fd Sci.* **29**, 629–30.

Maroc, J. (1967). *Physiol. Végét.* **5**, 37–46.

Mazliak, P. and Salsac, L. (1965). *Phytochemistry* **4**, 693–703.

Mehlitz, A. and Matzik, B. (1957). *Ind. Obst. u. Gemüseverwert.* **42**, 127–31.

Menard, P. and Devaux, G. (1963). *C.r. hebd. Séanc. Acad. Sci., Paris* **256**, 1551.

Meynhardt, J. T., Maxie, E. C. and Romani, R. J. (1964). *S. Afr. J. agric. Sci.* **7**, 485–96.

Millerd, A., Bonner, J. and Biale, J. B. *Plant Physiol., Lancaster* **28**, 521–31.

Neal, G. E. and Hulme, A. C. (1958). *J. exp. Bot.* **9**, 142–57.

Nelson, E. K. (1927). *J. Amer. chem. Soc.* **49**, 1300–2.

Niethammer, A. (1931). *Z. Unters. Lebensmittel* **61**, 103–5.

Nitsch, J. P. (1953). *A. Rev. Pl. Physiol.* **4**, 199–236.

Nitsch, J. P. and Nitsch, C. (1959). *Bull. Soc. bot. Fr.* **106**, 414–17.

Paillard, N. (1968). *Fruits* **23**, 383–7.

Pearson, J. A. and Robertson, R. N. (1954). *8ème congrès Inter. Bot. Paris*, Sect. 11–12, 380–9.

Peynaud, E. (1946). Thèse Ingr Docteur, University of Bordeaux. *Indust. Agric. Alim.* (1947). **64**, 87, 167, 301, 399.

Peynaud, E. (1950). *Annls agron.* **1**, 775–91.

Poapst, P. A. and Phillips, W. R. (1960). *Can. J. Pl. Sci.* **40**, 736–44.

Rentschler, H. and Tanner, H. (1956). *Fruchtsaft-Ind.* **1**, 30–5.

Rhodes, M. J. C., Wooltorton, L. S. C., Galliard, T. and Hulme, A. C. (1968). *Phytochemistry* **7**, 1439–51.

Ribereau-Gayon, G. and P. (1965). *C.r. hebd. Séanc. Acad. Sci., Paris* **261**, 1764–6.

Ribereau-Gayon, G. (1966). Thèse Sciences physiques, University of Paris.

Ribereau-Gayon, G. (1968). *Phytochemistry* **7**, 1471–82.

Ribereau-Gayon, G. and Lefebvre, A. (1967). *C.r. hebd. Séanc. Acad. Sci., Paris* **264,** 1112–15.
Robertson, R. N. and Turner, J. F. (1951). *Aust. J. Scient. Res.* B. **4,** 92–107.
Roux, L. and Lesaint, C. (1959). *Annls Physiol. vég., Brux.* **1,** 83–91.
Saito, K. and Kasai, Z. (1968). *Pl. Cell Physiol., Tokyo* **9,** 529–37.
Sinclair, W. B. (1961). "The orange. Its Biochemistry and Physiology". University of California.
Sinclair, W. B. and Ramsay, R. C. (1944). *Bot. Gaz.* **106,** 140–8.
Sober, H. A. (1968). "Handbook of Biochemistry. Selected Data for Molecular Biology". The Chemical Rubber Publishing Co., Cleveland, Ohio.
Sterling, C. (1958). *J. Fd Sci.* **23,** 380–3.
Steward, F. C., Hulme, A. C., Freiberg, S. R., Hegarty, M. P., Pollard, J. K., Rabson, R. and Barr, R. A. (1960). *Ann. Bot.* **24,** 83–116.
Tager, J. M. and Biale, J. B. (1957). *Plant. Physiol., Lancaster* **10,** 79–85.
Thimann, K. V. and Bonner, W. D. (1950). *A. Rev. Pl. Physiol.* **1,** 75–108.
Tishel, M. (1967). *Diss. Abstr.* **28,** 1836. B.
Tomkins, R. G. (1954). *J. Sci. Fd Agric.* **5,** 161–5.
Ulrich, R. (1952). "La vie des Fruits". Masson, Paris.
Ulrich, R. (1957). *J. Agric. trop. Bot. appl.* **4,** 12–30.
Ulrich, R. and Renac, J. (1950). *C.r. hebd. Séanc. Acad. Sci., Paris* **230,** 567–9.
Varma, T. N. S. and Ramakrishnan, C. V. (1956). *Nature, Lond.* **178,** 1358–9.
Vitte, G. and Guichard, C. (1955). *Revue gén. Bot.* **62,** 622–8.
Wager and Isherwood, F. A. (1941). *Analyst, Lond.* **86,** 260.
Walker, D. A. (1966). *Endeavour* **25,** 21–6.
Wejnar, R. (1967). *Ber. d. deutsch. bot. Ges.* **80,** 447–50.
Whiting, G. C. (1958a). *J. Sci. Fd Agric.* **9,** 244–50.
Whiting, G. C. (1958b). *Chemy. Ind.,* 710.
Williams, M. W. and Patterson, M. E. (1964). *J. agric. Fd Chem.* 80–3.
Wills, R. B. H. and McGlasson, W. B. (1968). *Phytochemistry* **7,** 733–9.
Wolf, J. (1938). *Planta,* **28,** 721–4.
Wolf, J. (1960). "Der Säurestoff Wechsel fleischiger Früchte". *In* "Handbuch der Pfanzenphysiologie" (Ruhland, ed.) XII/2, 720–808.
Wyman, H. and Palmer, J. K. (1964). *Plant Physiol., Lancaster* **39,** 630–3.
Young, R. E. and Biale, J. B. (1956). *Plant. Physiol., Lancaster* **31,** suppl. XXIII.
Young, R. E. and Biale, J. B. (1968). *Planta,* **81,** 253–63.

Chapter 5

Amino Acids

L. F. BURROUGHS

Department of Agriculture and Horticulture, University of Bristol, England

I. INTRODUCTION

Our present knowledge of amino acids in biological material has resulted almost entirely from the development of chromatographic methods of analysis, both on paper and in columns. The original paper-partition

119

chromatography of Consden *et al.* (1944) was applied to fruits by Joslyn and Stepka (1949) and has since been improved by many workers in various ways. It is not appropriate here to discuss experimental details of chromatographic techniques, but it is useful to be aware of the general capabilities and limitations of various types of procedure.

The free amino acids of fruits, being essentially water soluble, exist as such in the juice. Methods based on spotting a portion of filtered juice, or a 70–80% ethanolic extract of the fruit, directly on the paper are of limited use because of the presence of other juice constituents, particularly sugars, which restrict the loading on the chromatogram so that only the major amino acids can be detected. A better procedure is to separate the amino acids by means of a small column of cation exchange resin and so obtain a concentrate that can be chromatographed more easily. Such methods are simple, rapid and applicable to surveying numbers of samples. Many solvent systems have been proposed, but those most frequently used for two-dimensional chromatograms are *n*-butanol/acetic acid/water, and water saturated phenol. These resolve most of the common amino acids except leucine and isoleucine, which are usually reported simply as "leucine(s)". Although these methods have been widely used, their reliability depends very much on the details of the experimental procedure, which are not always adequately described in the original papers. Thus the failure to find a particular amino acid in a fruit does not establish its absence but only that it was below the limit of detection under those experimental conditions. Other workers using a different method may well get different results.

Provided that the resolution of amino acids is adequate, two-dimensional chromatograms can be interpreted in a semi-quantitative way by visual or photometric assessment of spot size and intensity. This sort of method is often quite sufficient for comparative purposes where precise determinations are not justified. If greater accuracy is required, the conditions of colour development with ninhydrin should be carefully standardized and the spots eluted to give solutions that can be measured spectrophotometrically. The best accuracy is obtained with the modern quantitative methods of column chromatography, with automated monitoring of the eluate, but even these are not without pitfalls. It is important, for example, to check the identity and homogeneity of peak solutions by paper chromatography.

The recently developed methods of thin-layer chromatography have not been widely applied to fruits, but would no doubt be entirely suitable where the particular advantages of speed and good resolution are required.

In general, not much work has been done on the amino acids of fruit, probably because fruit is essentially a low-nitrogen product and of little nutritional significance as a protein food. Considerable interest arises, however, when the amino acid content influences the processing of the fruit, for example, in the fermentation industries of wine and cider and in the browning reactions of citrus products and dehydrated fruits.

The role of the free amino acids in relation to metabolic changes during growth and ripening, processes that are of fundamental importance in understanding and controlling the post-harvest behaviour of fruits, has received little attention. The experimental study of enzyme systems in fruits is difficult because of the low pH and the presence of polyphenols. The solution of these problems must remain the ultimate objective of work in this field, but in the meantime one can only view the situation in more general terms. Undoubtedly the free amino acids are to be regarded as in metabolic equilibrium with the processes of protein synthesis and degradation (Hulme, 1954a) and it is reasonable to assume that the mechanisms involved are similar to those in other plant tissues. The general topics of the biosynthesis of protein and non-protein amino acids have been reviewed by Greenberg (1964) and Fowden (1964) respectively.

In this chapter an attempt is made to give the average distribution of amino acids in each of the fruits concerned. How good this is depends on the amount and quality of the published work in each case. For some, such as the grape, the information is adequate, but for others it may be very scanty and contradictory. If the contradictions are accepted as real differences, the reasons must be sought in terms of fruit variety, environmental or nutritional conditions of growth, degree of ripeness, etc. It is easy to attribute differences to factors of this sort in a general way, but such effects are rarely investigated experimentally; where they are, the results are particularly valuable.

The question of nitrogenous compounds other than amino acids is strictly outside the scope of this chapter; proteins in fruits are discussed in Section I, Chapter 9. Tercelj (1965) has shown the presence of purines, nucleosides and nucleotides in wine, and Burroughs (1957a) found evidence for such compounds in apple juice. Deibner (1964) reported hexosamines in grape juice and wines. There is also the possibility of peptides, of which Ribereau-Gayon and Peynaud (1961) reported appreciable amounts in grapes. These have not been found generally by other workers, either in grapes or other fruits, possibly because they have not been looked for specifically. Their occurrence at least in small amounts is inherently possible or even probable. The first approach to the presence of these and other non-amino acid nitrogenous substances would be to establish a balance sheet for the total soluble nitrogen of the juice. Investigations of this sort would be valuable.

II. POME FRUITS

A. Apple (*Malus pumila*)

The first reasonably complete accounts of the free amino acids of apples were given by Hulme and Arthington (1950, 1952) for the varieties Bramley's Seedling and (immature) Worcester Pearmain. The second paper, however, was concerned mainly with the presence of pipecolic acid and methylproline. McKee and Urbach (1953) examined the changes in the free amino acids of Granny Smith apples during growth on the tree. Their results agreed well with those of Hulme and Arthington with a few minor omissions and additions. The chief amino acids in ripe fruit were asparagine, aspartic acid, glutamic acid, serine, threonine and α- and β-alanine, with lesser amounts of valine, γ-aminobutyric acid, leucine(s) proline, methionine sulphoxide and pipecolic acid; a further unknown spot was later shown to be homoserine. They also reported an "unknown" amino acid which later work (Hulme, 1954b; Urbach, 1955; Hulme and Steward, 1955) showed was either 4-methyl-4-hydroxyproline or 4-hydroxymethylproline. The same amino acid was found by Burroughs (1957a), and its structure was finally elucidated by Abraham *et al.* (1961) as 4-hydroxymethylproline. The —CH_2OH group on the C_4 carbon is probably *cis* with respect to the carboxyl group (Bethell *et al.*, 1963). The closely related 4-methylproline originally reported by Hulme and Arthington (1954) was shown to have the *trans* configuration (Burroughs *et al.*, 1961). Hydroxyproline was found in immature Worcester Pearmain apples (Hulme and Arthington, 1952).

Most of the free amino acids recorded by the earlier workers were also found by Burroughs (1957a) in an extensive survey of twenty varieties of cider apple. The soluble nitrogen content of these juices varied from 4 to 33 mg N/100 ml. Asparagine was the predominant amino acid of all juices except those of very low N content, and in high N juices up to half the soluble N content was attributed to asparagine. Aspartic and glutamic acids were prominent in all juices. Most juices contained moderate amounts of serine, α-alanine, γ-aminobutyric acid, valine, isoleucine and 4-hydroxymethylproline. The leucine/isoleucine spot noted by previous workers was shown to be due exclusively to isoleucine in these juices. Most juices contained small amounts of threonine, glutamine, β-alanine, lysine and arginine. About half the juices also contained traces of glycine, phenylalanine, pipecolic acid and methionine sulphoxide. Proline was usually absent or present only as traces, but occasionally reached small to medium amounts. These observations on their relative abundance merely grade the amino acids into major, moderate and minor constituents. The fact that certain amino acids were sometimes not detected does not mean that they were absent, but only that they were below the practical limit of detection in the presence of larger amounts of other amino acids.

In this study of cider apple juices there was no evidence for any specific varietal influence on the pattern of amino acids, except in so far as some varieties tend to have a high total nitrogen content, which always manifests itself in a high content of asparagine and aspartic acid. Conversely in varieties of low nitrogen content the otherwise minor amino acids tend to be relatively more prominent. Dessert and culinary apples are usually grown under good conditions of nitrogen nutrition so that they resemble the high nitrogen cider varieties.

The occurrence of appreciable amounts of 4-hydroxymethylproline in apple and pear fruits appears to be unique; only traces of this substance have been tentatively reported in other fruits, for example, in apricots (Ingles and Reynolds, 1958) and in cherries (Thale and Rateau, 1957). The metabolic origin of 4-hydroxymethylproline has not been studied, but Fowden (1964) suggests that the metabolism of hydroxyimino acids in plants may well be similar to known pathways in animal tissues.

Cuzzoni and Lissi (1965) reported hydroxyproline in apples and pears but this may possibly have been a wrong identification of 4-hydroxymethylproline. Free hydroxyproline has not been found in apple and pear by other workers, although it occurs in apple protein (McKee and Urbach, 1953).

B. Pear (*Pyrus communis*)

Ulrich and Thaler (1955, 1957) examined the sugars, organic acids and amino acids of William and Passe Crasanne pears during growth and maturing. In ripe pears they found chiefly aspartic acid and asparagine with smaller amount of proline, glutamic acid, serine, threonine, alanine valine and leucine, and traces of lysine and phenylalanine. Proline increased markedly during growth and maturing.

Burroughs (1957a) examined about twenty perry pear juices and found the free amino acids to be very similar to those of apples. The main difference was that the pears contained more proline, which was sometimes the dominant amino acid. They also contained rather more serine and alanine and less asparagine, aspartic acid and glutamic acid, probably because the total nitrogen of these pears (3–17 mg N/100 ml) was less than that of the apples examined. In one sample of William pears of high nitrogen content (28 mg/100 ml) asparagine and aspartic acid were very prominent. In general, the pears contained similar amounts of 4-hydroxymethylproline to cider apples and most of them also contained small amounts of 1-aminocyclopropane-1-carboxylic acid (Burroughs, 1957b, 1960). Neither of these compounds was detected in the William pear.

HOCH$_2$—CH——CH$_2$ CH$_2$ NH$_2$

       CH$_2$ CH—COOH   C

             N   CH$_2$ COOH

           H

4-hydroxymethylproline   1-aminocyclopropane-1-carboxylic acid

Table I shows the relative proportions of amino acids in apple and pear juices, based on the average results of visual assessments of chromatograms (Burroughs, 1958).

TABLE I. Relative proportions (%) of individual amino acids in cider apple and perry pear juices

No. of Samples		Apple 15	Pear 15
Soluble N	range	1·7–31·9	2·4–17·5
(mg/100 ml)	average	9·4	8·4
Amino acids			
Aspartic acid		*21*	10
Asparagine		*17*	9
Glutamic acid		*15*	10
Serine		10	11
α-Alanine		7	9
4-hydroxymethylproline		6	6
γ-Aminobutyric acid		5	3
Isoleucine		5	7
Valine		4	6
Threonine		3	2
Glutamine		2	2
β-Alanine		2	1
Proline		2	*14*
Lysine		2	3

The dominant amino acids are shown in italics

C. Medlar (*Mespilus germanica*)

Only one sample of medlar has been examined (Burroughs, 1960). This fruit is of no commercial importance and is only mentioned because of a dramatic change in nitrogen content associated with the sudden ripening of the fruit. The alcohol soluble nitrogen (approximately 50 mg N/100 g) of the hard, green, unripe medlar decreased to 10 mg/100 g in the soft, yellow-brown, edible fruit. Much of the soluble nitrogen of the unripe medlar was due to asparagine which disappeared almost completely on ripening. Both ripe and unripe fruits contained traces of 4-hydroxymethylproline.

III. GRAPE (*Vitis species*)

The world production of grapes is about twice that of citrus fruit and is of the order of 50 million tons per year, of which 80–85% is used for wine making (Anon, 1968). Much the greatest proportion of this comes from the species *Vitis vinifera* but in certain regions other species or hybrids are grown because of their resistance to fungal or insect (phylloxera) attack. The best known of these are the North American species *V. labrusca* and *V. rotundifolia* grown in the Eastern United States (varieties Concord, Niagara, Delaware); hybrids of these with *V. vinifera* give the so-called "direct producers", widely planted in America and even in certain regions of France (Amerine *et al.*, 1967).

The amino acids of grapes have been studied mainly on account of their importance as yeast nutrients in wine fermentation. Because of this it is necessary when reading papers in this field to distinguish clearly between results for unfermented juices ("musts") and those relating to fermented wines. Earlier work on nitrogenous compounds in grapes and wines was summarized by Amerine (1953).

The distribution of nitrogenous compounds in the grape as a whole is described by Ribereau-Gayon and Peynaud (1961). The free amino acids being essentially water soluble occur in the juice of the grape. Although the juice represents about 75% of the weight of the fruit, it contains only one-fifth of the total nitrogen, the remaining four-fifths being in the skin and seeds. According to the same authors, there is some release of nitrogenous compounds from the seeds into the pulp of the mature grape. Usually, less than half the nitrogen content of the juice of ripe grapes is due to free amino acids, there being substantial amounts of ammonium ion, peptide and protein. There are important changes in these fractions during the ripening of the grape; in the juvenile fruit most of the soluble nitrogen is present as ammonium ion and synthesis of amino acids, peptides and protein occurs mainly during the last six to eight weeks of development (after the "véraison" stage). The nature of the protein in grape juice, and the consequent problems of turbidity in the wine, have been studied by Diemair *et al.* (1962).

The free amino acids of the juices of seven varieties of grape were determined by Castor (1953) using microbiological assays. Glutamic acid was the most prominent (mean 69 mg/100 ml; range 27–107) followed by arginine (mean 40; range 7–113); histidine, leucine, isoleucine, valine, aspartic acid, phenylalanine and tryptophane each averaged 5–10 mg/100 ml; tyrosine, lysine, methionine, glycine and cystine each averaged less than 2 mg/100 ml. The importance of proline, serine and threonine was shown later (Castor and Archer, 1955) when the main amino acids of the French Colombard juice were given as proline 349 mg/100 ml, arginine 103, serine 48, glutamic acid

27, and threonine 21. It was also shown that, unlike most other amino acids, proline was not readily assimilated by the yeasts during fermentation.

A similar range of amino acids in grape juice and wine was reported from Russia by Sisakian and Bezinger (1953) and the same general picture has been amply confirmed by many workers (Hennig and Venter, 1958; Lafon-Lafourcade and Peynaud, 1959; Lafon-Lafourcade and Guimberteau, 1962). There are, however, some inconsistent reports, for example Van Wyck and Venter (1965) found relatively little proline and arginine and larger amounts of alanine and valine in a Riesling from South Africa. Tercelj (1965) found much more arginine than proline in grape juice (variety Servant); arginine 186 mg/litre, proline 58, glutamic acid 47, glutamine 44, aspartic acid, alanine, threonine and leucine(s) each about 30, γ-aminobutyric acid and serine both 24 mg/litre. Amino acids accounted for 37%, protein 35% and ammonia 14% of the total nitrogen of this juice. Tercelj also studied the changes in amino acids during fermentation and gives some data on nucleic acid components in wine.

The wide differences in composition of grape juice are mentioned by Kliewer (1968) both in total nitrogen (10–200 mg N/100 ml) and in the proportion due to amino acids. In a study of 28 varieties, Kliewer (1969) found that amino acids accounted for 60–90% of the total nitrogen. This is considerably higher than in the older (European) data of Ribereau-Gayon and Peynaud (1961) and does not leave much room for ammonia, peptide and protein nitrogen. Kliewer (1968) examined the changes in amino acid content during the later stages of ripening for 18 varieties of grape. Total free amino acids increased two- to five-fold during development from under-ripe to ripe and over-ripe stages, and ranged from 200–800 mg/100 ml (as leucine equivalents). Eight amino acids accounted for 60–95% of the total amino acids present. Arginine and proline were the two most prominent amino acids at the ripe stage of most varieties. The concentration of arginine usually increased rapidly during the early stages of ripening (after véraison) and then sometimes decreased as the fruit became over-ripe. Proline, on the other hand, generally increased rapidly throughout, even to senescence as previously shown by Lafon-Lafourcade and Guimberteau (1962). Changes in other amino acids were less spectacular. Kliewer divided his varieties into three groups according to whether they were proline or arginine dominated, or intermediate. Although the vines were virus-free and all grown under the same conditions, it would seem that more samples are needed to decide whether this represents real and constant varietal differences or whether it is a logical consequence of the extreme variability of two independent parameters. Kliewer discusses possible metabolic relationships between arginine and proline but direct evidence is lacking, and he concludes that the biochemical implications remain to be determined. The amounts of both arginine and

TABLE II. Free amino acids in ripe grapes (mg/100 ml juice)

Variety	Type	Alanine	γ-Amino-butyric acid	Arginine	Aspartic acid	Glutamic acid	Proline	Serine	Threonine	Total
Cabernet Sauvignon	RW	22	18	33	15	14	*305*	9	13	429
Chardonnay	WW	59	30	93	16	64	*277*	28	28	595
Perlette	T	36	14	103	17	72	*196*	9	33	480
Cardinal	T	64	32	*183*	13	133	*183*	16	22	646
Carignane	RW	38	29	51	13	34	*124*	19	32	340
Chemin Blanc	WW	58	19	*119*	24	31	123	27	37	438
Pinot Blanc	WW	33	25	*125*	7	55	111	22	23	401
Thompson Seedless	T	32	11	95	9	58	99	7	26	337
Malbec	RW	31	17	79	14	15	94	13	17	280
Palomino	WW	26	28	97	9	48	86	27	25	346
Muscat Hamberg	T	37	15	92	10	70	83	14	27	348
Pinot Noir	RW	32	17	88	13	37	79	25	30	321
White Riesling	WW	25	18	52	7	28	77	14	15	236
Tokay	T	19	10	40	12	56	55	7	11	210
Alicante Bouschet	RW	22	30	84	20	58	66	13	17	310
Flora	WW	31	43	*178*	9	43	105	38	18	465
Black Corinth	T	35	15	*201*	14	54	98	18	34	469
Gewurztraminer	WW	32	26	*236*	14	49	85	26	33	501
Average Composition		35	22	108	13	51	125	18	24	398

Abbreviations used: RW = Red wine; WW = White wine ; T = Table
Figures in italics indicate dominance of proline or arginine
Data quoted with permission from Kliewer (1968)

proline are strongly influenced by the ripeness of the grapes and possibly also by seasonal factors. Flanzy and Poux (1965) found that a grape juice contained much less proline (55 mg/litre) in a cool year than juice from the same source in the preceding, hot year (215 mg/litre), other amino acids being largely unaffected. Whatever the significance of the arginine/proline ratios, Kliewer's data are the most comprehensive available, and his figures for ripe grapes are therefore given in Table II. Other amino acids, apart from arginine and proline, do not vary much and the overall average composition can be regarded as well established, subject to possible seasonal effects.

It is to be noted that certain varieties in Table II have relatively more total amino acids (Cardinal and Chardonnay) while others have relatively little (Tokay and White Riesling). Since they were all grown under the same conditions, this is probably a true varietal effect.

Kliewer et al. (1966) examined the free amino acids in leaves and berries of 23 different species of Vitis at different stages of ripeness. Five of the species contained very large amounts of hydroxyproline and an unidentified amino acid in mature leaves and immature berries. These were virtually absent from all other varieties—a very clear-cut example of chemical taxonomy. Other amino acids showed less dramatic differences, both qualitative and quantitative, between the species.

IV. SOFT FRUITS

There are very few reports of amino acids in soft fruits. Burroughs (1960) examined seven different sorts available in Britain, making visual estimates of the relative spot size and intensity on two-dimensional chromatograms. Most of the common amino acids were present, alanine and glutamine being the two most generally prominent. (See Table III.) Other information where available is given below.

A. Strawberry (*Fragaria species*)

Rockland (1959) found medium amounts of asparagine, glutamine and alanine and small amounts of aspartic and glutamic acid and serine. Silber et al. (1960) report medium amounts of alanine, arginine, asparagine and glutamic acid, and small amounts of cystine/cysteine, γ-aminobutyric acid, glycine, lysine, methionine and ornithine. Tinsley and Bockian (1959) made quantitative determinations on the variety Marshall, and found asparagine 59 mg/100 g, glutamine 15, alanine 12, glutamic acid 8, aspartic acid 3, and serine, valine, threonine, leucine(s), cystine/cysteine, all less than 2 mg/100 g. It seems generally agreed that asparagine and glutamine predominate and that proline seems to be absent from strawberries. Since most fruits contain proline, this might be useful in detecting adulteration.

TABLE III. Amino acids of soft fruits

	Straw-berry	Goose-berry (green)	Black-currant	Red-currant	Logan-berry	Rasp-berry	Black-berry
			(mg N/100 g fruit)				
Total N	148	256	290	183	278	177	181
Alcohol-soluble N	44	165	53	15	94	44	40
Alcohol-insoluble N	104	91	237	168	184	133	141
Amino acids							
(visual assessments on arbitrary scale 0–10)							
Aspartic acid	3	2	2	3	2	2	3
Asparagine	7	3	3	1	*6*	3	6
Glutamic acid	5	5	3	3	2	3	6
Glutamine	*8*	*10*	5	5	2	3	5
Serine	2	5	4	3	3	5	5
Glycine	tr.	1	1	1	tr.	0	0
Threonine	1	2	2	1	1	1	1
α-alanine	3	*8*	7	*8*	*6*	*8*	5
β-alanine	tr.	tr.	2	1	0	tr.	0
γ-aminobutyric acid	1	3	3	3	1	3	4
Valine	tr.	2	2	1	2	2	2
Leucine(s)	tr.	2	2	1	1	1	1
Proline	0	A	A	A	tr.	tr.	tr.
Arginine	0	tr.	1	tr.	1	tr.	tr.
Lysine	0	tr.	tr.	tr.	0	tr.	0
Tyrosine	0	tr.	0	0	tr.	tr.	tr.

Abbreviations used: tr. = trace; A = small amount
Figures in italics indicate dominant amino acid

B. Blackcurrant (*Ribes nigra*)

Ayres *et al.* (1961) gave a most useful survey of the composition of black-currant juice based on the experience of large-scale commercial processing. They quote the following approximate concentrations:

	mM	mg/100 ml
Alanine	2·3	21
Glutamine	2·0	29
Glutamic acid	1·4	21
γ-aminobutyric acid	1·4	14
Proline	0·9	10
Asparagine	0·6	8
Serine	0·6	6
Leucine(s)	0·4	5
Arginine	0·2	4
Aspartic acid	0·15	2
Valine	0·1	1

In view of the number of samples, these results can be regarded as well established.

C. Raspberry (*Rubus species*)

Silber *et al.* (1960) reported a very wide range of amino acids in the American red raspberry (*Rubus strigosa*); large amounts of α-alanine, valine and isoleucine, medium amounts of asparagine, β-alanine, γ-aminobutyric acid, glutamic acid, glutamine, glycine, proline, threonine and leucine, and small amounts of α-aminobutyric acid, aspartic acid, cystine/cysteine, histidine, phenylalanine and pipecolic acid. This was obviously very different from the European sample (*R. idaeus*) examined by Burroughs (see Table III), where α-alanine and serine were the major constituents and valine and leucine(s) were present in only small amounts.

The closely related blackberry (*Rubus spp.*) and loganberry (*R. loganobaccus*) were similar in composition to the raspberry, but both contained more asparagine. This may be attributed to the fact that these fruits do not separate from the "plugs" (receptacles). Raspberry plugs were analysed separately and found to be particularly rich in asparagine.

D. Gooseberry (*Ribes Grossularia*)

The gooseberries recorded in Table III were unripe, and in this way differed from the other fruits examined; they differed also in their very high soluble nitrogen content, much of which was due to glutamine. Further samples of fruit were therefore examined to see if these features were related to maturity; both green and ripe gooseberries were picked from the same bush at an interval of 33 days. The results (Table IV) showed a marked decrease in the concentration of alcohol soluble nitrogen and in the glutamine content with ripening, while alanine, glutamic and γ-aminobutyric acids increased. The results for ripe gooseberries resembled those of Silber *et al.* (1960) who found large amounts of alanine, γ-aminobutyric and glutamic acids, a medium amount of asparagine and a small amount of cystine/cysteine.

E. Vaccinium Species

Blueberries (*V. corymbosum*). Six cultivated varieties of blueberry were examined (Burroughs, 1960) and were unusual in that arginine was much the most prominent amino acid, particularly in varieties of high nitrogen content. Other amino acids present, in decreasing order of prominence, were γ-aminobutyric acid, alanine, serine, glutamic acid, glutamine, valine, leucine(s) and aspartic acid.

Wild bilberries (*V. myrtilis*) were much lower in alcohol soluble nitrogen (5 mg N/100 g) than the cultivated blueberries (15–60 mg N/100 g). The main amino acids were glutamic acid and valine, with smaller amounts of alanine, serine, γ-aminobutyric and aspartic acids. There was no arginine.

TABLE IV. Changes in nitrogen content of gooseberries during ripening

Average weight per fruit, g	Green 6·9		Ripe 15·4	
	per 100 g	per fruit	per 100 g	per fruit
Total N, mg	157	10·8	117	18·0
Alcohol-soluble N, mg	77	5·3	36	5·5
Alcohol-insoluble N, mg	80	5·5	81	12·5
Amino acids				
(visual assessment)				
Aspartic acid	3		3	
Asparagine	6		6	
Glutamic acid	5		8	
Glutamine	10		6	
Serine	3		3	
Threonine	2		2	
Alanine	4		10	
γ-aminobutyric acid	tr.		4	
Valine	1		2	
Leucine(s)	1		2	
Proline	0		A	
Lysine	0		tr.	
Tyrosine	0		tr.	

Abbreviations used: tr. = trace; A = small amount

Cowberries (*V. vitis-idaea*) are unusual in containing 1-aminocyclopropane-1-carboxylic acid and 5-hydroxypipecolic acid (Vähätalo and Virtanen, 1957a, b). The former was also found in perry pears and cider apples (Burroughs, 1957b) and has not been reported in any other natural material; the latter occurs in dates (Rinderknecht, 1959). Both substances were present in small amounts in a sample of *V. vitis-idaea* grown in Scotland; the main amino acids were serine and γ-aminobutyric acid, with smaller amounts of glutamine, threonine, alanine, valine, leucine(s), arginine, lysine, tyrosine and several others (Burroughs, 1960). Thus the high arginine pattern of *V. corymbosum* does not extend to these other two species.

V. STONE FRUITS

A. Cherry (*Prunus cerasus*; *Prunus avium*)

Three semi-quantitative reports of the relative amounts of free amino acids in cherries are summarized in Table V.

Of these, the work of Thaler and Rateau is the most complete; they examined the changes in free amino acids at four stages of ripeness (green to red). Most of the 16 amino acids decreased during ripening but asparagine and proline increased slightly. They tentatively reported 4-hydroxymethyl-proline in cherries, but this still requires confirmation. It seems established from the results in Table V that proline is a main constituent and that pipecolic acid can occur.

TABLE V

	Thaler and Rateau (1957)				Rockland (1959)	Silber et al. (1960)
	green	green	yellow	red		
Aspartic acid	X X	X X X	X X X	X X X	X	
Asparagine	X X	X	X	X	X X	X
Glutamic acid	X X	X	X	X	X	X
Glutamine					X X	
Serine	X	X	X	X	X	X
Glycine		X	X	X		X
Threonine	X	X	X	X		
α-alanine	X X	X	X	X	X X	X X X
β-alanine	X	X	X	X		X
γ-aminobutyric acid	X X	X X	X	X	X	X X
Valine	X X	X X	X	X		X X
Leucine(s)	X X	X	X	X		X X
Proline	X	X	X	X X	X X X	X X
Arginine	X X X	X	X	X		
Tyrosine	X X		X			X X
Phenylalanine	X X	X X	X			X
Pipecolic acid	X X	X X	X	X		X X X

B. Plum (*Prunus domestica*)

Joslyn and Stepka (1949) examined two varieties of prune, French and Imperial, and found the chief amino acids to be asparagine and aspartic acid, with smaller amounts of glutamic acid, glutamine, serine, threonine, α-alanine, γ-aminobutyric acid, valine, leucine(s) and proline. They also reported a trace of hydroxyproline, but this is unusual in plant material and needs to be confirmed. Silber *et al.* (1960) found medium amounts of aspartic acid, α-alanine, β-alanine and γ-aminobutyric acid with smaller amounts of 12 other amino acids. The presence of a substantial amount of β-alanine is unusual and also needs confirmation.

The amino acids of the closely related damson (*P. insititia*) were found to be chiefly asparagine, α-alanine and γ-aminobutyric acid, with smaller amounts of aspartic and glutamic acids, glutamine, serine, threonine, valine, leucine(s), proline and traces of tyrosine, phenylalanine and pipecolic acid (Burroughs, unpublished).

C. Apricot (*Prunus armericus*) and Peach (*P. persica*)

Joslyn and Stepka (1949) examined two varieties of apricot, Blenheim and Moorpark, and found relatively large amounts of asparagine, aspartic acid, glutamic acid and alanine, and smaller amounts of glutamine, serine, proline, valine, leucine and γ-aminobutyric acid. Reynolds (1957) and Ingles and Reynolds (1958), using the Moore and Stein column procedure, found an overwhelming predominance of asparagine (57% of the total amino acids) followed by aspartic acid, alanine and proline and small amounts of serine, γ-aminobutyric and glutamic acids, valine, leucine and threonine. The last two were present at less than 0·1 mM/g dry weight of fruit. In freeze-dried apricot purée, the free amino acids reacted with sugars during storage (12 months at 25°C and 70% relative humidity) to form 1-(N-amino acid)-1-deoxysugars; these Amadori rearrangement products are the first stage of the complex changes leading to non-enzymic browning.

Casoli and Bellucci (1964) confirmed the large excess of asparagine in a study of five Italian varieties of apricot. The average composition was asparagine 116 mg/1C0 g fresh weight, aspartic acid 19, alanine 11, glutamic acid 10, proline 8, threonine 4, valine 3, leucine 2, serine 2, glycine 1, phenylalanine 1. The free amino acids represented 38% of the total amino acids after hydrolysis of the puréed fruit, including skins. In this paper, Casoli and Bellucci found that asparagine and serine formed a mixed peak in their fractionation by the Moore and Stein procedure. This undoubtedly accounts for an earlier report by Poretta and Giannone (1963), who used the same method, of an overwhelming predominance of serine and threonine in apricots and peaches. Apart from this, the results of these two groups of workers were in general agreement.

Reynolds (1957) found that the amino acids of peaches were closely similar to those of apricots except that peaches contained much less proline. Porretta and Giannone (1963) also noted that proline was almost absent from peaches, although present in quite large amounts in apricots, and that the two fruits were quite similar in their content of all the other amino acids.

Silber *et al.* (1960) found medium amounts of alanine, aspartic acid, γ-aminobutyric acid, valine and leucine in peaches, but only a small amount of asparagine and eight other amino acids. In nectarines they found medium amounts of alanine and arginine and small amounts of twelve other amino acids, including asparagine.

VI. CITRUS FRUITS

Because of the commercial importance of citrus fruits, a great many studies have been made of their composition in various respects. A comprehensive

TABLE VI. Soluble nitrogen compounds in citrus fruits

Compound	Conc. (mg/100 ml) in juice Orange[a]	Grapefruit[b]	Lemon[c]	Notes on occurrence
Alanine	3–26	—	1–31	This group of amino acids appears
γ-Aminobutyric acid	4–73	—	4–20	to be present generally in citrus
Arginine[d]	23–150	76	25–106	fruits; e.g., in American oranges,
Asparagine	20–188	—	—	grapefruit, mandarins, lemons,
Aspartic acid	7–115	470	19–60	limes and some hybrids;[a,q,e] in
Glutamic acid	6–71	280	6–35	Italian oranges, mandarins and
Glutamine	3–63	—	—	lemons;[f] in Spanish oranges and
Glycine	5	—	—	lemons;[g] and in Japanese man-
Proline	6–295	—	27–53	darins and natsudaidai[h,i,j]
Serine	4–37	310	12–28	
Valine	10	24	—	
β-Alanine	—	—	—	In mandarins and natsudaidai[j,j,k]
α-Aminobutyric acid	—	—	—	In Navel tissues[e]
Citrulline	—	—	—	In Spanish oranges and lemons[g]
Histidine	—	14	—	In oranges,[q] grapefruit,[b] manda- rins[j] and lemons[g]
Hydroxyproline	—	—	—	In natsudaidai[i]
Leucines	—	24	—	In oranges, lemons, mandarins[f] and grapefruit[b]
Lysine	—	16	—	In oranges, lemons and grape- fruit[b,d,e,f,g]
Ornithine	—	—	—	In Spanish oranges and lemons[g]
Phenylalanine	—	12	—	In oranges,[e] grapefruit,[b] lemons[f] and natsudaidai[i]
Threonine	—	10	—	In oranges, grapefruit and lemons[b,e,f,g,l]
Tryptophan	—	4	—	In grapefruit,[b] mandarins and natsudaidai[i,k]
Tyrosine	—	6	—	In oranges, grapefruit, lemons,[b,e,g] and mandarins[j]
Cysteine	0·3–0·8		—	Range of values for oranges, grapefruit, lemons and limes[m]
Cystine	—	0·18	—	In grapefruit[b]
Glutathione	2·8–7·8		—	Range of values for oranges, grapefruit, lemons and limes[m]
Methionine	—	0·35	—	In grapefruit[b]
Betaine	39–63	—	—	Range of values for orange juice[l]
Choline	7–16	—	—	Range of values for orange juice[l]
Putrescine	—	—	—	In canned orange juice[n]
Stachydrine	—	—	—	In oranges[o] and pumelos[p]

[a] Extremes of ranges from Wedding and Sinclair (1954); Wedding and Horspool (1955); Rockland and Underwood (1956).

[b] From Burdick (1954).

[c] Rockland (1959).

[d] Probably arginine and lysine, cf., Rockland and Underwood (1956).

[e] Townsley et al. (1953).

[f] Safina (1953).

review by Kefford (1959) describes the botanical classification of citrus fruits and contains a section on nitrogenous compounds with a useful table, reproduced opposite (Table VI), of the ranges of concentration of the principal amino acids of orange, grapefruit and lemon, and references to the occurrence of less prominent constituents. The concentration ranges quoted for the main amino acids are, however, very wide and give no clear indication of the order of prominence of individual compounds. The reasons for such extreme variability from one sample to another are not immediately obvious.

Underwood and Rockland (1953) suggested that the relative proportions of the different amino acids appeared to be characteristic of the variety of orange; although this may be true to some extent this view has not received much support in later work. It seems that variability due to environmental and physiological factors is likely to obscure any characteristic varietal influence on the amino acid pattern. Rockland (1961) reviewed the earlier work on nitrogenous compounds in orange and other citrus fruits. Much of this information, however, was obtained before the development of the more refined chromatographic methods of more recent years.

A comprehensive study by Clements and Leland (1962a) of Navel and Valencia oranges, Eureka and Lisbon lemons, Marsh grapefruit and Dancy tangerines, gave values generally within the ranges quoted by Kefford. These results, by quantitative column chromatography (Moore *et al.*, 1958) on duplicate samples of commercially mature fruit, showed that (a) alanine, asparagine, aspartic acid, glutamic acid, proline, serine, γ-aminobutyric acid and arginine occurred in substantial amounts in all the fruits; (b) proline was the most prominent amino acid in every fruit except the grapefruit and was especially prominent in Valencia oranges; (c) aspartic acid predominated in the grapefruit; (d) amino acids accounted for approximately 70% of the total nitrogen of the juices. In particular, their results for grapefruit were markedly lower, and probably more reliable, than those of Burdick (1954) for aspartic and glutamic acids and serine.

One possible source of variability in amino acid pattern is the effect of fruit maturity; Clements and Leland (1962b) made a detailed study of the

---

[g] Caabeiro (1956).
[h] Nomura and Munechika (1952).
[i] Nomura (1953).
[j] Iseda and Matsushita (1953).
[k] Ito and Sakasegawa (1952b).
[l] Rakieten *et al.* (1952).
[m] Miller and Rockland (1952).
[n] Herbst and Snell (1949).
[o] Nelson *et al.* (1933).
[p] Hiwatari (1927).
[q] Underwood and Rockland (1953).

Reproduced by permission of the Editor (Copyright Academic Press Ltd.).

free amino acids in the juice of Valencia oranges during development on the tree. The concentrations of asparagine, aspartic acid and serine stayed fairly constant throughout, but the amounts of proline, arginine and γ-aminobutyric acid increased progressively; the last three, particularly proline, were predominant in mature fruit and increased further with over-maturity. The predominance of proline was convincingly demonstrated by Ting and Deszyck (1960); they examined 199 samples of orange juice and 163 samples of concentrate and found the mean concentration of proline was 0·49 m mole/100 ml with a mean total amino acid content of 0·9 m mole/100 ml (range 0·61–1·20).

Averna (1960) examined the amino acids of Italian lemons (variety Feminello), oranges (Sanguinello) and mandarins (Tardivo). He found most of the amino acids reported by Clements and Leland (1962a) but unfortunately did not give figures for proline, arginine and γ-aminobutyric acid. Aspartic acid was predominant in all his samples. Averna also determined the free amino acids in aqueous homogenates of the flavedo, albedo and pulp tissues of his fruits.

Another investigation of Italian citrus juices was made by Casoli (1963) using quantitative column chromatography. Proline, arginine and aspartic acid were the main amino acids in three varieties of orange together with a mixed peak of serine and asparagine (Casoli and Bellucci, 1964); lemons contained more aspartic acid, but much less proline and only a trace of arginine.

Calvarano (1963a) made a survey of 47 samples of Biondo oranges, the commonest Italian variety used for juice processing. On average, proline, aspartic acid, asparagine and arginine in decreasing order made up 75% of the total amino acids (254 mg/100 ml).

Vandercook et al. (1963) confirmed the high aspartic acid and low arginine pattern of lemon juice from California and Arizona; in 61 samples these amino acids averaged 32% and 3% respectively of the total free amino acids; serine (24%) and alanine plus proline (18%) were second and third in prominence. Bogin and Wallace (1966) also found aspartic acid predominating in the juice of Eureka lemon (Citrus limon); they also examined Tunisian sweet lemon (Citrus limettioides), a quite different low acid fruit, with alanine, proline and glutamine as main amino acids, lesser amounts of valine, serine and cysteine and only traces of aspartic acid. Datta (1963) found no aspartic acid in the Indian lemon (Citrus medica); the shaddock (Citrus decumana) and orange (Citrus sinensis) were remarkable for a high content of γ-aminobutyric acid.

The most recent report of amino acids in citrus fruit is that of Coussin and Samish (1968). They found that aspartic acid and serine were particularly prominent in Israel Shamouti oranges, so much so that this may be a varietal tendency. Unfortunately, they do not give figures for proline, asparagine or γ-aminobutyric acid, possibly due to interference by other juice constituents

TABLE VII. Free amino acids in citrus juices (mg/100 ml)

	Authors	Aspartic acid	Aspara-gine	Glutamic acid	Serine	Glycine	Threo-nine	α-Alanine	γ-Amino-butyric acid	Valine	Leucine(s)	Proline	Arginine	Lysine	Phenyl-alanine	Cystine
Orange																
Valencia	a	71	—	49	15	—	—	17	30	—	—	123	120	—	—	—
Valencia	b	33	50	18	22	2	—	13	32	2	—	239	57	4	—	—
Valencia	c	31	36	19	19	2	—	12	25	—	—	172	73	6	—	—
Navel	a	42	—	20	26	—	—	18	29	2	—	199	77	—	—	—
Navel	b	27	67	12	18	2	—	12	24	1	—	107	54	3	1	—
Sanguinello	d	16	6	7	6	—	—	8	—	1	1	*	—	1	—	—
(see notes)	e	34	(49)	16	(49)	1	2	8	—	1	2	70	44	4	—	—
Biondo	f	48	45	21	16	—	—	14	14	—	—	57	41	—	—	—
Shamouti	g	115	*	28	70	*	*	36	*	12	6	*	45	10	—	—
Lemon																
Eureka	a	38	—	21	17	—	—	12	7	—	—	40	45	—	—	—
Eureka	b	36	16	19	17	1	—	9	7	1	—	41	3	1	2	—
Lisbon	b	32	17	18	19	1	—	10	7	1	—	47	3	1	3	—
(see notes)	h	32	10	10	24	—	—	(18)	3	—	—	(18)	3	—	—	—
Feminello	d	41	6	29	17	—	—	9	—	4	1	*	—	—	—	*
Primo Fiore	e	51	(38)	26	(38)	1	1	13	—	2	2	29	2	1	—	—
Others																
Marsh grapefruit	b	81	42	22	15	2	—	9	19	2	—	59	47	3	3	—
Dancy tangerine	b	36	85	16	19	2	—	7	18	2	—	100	84	4	5	—
Mandarin	d	24	18	17	12	—	—	8	—	3	5	*	—	4	6	*

a Rockland (1959)

b Clements and Leland (1962a)

c Clements and Leland (1962b)

d Averna (1960); * = present but not measured.

e Casoli (1963); mixed peak of serine and asparagine, orange represents average of 3 varieties, Biondo di Sicilia, Moro and Tarocco.

f Calvarano (1963a); average of 47 samples.

g Coussin and Samish (1968)

h Vandercook et al. (1963); average of 61 samples from California or Arizona, expressed as % of total amino acids; mixed peak of alanine and proline.

*Present but not measured.

since they chromatographed their juices directly without previous ion-exchange treatment. This casts some doubt on the accuracy of their quantitative determinations.

Discussing the occurrence of free amino acids in citrus juices generally, Calvarano (1963b) concludes that 90% of the total amino acids are accounted for by aspartic and glutamic acids, alanine, γ-aminobutyric acid, arginine, asparagine, proline and serine. This agrees with Clements and Leland (1962a) and seems to be a fair statement of the situation. The relative proportions of the free amino acids, however, vary widely in different samples and varietal, or even species differences are sometimes difficult to establish.

Table VII summarizes the quantitative results for free amino acids in citrus juices quoted in the preceding paragraphs.

There is considerable interest in the measurement of total amino acids in citrus juices by formol titration and chloramine values as a means of detecting adulteration in commercial products (Vandercook et al., 1963; Wucherpfennig and Franke, 1966). Rapid routine chromatographic tests for detecting added amino acids, for example, glycine, are useful in this respect (Alvarez, 1967).

Specific determination of serine has been proposed as an index of the fruit content of orange products (Morgan, 1966). This method is claimed to be applicable even to comminuted juices since the free serine content of the orange is fairly uniform throughout all its tissues.

VII. BANANA (*Musa acuminata*)

Steward et al. (1960a) made an extensive study of nitrogenous and other components of the cultivar Gros Michel examining roots, rhizome, leaves, floral parts and the fruit. Total free amino acids amounted to 515 μg/g of edible fruit tissue. Of these, asparagine accounted for over 15%; glutamine and histidine each 10–15%, aspartic, γ-aminobutyric and pipecolic acids each 5–10%; smaller amounts of glutamic acid, serine, glycine, alanine, threonine, lysine, arginine, proline, valine, leucine(s) and tyrosine were also present. The remarkable feature was the high proportion of histidine, which is unusual in plant tissues.

In a further paper, Steward et al. (1960b) studied the changes in the nitrogenous compounds of banana fruit after harvesting. Throughout the ripening process the proportion of alcohol soluble to alcohol insoluble (protein) nitrogen remained constant. Before the onset of ripening of the green banana, asparagine, glutamine and histidine accounted for 32%, 28% and 15% of the alcohol soluble nitrogen, and as ripening proceeded the amides, especially glutamine, decreased while histidine increased (to 30%). The same three compounds accounted for 70% of the alcohol soluble nitrogen of the ripe fruit, so that any changes in the other amino acids present (14 of them) had little effect. The relative proportions of the amides and histidine, however, were markedly affected by the time of year at which the fruit developed. Winter-grown fruit (October to February) contained less aparagine (20%), less glutamine (6%) and more histidine (30%) at harvesting than the summer-grown fruit referred to above; histidine remained the dominant amino acid after ripening. The samples of fruit on which the above observations were made were grown in Central America. Other samples of the same variety, *Gros Michel*, grown in Jamaica and British Cameroons, and of two other varieties *Lacatan* and *Cavendish*, contained much less glutamine (1–2%) and tended to be rich in asparagine (20–30%) and arginine (10–20%) rather than histidine (5–15%). They also contained a higher proportion (over 50%) of the soluble nitrogen as a variety of common amino acids, especially leucine(s), valine and serine. Thus the histidine dominance of the high-glutamine Gros Michel from Central America was by no means universal. It is not clear what factors (nutritional, climatic or environmental) determine whether the fruit will follow the high-glutamine or low-glutamine metabolic pattern. Certain differences were noted in the amino acid composition of the protein of these two types of fruit.

Steward *et al.* (1960b) further observed that there were differences in the distribution of amino acids, and therefore in metabolic activity, between the inner placental region and the surrounding fleshy pericarp (endocarp). The inner region was much richer in total soluble nitrogen, 454 μg N/g compared with 122 μg N/g in the endocarp; this difference was reflected in the presence of more of the individual amino acids, particularly the amides glutamine and asparagine which were virtually absent from the endocarp.

Further work is needed to understand the metabolic implications of the changes in amino acid composition during the development and post-harvest ripening of the banana.

From the compositional point of view the chief amino acid in ripe bananas is usually asparagine but in certain cases it can be histidine, and these two can account for 50% of the soluble nitrogen. Where histidine is less prominent other amino acids become more important, particularly leucine(s), arginine, valine and serine. Occasionally pipecolic acid occurs in moderate amount as also does γ-aminobutyric acid. The latter is dominant in the skin of unripe bananas and can amount to 70% of the total soluble nitrogen (Steward *et al.*, 1960b).

VIII. PINEAPPLE (*Ananas comosus*)

Gortner and Singleton (1965) studied the chemical and physical development of Hawaiian pineapple, including nitrogenous constituents and enzymes. There were distinct trends in the amino acid content of the flesh and shell tissues, corresponding to physiological stages of development. The concentration of amino acids in the juice was minimal (25 mg N/100 ml), about six weeks before ripeness, when it reached 50 mg N/100 ml. During this period, alanine and methionine increased greatly and were among the major amino acids in ripe fruit, an increase which continued into senescence. No quantitative determinations were made of aspartic and glutamic acids but they were said to occur in very high amounts at all stages of development; asparagine and glutamine were present in smaller amounts. These four, together with alanine, methionine and possibly γ-aminobutyric acid were presumably the major free amino acids of ripe pineapples; peptides were also present.

Gawler (1962) had previously examined the amino acids of canned Malayan pineapple juice and found more proline and isoleucine, but no methionine or glutamine. Gortner and Singleton attributed these differences to varietal factors.

IX. DATE (*Phoenix dactylifera*)

The changes in free amino acids in dates during ripening from the green to the brown stages were studied by Rinderknecht (1959) in relation to the darkening of the fruit by formation of Maillard condensation products. Aspartic and glutamic acids, serine, leucine and pipecolic acid decreased, while γ-aminobutyric acid, glycine and proline increased during four stages of ripening (green, yellow, red and brown). The most striking features, however, were sharp increases in glutamine, arginine and glutathione at the red stage and their subsequent decline at the brown stage and beyond. The chief amino acids of brown dates were alanine, arginine and 5-hydroxypipecolic acid, with smaller amounts of proline, γ-aminobutyric, aspartic and glutamic acids, asparagine, glutamine, glutathione, glycine and citrulline. Presumably there must also be a considerable amount of "amino" nitrogen in the form of Maillard compounds. Dates appear to be the richest natural source of 5-hydroxypipecolic acid, a relatively rare amino acid probably derived from 5-hydroxylysine (Grobbelaar et al., 1955). The other unusual feature of dates is the presence of citrulline.

Further information was given by Al-Rawi et al. (1967) who reported on the free and total amino acids of three varieties of Iraqi dates, in relation to their nutritive value. The chief free amino acids were proline (37 mg/100 g) and alanine (20 mg/100 g) but the main component (80 mg/100 g) formed a mixed peak with phenylalanine on the auto-analyser and was hydrolysable. It was therefore presumed to be a peptide but was not further examined. Although Rinderknecht (1959) had reported small to medium amounts of glutathione in dates, it would be surprising to find it as a major constituent to this extent.

X. CUCURBITACEOUS FRUITS

Melons, marrows, cucumbers, pumpkins, squashes and gourds are widely grown, and in some tropical and sub-tropical areas may be quite important foods. Botanically they are a diverse group, but most of the edible fruits belong to the species *Citrullus vulgaris*, *Cucumis melo* or *Cucurbita pepo*.

Very little information has been published on their nitrogenous constituents. The best known and most interesting fact is that citrulline was first isolated from the water melon (*Citrullus vulgaris*) by Wada as long ago as 1930. Selim *et al.* (1966) examined the amino acids in the protein of the edible seeds of three varieties of melon. Noe and Fowden (1960) discovered β-pyrazol-1-ylalanine, isomeric with histidine, in the seeds of watermelon. Dunnill and Fowden (1965) made a chemo-taxonomic survey of a wide range of Cucurbitaceous species based on the non-protein amino acids of the seeds. These were: citrulline, β-pyrazol-1-ylalanine and its γ-glutamyl peptide, *m*-carboxyphenylalanine, cucurbitin, and three N_4-alkylasparagines. Citrulline was present in all species but the amounts varied widely; the occurrence of the other seven amino acids depended on the taxonomic relationships of the species. There was however, no direct evidence that these compounds occur in the flesh of the edible species, nor were the commoner amino acids investigated.

Hadwiger and Hall (1961) examined the free amino acids in the skin tissues of watermelon (*Citrullus vulgaris*) and found more citrulline, glutamine, aspartic and glutamic acids, alanine, serine and threonine in the dark green stripes than in the lighter areas; the darker areas were more susceptible to fungal attack.

None of these investigations give direct evidence of amino acids in the edible tissues. Accordingly, the writer obtained two melons, a dark green Spanish Honeydew and a pale yellow South African Honeydew. Both were presumably *Cucumis melo* and it was not possible to get a watermelon, *Citrullus vulgaris*. The total nitrogen contents were 160 and 82 mg/100 g fresh weight and alcohol soluble nitrogen 130 and 50 mg/100 g respectively. The free amino acids were similar in both, glutamine and alanine were the main components, followed by γ-aminobutyric acid, small amounts of aspartic and glutamic acids, serine and citrulline, together with traces of asparagine, valine, leucine(s) and possibly histidine. Citrulline was not resolved from the closely adjacent glutamine in the solvents used (*n*-butanol/acetic acid/water and 80% phenol with ammonia) and it was therefore necessary to hydrolyse the concentrate before chromatographing. The presence of citrulline was confirmed by spraying with Ehrlich's reagent.

The amino acids found in these melons were similar to those reported by Hadwiger and Hall (1961) in their sample of *Citrullus vulgaris*. These authors however, gave no details of the relative proportions of amino acids apart from implying that citrulline and glutamine were major constituents.

XI. TOMATO (*Lycopersicum esculentum*)

All workers on the free amino acids of tomato have found glutamic acid as the main component, but the amounts of other amino acids have been variable. This may be because most investigations have been concerned with the effects of fertilizer treatment, degree of ripening or other cultural factors, all of which seem to influence the free amino acids of the fruit.

Carangal *et al.* (1954) reported tryptophane as a main constituent but the amounts varied extremely (5–80 mg/100 g) according to fertilizer treatment. Tryptophane has not been found by other workers, although specifically mentioned by Possingham (1956) when dealing with the effect of micronutrient deficiency on the whole plant, and by Saravacos *et al.* (1958).

Saravacos *et al.* (1958) studied the amino acids of tomatoes in relation to fertilizer treatment. They found glutamic acid 160 mg/100 ml, aspartic acid 30, valine, glycine and (asparagine + glutamine) each about 20, and leucine, serine, threonine and alanine variable between 5–20 mg/100 ml. These figures are for the control plants; addition of nitrogen increased the free amino acids, particularly the amides, aspartic acid and alanine.

Gulyakin *et al.* (1965) studied the effects of fertilizers (NPK) on yield, sugars, organic and amino acids in tomatoes. Low nitrogen decreased the total amino acids, especially γ-aminobutyric acid, alanine, valine, leucine and the amides. High potassium decreased the total amino acids and amides but increased alanine. High phosphate increased the total amino acids and amides but decreased γ-aminobutyric acid. This last correlation had previously been found by Saito (1959).

Freeman and Woodbridge (1960) examined the changes in free amino acids of tomatoes during ripening, on and off the plant, and the effect of truss height. The average composition of fruit ripened on the plant was, glutamic acid 77 mg/100 g, arginine 58, asparagine 30, aspartic acid 26, γ-aminobutyric acid 22, serine 13. Aspartic and especially glutamic acids increased during ripening, particularly in fruit ripened off the plant. Arginine, γ-aminobutyric acid, alanine, leucine and valine all decreased during ripening. Total amino acids decreased with truss height. This work is notable for the high concentration of arginine, scarcely mentioned by previous authors, and the presence of γ-aminobutyric acid. Burroughs (1960) also found a relatively large amount of γ-aminobutyric acid.

Because of the very variable composition of tomatoes, depending on the conditions of growth and ripening, it is not possible to give a useful average amino acid content. It seems, however, that glutamic acid is always predominant and proline is virtually absent.

XII. MISCELLANEOUS FRUITS

A. Passion Fruit (*Passiflora edulis*)

Pruthi (1963) reviewed the composition and technology of passion fruit juice. He gives the total nitrogen content as ranging from 96–192 mg/100 ml, of which about half is amino nitrogen. The chief free amino acids are leucine(s), proline and threonine, with smaller amounts of valine, tyrosine, aspartic acid, glycine, arginine and lysine.

B. Mango (*Manganifera indica*)

Johnson and Raymond (1965) summarized the chemical composition of mangoes, including details of the amino acids in the seeds, but not in the flesh or juice. Govindarajan and Sreenivasaya (1950) examined four varieties of mango and found the free amino acids to be chiefly aspartic and glutamic acids, glycine and alanine, with smaller amounts of leucine(s) and methionine.

C. Brazilian Fruits

Xavier Filho *et al.* (1962) examined the free amino acids in the following local fruit: genipap (*Genipa americana*), sapodilla (*Achras sapota*), imbu (*Spondias tuberosa*), bacuri (*Platonia insignis*) and cashew apple (*Anacadium occidentale*). All these fruits contained aspartic and glutamic acids, alanine, α-aminobutyric acid, proline, arginine, lysine; arginine was the major basic amino acid, followed by lysine and traces of ornithine. An earlier paper by Ventura and Lima (1959) reports the cashew apple to contain asparagine, serine, threonine, γ-aminobutyric acid, leucine(s) and tryptophane, in addition to those listed above. Citrulline and valine were not detected in any of these fruits. Ventura and Lima (1961) examined the sugar apple (*Annona Squamosa*) which was unusual and metabolically interesting in that γ-aminobutyric acid and citrulline predominated among a total of 14 amino acids, including arginine and ornithine; in the soursop (*Annona muricata*) proline and γ-aminobutyric acid were the major amino acids, with nine others in smaller amounts.

D. Litchi (*Litchi chinensis*)

Farooqi and Kaul (1964) found that an ethanolic extract of the defatted litchi aril contained free lysine, leucine, valine, alanine, glutamic acid, serine and proline; acid hydrolysis of the extract liberated also isoleucine, tyrosine, aspartic acid, threonine and arginine. Datta (1963) reported the presence of arginine and tryptophane in the litchi.

E. Persimmon (*Diaspyros species*)

Rockland (1959) found proline to be the chief amino acid of persimmon (*D. virginiana*), with smaller amounts of glutamine, serine and arginine and traces of aspartic and glutamic acids and alanine.

REFERENCES

Abraham, R. J., McLauchlan, K. A., Dalby, S., Kenner, G. W., Sheppard, R. C. and Burroughs, L. F. (1961). *Nature, Lond.* **192**, 1150–3.
Al-Rawi, N., Markakis, P. and Bauer, D. H. (1967). *J. Sci. Fd Agric.* **18**, 1–2.
Alvarez, B. M. (1967). *Analyst, Lond.* **92**, 176–9.
Amerine, M. A. (1953). *Adv. Fd Res.* **5**, 448–56.
Amerine, M. A., Berg, H. W. and Cruess, W. V. (1967). "The Technology of Wine Making", p. 4. Avi Publishing Co. Inc., Westport, Connecticut.
Anon. (1968). *In* "Fruit", pp. 76–86. The Commonwealth Secretariat, London.
Averna, V. (1960). *Conserve Deriv. agrum.* **9**, 83–93.
Ayres, A. D., Charley, V. L. S. and Swindells, R. (1961). *Fd Process. Packag.* (*Nov.*), 413–22.
Bethell, M., Bigley, D. B. and Kenner, G. W. (1963). *Chemy Ind.* 653–4.
Bogin, E. and Wallace, A. (1966). *Proc. Am. Soc. hort. Sci.* **88**, 298–307.
Burdick, E. M. (1954). *In* "The Chemistry and Technology of Fruit and Vegetable Juice Production" (D. K. Tressler and M. A. Joslyn, eds), pp. 381–410. Avi Publishing Co., New York.
Burroughs, L. F. (1957a). *J. Sci. Fd Agric.* **8**, 122–31.
Burroughs, L. F. (1957b). *Nature, Lond.* **179**, 360–1.
Burroughs, L. F. (1958). Ph.D. Thesis, University of Bristol.
Burroughs, L. F. (1960). *J. Sci. Fd Agric.* **11**, 14–18.
Burroughs, L. F., Dalby, S., Kenner, G. W. and Sheppard, R. C. (1961). *Nature, Lond.* **189**, 394–5.
Caabeira, J. C. (1956). *An. Inst. nac. Invest. agron.* (*Madrid*) **5**, 211–16.
Calvarano, I. (1963a). *Essenze* **33**, 22–33.
Calvarano, I. (1963b). *Essenze* **33**, 208, 209, 218–27.
Carangal, A. R., Alban, E. K., Varner, J. E. and Burrell, R. C. (1954). *Pl. Physiol., Lancaster* **29**, 355–60.
Casoli, U. (1963). *Industria Conserve* **38**, 113–16.
Casoli, U. and Bellucci, G. (1964). *Industria Conserve* **39**, 36–8.
Castor, J. G. B. (1953). *J. Fd Sci.* **18**, 139–45.
Castor, J. G. B. and Archer, T. E. (1956). *Am. J. Enol. Vitic.* **7**, 19–25.
Clements, R. C. and Leland, H. V. (1962a). *J. Fd Sci.* **27**, 20–5.
Clements, R. C. and Leland, H. V. (1962b). *Proc. Am. Soc. hort. Sci.* **80**, 300–7.
Consden, R., Gordon, A. H. and Martin, A. J. P. (1944). *Biochem. J.* **38**, 224–32.
Coussin, B. R. and Samish, Z. (1968). *J. Fd Sci.* **33**, 196–9.
Cuzzoni, M. T. and Lissi, P. T. (1965). *Farmaco Edizione Pratica* **20**, 488–96.

Datta, S. C. (1963). *Bull. bot. Soc. Beng.* **17**, 8–9.
Deibner, L. (1964). *Revue Ferment Ind. aliment.* **19**, 141–4, 201–7.
Diemair, W., Koch, J. and Sajak, E. (1962). *Z. Lebensmittelunters u.-Forsch.* **116**, 209–15, 327–35.
Dunnill, P. M. and Fowden, L. (1965). *Phytochem.* **4**, 933–44.
Farooqi, M. I. H. and Kaul, K. N. (1964). *Curr. Sci. (India)* **33**, 183–4 (via *Chem. Abs.* **60**, 14,827a).
Flanzy, C. and Poux, C. (1965). *Annls Technol. agric.* **14**, 35–48.
Fowden, L. (1964). *A. Rev. Biochem.* **33**, 173–204.
Freeman, J. A. and Woodbridge, C. G. (1960). *Proc. Am. Soc. hort. Sci.* **76**, 515–23.
Gawler, J. H. (1962). *J. Sci. Fd Agric.* **13**, 57–61.
Gortner, W. A. and Singleton, V. L. (1965). *J. Fd Sci.* **30**, 24–9.
Govindarajan, V. S. and Sreenivasaya, M. (1950). *Curr. Sci. (India)* **19**, 234–6.
Greenberg, D. M. (1964). *A. Rev. Biochem.* **33**, 633–66.
Grobbelaar, N., Pollard, J. K. and Steward, F. C. (1955). *Nature, Lond.* **175**, 703–708.
Gulyakin, I. V., Gusev, M. I. and Pogosyan, E. A. (1965). *Dokl. TSKhA (Timiryazevsk. Sel'skokhoz. Akad.)* **103**, 247–51 (via *Chem. Abs.* **65**, 6242 f).
Hadwiger, L. A. and Hall, C. V. (1961). *Pl. Dis. Reptr.* **45**, 373–4.
Hennig, K. and Venter, P. (1958). *Naturwissenschaften* **45**, 130.
Herbst, E. J. and Snell, E. E. (1949). *J. biol. Chem.* **181**, 47–54.
Hiwatari, Y. (1927). *J. Biochem., Tokyo* **7**, 169–73.
Hulme, A. C. (1954a). *J. exp. Bot.* **5**, 159–72.
Hulme, A. C. (1954b). *Nature, Lond.* **174**, 1055–6.
Hulme, A. C. and Arthington, W. (1950). *Nature, Lond.* **165**, 716–17.
Hulme, A. C. and Arthington, W. (1952). *Nature, Lond.* **170**, 659 60.
Hulme, A. C. and Arthington, W. (1954). *Nature, Lond.* **173**, 588–9.
Hulme, A. C. and Steward, F. C. (1955). *Nature, Lond.* **175**, 171.
Ingles, D. L. and Reynolds, T. M. (1958). *Aust. J. Chem.* **11**, 575–80.
Iseda, S. and Matsushita, A. (1953). *J. Home Econ., Tokyo* **3**, 15–17.
Ito, S. and Sakasegawa, H. (1952). *Bull. hort. Div. Tokai-Kinki agric. exp. Stn.* **1**, 236.
Johnson, R. M. and Raymond, W. D. (1965). *Trop. Sci.* **7**, 156–64.
Joslyn, M. A. and Stepka, W. (1949). *J. Fd Sci.* **14**, 459–67.
Kefford, J. F. (1959). *Adv. Fd Res.* **9**, 286–372.
Kliewer, W. M. (1968). *Am. J. Enol. Vitic.* **19**, 166–74.
Kliewer, W. M. (1969). *J. Fd Sci.* **34**, 274–8.
Kliewer, W. M., Nassar, A. R. and Olmo, H. P. (1966). *Am. J. Enol. Vitic.* **17**, 112–17.
Lafon-Lafourcade, S. and Peynaud, E. (1959). *Vitis* **2**, 45–56.
Lafon-Lafourcade, S. and Guimberteau, G. (1962). *Vitis* **3**, 130–5.
McKee, H. S. and Urbach, G. E. (1953). *Aust. J. biol. Sci.* **6**, 369–78.
Miller, J. M. and Rockland, L. B. (1952). *Archs Biochem. Biophys.* **40**, 416–23.
Moore, S., Spackman, D. H. and Stein, W. H. (1958). *Analyt. Chem.* **30**, 1185–90.
Morgan, R. H. (1966). *J. Ass. Public Anal.* **4**, 73–80.
Nelson, E. K., Mottern, H. H. and Eddy, C. W. (1933). *Fruit Prod. J.* **12**, 231–5.
Noe, F. F. and Fowden, L. (1960). *Biochem. J.* **77**, 543–6.
Nomura (1953). *J. Ferment. Technol., Osaka* **31**, 429–34.
Nomura, D. and Munechika, T. (1952). *J. Ferment. Technol., Osaka* **30**, 449–52.
Pruthi, J. S. (1963). *Ads. Fd Res.* **12**, 203–83.

Porretta, A. and Giannone, L. (1963). *Industria Conserve* **38**, 7–20.

Possingham, J. V. (1956). *Aust. J. biol. Sci.* **9**, 539–51.

Rakieten, M. L., Newman, B., Kalk, K. B. and Miller, I. (1952). *J. Am. diet. Ass.* **28**, 1050–3.

Ribereau-Gayon, J. and Peynaud, E. (1961). "Traite d'Oenologie", Vol. 1, pp. 62–3, 111–12. Béranger, Paris.

Rinderknecht, H. (1959). *J. Fd Sci.* **24**, 298–304.

Reynolds, T. M. (1957). *Aust. J. Chem.* **10**, 198–202.

Rockland, L. B. (1959). *J. Fd Sci.* **24**, 160–4.

Rockland, L. B. (1961). *In* "The Orange" (W. B. Sinclair, ed.), pp. 230–64. University of California, Division of Agricultural Sciences.

Rockland, L. B. and Underwood, J. C. (1956). *Analyt. Chem.* **28**, 1679–84.

Safina, G. (1953). *Conserve deriv. agrum.* **2**, 178–81.

Saito, S. (1959). *Tokyo Nogyo Daigaku Nogaku Shuho* **5**, 32–9.(via *Chem. Abs.* **61**, 3646h).

Saravacos, G., Luh, B. S. and Leonard, S. J. (1958). *J. Fd Sci.* **23**, 329–37.

Selim, A. S. M., Ikbaal Zaki and Ali Hassan (1966). *J. Chem. U.A.R.* **9**, 103–15. (Via *Chem. Abs.* **66**, 75,088 f).

Silber, R. L., Becker, M., Cooper, M., Evans, P., Fehder, P., Gray, R., Gresham, P., Rechsteiner, J. and Searles, M. A. (1960). *J. Fd Sci.* **25**, 675–80.

Sisakian, N. M. and Bezinger, E. N. (1953). *Biokhimiya* **18**, 412–22.

Steward, F. C., Hulme, A. C., Freiberg, S. R., Hegarty, M. P., Pollard, J. K., Rabson, R. and Barr, R. A. (1960a). *Ann. Bot.* **24**, 83–116.

Steward, F. C., Hulme, A. C., Freiberg, S. R., Hegarty, M. P., Pollard, J. K., Rabson, R. and Barr, R. A. (1960b). *Ann. Bot.* **24**, 117–46.

Tercelj, D. (1965). *Annls Technol. agric.* **14**, 307–19.

Thaler, O. and Rateau, J. (1957). *Mitt. Klosterneuburg Ser. B: Obst Garten.* **7**, 191–6.

Ting, S. V. and Deszyck, E. J. (1960). *Proc. Fla St. hort. Soc.* **73**, 252–7 (via *Chem. Abs.* **56**, 1815e).

Tinsley, I. J. and Bockian, A. H. (1959). *J. Fd Sci.* **24**, 410–12.

Townsley, P. M., Joslyn, M. A. and Smit, C. J. B. (1953). *J. Fd Sci.* **18**, 522–31.

Ulrich, R. and Thaler, O. (1955). *C.r. hebd Acad. Sci., Paris* **240**, 1625–6.

Ulrich, R. and Thaler, O. (1957). *J. Agric. trop. Bot. appl.* **4**, 12–30.

Underwood, J. C. and Rockland, L. B. (1953). *J. Fd Sci.* **18**, 17–29.

Urbach, G. E. (1955). *Nature, Lond.* **175**, 170–1.

Vähätalo, M. L. and Virtanen, A. I. (1957a). *Acta chem. scand.* **11**, 747–8.

Vähätalo, M. L. and Virtanen, A. I. (1957b). *Acta chem. scand.* **11**, 741–3.

Vandercook, C. E., Rolle, L. A. and Ikeda, R. M. (1963). *J. Ass. off. agric. Chem.* **46**, 353–8.

Van Wyk, C. J. and Venter, P. J. (1965). *S. Afr. J. agric. Sci.* **8**, 57–72.

Ventura, M. M. and Holanda Lima, I. (1959). *Phyton, B. Aires* **12**, 31–4.

Ventura, M. M. and Holanda Lima, I. (1961). *Phyton, B. Aires* **17**, 39–47.

Wada, M. (1930). *Biochem. Z.* **224**, 420–9.

Wedding, R. T. and Horspool, R. P. (1955). *Calif. Citogr.* **40**, 106–7.

Wedding, R. T. and Sinclair, W. B. (1954). *Bot. Gaz.* **116**, 183–8.

Wucherpfennig, K. and Franke, I. (1966). *Fruchtsaft-Ind.* **11**, 60–5.

Xavier Filho, J., Holanda Lima, I. and Ventura, M. M. (1962). *Phyton, B. Aires* **19**, 121–5.

Chapter 6

Proteins

ELMER HANSEN

Department of Horticulture, Oregon State University, Corvallis, Oregon U.S.A.

I. INTRODUCTION

The protein constituents of fruits, although occurring in low concentrations, are of primary importance not only as components of nuclear and cytoplasmic structures which take part in determining and maintaining cellular organization, but also including, as they must, the full complement of enzymes involved in metabolism during growth, development, maturation and the post-harvest life of the fruit. A major portion of the interest in fruit proteins has, in fact, been in relation to various physiological aspects, including respiration, enzyme activity, ripening, as well as the overall problem of senescence. Information on the nature of proteins and their metabolism in fruits, however, is fragmentary compared to that in some other plant tissues. Fortunately, the basic features of protein synthesis: DNA → RNA → Protein, are the same in all organisms studied (Chantrenne, 1961; Wanner and Soriro, 1967), and fruits should be no exception. As stated by Steward and Bidwell(1966), "genetics endows each cell with the information that makes its biochemical reactions feasible; the organization of the cells determine how far the feasible becomes practised in any given situation". It is especially in relation to this latter aspect that proteins in fruits need to be considered.

Studies on proteins in fruits have been impeded to some extent by the inherently low concentrations and interference from vacuolar contents, principally phenolic compounds and organic acids. These problems have been largely overcome by the development of new materials and analytical

147

techniques, so that separations and isolations of proteins, specific enzymes and organelles involved in their synthesis are comparable in quality to those obtained from other types of tissues.

II. QUALITATIVE RANGE IN DISTRIBUTION

As indicated, fruits are characteristically low in proteins, as well as in total nitrogen, compared to seeds, leaves and some other plant parts and tissues. The concentration, furthermore, can vary widely according to species, area where grown, season, cultural practices and environmental influences. Comparisons are even more difficult because the protein content of fruits has been expressed in various ways, not all of which are truly indicative of the actual protein contained. Thus, in food compilation tables, values are commonly listed as total nitrogen $\times$ 6·25. These values, while of interest to the dietician, provide only an approximation of the true protein content, which may vary from approximately 40–85% of the total nitrogen present. Values calculated from the data of Robertson and Turner (1951) show that protein nitrogen in Australian grown mature Granny Smith apples of different sizes picked from the same tree varied from 45 to 87% of the total nitrogen. Protein values of specific fruits also tend to vary regionally and seasonally. This is evident in the composition listed for various fruits grown in five Central American countries (Munsell et al., 1950). Kenworthy and Harris (1963) also found differences in McIntosh, Red Delicious and Golden Delicious apples according to season as well as region of growth. Recognizing the influence of these factors, there are, however, genetic variations in protein content among the various species of fruits. As shown in Table I, per cent protein (total nitrogen $\times$ 6·25) varies from approximately 0·4–0·6% in the cranberry, pineapple, watermelon, grapefruit, peach and papaya to more than 1% in the date, avocado, black raspberry, tomato, currant, banana and cherry.

In physiological studies of fruits during growth, maturation, ripening and storage, protein generally has been determined on the fraction insoluble in 80% alcohol. Hulme (1954) introduced, also, the expression "protein N as per cent of total N", considering that since the total nitrogen content in apple tissue does not change significantly in storage, protein nitrogen calculated on this basis provides true values and avoids complications of sample variability and changes in moisture content during prolonged storage. Similar tabulations of protein data have been used for banana (Steward et al., 1960) and tomato (Rowan et al., 1960). It would be helpful where this method of expression is used if total nitrogen values were included, so that actual protein nitrogen content could be calculated. Need for some degree of standardization of methods for determining and expressing the protein content of fruits is indicated.

TABLE I. Protein content of fruits expressed as total nitrogen $\times$ 6·25[a]

Fruit	% Moisture	% Protein
Apple (*Malus sylvestrus*)	84·8	0·2
Apricot (*Prunus armeniaca*)	85·3	1·0
Avocado (*Persea gratissima*)	74·0	2·1
Banana (*Musa sapientum*)	75·7	1·1
Blackberry (*Rubus sp.*)	84·5	1·2
Blueberry (*Vaccinium corymbosum*)	83·2	0·7
Cherry		
sour (*Prunus cerasus*)	83·7	1·2
sweet (*Prunus avium*)	80·4	1·3
Cranberry (*Oxycoccus macrocarpus*)	87·9	0·4
Currant		
European (*Rubus nigrum*)	84·2	1·7
Red and White (*Rubus* hybrid)	85·7	1·4
Dates, dried (*Phoenix dactilifera*)	22·5	2·2
Figs (*Ficus carica*)	77·5	1·2
Gooseberry (*Rubus grossularia*)	88·9	0·8
Grapefruit (*Citrus paradisi*)	88·4	0·5
Grape		
American (*Vitis labrusca*)	81·6	1·3
European (*Vitis vinifera*)	81·4	0·6
Guava (*Psidium guajava*)	83·0	0·8
Lemon (*Citrus limonia*)	87·4	1·2
Lime (*Citrus aurantifolia*)	89·3	0·7
Mango (*Mangifera indica*)	81·7	0·7
Melon		
Cantaloup (*Cucumis melo*)	91·2	0·7
Nectarine (*Prunus Persica nectarina*)	81·8	0·6
Olive (*Olea europoea*)		
green	78·2	1·4
ripe	73–84	1–1·2
Orange (*Citrus sinensis*)	86·0	1·0
Papaya (*Carica papaya*)	88·7	0·6
Peach (*Prunus persica*)	89·1	0·6
Pear (*Pyrus communis*)	83·2	0·7
Pineapple (*Ananas cosmosus*)	85·3	0·4
Plum (*Prunus sp.*)	79–87	0·5–0·8
Pomegranate (*Punica granatum*)	82·3	0·5
Raspberry		
red (*Rubus strigosus*)	84·2	1·2
black (*Rubus occidentalis*)	80·8	1·5
Strawberry (*Fragaria* hybrids)	89·9	0·7
Tomato (*Lycopersicon esculentum*)		
green	93·0	1·2
ripe	95·5	1·1
Watermelon (*Citrullus vulgaris*)	92·6	0·5
Tangerine (*Citrus* hybrid)	87·0	0·8

[a] Watt and Merrill (1963)

The protein nitrogen concentration in various fruits, calculated as mg/100 g fresh weight and/or as per cent of total nitrogen are shown in Table II.

TABLE II. Protein N content of fruits, expressed as mg/100 g and/or as per cent of total N

Fruit	Source	mg/100 g	% of total N	Reference
Apple, Bramley Seedling	England			
50–100 days postbloom		55–25	77–63	Hulme (1954)
Apple, Granny Smith	Tasmania			
0–190 days postbloom		——	50–80	Martin et al. (1967)
Apple, Granny Smith	Australia			
stored 0–400 days at 0°C		101–137	62–74	Turner (1949)
Avocado, Anaheim variety	Australia	——	50–80	Rowan et al. (1960)
Banana, Gros Michel	Honduras, C.A.			
green		94	65	Steward et al. (1960)
yellow		105	67	
Orange, Valencia	Australia			
whole fruit		125	52	Bain (1958)
pulp		60	43	
Pear, Bartlett	Oregon (U.S.A.)			
8 days at 20°C		30–60	——	Hansen (1967)
Tomato, King of All	Australia	——	35–50	Rowan et al. (1960)

The gradient distribution of protein in fruits has not been studied extensively. Probably there exists more uniformity than in seeds or leaves where storage or translocation would be of significance. On the basis of the limited data available, the concentration of protein tends to be higher in the peel than in that portion of the fruit comprising the greater bulk of tissue, normally the edible portion. Hulme (1936) found 100–150 mg/100 g in the pulp and 320–360 mg/100 g in the peel of Bramley's Seedling apples, depending on stage of development. The peel of mature Anjou pears was reported to contain 101 mg/100 g, approximately three times the amount normally present in the pulp (Hansen, 1955). In developing oranges Bain (1958) found more protein nitrogen in the peel than in the pulp segments, but in mature fruit, approximately equal amounts were present in both types of tissue.

III. AMINO ACID COMPOSITION

The amino acid composition of proteins has been determined in only a few species of fruits. Generally, the hydrolysates reveal most of the amino acid present in the free state. Amino acid composition of proteins from apple, banana and orange are shown in Table III.

TABLE III. Amino acids in proteins from various fruits

Amino Acid	Apple[a]	Banana[b]	Navel orange[c]	Valencia orange[c]
		Fruit		
Alanine	——	+	+	+
γ-Aminobutyric Acid	——	——	——	+
Aspartic Acid	+	+	+	+
Arginine	+	+	——	——
Cystine(s)	+	+	——	——
Glutamic Acid	+	+	+	+
Glycine	+	+	+	+
Hydroxyproline	——	+	——	——
Leucine(s)	+	+	+	+
Histidine	+	+	——	——
Lysine	+	+	+	+
Methionine	+	——	——	——
Ornithine	——	——	+	——
Phenylalanine	+	——	+	+
Proline	+	+	+	+
Serine	+	+	+	+
Threonine	+	+	+	+
Tyrosine	——	+	+	+
Valine	+	+	+	+

[a] Davis et al., 1949; Hulme, 1951.
[b] Steward et al., 1960.
[c] Wedding and Sinclair, 1954.

Hulme (1951) examined the hydrolysates of two crude protein fractions of immature Bramley Seedling apples, obtained by preliminary extraction with phosphate solution (pH 9·0). The first fraction obtained by centrifugation contained aspartic and glutamic acids, serine, glycine, threonine, alanine, arginine, proline, tyrosine, valine, leucine (possibly isoleucine), phenylalanine and lysine. The second fraction obtained by ammonium sulphate precipitation differed from fraction 1 by the absence of aspartic acid and the presence of an unknown amino acid.

Davis et al. (1949) determined the amino acid composition of Baldwin apple protein obtained by a foam fractionation technique and found sixteen amino acids: leucine, isoleucine, valine, phenylalanine, tryptophan, glutamic acid, histidine, arginine, threonine, methionine, lysine, aspartic acid, serine, glycine, proline and cystine.

Chaplin (1966) conducted a comprehensive analysis of the amino acid composition of Stayman apple peel tissue in relation to maturity, ripening, and senescence (Table IV). Although the total amino acid content increased slightly as the fruits matured on the tree and increased markedly as they ripened during low temperature storage, the profile remained constant. The

TABLE IV. Total amino acid (free plus protein) composition of Stayman apple peel tissue in relation to harvest date and following storage[a]

Amino Acid	Days at 0°C	5 Oct.	12 Oct.	Harvest Date 19 Oct. (% distribution)	26 Oct.	Average
Aspartic acid	0	13·2	9·7	10·6	11·7	11·3
	150	11·2	12·3	12·1	12·6	12·1
Threonine	0	6·6	5·3	7·4	6·8	6·5
	150	6·7	6·8	6·4	6·0	6·5
Serine	0	10·1	7·0	10·2	9·1	9·1
	150	9·4	8·5	8·4	7·9	8·6
Glutamic acid	0	6·3	5·8	5·6	7·3	6·2
	150	9·4	6·9	7·5	6·9	7·7
Proline	0	6·0	6·2	7·3	6·7	6·6
	150	6·7	6·5	6·2	6·7	6·5
Glycine	0	10·9	7·5	10·8	9·1	9·6
	150	9·6	10·1	11·0	9·3	10·0
Alanine	0	12·2	10·5	11·0	11·1	11·2
	150	11·0	11·2	11·6	11·5	11·3
Valine	0	7·5	6·3	7·6	7·6	7·2
	150	7·3	7·3	6·9	7·5	7·2
Isoleucine	0	5·3	4·2	5·5	5·7	5·2
	150	5·6	5·6	5·5	5·6	5·6
Leucine	0	8·4	6·6	9·3	9·0	8·3
	150	8·7	6·9	8·6	7·9	8·0
Tyrosine	0	2·6	2·0	2·6	2·4	2·4
	150	2·5	2·5	2·6	2·8	2·6
Phenylalanine	0	3·0	2·4	3·6	3·6	3·2
	150	3·6	3·8	3·5	3·2	3·5
Lysine	0	4·8	4·0	4·6	4·8	4·6
	150	5·1	6·1	5·5	6·6	5·8
Histidine	0	1·7	1·2	1·8	2·2	1·7
	150	2·1	2·4	2·0	2·3	2·2
Arginine	0	1·4	2·0	2·1	2·6	2·0
	150	2·5	3·0	2·1	2·9	2·6
		(μmole per g dry weight)				
Total amino acid content	0	77·2	100·7	105·9	100·7	
	150	124·6	171·2	144·4	114·3	

[a] Chaplin, 1966.

increase in total amino acid content with ripening following harvest is probably the result of mobilization of amino acids from the subjacent pulp tissue. In view of the fact that the non-protein N is converted to protein N during ripening, the constancy of the amino acid content clearly indicates that there is no major change in the amino acid pools during ripening.

Klein (1969) analysed the amino acid composition of highly purified malic enzyme from Bartlett pear fruit. The analysis was made following isoelectric focusing separation which resolved the enzyme activity into two clearly distinct isozymes (Fig. 1). The pI of the major fraction was 4·6 and the pI of the minor fraction was 5·7. The amino acid analysis of the pI 4·6 enzyme and combined 4·6 and 5·7 enzymes is given in Table V. Of particular interest

TABLE V. Amino acid composition of Bartlett pear fruit[a] malic enzyme[b]

Amino acid	μmole/mg protein	
	pI 4·6 + pI 5·7[c]	pI 4·6[d]
Aspartic acid	1·540	1·150
Threonine[e]	est. 0·5	0
Serine	0·439	0·451
Glutamic acid	1·092	1·066
Proline	0	0
Glycine	0·707	0·708
Alanine	0·756	0·716
Valine	0·776	0·719
Cysteine	trace	trace
Methionine	0·091	0·112
Isoleucine	0·469	0·433
Leucine	0·870	0·916
Tyrosine	0·310	0·291
Phenylalanine	0·315	0·314
Lysine	0·686	0·572
Histidine	0·148	0·139
Arginine	0·375	0·368

[a] Klein, 1969.
[b] Enzyme was purified from pear fruit after 5 months storage at 0°C.
[c] Enzyme from sucrose gradient electrophoresis: 1·51 mg protein hydrolysate loaded on column.
[d] Enzyme from isoelectric focusing: 0·619 mg protein hydrolysate loaded on column.
[e] Threonine was present but was insufficiently separated from aspartic acid to obtain a reliable measurement of quantity. Estimated to be about equal to that of serine.

is the absence of threonine in the pI 4·6 enzyme. Other than having threonine and more aspartic acid and lysine, the pI 5·7 enzyme exhibits an amino acid composition similar to the pI 4·6 enzyme.

The amino acid composition of Navel and Valencia orange protein was reported by Wedding and Sinclair (1954). Hydrolysates of proteins from both varieties contained similar amino acids with the exception of γ-aminobutyric acid and ornithine. Townley *et al.* (1953) found the same amino acids in the peel and chromatophore tissue of Valencia oranges with the exception of valine, which was absent in the latter. Proteins of lemons appear to be similar to those of oranges in general chemical properties.

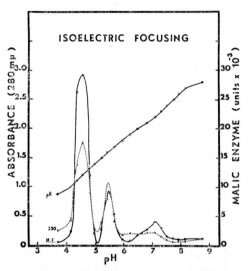

FIG. 1 Resolution of malic enzyme by isoelectric focusing

TABLE VI. Changes in the amino acid content of the protein of the banana fruit (Gros Michel) during ripening[a]

Days ripened	0	2	4	6	9	12
	N in each amino acid as % of total protein N					
Amino acid						
Aspartic acid	13·7	14·2	11·6	13·5	9·9	9·4
Glutamic acid	10·7	11·1	11·5	11·0	10·8	10·8
Serine	4·0	6·2	4·7	5·4	6·0	5·2
Glycine	7·3	6·3	7·4	7·1	9·7	8·6
Threonine	3·8	3·8	3·9	4·4	4·9	4·8
Alanine	8·0	7·5	8·2	8·9	10·4	9·6
Histidine	6·1	6·9	5·4	5·3	4·0	3·3
Lysine	8·5	7·7	9·2	8·5	8·3	8·6
Arginine	10·3	7·5	10·0	6·8	5·7	8·9
Proline	8·3	8·0	6·2	5·0	4·8	4·9
Valine	5·0	4·9	5·6	6·1	6·7	7·0
Leucine(s)	12·6	13·0	12·7	13·9	15·7	15·1
Tyrosine	1·6	1·6	2·2	2·9	3·0	2·8
Hydroxyproline	trace	1·3	1·3	1·3	trace	1·1

[a] Steward *et al.*, 1960.

In their extensive physiological investigations of the banana plant, Steward *et al.* (1960) found that the amino acid composition of the total protein in the fruit remains relatively constant during ripening (Table VI), although specific trends were observed in certain plants. This is indicative of a certain amount of protein turnover during ripening, even though the total amount remains constant. With the exception of the protein in Gros Michel fruit from Central America being lower in arginine and higher in aspartic and glutamic acids, proteins in all other tissues examined were remarkably uniform in amino acid composition, regardless of variety and region where grown. Insufficient data are available to determine if this generalization could be applied to other fruit species.

IV. STRUCTURAL PROTEINS

The distribution of proteins in particulate fractions has been investigated in only a few kinds of fruit. In Bartlett pears, Miller and Romani (1966) found mitochondrial protein at the pre-climacteric state was in the denser region of the sucrose density gradient and had a higher and sharper distribution peak compared to mitochondria from fruit at the climacteric maximum. Similar patterns were reported for avocados and Bing cherries. A decrease in mitochondrial protein of pear, Romani and Fisher (1966) and tomato tissue, Dickinson and Hanson (1965) during the climacteric rise in respiration and ripening has been observed.

Ribosomes isolated from Anjou pears by Ku and Romani (1966) were similar in sedimentation gradients and constants as well as to electron micrographs to ribosomes from other living tissues. Several ribosomal components, including 60S and 80S particles, were isolated. Characteristic dissociation of the ribosomes into 42S and 60S sub-units on lowering of Mg^{2+} concentration took place. Light and heavy ribosomal RNA were tentatively identified by Richmond and Biale (1967) from elution profiles on a MAK (methylated albumen on kieselguhr) column. In addition DNA, transfer RNA and a precursor for transfer RNA were separated.

V. METABOLISM IN RELATION TO DEVELOPMENT

Growth and development of fruits occur in sequential stages of cell division, enlargement, maturation and senescence. Genetic expression of anatomical and morphological features during development are readily apparent, but a similar relation to biochemical patterns is more difficult to recognize. Brown and Robinson (1955) proposed the hypothesis that the growth of the cell is determined by a development involving a succession of metabolic states in which changes in the metabolic pattern are a reflection of corresponding changes in protein complements. According to this concept, the metabolic patterns during the life of a fruit could be considered as developing in a continuous, orderly process, programmed according to the specific genetic information contained in the cell, and reacting and influenced by the internal and external environment. Thus, information on protein metabolism during the pre- and post-harvest life of fruits assumes a special significance in relation to changes occurring at different stages of ontogeny. Direct evidence of progressive changes in genetic expression reflected in metabolism during development would be the concomitant changes in the protein complement of the cells, especially in the specific enzymes contained. This aspect is considered in Chapter 8.

In the cells of Granny Smith apples, Pearson and Robertson (1953) found changes in nitrogen compounds, including proteins, to be similar during three seasons, suggestive at least of a recurring metabolic pattern. In all three seasons, protein and soluble nitrogen increased up to 120 days after bloom, remained stationary until 190 days, when protein nitrogen only increased, suggesting that some factor other than nitrogen supply was exerting a control over protein synthesis. Davies and Cocking (1965) found considerable changes occurring in the levels of nucleic acid and protein per cell during the development of tomato locule tissue. Similar trends were observed in summer- and winter-grown (greenhouse) fruits, except for the time sequence.

The capacity for protein synthesis in fruits appears to be retained until late in the senescent stage. Hulme (1936) was the first to observe a net protein increase in mature apples, which he considered quite unexpected in a senescent organ. A similar increase in protein nitrogen was reported by Turner (1949) to occur during the cool storage of apples. Pears (Hulme, 1936; Li and Hansen, 1964), avocados and tomatoes (Rowan et al., 1960) show net increases in protein nitrogen during ripening. Richmond and Biale (1966) found significant changes in the capacity for avocado fruit to incorporate amino acids during the climacteric rise in respiration. Incorporation was rapid during the early stages but later diminished and was virtually absent at the peak. A marked increase in total ribonucleic acid was also observed during the climacteric rise in respiration in Yellow Transparent apples (Looney and Patterson, 1967). A net increase in protein nitrogen apparently does not develop in the banana fruit during ripening (Sacher, 1967). It has recently been determined for apple and pear (Frenkel et al., 1968) and banana (Smillie et al., 1969) fruits that the observed increases in protein involves both an increase in the rate of synthesis and a change in the nature of the protein complement. The latter is considered to be of special significance with respect to ripening and conceivably could occur without a net gain in protein content. The significance of protein synthesis in relation to fruit ripening is considered elsewhere (Chapter 17).

VI. SUMMARY

Investigations of protein content in fruits in relation to fruit development and ripening have established the dynamic nature of the changes taking place. Those studied served as the basis for working hypotheses concerning the involvement of proteins as enzymes catalysing the ripening process. Only recently has technology been achieved to ascertain the dependency of ripening on synthesis of the ripening enzymes. Elucidation of the hormonal control mechanism which results in specific enzyme synthesis during ontogeny remains a challenging task for the future.

REFERENCES

Bain, Joan M. (1958). *Aust. J. Bot.* **6**, 1–24.
Brown, R. and Robinson, E. (1955). *In* "Specificity of Growth" (E. G. Butler, ed.), pp. 93–118. Princeton University Press.
Chantrenne, H. (1961). *In* "Protein Biosynthesis" (R. J. C. Harris, ed.), pp. 385–92. Academic Press, London and New York.
Chaplin, M. H. (1966). M.Sc. Thesis, Rutgers University, New Brunswick.
Davies, J. W. and Cocking, E. C. (1965). *Planta*, **67**, 242.
Davis, S. G., Fellers, C. R. and Esselen, W. B. (1949). *Fd. J. Sci* **14**, 417–28.
Dickinson, D. B. and Hanson, J. B. (1965). *Plant Physiol., Lancaster* **40**, 161–5.
Frenkel, C., Klein, I. and Dilley, D. R. (1968). *Pl. Physiol., Lancaster* **43**, 1146–53.
Hansen, E. (1967). *Proc. Am. Soc. hort. Sci.* **91**, 861–7.
Hansen, E. (1955). *Proc. Am. Soc. hort. Sci.* **66**, 118–24.
Hulme, A. C. (1936). *Biochem. J.* **30**, 258–68.
Hulme, A. C. (1951). *J. Sci. Fd Agric.* **2**, 160–6.
Hulme, A. C. (1954). *J. exp. Bot.* **5**, 159–72.
Kenworthy, A. L. and Harris, N. (1963). *Mich. St. Univ. Agric. Expt. Sta. Bul.* **46**, 293–334.
Klein, I. (1969). Ph.D. Thesis, Michigan State University, East Lansing.
Ku, Lily (Lim) and Romani, R. J. (1966). *Science, N.Y.* **154**, 408–9.
Li, P. H. and Hansen, E. (1964). *Proc. Am. Soc. hort. Sci.* **85**, 100–11.
Looney, N. E. and Patterson, M. E. (1967). *Phytochem.* **6**, 1517–20.
Martin, D., Lewis, T. L. and Cerny, J. (1967). *Aust. J. agric. Res.* **18**, 271–8.
Miller, L. A. and Romani, R. J. (1966). *Pl. Physiol., Lancaster* **41**, 411–14.
Munsell, H. E., Williams, L. O., Guild, L. P., Kelly, L. T., Troescher, C. B., McNally, A. M., Harris, R. S. and Nightingale, G. (1950). *Fd. J. Sci* **15**, 263–96, 379–464, 439–53.
Pearson, Judith A. and Robertson, R. N. (1953). *Aust. J. biol. Sci.* **6**, 1–20.
Richmond, A. and Biale, J. B. (1966). *Pl. Physiol., Lancaster* **41**, 1247–53.
Richmond, A. and Biale, J. B. (1967). *Biochem. biophys. Acta* **138**, 625–7.
Robertson, R. N. and Turner, J. F. (1951). *Aust. J. scient. Res.* Series B. **4**, 92–107.
Romani, R. J. and Fisher, L. K. (1966). *Life Sci.* **5**, 1187–90.
Rowan, K. S., Pratt, H. K. and Robertson, R. N. (1960). *Aust. J. biol. Sci.* **11**, 329–35.
Sacher, S. A. (1967). *In* "Aspects of the Biology of Aging", (H. W. Woolhouse, ed.), pp. 269–303. Academic Press, New York.

Smillie, R. M., Palmer, J. K., Brady, C. J. and O'Connell, P. B. H. (1969). *Phytochem.* **8** (in press).

Steward, F. C. and Bidwell (1966). *J. exp. Bot.* **17,** 726–41.

Steward, F. C., Freiberg, S. R., Hulme, A. C., Hogarty, M., Barr, R. and Robson, R. (1960). *Ann. Bot.* **24,** 83–116.

Townley, P. M., Joslyn, M. A. and Smit, C. J. B. (1953). *J. Sci Fd* **18,** 522–31.

Turner, J. F. (1949). *Aust. J. scient. Res.* **2,** 138–53.

Wanner, J. R. and Soriro, Ruy (1967). *New Engl. J. Med.* **276,** 563–70, 613–19, 675–80.

Watt, Bernice K. and Merrill, Annabel K. (1963). U.S.D.A. Agric. Handbook No. 8, 1–190.

Wedding, R. T. and Sinclair, W. B. (1954). *Bot. Gaz.* **116,** 183–8.

Chapter 7

Protein Patterns in Fruits

R. L. CLEMENTS

Institute of Nutrition, Ohio State University, Columbus, Ohio, U.S.A.*

I. INTRODUCTION

The non-seed tissues of a fruit may be expected to contain cytoplasmic protein "normally" associated with vital processes of cells, as well as less ubiquitous proteins peculiar to the tissue. In fruits such as the pome fruits, the protein complement has been presumed to be essentially "functional", with a relatively small (and speculative) proportion assigned to "nonfunctional" structural and storage duties. Studies of these proteins, however, have been handicapped by several difficulties. Among the factors are the small volume of cytoplasm relative to total cell volume, acidic vacuolar contents, and a prevalence of tannins and other substances which exert deleterious effects on the proteins upon rupture of the cell membranes. The general problem has been reviewed by several authors (Loomis and Battaile, 1966; Anderson, 1968). The difficulties are exemplified by the pome fruits, which characteristically contain high levels of phenols and phenoloxidases. In general, attempts to isolate proteins in their native states from apple and pear fruits have been unsuccessful. The phenols also present a major problem in the banana. In the citrus fruits, a primary difficulty is the overwhelming volume of acidic cell sap relative to cytoplasmic material. In any case, preparation of such tissues by conventional means invariably leads to mixing

---

* Present Address: U.S. Dept. of Agriculture, Soft Wheat Quality Laboratory, Wooster, Ohio.

of the cytoplasm with vacuolar contents, and the consequence is a high degree of denaturation and inactivation. Because of these obstacles, advances in knowledge of the fruit proteins have not paralleled the general progress in protein chemistry brought about through recent developments in methodology. Characterization of these proteins has thus awaited (a) development of sensitive analytical techniques capable of resolving the minute levels and great array of albumins and globulins which appear to comprise the protein complement of a fleshy fruit, and (b) development of preparative procedures which circumvent interference by harmful agents.

The first requisite has been satisfied to a great extent by the development of new electrophoretic techniques, notably that of Ornstein and Davis, which has been termed *disc electrophoresis* (Ornstein and Davis, 1962; Davis, 1964; Ornstein, 1964). This procedure, which employs small cylindrical columns of polyacrylamide gel as a medium, has limited capabilities as a quantitative method, but it has several advantages which make it an excellent tool for application to problems such as those encountered in fruit biochemistry. The method is sensitive, requiring less than 100 μg protein, and the load can be applied in a relatively large volume, i.e., up to 300 μl. The technique is inherently capable of great resolution (up to thirty bands have been detected by the author in a single gel specimen from apple cortical tissue). Moreover, the method is sufficiently rapid to be used as a means for evaluating and monitoring new preparative procedures. For enzyme studies, the gels are especially amenable to the application of the many specific enzyme stains which have been developed for histochemical purposes. Although media other than polyacrylamide may be useful for fruit protein studies, the results presented in this discussion were obtained solely by disc electrophoresis, and any demonstrations of success can largely be ascribed to the unique capabilities of this technique.

In spite of its potential value, successful application of the preceding technique to fruits is contingent upon a satisfactory method for preparation of tissues prior to analysis. Attempts in this direction have resulted in a variety of innovations, generally based on incorporation of chemical agents designed to neutralize harmful substances before damage can occur (Loomis and Battaile, 1966; Anderson, 1968). Such techniques have been especially useful for isolation of active particulates, such as mitochondria (Jones *et al.*, 1965), but have also resulted in reports of success in protein studies (Loomis and Battaile, 1966). Recently, the author reported a preparative procedure which does not rely on such additives, and which was used in conjunction with disc electrophoresis to obtain protein patterns from several fruits (Clements, 1965, 1966a, b, c). This procedure is based on comminution of tissues at low temperatures (approximately $-70°$C) in acetone, followed by equilibration at $-25°$C. The water and low molecular weight solutes pass into the liquid phase, which is drawn off, and the resulting powder is dried under vacuum. Presumably, under these conditions, phenols, acids, sugars and other soluble components are extracted in an environment which minimizes interaction with the proteins. The efficacy of the procedure is suggested by an abundance of reproducible protein bands when extracts of the powders are subjected to electrophoresis, and by demonstration of enzyme activities. The results suggest the potential value of such an approach to problems of fruit biochemistry.

II. PROCEDURES

The patterns illustrated were derived from powders prepared by the above procedure. Proteins were extracted by suspension of the powders (100–500 mg) in 5 ml 0·1M potassium phosphate buffer, pH 7·5, containing 5% sucrose and 50 μmole EDTA. After one hour at 0°C, suspensions were centrifuged at 20,000 × **g**, and supernatants were applied to the electrophoretic columns. Electrophoresis was performed essentially as described by Ornstein and Davis (1962), but usually with the following modifications. Gel tubes were 0·5 cm internal diameter × 8 cm long, with a frontal migration of 3 cm in the lower gel. The spacer gel was 1·2 cm deep, and depth remaining for sample was 1·6 cm. Sucrose (25%) was incorporated into the spacer gel to provide added support for the sample. Samples (100–300 μl) were applied without addition of gel medium, and voltage was applied immediately. Reservoir buffer was used at full strength (*not* diluted 1 : 10). Current was generally restricted to 2 mA per tube, and tubes were maintained at 5°–10°C by immersion in the lower reservoir, which was cooled by addition of frozen buffer and application of external ice. Proteins were stained with Amido Schwartz in 7% acetic acid, and gels were destained by electrophoresis. Enzymes were detected by conventional histochemical staining procedures (Burstone, 1962) unless otherwise noted.

III. ELECTROPHORETIC PATTERNS

A. Proteins

Figures 1 to 7 illustrate typical results from the conventional Ornstein and Davis procedure when a non-specific protein stain (Amido Schwartz) is applied. In general, a given tissue can be expected to exhibit a multitude of bands with a broad range of mobilities. With a proper selection of operating parameters, most fruit proteins migrate into 7·5% polyacrylamide, indicating a preponderance of relatively low molecular weights (considerably less than 10^6). Some tissues (for example, citrus peel) exhibit many bands of rather uniform intensity, with no predominant components (Figs 5 and 7),

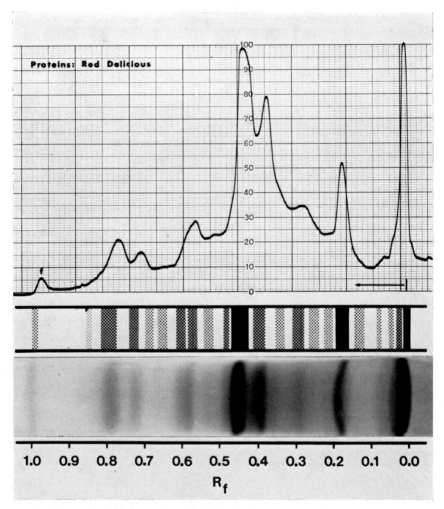

Fig. 1. Photograph, diagram and densitometric scan of proteins in cortex of ripe Red
Delicious apple.

whereas other tissues (for example, citrus vesicles) appear to contain one or
more components in relatively high concentrations (Figs 5 and 6). It remains
to be established whether such bands are pure. Repeated application to a
particular tissue of a given variety at a particular physiological stage generally results in a reproducible and predictable pattern (Fig. 1). When this
precision is attained, the technique can be extended to comparisons of
varieties (Figs 2, 3, 4, 6 and 7), tissues (Fig. 5) and physiological stages
(Fig. 2). However, the sensitivity of the method and the complexity of the

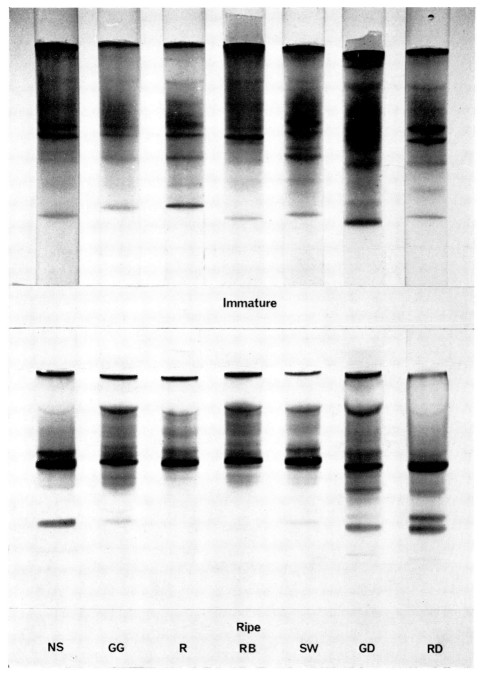

Immature

Ripe

NS   GG   R   RB   SW   GD   RD

FIG. 2. Proteins in seven varieties of apple, immature v. ripe. Abbreviations used: GD = Golden Delicious; GG = Grimes Golden; NS = Northern Spy; R = Ruby; RB = Rome Beauty; RD = Red Delicious; SW = Stayman Winesap.

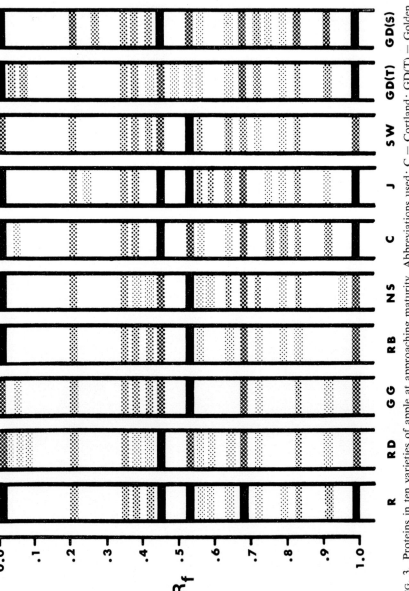

FIG. 3. Proteins in ten varieties of apple at approaching maturity. Abbreviations used: C = Cortland; GD(T) = Golden Delicio us (Orchard 1); GD(S) = Golden Delicious (Orchard 2); GG = Grimes Golden; J = Jonathan; NS = Northern Spy; R = Ruby; RB = Rome Beauty; RD = Red Delicious; SW = Stayman Winesap.

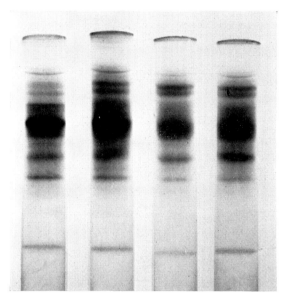

FIG. 4. Proteins in placental tissue of four varieties of tomato (ripe).

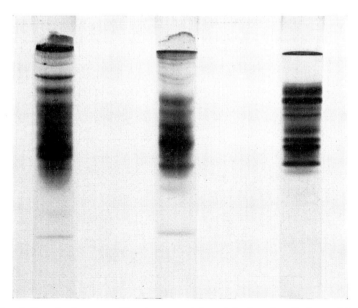

FIG. 5. Proteins in mature Navel orange: *left to right*, flavedo, albedo, vesicles.

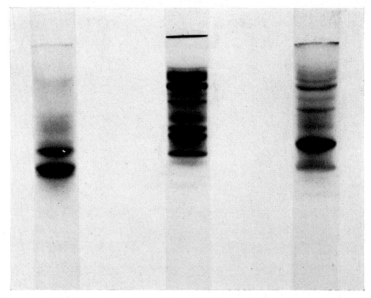

FIG. 6. Proteins in mature citrus vesicles: *left to right*, lemon, orange, grapefruit.

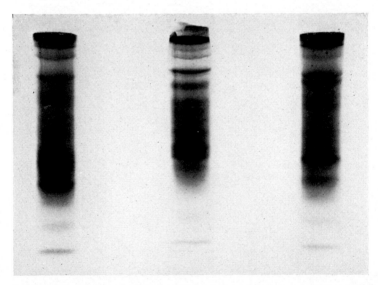

FIG. 7. Proteins in whole peel of mature citrus: *left to right*, lemon, orange, grapefruit.

patterns require strict standardization and control of parameters. Many variations in electrophoretic procedure are possible, and a particular separation may require modification of supporting medium, buffer or other components. Figure 8 illustrates results of application of a cationic system to separation of citrus proteins (Clements, 1966a). Adjustment of gel pore size by variation of polyacrylamide concentration, and incorporation of denaturing agents, such as urea, are other modifications which have been employed.

B. Enzymes

As a rule, conventional enzyme assay methods measure *total* activity, without regard for possible variants (isoenzymes). However, in recent years, high-resolution electrophoresis has stimulated interest in electrophoretic variations in enzymes (Shaw, 1965). The development of suitable preparative procedures should permit such an approach to fruit biochemistry (Clements, 1966c). Disc electrophoresis has found wide application as an adjunct in enzyme characterization, and has been employed to some extent in studies of fruit enzymes. However, in this discussion, we are concerned with utilization of the technique to produce enzyme histograms or *zymograms* (total profiles of more or less specific enzyme activities obtained from whole-tissue extracts). Such patterns are analogous to protein profiles, and result when electrophoretic specimens are subjected to specific enzyme stains rather than to general protein dye. Enzyme variants detected in this manner may be of value in interpreting genetic relationships, as well as changes associated with growth and maturation, host-pathogen interactions, and other aspects of fruit biochemistry. Enzyme detection methods are generally far more sensitive than protein stains, since a minute level of enzyme can catalyse a relatively high turnover of substrate, and consequently generate almost unlimited dye, dye precursor or activator, whereas protein stains react only with the protein molecule. As a result, enzyme and protein patterns do not necessarily show any correlation, and intense bands of enzyme activity may appear in zones in which protein bands are not evident. The generally large number of bands detected on application of a given enzyme test leads to the conclusion that, qualitatively, the actual protein complement of these tissues is far greater than evidenced by protein profiles alone.

Various zymograms are presented in Figs 8 to 17. Although these patterns may be rather tentative and preliminary, they reveal differences which permit some speculation regarding the occurrence of isoenzymes in fruit tissues. Enzymes detected by such zymograms can be classified as "specific" or "nonspecific" (Shaw, 1965). The use of naphthol esters as synthetic substrates for detection of esterases results in a rather broad response, since many enzymes

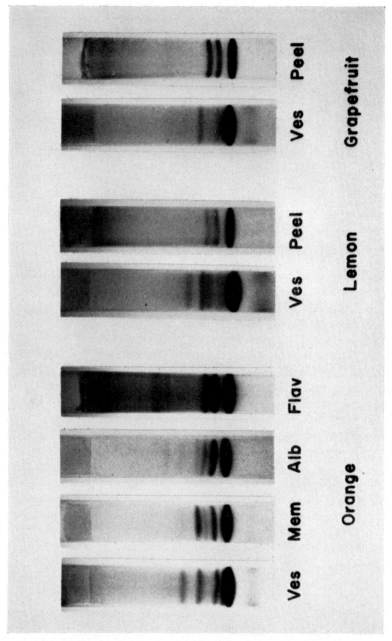

Fig. 8. Citrus proteins, cationic system.

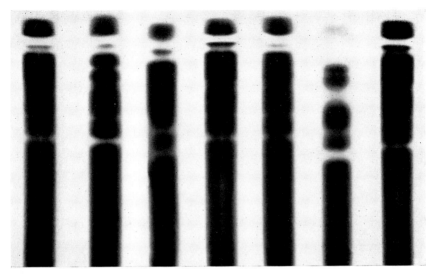

FIG. 9. Amylases in cortex of seven apple varieties (ripe).

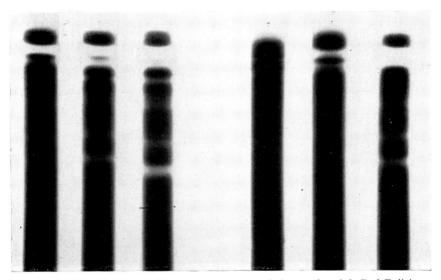

FIG. 10. Amylases in cortex of immature, mature and ripe apples: *left*, Red Delicious; *right*, Stayman Winesap.

(for example, lipases, phosphatases) may be capable of hydrolysing these esters. On the other hand, the use of a natural substrate, along with specific co-factors, results in a narrow response, and the enzymes detected will be relatively specific (for example, dehydrogenases). The zymograms cannot be interpreted in terms of natural functions unless the *natural* substrates are known, and in the case of such non-specific enzymes as the esterases this may be difficult to ascertain. Nevertheless, the profiles provide interesting comparisons and suggest avenues of approach.

The literature relating to enzyme histochemical tests and their application to studies of variants is extensive, and space does not permit a discussion of procedures and isoenzymes. However, some comments should be made regarding individual zymograms.

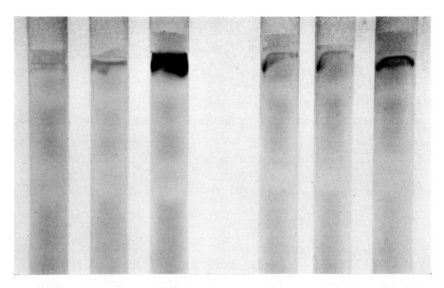

FIG. 11. Phosphorylase in immature, mature and ripe apples: *left*, Red Delicious; *right*, Golden Delicious.

1. *Amylases*

Amylases were detected by incorporating starch (0·1%) into the acrylamide before polymerization. After electrophoresis, gels were incubated at pH 5·3 and stained with iodine. Eight bands were usually evident in the apple (Figs 9, 10 and 12) and in the tomato. Qualitative variations were not apparent among varieties, but quantitative differences were evident, and a substantial increase was noted during ripening.

2. *Phosphorylase*

Phosphorylase was detected by incorporating starch (0·01% as primer) into the acrylamide before polymerization, and following electrophoresis,

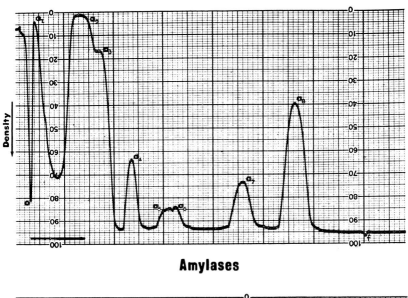

Amylases

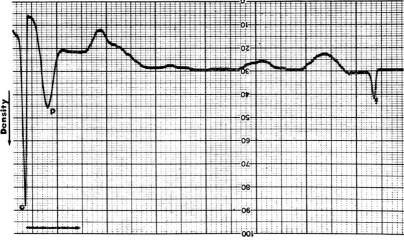

Phosphorylase

FIG. 12. Densitometric scan (inverted) of amylases and phosphorylase in cortex of ripe Red Delicious apple.

specimens were incubated in 0·1M sodium citrate, pH 6·0, containing 5 µmole glucose-1-phosphate. Starch was then detected with iodine (Figs 11 and 12). The nine apple varieties studied produced a single band, but quantitative differences were evident, and activity increased markedly during ripening.

3. *Malic dehydrogenase*

Apple cortical tissue produced many fine bands (Fig. 13). Both qualitative and quantitative differences were noted among varieties, but the complexity of the patterns makes comparison difficult.

4. *NADP-dehydrogenase (malic enzyme)*

This enzyme appeared in all varieties of apple and at all maturation stages (Fig. 14), with increasing activity evident during maturation. In the tomato, activity declined during maturation.

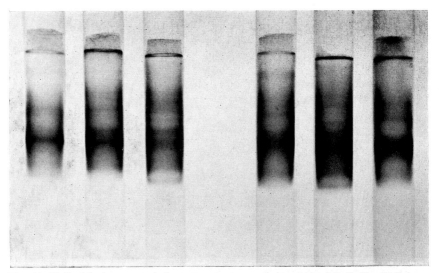

FIG. 13. Malic dehydrogenases in immature, mature and ripe apple: *left*, Golden Delicious; *right*, Red Delicious.

5. *Esterases*

Although relatively non-specific, esterase patterns demonstrated definite qualitative differences among apple varieties (Fig. 15) and among tomato varieties. Maturation produced quantitative changes.

6. *Acid phosphatases*

Slight quantitative differences in phosphatase activity appeared among apple varieties (Fig. 16). However, heavy staining near the origin indicates limited migration of much of the enzyme.

7. *Phenoloxidases*

Phenoloxidase activity was detected by incubating specimens in buffered solutions of residue from acetone extracts obtained during powder preparation,

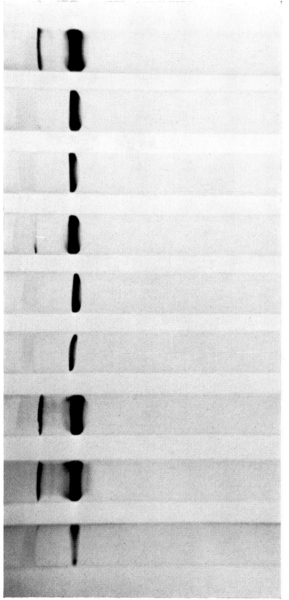

FIG. 14. NADP-dehydrogenase (malic enzyme) in cortex of immature, mature and ripe apple: 1–3, Cortland; 4–6, Golden Delicious; 7–9, Grimes Golden.

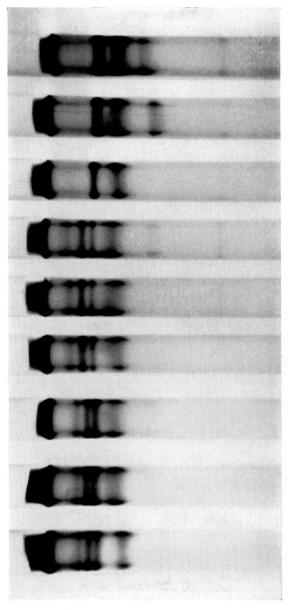

FIG. 15. Esterases in cortex of immature, mature and ripe apple: 1–3, Cortland; 4–6, Golden Delicious; 7–9, Grimes Golden.

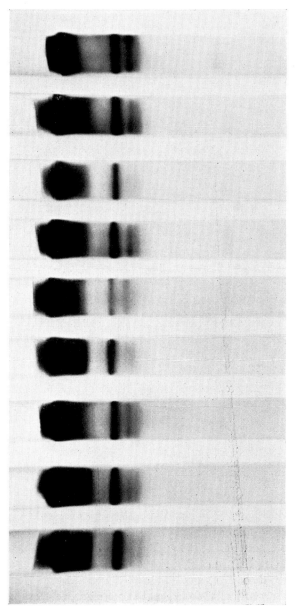

FIG. 16. Acid phosphatases in immature, mature and ripe apple: 1–3, Cortland; 4–6, Golden Delicious; 7–9, Grimes Golden.

thus producing bands through oxidation of the natural substrates. Figure 17 illustrates the bands resulting from incubation of gels from pome fruits in extracts from apple tissues.

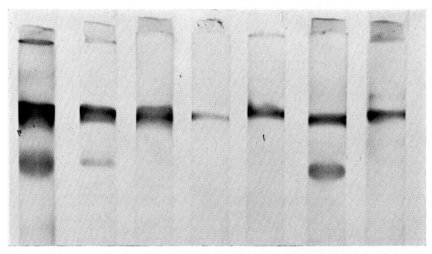

Fig. 17. Phenoloxidases in ripe pome fruits: *left to right*, apple cortex, apple cortex, apple peel, pear cortex, pear peel, quince cortex, quince peel (first gel incubated in apple peel extract remainder incubated in apple cortical extract).

IV. CONCLUSION

High-resolution electrophoresis, when used in conjunction with satisfactory preparative and extraction procedures, should be a valuable tool for studies of fruit tissues. Results must be interpreted in terms of the limitations of the methods, however, and each fruit tissue presents its own unique difficulties. The processes of tissue preparation, protein extraction, electrophoresis and detection present many parameters, and the conditions must often be selected by trial and error. When reproducible patterns are obtained, effects of such factors as chemical environment, temperature, and mechanical manipulations during tissue preparation must be considered. When a highly sensitive electrophoretic technique is employed, such considerations are of particular importance. Freezing, for example, may affect the distribution of certain isoenzymes (Chilson *et al.*, 1965). Moreover, a given set of conditions cannot be expected to effect a quantitative extraction of the entire protein complement of a particular tissue, and more rigorous treatment may be required for solubilization of proteins associated with cell walls, nuclei, mitochondria, and other organelles. However, a reproducible pattern can represent a starting point, and permit the development and evaluation of modifications designed for specific problems. The vast amount of information regarding proteins and isoenzymes in other areas may then be applied to studies of fruit biochemistry.

A Note Regarding Photography

All photographs were taken by the author on 35 mm Kodachrome II film with a Contaflex-I camera and close-up lens. Specimens were placed in glass tubes and photographed with transmitted light from a 15 watt GE Daylight fluorescent tube fitted with diffusion panels. Black and white photographs were printed from negatives prepared from the colour transparencies.

Acknowledgements

The author wishes to acknowledge the support of the Institute of Nutrition, Ohio State University, and the co-operation of the director, Dr. Ralph Johnson, in this research. The author would also like to thank Miss Carrie Voiers for preparation of the manuscript.

REFERENCES

Anderson, J. W. (1968). *Phytochemistry* **7**, 1973–88.
Burstone, M. S. (1962). "Enzyme Histochemistry". Academic Press, New York.
Chilson, O. P., Costello, L. A. and Kaplan, N. O. (1965). *Fedn. Proc. Fedn. Am. Socs. exp. Biol.* **24**, Part *III*, S55–S65.
Clements, R. L. (1965). *Analyt. Biochem.* **13**, 390–401.
Clements, R. L. (1966a). *Phytochemistry* **5**, 243–9.
Clements, R. L. (1966b). *Proc. XVII int. Hort. Congr.* **1**, Paper 55.
Clements, R. L. (1966c). *Proc. XVII int. Hort. Congr.* **1**, Paper 127.
Davis, B. J. (1964). *Ann. N.Y. Acad. Sci.* **121**, 404–27.
Jones, J. D., Hulme, A. C. and Wooltorton, J. S. C. (1965). *Phytochemistry* **4**, 659.
Loomis, W. D. and Battaile, J. (1966). *Phytochemistry* **5**, 423–38.
Ornstein, L. (1964). *Ann. N.Y. Acad. Sci.* **121**, 321–49.
Ornstein, L. and Davis, B. J. (1962). "Disc Electrophoresis", Parts I and II. Preprinted by Distillation Products Industries, Rochester, New York.
Shaw, C. R. (1965). *Science, N.Y.* **149**, 936–43.

Chapter 8

Enzymes

DAVID R. DILLEY

Department of Horticulture, Michigan State University,
East Lansing, Michigan, U.S.A.

I. INTRODUCTION

More than fifty years have passed since Thatcher (1915) reported his observations on the enzymes in apples and their relation to the ripening process.

He reported difficulties still encountered in obtaining active enzyme preparations from fruits of this type and was probably the first investigator to
employ the acetone-dried powder technique to overcome them and demonstrate the activity of several enzymes in this tissue. Whereas he was not
successful in demonstrating activity of pectinase, diastase (amylase), invertase,
tannase, or emulsin (glucosidase), he did observe esterase, protease and
polyphenol oxidase activity in preparations from apple cortical tissue. In
addition, he obtained some evidence from apple seed preparations for diastase, emulsin, lipase and protease activity. In retrospect his investigations
were truly remarkable and to quote " . . . the changes taking place (during
ripening) in the apple were not simple respiratory changes, but probably in
large part were internal enzymic activities", reflects his hypothesis which only
quite recently is being substantiated with experimental observation.

The objectives of this Chapter are threefold: (a) to describe briefly the
reactions and location of the enzymes within the cells and, if possible, the
biological function of the enzyme; (b) to describe pertinent investigations of
the respective enzymes in fruit tissue, and (c) to relate changes in activity,
where possible, to the physical and chemical transformations that occur in
fruits during development, ripening and senescence. No attempt will be made
to document all studies that have been conducted or all enzyme activities
that have been observed. Enzyme activities of mitochondria will not be
covered since this subject is dealt with in chapters dealing with individual
fruits (Volume 2).

It is becoming increasingly evident from comparative biochemistry that
plants and animals are endowed with most of the same enzymes. Therefore, it
is more important to relate specific enzyme activities to physiological function, or failure as the case may be, than merely to note similarities that
probably exist with no attention to biological function. The aspect of control
of enzyme activity or synthesis will be treated in relation to cellular development as this represents a significant new area of the utmost importance with
great promise of future development toward the goal of understanding fruit
biochemistry. The reader is referred to the chapters devoted to particular
fruits for a more comprehensive discussion of this subject.

II. INTRACELLULAR DISTRIBUTION OF ENZYMES

It is becoming increasingly apparent that the intracellular distribution of
enzymes in plant cells is much more complex than was once believed. Until
quite recently it was sufficient to categorize enzyme location as either soluble
or particulate based upon sedimentation behaviour during centrifugation.
Generally speaking, an enzyme was considered to be a soluble component
of the cytoplasmic fluid if it was found in the supernatent solution following

centrifugation of a crude extract at 10,000 to 20,000 $\times$ **g** for 15 minutes. And if present in the precipitated material it was designated as particulate or mitochondrial. Later refinements were introduced to prepare several sub-cellular fractions based on differential centrifugation generally designated as cell-wall fragments, nuclear, chloroplast, mitochondrial, ribosomal and "soluble". Only quite recently has it been found that many enzymes which were once considered to be soluble are, in fact, located in particles readily disrupted by extracting procedures commonly employed and thus become solubilized. These particles are currently referred to as peroxisoms, glyoxisomes and lysosomes depending upon the types of enzyme activities found within them. These particles, generally larger than mitochondria but smaller than chloroplasts, although quite labile, can be stabilized by extracting in 0·5M sucrose and separated from mitochondria and other plastids by the isopycnic centrifugation technique (Tolbert et al., 1968).

Lysosomes may be ruptured by exposure to distilled water, salt solutions, freezing and thawing, sonication, detergents, digitonin and carbon tetra-chloride (Weissmann, 1964). Proteases and lecithinase increase lysosomal permeability (de Duve et al., 1962). Tappel et al. (1963) has shown that the lysosomal membrane is made more permeable by treatments that promote free radicals such as ionizing radiation, ultra-violet irradiation, exposure to H_2O_2 and lipid peroxides. The lysosomal membrane is stabilized by choles-terol, cortisone and chloroquine (Weissmann, 1964). It has been observed (Grunwald, 1968) that certain sterols promote, while others retard, mem-brane permeability of red beet cell vacuoles as judged by pigment leakage. Similarity of behaviour of the vacuolar membrane and lysosomal membrane with respect to steroids suggests a common origin for the two membranes. Furthermore, vacuoles and lysosomes behave as osmometers.

Matile (1968) has obtained evidence for several types of microbodies in corn root tip cells (he refers to them as lysosomes) which differed in size and density and enzyme activities. The different types of particles were con-sidered to represent various stages of lysosome development with the vacuole of parenchymatous cells being the product of progressive fusion of these particles. It is premature to extrapolate from such limited data that all plant cells contain lysosomes. However, it is tempting to speculate from this premise, for, together with the chloroplast, mitochondrion, peroxisome, leucoplast, nucleus, vacuole and perhaps other membrane enclosed sub-cellular organelles one can begin to account for the speciality of function and interplay among these diverse compartments that must exist, and gain further appreciation of the co-ordinated biochemical control of cellular processes.

The following scheme outlines the various subcellular fractions that have been identified with certain enzyme activities as a progression is made from the "outside" to the "inside" of the cell.

Intracellular distribution
>   Cell wall
>   Plasmalemma
>   Cytoplasmic fluid
>>   Soluble fraction
>>   Nucleus
>>   Endoplasmic reticulum
>>   Ribosome
>>   Chloroplast
>>   Leucoplast
>>   Mitochondria
>>   Peroxisome
>>   Glyoxisome
>>   Lysosome
>>   Membrane
>>   Vacuole

III. SPECIFIC ENZYMES

A. Pectic Enzyme Complex

It is clear that the pectic enzymes play a vital role in fruit ripening. Investigations by Hobson (1963, 1964) establish a close association between textural changes and the activity of pectinesterase and polygalacturonase during maturation and ripening of tomato fruits. The pectinesterase activity increases approximately 40% as the tomato fruit progresses from mature green to the fully red stage. Kertesz (1938) and Pithawala *et al.* (1948) observed two-fold and 30% increases, respectively, in tomato fruit pectinesterase activity with ripening. Recent studies by Markakis (1969) indicate a five-fold increase in pectinesterase activity in tomato fruit (Fireball variety) from the mature green to the red ripe stage of development. Polygalacturonase activity was not found in green fruits, but increased 200-fold in tomato fruits as they passed from the green-orange to the red stage and continued to increase beyond the fully red stage for nearly two weeks before a gradual decline occurred (Hobson, 1964). A similar trend in polygalacturonase activity with ripening tomatoes was found by Foda (1957).

Properties of purified citrus fruit pectinesterase have been studied quite extensively (MacDonnell *et al.*, 1950). Orange pectinesterase is quite specific for pectin and methyl and ethyl esters of polygalacturonic acid. A high degree of substrate specificity for pectin was also observed for tomato fruit pectinesterase. These investigators also found evidence in citrus and tomato fruits for esterases other than pectinesterase which exhibited activity towards a wide range of non-galacturonide esters.

The positive correlation between ripening (loss of firmness and colour development) and increased polygalacturonase and pectinesterase activity may be due to *de novo* protein synthesis during ripening. Hobson (1964) suggests that breakdown in the mechanism for polygalacturonase synthesis may explain ripening failure of tomato fruits afflicted with "blotchy" ripening, a common physiological disorder. This malady is characterized by the presence of firm, poorly coloured sections of locule wall interspersed with the soft red locule walls of ripe fruits. Polygalacturonase activity of affected areas was only 5–17% of that found in adjacent normal tissue.

Employing the same enzyme extraction procedure successful for tomato, Hobson (1962) demonstrated polygalacturonase activity in avocado, medlar, pear and pineapple but not melon or grape. The absence of enzyme activity, however, may be due to inactivation during extraction or the presence of inhibitors. McCready and McComb (1954) could not detect polygalacturonase in unripe Fuerte avocado or Bartlett pear, but both fruits contained abundant activity when fully ripe.

Weurman (1954a) made a rather extensive study on "pectase" (pectinesterase) activity during development and ripening of Doyenné Boussoch pears. He found activity (based on a given weight of fresh cortical tissue) reached a peak during early development on the tree and subsequently decreased to a low and relatively unchanging level about two weeks prior to commercial maturity. Since the fruit undergoes a tremendous increase in size during the development period studied by Weurman, and exclusively by cell enlargement, the enzyme activity versus fruit development relationship noted above does not adequately reflect possible changes in pectinesterase on a per cell or protein N basis. In ripening studies following harvest, activity expressed on a tissue weight basis more appropriately reflects actual changes. Pectinesterase activity of fruits harvested approximately one month prior to the commercial harvest period and allowed to ripen did not change appreciably from that observed at harvest. However, pectinesterase activity increased approximately 50% during low temperature storage of pears harvested at a mature, but unripe condition. This can be taken as evidence that pectinesterase activity of pears increases during ripening, providing the fruits have attained a certain minimal maturation stage.

Pectinase (polygalacturonase) activity of pears was also investigated by Weurman (1954b). He reported an increase in polygalacturonase activity as fruits of the Doyenné Boussoch variety passed from an unripe to a ripe condition. Nagel and Patterson (1951) observed both pectinesterase and polygalacturonase in Bartlett pears during development and ripening but were unable to relate activity with development in a definitive manner.

Pollard and Kieser (1951) studied the pectinesterase activity of several apple varieties and partially purified the enzyme from Worcester Permain,

The enzyme exhibited a pH 6·6 optimum. Pectinesterase activity varied widely among apple varieties although maturity or stage of ripeness was not stated and may be responsible for some of the variations found.

Banana fruit pectinesterase activity increases during ripening (Hultin and Levine, 1965), particularly during the period when the skin colour turns from green to yellow. This increase in activity was judged to be real and not due to tannin inactivation in the green fruits. Pectic enzymes are considered in detail in Chapter 3.

B. Cellulase

The role of cellulase in cell-wall softening during fruit ripening is not clear. While it might justly be presumed that cellulose hydrolysis would structurally weaken the cell wall, several lines of experimental evidence militates against this being a primary cause of flesh softening. Cellulase activity of tomato fruit has been observed to increase during ripening (Dickinson, 1962; Hall, 1964; Hobson, 1968). It is possible that the enzyme is a component of the cell wall protein. However, cellulose micelles undergo little degradation in pears (Jermyn and Isherwood, 1956) or peaches (Sterling, 1961) during ripening. Furthermore, the cellulose content of apples decreases only slightly as they ripen in storage (Kertesz, et al., 1959).

The study of Hobson (1968) is perhaps the most definitive investigation into the role of cellulase during fruit ripening. He found cellulase activity to be high in immature fruits (approximately $\frac{1}{2}$ inch diameter) and that activity declined with growth, but subsequently increased more than two-fold as fruits passed from the mature green to red ripe state. In contrast to polygalacturonase activity which continued to increase as fruits went from ripe to over-ripe, cellulase activity remained at the same level. Hobson (1968) found no correlation between cellulase activity and firmness among several tomato varieties. In fact, Potentate, a firm variety, was found to contain more than twice as much cellulase activity as Harbinger, a characteristically soft variety. Hobson concludes that cellulase may complement the action of pectinesterase and polygalacturonase but flesh softening during ripening of tomato is primarily controlled by the action of the pectic enzyme complex.

C. Amylase and Phosphorylase

The disappearance of starch is one of the most dramatic chemical changes associated with ripening of many fruits. Bananas, which may contain up to 20% starch by weight at the mature green stage possess less than 1% at the fully ripened stage (Biale, 1964). The starch content of pome fruits (apple and pear) reaches a maximum during the growing season, declines to approximately 1% at maturity, and undergoes a precipitous drop during ripening.

Enzymatic hydrolysis of starch can be performed by amylases (in most cases a mixture of amylases) and phosphorylases. The primary forms of amylase are denoted as alpha and beta. α-Amylase hydrolyses the α-1,4-glucosidic linkages whereas β-amylase hydrolyses alternate α-1,4-glucosidic bonds from the non-reducing end of the molecule resulting in maltose formation. Neither α- nor β-amylase is capable of transversing or hydrolysing the α-1,6-glucosidic bonds at branching points in amylopectin. These bonds are broken by isoamylase—an α-1,6-glucosidase.

Phosphorylases degrade starch in a distinctly different manner than amylases. The reaction is a tranglucosidation wherein a glucose residue is reversibly transferred from amylose to phosphate with conservation of most of the glucosidic bond energy. Phosphorylase like α-amylase degrades amylose completely but also is not capable of handling the α-1,6-glucosidic linkages at branching points in amylopectin.

The relative contribution of amylase and phosphorylase in starch degradation in fruits is not known. Maris McArthur-Hespe (1956) studied amylase activity in cortical tissue of several pear varieties during growth and maturation and storage and ripening following storage. As noted by Hulme (1958) her assay procedure was not sufficiently specific to rule out participation of phosphorylase. None the less, pear fruits exhibited an increase (per fruit) in starch hydrolytic activity with development. The most significant increase in activity occurred during the month preceding commercial harvest maturity and not during the earlier period when most of the accumulated starch was being degraded. Maris McArthur-Hespe found that activity continued to increase in fruits during storage for 3 months at $-0.5°C$ but not during ripening following removal from storage. A dramatic increase in starch hydrolytic activity during storage (long after starch had disappeared from the fruits) in relation to values at harvest was associated with failure of these fruits to ripen normally upon removal from storage. This phenomena may have important bearing on Li and Hansen's (1964) observation that failure of Bartlett pear fruits to ripen following long term storage was associated with the failure of protein synthesis upon removal from storage. In both studies protein synthesis took place during storage. This may represent synthesis of particular enzymes at the expense of others required for ripening and for which synthesis is not favourable at low temperature, and may reflect a differential effect of temperature on synthesis of specific enzymes. If so, it may be a possible cause of "low temperature injury", an abnormal ripening malady, common to fruits of many species when exposed to low temperatures following harvest.

Of particular significance in Maris McArthur-Hespe's study was her

observation that less mature fruits of the Comptesse de Paris variety underwent a greater increase in starch hydrolytic activity than those of *later* picked
fruits which were capable of ripening after a much longer storage period.
This is an apparent inconsistency with the thesis that potential "storage
life" diminishes as fruits progress beyond a critical stage of maturation.
However, this may be nothing more than absence of complete ripening potential in the early picked fruit. Perhaps those proteins (starch hydrolysing
proteins included) for which the mechanism for synthesis is present utilize
amino acid reserves at the expense of other enzymes for which the synthesic
mechanism is not yet developed at the more immature stage. Fruits of the
later harvest would still be endowed with the capacity to synthesize starch
enzyme, but in addition would have gained capacity to synthesize still
other "ripening enzymes", and thus a more favourable complement of proteins would ensue.

Mattoo and Modi (1969) observed an increase in amylase activity in mango
which they attributed to a decrease in an inhibitor as the fruits ripened.
Starch hydrolysing enzymes are present in plastids in fruits, and according
to Davies and Cocking (1967) are synthesized in them. Soluble amylases also
exist within the cell. We have detected an enzyme with starch-splitting
activity in acetone-dried powders of apple fruits and in fresh extracts of
Bartlett pears but have not characterized it further. Our preliminary studies
suggest that this enzyme lends itself well to electrophoretic separation on
acrylamide gel which should facilitate further investigations.

D. Invertase

In spite of extensive investigations into changes in reducing and non-
reducing sugars during development, ripening and senescence of fruits, few
studies have been made of the enzymes catalysing sugar transformations
(Hulme, 1958). Invertase, the enzyme which hydrolyses sucrose into fructose
and glucose is termed β-fructofuranosidase, is also capable of transglycosidation activity whereby a hexose moiety is transferred to a primary alcohol
group of mono- or disaccharides. Transferase activity may account for the
synthesis of certain trisaccharides or oligosaccharides observed in fruits
during ripening as was reported in banana by Henderson *et al.* (1959). These
investigators partially purified invertase from ripe banana fruits and this
preparation in addition to hydrolysing sucrose gave an *in vitro* enzymatic
formation of a trisaccharide tentatively identified as a fructosylsucrose,
similar to that formed from yeast invertase. The presence in banana fruits of
the same trisaccharide, which increased with sucrose, glucose and fructose
during ripening, strongly suggests that transglycosidation is an *in vivo*
enzymatic activity of invertase. The pH activity curve of banana invertase

showed a broad peak around pH 4 similar to that for yeast invertase. However, the K_m values for sucrose hydrolysis by banana and yeast invertase are markedly different being 0·0005M and 0·2M, respectively, at pH 5·1.

Hulme (1951) reported the presence of invertase activity in young apple fruits (approximately 15 g size) but enzyme activity was not studied in relation to fruit development. In view of the marked increase and subsequent rapid decline in sucrose content of apples and pears during ripening a study of invertase activity should be most interesting, particularly since sucrose accumulates in quantities far greater than can be accounted for by starch hydrolysis during this period (Hulme, 1958).

E. Enzymes of the Pentose Phosphate Pathway

Contribution of the pentose phosphate pathway to the ripening process in fruits is inferred from the fact that considerable ribose synthesis would be required to sustain the RNA synthesis that occurs during ripening. In addition, other syntheses (protein, anthocyanins and phenols) draw precursors from this cycle. Evidence for the operation of the pentose pathway has been obtained from C_1- and C_6-glucose feeding studies in tomato, cucumber, lime and orange fruits (Bradbour et al., 1958; Wang et al., 1962), apple (Burg and Thimann, 1961, Faust, 1965) and pear (Meynhardt et al., 1965a). The investigation by Meynhardt et al. (1965), indicates active participation of the pentose cycle particularly during the early stages of ripening in Bartlett pear. These workers demonstrated activity of the following pentose phosphate pathway enzymes; glucose-6 phosphate and phosphogluconate dehydrogenase, phosphoribose isomerase, phosphohexose isomerase, phosphoribulose epimerase and transketolase. Enzyme activity in peel extracts was assayed in relation to fruit ripening with the following results; glucose-6 phosphate dehydrogenase decreased with ripening but was again high in senescent fruit, phosphogluconate dehydrogenase decreased with ripening and senescence, phosphoribose isomerase increased with ripening and then declined in senescent fruit. Phosphohexose isomerase activity was high at the onset of ripening and declined as fruits reached full ripeness and became senescent. The activity changes should be considered as tentative since quantitative extraction of the enzymes from the tissue was not attempted. The significant feature of their study was that the pentose pathway was most active during the early stage of fruit ripening. This is consistent with the thesis that it is during this period that induction of the ripening processes is taking place. This thesis maintains that the components for protein synthesis required for synthesis of the enzymes catalysing the ripening process are fabricated at the early stages of the climacteric. Recent studies of Ku and Romani (1969) indicate that ribosomal RNA synthesis is active during the early phase of Bartlett pear ripening and ceases by the time the climacteric peak is reached.

F. Enzymes of the Glyoxylate Cycle

The presence of isocitrate lyase in Bartlett pear fruit at various ripening stages (Meynhardt et al., 1965b) raises an interesting question regarding its location within the cell. Breidenbach et al. (1968) established that isocitrate lyase, malate synthetase, catalase and glycolate oxidase are present in glyoxysomes from castor bean endosperm. It is possible that pear fruits contain similar particles, currently being referred to as peroxisomes or glyoxisomes with similar enzyme activities.

G. Chlorophyllase

It has long been presumed that chlorophyllase may be involved in the destruction of chlorophyll which is so characteristic during ripening of fruits. The enzyme catalyses the removal of the phytol group of chlorophyll forming the corresponding chlorophyllide. This reaction proceeds reversibly in vitro. The enzyme activity is high in tissues undergoing chlorophyll synthesis and this has lead to suggestions that it may normally have a role in synthesis (Holden, 1965). A catabolic role in fruit ripening has been suggested by Looney and Patterson (1967a) in the banana, and by Rhodes and Wooltorton (1967) in apple tissue. In banana, chlorophyllase activity paralleled the respiratory climacteric. Looney and Patterson suggest that since chlorophyllase is present in the chloroplast and that this organelle undergoes degeneration quite early in the ripening process the increased activity may possibly be accounted for by release of the enzyme. They alternatively hypothesize that the increase in activity is the result of new enzyme synthesis at the onset of ripening. Chlorophyllase activity of apple tissue was found to increase somewhat before the climacteric commenced, increased three-fold during the climacteric rise while the chlorophyll content was declining, and continued to increase beyond the peak (Rhodes and Wooltorton, 1967). Apple fruit chlorophyllase exhibited a pH optimum at about 7·5 and activity was maximum in acetone at a concentration of 40% (v/v).

The question as to whether or not the increase in chlorophyllase activity during ripening is the result of new protein synthesis or release of an existing membrane bound enzyme has not been resolved.

Ripening and chlorophyll destruction is blocked when preclimacteric pome fruits are exposed to high CO_2 levels. This treatment delays the normal increase in protein nitrogen observed during ripening. Chlorophyll breakdown is also blocked when protein synthesis is stopped by treating pre-climacteric pear fruits with cycloheximide or when RNA synthesis is in-hibited with actinomycin-D whereas the respiratory climacteric proceeds in an apparently normal manner (Frenkel et al., 1968). However, these fruits do not ripen even in the presence of an exogenous supply of ethylene. There-fore, chlorophyll degradation may be viewed as a normal consequence of the ripening process in certain fruits but as a fortuitous coincidence with the respiratory climacteric in others. Chlorophyll degradation is commonly ob-served in Bartlett pears during prolonged low temperature storage when flesh softening or other attributes of ripening are absent. This may be taken as evidence that chlorophyll degradation is not necessarily an essential pro-cess in ripening or that the mechanism of breakdown is distinctly different from that catalysed by chlorophyllase, perhaps via an unsaturated fatty acid system which has been studied by Holden (1965).

H. Fatty Acid Synthetase

The synthesis of long-chain fatty acids during ripening of apples is well documented by the studies of Meigh and Hulme (1965) and more recently in ageing peel discs prepared from pre-climacteric apples (Galliard et al., 1968; Hulme et al., 1968). Peel discs of pre-climacteric apples appear to progress through similar biochemical changes with ageing as intact fruit during the respiratory climacteric. Although the specific enzymes involved in fatty acid synthesis in apple fruits have not been elucidated, increased activity of fatty acid synthase has been suggested by Galliard et al. (1968) on the basis of acetate incorporation studies. They demonstrated that the increased activity is dependent upon new protein synthesis during the develop-ment of respiratory climacteric.

Stumpf and co-workers (Stumpf and Barber, 1957; Yang and Stumpf, 1965) described a particulate and soluble enzyme system from ripe avocado fruit which incorporated acetate and malonyl-CoA respectively into palmitic and stearic acids. The scheme for fatty acid synthesis in avocado and, pre-sumably, for other fruit tissues is probably similar to that described by Stumpf (1965). Of particular interest with respect to fruit ripening is the fact that newly synthesized fatty acids are readily incorporated into phospholipids, but not galactolipids. Since both are important components of the plastid membranes this indicates, perhaps, a loss of co-ordination in lipid synthesis (Galliard et al., 1968).

I. Lipase

Studies of lipase activity in relation to ripening of fruits are limited. With the exception of the avocado, our common fruits are typically low in fats and oils and this perhaps explains the paucity of knowledge about lipase activity in fruits. Lipase catalyses the hydrolysis of tri-, di- and mono-glycerides to the component fatty acids and free glycerol. Galliard (1968) found that the lipids of apple fruit pulp are typical of those from leaves and storage organs of plants in general. Meigh and Hulme (1965) found that the content of free C-18 fatty acids increased markedly in the peel of apples as they progressed through the climacteric, but they were always in much lower amounts than the esterified fatty acids. Rhodes and Wooltorton (1967) found that lipase activity paralleled the increase in respiration rate in the early stages of the climacteric but subsequently declined before the climacteric peak of respiration was reached. Lipase activity was primarily restricted to the soluble fraction throughout the ripening period of 40 days at 12°C. Some lipase activity (approximately 10% of the total) was found to be associated with the ribosomal fraction, but this may be attributed to contamination. The increase in lipase activity may be responsible for the increase in free fatty acids noted above by Meigh and Hulme (1965).

J. Lipoxidase

Lipoxidase may play a vital role in fruit ripening and senescence. Wooltorton et al. (1965) found that lipoxidase activity increases significantly during the respiratory climacteric of apples and fatty acids may serve as a source of ethylene in this tissue (Galliard et al., 1968). Lieberman and Mapson (1964) suggested earlier that lipoxidase acting on linolenic acid might be involved in ethylene production in fruits. This enzyme catalyses the initial reaction in the degradation of poly-unsaturated fatty acids that contain the cis, cis-1,4-pentadiene system. Arachidonic, linoleic and linolenic acids are of primary importance as substrates whereas fatty acids with single or conjugated double bonds or poly-unsaturated fatty acids with trans double bonds are not substrates for lipoxidase (Holman, 1960).

Linoleic and linolenic acids are quantitatively significant as components of membranes in cell organelles. The chloroplast, but not the mitochondria, undergoes degeneration with loss of structure, chlorophyll, integrity and function during ripening of apples and pears (Bain and Mercer, 1964; Rhodes and Wooltorton, 1967) and presumably other fruits. Galliard's investigation (1968) revealed that there is a loss of galactolipids associated with plastid membrane breakdown during apple ripening. The increase in lipoxidase activity was related to a general increase in fatty acid metabolism (Galliard et al., 1968). The increased lipoxidase activity observed in preclimacteric apple peel discs during ageing was prevented when protein synthesis was stopped with cycloheximide. This strongly suggests that lipoxidase is among the enzymes undergoing synthesis during the onset of ripening.

Our own studies lend support to this conclusion to the extent that lipoxidase has been isolated from ripening pears and apple fruits, increases in quantity as judged by disc electrophoresis studies and undergoes synthesis as measured by ^{14}C-phenylalanine incorporation during ripening.

K. Phosphatase

Phosphatases as a class of enzymes are categorized according to substrate specificity and pH optima. There are specific and non-specific phosphomono-esterases, and within the non-specific group they are further differentiated with respect to having acid or alkaline pH optima. An excellent treatise on the phosphatases is available (Schmidt and Laskowski, 1961). For the purpose of this review it is sufficient to note that phosphatases hydrolyse phosphoric acid esters making phosphate available for other metabolic processes.

Alexrod (1947) made an extensive investigation of the properties of phosphatase obtained from Navel orange juice. This was the first reported instance of enzyme activity present in citrus juice. Fractionation of the enzyme activity within the various tissue of citrus fruits revealed that most of the enzyme was in the juice. This particular enzyme was judged to be an acid phosphatase or, more specifically, a non-specific acid phosphomonoesterase. His preparation also contained phosphodiesterase activity as evidenced by its ribonuclease activity (see ribonuclease section), however diphenyl-1-phosphate was not a substrate.

Rhodes and Wooltorton (1967) observed an increase in an acid phosphatase during the respiratory climacteric of apple fruit. The increase in acid phosphatase activity was not as clearly defined as was the case for chlorophyllase, ribonuclease and lipoxidase. They discount, but do not rule out, the possibility of the phosphatase activity residing in "lysosome-like" particles within the cell. It is well documented (De Duve and Bandhiun, 1966) that peroxisomes of animal cells contain an acid phosphatase which is readily solubilized by low tonicity extracting solutions commonly employed in preparing enzyme extracts. Miller and Romani (1966) observed acid phosphatase activity in a particular fraction of Bartlett pear extract subjected to sucrose density centrifugation. As ripening progressed the phosphatase was obtained in the fraction from a somewhat lower sucrose density than in the earlier stages.

L. Ribonuclease

Interest in ribonuclease in relation to fruit ripening and senescence arises from the fact that the activity of this enzyme might initiate general cellular degradation by digesting the RNA required for protein synthesis. All plant ribonucleases thus far investigated degrade RNA completely to nucleo-side-2',3'-cyclic phosphates and the purine nucleosides to the corresponding 3'-nucleotides (Anfinsen and White, 1961).

Alexrod (1947) observed ribonuclease activity in a partially purified citrus fruit phosphatase preparation. The enzyme was stable to heating for 5 min at 75°C at pH 4·3. Heat stability is a common characteristic of ribonuclease from many plant sources. Bolomey and Allen (1942) had shown previously that a phosphatase preparation from almonds contained considerable ribonuclease activity.

Rhodes and Wooltorton (1967) found that ribonuclease activity increased and closely paralleled the respiration rate during the climacteric of apple fruits and that the bulk of activity was found in the soluble protein fraction which is typical of other plant tissues. The pH optimum of apple RNAase was 6·6 which is somewhat higher than that generally observed (pH 4·5–5·5) for most plant RNAases.

The increase in apple fruit RNAase activity observed by Rhodes and Wooltorton (1967) is interesting in view of the marked increase (approximately 50%) in total RNA found by Looney and Patterson (1967b) during the climacteric of apples. The molar ratios of nucleotides remained essentially constant during maturation and ripening of Yellow Transparent apples. The molar percent of each was: cytidylic acid 22·5, adenylic acid 27·1, uridylic acid 20·6, guanylic acid 29·8. Apparently the rate of RNA synthesis far exceeded that of degradation to account for the marked increase in total RNA. Richmond and Biale (1967) found that ^{32}P incorporation into RNA of avocado fruit slices was highest in the early stages of the climacteric and progressively decreased as the respiratory peak was attained. Ribosomal RNA accounted for 70–90% of the total RNA, but total RNA content of avocado did not change markedly with ripening. It is perhaps significant that the rate of RNA synthesis as measured by ^{32}P incorporation (Richmond and Biale, 1967) and rate of protein synthesis as measured by leucine or valine incorporation (Richmond and Biale, 1966a, 1966b) followed the same pattern both markedly diminishing as the climacteric peak was attained. This may indicate a fairly rapid rate of turnover of the components of protein synthesis. The decline at or near the peak may be due to RNAase digestion of RNA required to maintain protein synthesis.

M. Ethylene Synthesizing Enzymes

The significance of the ethylene synthesizing system in relation to fruit ripening is self-evident since ethylene is the ripening hormone. Within the past five years considerable progress has been made towards elucidating the mechanism of ethylene biosynthesis particularly through the efforts of Lieberman, Mapson and Yang. Many substrates yield ethylene when administered to plants (see review by Pratt and Goeshl, 1969) and some insight into possible pathways has been achieved in this manner. Recently, Jacobson and Wang (1968) described a pathway in *Penicillium digitatum* which indicates that acrylic acid may be a direct precursor for ethylene. Further details of the biogenesis of ethylene appear in Chapter 16.

The present status of enzymes directly involved in ethylene biosynthesis is not clear, but at least two general pathways appear probable. One appears to involve linolenic acid as substrate with the reaction sequence being initiated by lipoxidase with subsequent degradation to propanal (Lieberman and Kunishi, 1967) which then gives rise to ethylene. Lipic hydroperoxides are also converted to ethylene via the methional-cleaving enzyme of Mapson and Wardale (1968). The quantitative aspects of substrate-product considerations tend to favour linolenic-ethylene as the major pathway for ethylene production in ripening fruits, particularly in view of the magnitude and direction of changes in lipoxidase activity, linolenic acid and ethylene that occurs during ripening. Furthermore, it is apparent that this system is associated with chloroplasts or other plastids undergoing degradative changes as ripening progresses. There must be rigid compartmentation of enzyme and substrate or a missing link in the linolenic acid-ethylene system to explain why tissues such as soybean cotyledons which are rich in linolenic acid and lipoxidase activity produce ethylene only sparingly. It is known that cotyledons contain glyoxisomes which possess the glyoxylate cycle enzymes plus a α-β-oxidation system which together may account for glucogenesis from lipid reserves.

The second pathway and one which may be involved in ethylene production prior to the induction of the ripening processes is the methionine-methional-ethylene system which may involve a peroxidase. It would appear important to determine whether or not this system is a component of peroxisomes within the cell. Peroxisomes of plants are known to contain catalase (Tolbert *et al.*, 1968) but not peroxidase. However, catalase can function as a hydroperoxidase utilizing enzymatically generated H_2O_2 in the oxidation of phenols and certain other H-donors among which some may be substrates for ethylene production. All known peroxidases and catalases are iron-containing proteins; however, a copper-containing protein has been implicated as being involved in ethylene synthesis. Several enzymes may be involved in the terminal steps of ethylene production including a H_2O_2 generating oxidase (amino acid oxidase or ascorbic acid oxidase) requiring Cu for activity and a hydroperoxidase (for example, peroxidase or catalase) utilizing H_2O_2 in the oxidation of a substrate yielding ethylene as the product.

N. Catalase

Catalase decomposes hydrogen peroxide to water and oxygen. The enzyme is closely related to peroxidase in structure and function, and both enzymes are sometimes considered together as hydroperoxidases. There appear to be two functions of catalase in plants; first to dispose of excess H_2O_2 produced during oxidative metabolism of all organisms, and, secondly, to utilize H_2O_2 in the oxidation of alcohols, phenols and other H-donors in a manner similar to peroxidase.

There is increasing evidence that a great abundance of catalase resides in subcellular organelles referred to as peroxisomes (de Duve and Bandhuin, 1966; Tolbert et al., 1968). Whether or not a substantial amount of catalase is present in cells other than in peroxisomes is difficult to ascertain from much of the previous work since enzyme extraction procedures employed would disrupt and solubilize the peroxisomal enzymes.

Non-enzymic decomposition of H_2O_2 by certain chelated metal compounds such as Fe-heme is possible; thus, assays based on O_2 generation (Ezell and Gerhardt, 1937) in the absence of adequate controls may not truly reflect catalase activity. Ezell and Gerhardt (1942) made an extensive investigation of catalase activity in relation to development and ripening of apple and pear fruits. They found that catalase activity was positively correlated with the respiration rate of Bartlett pears during ripening on the tree, but not if harvested at various maturation stages and ripened. However, Bosc pears harvested from three different growing areas and stored at $2 \cdot 2°C$ for 3 months had higher catalase activity than those stored at $-1°C$ indicating, perhaps, that the increase may be in response to ripening changes at the higher temperature. An increase in catalase activity during storage of Anjou pears at $0°C$ was also observed by these workers.

Studies of catalase activity to determine its relevance to processes attending fruit ripening would be more definitive if attention were paid to intracellular distribution of activity in view of the likelihood that catalase may be a normal constituent of peroxisome-like particles within the cell. Miller and Romani (1966) found catalase activity in a particulate fraction of Bartlett pear fruit obtained by sucrose density centrifugation. Catalase distribution in relation to cytochrome oxidase distribution throughout the gradient suggests that the enzymes reside in particles of slightly different densities. Further work is needed to clarify this point. As mentioned elsewhere, catalase acting in a peroxidative manner may, in conjunction with an appropriate oxidase such as an amine oxidase or an α-hydroxy acid oxidase which have also been designated as peroxisomal enzymes, be involved in ethylene production. If this speculation is borne out by experimental evidence, the relevance of catalase to fruit ripening would be clearly evident. Mattoo and Modi (1969) found that ethylene promoted a three-fold increase in catalase and peroxidase activities in pre-climacteric mango fruit slices during a 24 hour period of exposure to the gas. Preclimacteric mango did not show catalase activity but possessed peroxidase activity. Ethylene treatment (10 and 50 p.p.m.) also inactivated a heat-labile non-dialysable inhibitor of catalase and peroxidase.

O. Peroxidase

There are many reports of peroxidase activity in all of the common fruits (Saunders *et al.*, 1964). In the presence of H_2O_2, peroxidase catalyses the oxidation of substrates such as phenols, aromatic-, primary-, secondary- and tertiary-amines, leuco-dyes and certain heterocyclic compounds such as ascorbic acid and indole. In addition, a wide range of H-donors are oxidized in coupled oxidation in which the peroxidase system results in the formation of an oxidation product which, in turn, oxidizes another compound. Thus, peroxidase, although limited to some degree with respect to substrates for the initial reaction, promotes a very wide range of reactions. In addition to catalysing peroxidatic reactions, peroxidase catalyses certain oxidatic reactions, an example of which is the oxidation of oxalacetate to malonate and CO_2 (Kay *et al.*, 1968) in which molecular O_2 is utilized rather than H_2O_2.

Despite the ubiquity of peroxidase, and extensive study, its physiological role remains obscure. At least seven distinct peroxidase isozymes are known (Shannon *et al.*, 1966). The oxidatic reaction catalysed by peroxidase may be extremely relevant to enzymic ethylene synthesizing systems described elsewhere. Of particular interest is the observation (Goldacre *et al.*, 1953) that the oxidatic type of peroxidase-catalysed reactions have an aromatic phenol co-factor requirement which presumably serves to generate free radicals. The apple fruit methional-ethylene synthesizing enzyme has a similar phenol co-factor requirement (Lieberman, 1969) as also does the enzyme system described by Mapson and Wardale (1968) and Yang (1967). Autocatalytic synthesis of ethylene via a peroxidase system following exogenous application of ethylene may occur since Matoo and Modi (1969) found a marked increase in peroxidase activity of pre-climacteric mango fruit 24 hours following ethylene treatment.

Peroxidase catalysed reactions may be envisioned as an integral aspect of the biochemistry of ageing cells since subcellular organelles undergo degeneration with subsequent decompartmentation of enzymes and substrates. Peroxidase is considered to be a membrane bound or soluble enzyme.

P. Phenolase Complex

Interest among fruit physiologists and food scientists in the phenolase enzymes stems largely from the action of these enzymes in promoting tissue browning subsequent to bruising, or during the preparation of many fruit tissues for processing. The browning is the result of phenol oxidation and eventual non-enzymatic polymerization of the quinones formed into tannins or "melanins". Tannins are also a serious deterrent to the successful extraction of "active" mitochondria and soluble enzymes as they may co-precipitate or are otherwise bound to protein surfaces rendering the mitochondria or enzyme inactive. Hulme and co-workers at the Ditton Laboratory, England, conducted extensive investigations into tannin inhibition of mitochondrial enzyme activity particularly with respect to the use of polyvinylpyrrolidone (PVP) in circumventing these difficulties. Anderson (1968) has prepared an excellent review article and guidelines for extracting enzymes and subcellular organelles from plant tissues in which phenols and tannins are troublesome. The control of enzymatic browning of fruits during food processing has been discussed by Ponting (1960). The review article by Mason (1955) is an excellent treatise on the phenolase complex.

The phenol oxidases are characteristically copper-containing proteins. As noted elsewhere in this chapter, the heme-proteins catalase and peroxidase capably oxidize many phenolic compounds, but should not be confused with the phenol oxidases. Substrate specificity is employed to categorize the phenolases into two broad groups. One group (tyrosinase) catalyses the oxidation of various mono- and di-phenoes, whereas the other group (polyphenoloxidase) is quite specific in catalysing the oxidation of O-dihydric phenols such as catechol and chlorogenic acid.

There is increasing evidence for the existence of several distinct isozymes of phenoloxidase in a given tissue. Walker and Hulme (1966) chromatographically separated polyphenoloxidase from apple peel tissue into two distinct components both exhibiting similar substrate specificity. Harel and Mayer (1968) fractionated apple fruit chloroplast polyphenol oxidase into three fractions and demonstrated interconversion among them, suggesting the three forms represented various degrees of enzyme sub-unit aggregation. Molecular weight estimations of the various fractions made by these workers supports this concept. Multiple forms (three) of apple fruit polyphenoloxidase was also observed by Constantinides and Bedford (1967) employing polyacrylamide gel electrophoresis. Aggregation and interconvertibility was not observed in their investigations but this possibility cannot be ruled out. Constantinides (1966) observed the same multiple form pattern of polyphenoloxidase of Northern Spy apples at stages of fruit development ranging from 30 to 130 days from full bloom, suggesting that the polyphenoloxidase system is an integral component of apple fruit throughout development.

An investigation of polyphenolase activity in relation to tomato fruit development and ripening was conducted by Hobson (1967). Enzyme activity increased continually during the growth phase and subsequently declined as the fruits ripened. Kidson (1958) observed a similar change in enzyme activity during fruit development in the tomato.

Banana fruit polyphenoloxidase was investigated by Palmer (1963) who purified the enzyme from ripe fruit and examined its properties. The enzyme was active on O-dihydric phenols but not on monophenols. The substrate specificity is of particular interest since dopamine is the dominant polyphenol in this fruit and was the most reactive of the substrates tested.

Polyphenoloxidase may play a vital role in the biochemical processes leading to fruit ripening and plant senescence in general as a means of controlling ethylene biosynthesis. Yang (1967) noted a stimulatory effect of certain monophenols and a marked inhibitory effect of selected O-diphenols on ethylene synthesis via the methional-peroxidase system. He proposed that phenolase, by oxidizing monophenols to O-diphenols, may inhibit ethylene synthesis, and oxidation of O-diphenols may alleviate the inhibition. Mapson and Wardale (1968) also observed an inhibition of ethylene synthesis by O-diphenols. This would place phenolase in a unique regulatory role in ethylene synthesis. Perhaps significant in this respect is the fact that the phenolic content of most fruits declines from high levels during early growth to low levels when the fruit is considered to be physiologically mature and, therefore, susceptible to the induction of ripening. This is an attractive hypothesis since it could account for the resistance of immature, detached fruits to ripening previously explained by catabolism of a substance antagonistic to the synthesis or action of ethylene. This may also be pertinent to the delaying action of Alar (N-dimethyl-amino-succinamic acid) on ripening of apple fruits. Alar has been shown to shift glucose catabolism towards the pentose pathway from which aromatic phenols are derived (Chaplin, 1968).

Q. Protease

The presence of protein hydrolysing enzymes in fruit is well documented (Greenberg and Winnick, 1945) and the properties of some of the proteases, for example, papain from papaya fruits, have been extensively studied. The reader is referred to the treatise by Smith and Kimmel (1960).

Protease activity in relation to growth and development of fruits has not received much attention but it certainly must be involved in protein turnover and particularly during the final stages of senescence when protein catabolism is responsible for increases in free amino acids and amides.

R. Transaminase

Transaminases catalyse the transfer of the amino group from an amino acid to an α-oxo acid. Substrate specificity is generally quite broad, but highly specific transaminases are known (Meister, 1960). Although inter-conversion and synthesis of amino acids is presumably a counterpart of protein metabolism during ripening, the role of transaminases in relation to fruit ripening has not been investigated *per se*. Biale (1960) suggested that transaminase activity could account for the incorporation of ^{14}C into aspartic acid in lemons subjected to $^{14}CO_2$ via oxalacetate.

Romani (1962) investigated transaminases in Bartlett pears and established the presence of aspartate-α-oxoglutarate and alanine-α-oxoglutarate trans-aminase in both peel and cortical tissue. Enzyme activity was not studied in relation to fruit development or ripening.

S. Aldolase

The conversion of fructose 1,6-diphosphate to triose phosphates is catalysed by aldolase. Young (1965) reported that the increase in aldolase activity during banana ripening was due to complexing of the enzyme with tannins which are abundant in unripe fruit but not in ripe fruit. Hartman (1963) found an increase in aldolase activity during ripening of apple and pear peel and pulp tissue, but the extraction procedure employed would not circumvent the difficulty noted by Young (1965).

T. Malic Enzyme

Malic enzyme catalyses the oxidative decarboxylation of l-malic, the primary organic acid of apples, certain pear varieties and of many other fruits, resulting in the formation of pyruvic acid which may eventually be oxidized via the tricarboxylic acid cycle or converted to acetaldehyde by pyruvate decarboxylase. See next section. Involvement of the enzyme in malic acid catabolism in apple fruits was indicated in the studies of Neal and Hulme (1958) to account for an increased ability to apple peel tissue to decarboxylate malic acid as fruits ripened. The possibility that the enzyme might function in dark fixation of CO_2 in apple fruits was suggested earlier by Allentoff *et al.* (1954). An increase in apple fruit malic enzyme activity during ripening was demonstrated by Dilley (1962) and Hulme and Wool-torton (1962). The physical properties were investigated following its puri-fication from apple fruit (Dilley, 1966) and were similar to those reported for the enzyme from other sources. Hulme and co-workers have conducted extensive investigations into the change in malic enzyme activity in apple fruit in relation to development, ripening and senescence.

De novo synthesis of malic enzyme during apple and pear ripening has been firmly established from the studies of Frenkel *et al.* (1968) based on amino acid incorporation into the enzyme which was electrophoretically separated from other proteins extracted from fruits at various ripening stages. These investigators established that protein synthesis is required for normal ripening of pome fruits and that the proteins synthesized early in the ripening process are, in fact, enzymes required for ripening. Further, ethylene will not induce ripening if protein synthesis is not allowed to proceed in a normal manner. The studies of Hulme *et al.* (1968) with apple and of Smillie *et al.* (1970) with banana to a large extent confirm and extend the thesis that proteins synthesized during the early stage of ripening are enzymes required to catalyse the ripening process.

U. Pyruvate Decarboxylase

This enzyme decarboxylates pyruvate to acetaldehyde and CO_2. The co-factor requirements are diphosphothiamine (DPT) and a divalent metal ion, and it appears likely that during the decarboxylation of pyruvate a complex between the pyruvate and DPT is involved. Tager and Biale (1957) showed that the activity of this enzyme increased in bananas during ripening. Hulme *et al.* (1963) found an increase in pyruvate carboxylase activity in the peel and pulp of apples during the climacteric especially near the climacteric peak. A similar rise during the climacteric period was found by Hartmann (1962) for pears. It had previously been shown that pyruvate is broken down in apple tissue to acetaldehyde and CO_2, and Hulme *et al.* (1963) suggested that malate metabolism during the climacteric involved the combined action of malic enzyme and pyruvate carboxylase. It has recently been shown that during the climacteric the acetaldehyde formed from pyruvate in apples may be converted to alcohol by alcohol dehydrogenase (Rhodes *et al.*, 1969).

V. O-methyltransferase

The synthesis of lignin, flavonoids and other methoxylated aromatic constituents in plants requires the participation of O-methyltransferase, an enzyme which catalyses the transfer of the methyl group from S-adenosyl-methionine to various methyl acceptors. Nelson and Finkle (1964) studied the action of this enzyme in methylating O-diphenols in apple juice and tissue sections. Methylation, the O-diphenols, prevented their oxidation by poly-phenoloxidase. The prevention of polyphenolase oxidation by phenols by substrate modification may be of practical importance in prevention of oxidative browning during processing of certain plant products. O-methyl-transferase activity was found in cambial scrapings of apple trees (Finkle and Nelson, 1963) and possibly in fruit tissue as well (Nelson and Finkle, 1964).

IV. ENZYME SYNTHESIS IN RELATION TO FRUIT RIPENING

The dramatic physical and chemical changes attending fruit ripening occur as a result of both catabolic and anabolic processes. The marked increase in metabolism coincident with the respiratory climacteric and ripening of many fruits is accompanied by an increase in rate of protein synthesis. In the preceding sections reference was often made to increase in activity of numerous enzymes during fruit development or ripening. In most instances the question of whether the increase in activity was the result of enzyme synthesis, activation, disappearance of inhibitory substances or extraction artifacts arising from marked differences in the physical nature of unripe *versus* ripe tissue was not resolved. Many investigators have speculated that the increase in rate of protein synthesis, the net increase in protein content and the increased activity of several enzymes was the result of synthesis of the enzymes involved in the various ripening reactions. Evidence of amino acid incorporation into protein of avocado at the early climacteric stage, but sharply falling thereafter, led Richmond and Biale (1966b) to propose induction of enzymes which catalyse the climacteric and final breakdown of the cell. According to Hansen (1967), "ripening is a sequential phase in the life of the fruit which requires induction in order to become active, but proceeds according to a predetermined pattern once set in motion". Ethylene is presumed to be the factor which sets the process in motion.

Recent investigations (Richmond and Biale, 1966a, b; Frenkel *et al.*, 1968; Hulme *et al.*, 1968; Smillie *et al.*, 1969) have shown quite conclusively that protein synthesis increases at the onset of ripening and that, if synthesis is inhibited, ripening does not occur. Monitoring the rate or extent of protein synthesis at various stages of fruit development can be achieved in a straightforward manner by measuring the increase in protein nitrogen as was done in the early experiments of Hulme for apples, Hansen for pears and, more recently, Davies and Cocking (1967) for tomatoes. Alternatively, incorporation of a labelled amino acid into the protein fraction has been used as evidence for protein synthesis in ripening avocado (Richmond and Biale, 1966a, b), pear (Frenkel *et al.*, 1968), apple (Hulme *et al.*, 1968), banana (Smillie *et al.*, 1969) and tomato (Davies and Cocking, 1967). Studies of this type can be useful in the determination of the status of protein synthesis if measures are taken to avoid complications and misinterpretation due to possible pool size changes, and if incorporation is differentiated from uptake into the tissue. Fortunately, the above investigators were cognizant of these difficulties, and the data reflects the dynamic change in protein synthesis that, indeed, does occur during fruit ripening. However, direct evidence for the synthesis of a specific enzyme (malic enzyme) was only recently obtained (Frenkel *et al.*, 1968), thus confirming the hypothesis that proteins synthesized early in the ripening process include enzymes involved in the ripening process. Evidence for synthesis of many important enzymes is still lacking, but efforts in many laboratories are currently being directed to this end. For example, Rior *et al.* (1969) have found that phenylalanine ammonia lyase activity increases in grapefruit flavedo when the fruit is treated with ethylene.

Davies and Cocking (1967) investigated protein synthesis in tomato fruit locule tissue and found two main phases of protein synthesis during development. The first phase occurs during the first five weeks of development while the chlorophyll content per cell is increasing. The second phase is during the fifth to sixth week, coinciding with the onset of the respiratory climacteric after which both protein content per cell and respiration rate per unit protein declines.

In an earlier study Davies and Cocking (1965) observed an increase in α-amylase activity associated with the period of rapid starch hydrolysis in tomato fruits. Examination of protein synthesis by various subcellular fractions revealed that during the climacteric (which precedes marked visual ripening changes in the tomato) the rate of mitochondrial and "soluble" protein synthesis increased seven-fold while the chloroplast protein synthesis rate remained fairly steady (Davies and Cocking, 1967). These observations were based on weight of protein in the various fractions and were not confirmed by ^{14}C-incorporation from bicarbonate or amino acids possibly because of amino acid pool size changes. Davies and Cocking conclude that amino acids synthesized during photosynthesis are more directly available for protein synthesis than exogenously supplied amino acids. This is consistent with the concept that two pools exist for amino acids *en route* to protein, one which is termed "active" and is derived from sugars and the other a "storage" pool from which amino acids are much less accessible for protein synthesis.

Recent work at Michigan State University (Frenkel *et al.*, 1968) revealed that protein synthesis is required for normal ripening, and the proteins synthesized early in the ripening process are, in fact, enzymes required for ripening. These studies were conducted with intact pear fruits. Fruit ripening and ethylene synthesis was inhibited when protein synthesis was blocked by treatment with cycloheximide at the early climacteric stage. Cycloheximide became less of a deterrent to ripening as the climacteric developed. Ethylene did not overcome inhibition of ripening by cycloheximide. The types of proteins synthesized change as fruits ripen. Certain proteins which are synthesized at a high rate early in the climacteric are synthesized at a lower rate as ripening proceeds while for other proteins the reverse is true. Malic enzyme is an example of a protein for which synthesis rate increases during the early stage of ripening.

One of the inherent difficulties is the paucity of protein in fruit tissues. Techniques to incorporate labelled amino acid into a sufficient quantity of enzyme protein and subsequently electrophoretically separate and positively identify the enzyme were recently reported (Frenkel *et al.*, 1969). Smillie *et al.* (1969) also employed acrylamide gel electrophoresis to ascertain a progressive change in protein complement during banana ripening.

Ribonucleic acid synthesis is also required for development of the ripening complex (Frenkel *et al.*, 1968). Pear fruits treated with actinomycin-D at the pre-climacteric stage fail to ripen. Actinomycin-D inhibits DNA dependent RNA synthesis. This may mean that the RNA synthesized during the initial stages of ripening represents specific RNA species necessary for synthesis of proteins of the ripening complex. Incorporation of uridine in RNA of mid-climacteric pear fruits is only partially inhibited by actinomycin-D and ripening continues. This may indicate that the RNA of ripening, once synthesized, is fairly stable and continued synthesis is not essential.

Hulme and his associates in England (1968) have investigated metabolic changes in peel tissue discs taken from pre-climacteric apples (see Volume 2, Chapter 10).

Research workers in the Post-Harvest Physiology section of the CSIRO in Sidney, Australia (Smillie *et al.*, 1969), have been investigating the ripening of banana fruit in which they employed a tissue-slice technique to discern the involvement of protein synthesis in the physiological changes of ripening following exposure of the fruits to ethylene (see Chapter 16).

The investigations of Maxie *et al.* (1966) on the inhibiting influence of γ-radiation on ripening of Bartlett pear are pertinent to our present understanding of the involvement of ethylene and protein synthesis in the ripening process. Whereas protein synthesis capacity was not studied by Maxie *et al.*, it has been shown to be a prerequisite for pear ripening (Frenkel *et al.*, 1968). It may be inferred from the data of Maxie *et al.* (1966) that protein synthesis was impaired by γ-radiation. Several lines of evidence support this inference; (a) γ-radiation effectively inhibited ripening only when applied to fruits before ripening began; (b) γ-radiation was progressively less inhibitory when applied to fruits at progressive ripening stages; (c) irradiated unripe fruits produced less ethylene and did not ripen even when supplied with ethylene exogenously. Collectively these observations suggest that ripening capacity or potential was impaired by γ-radiation, but once the potential was allowed to develop irradiation was of little consequence. This reasoning is compatible with the concept that capacity for fruit ripening is manifest by the synthesis of enzymes involved in the ripening process.

There is some evidence that ethylene may exert its influence by regulating the synthesis of RNA. Holm and Abeles (1967) found that ethylene enhanced RNA synthesis in green banana peel sections. They also suggest that ethylene may regulate abscission by regulating the synthesis of specific messenger RNA. This messenger RNA would be that involved in the synthesis of the enzymes necessary for the development of the abscission process.

Many similarities exist in the effects of ethylene on the development of leaf abscission, fruit ripening, and ageing of tissue discs from storage organs. Japanese workers have recently reported (Imaseki *et al.*, 1968) that ethylene induces increased metabolic activities in sliced sweet potato root tissue. Ethylene concentrations as low as 0·1 p.p.m. stimulated the development of peroxidase and phenylalanine ammonia lyase. The influence of ethylene on peroxidase activity was of particular interest because only three or four out of nine isozymes of the peroxidase separated were stimulated, indicating that ethylene may preferentially affect the synthesis of particular enzymes. Studies of Hall and Morgan (1964) several years ago revealed that ethylene treatment of cotton seedlings stimulated peroxidase and IAA-oxidase activity. They suggest that ethylene synthesized in response to 2,4-D treatment may alter the effectiveness of auxin transport or mediate auxin destruction and thereby induce the abscission process.

The mechanism of ethylene action in inducing the ripening of fruits has not been resolved. Also, unresolved is the mechanism of ethylene action in abscission, flowering, and a multitude of morphological effects on vegetative tissues. The biochemical processes attendent to ripening in fruits are similar in many respects to those of leaf abscission and ageing of storage tissues. Knowledge gained from studies of these diverse phenomena may be interchangeable. An understanding of biological activity of growth regulators, both natural and synthetic, in delaying or hastening fruit ripening and senescence would be of great value in developing and incorporating new technology to regulate the harvest period of horticultural commodities. Limited evidence for hormonal regulation of fruit ripening has recently been reported (Dilley, 1969). The practical implications of environmental and chemical regulation of ripening and senescence are obvious and must be considered as a means of conserving food resources which can often be produced abundantly, but which may be unnecessarily wasted as a result of natural deterioration both before and following harvest.

V. SUMMARY

Considerable progress has been made in recent years towards understanding the biochemical processes attending fruit ripening and senescence. Current efforts are still primarily aimed at taking systems apart to find what components are involved in the various processes. Much is yet to be learned about intracellular distribution and function of multiple enzyme systems such as appear to exist in microbodies and their interdependence in the highly co-ordinated cellular metabolism. Future efforts will be increasingly directed at piecing this information together and seeking the mechanism of regulatory control.

REFERENCES

Allentoff, N., Phillips, W. R. and Johnston, F. B. (1954). *J. Sci. Fd Agric.* **5**, 234–8.
Anderson, J. W. (1968). *Phytochem.* **7**, 1973–88.
Anfinsen, C. B. and White, E. H. (1961). *In* "The Enzymes" (P. D. Boyer, H. Lardy and K. Myrback, eds), Vol. 5, pp. 95–122. Academic Press, New York and London.
Axelrod, B. (1947). *J. biol. Chem.* **167**, 57–72.
Bain, J. M. and Mercer, F. V. (1964). *Aust. J. biol. Sci.* **17**, 78–85.
Biale, J. B. (1960). *Adv. Fd Res.* **10**, 293–354.
Biale, J. B. (1964). *Science, N.Y.* **146**, 880–8.
Bolomey, R. A. and Allen, F. W. (1942). *J. biol. Chem.* **144**, 113–19.
Bradbour, R. D., Buhler, D. R. and Wang, C. H. (1958). *Pl. Physiol.* **33**, 396–400.
Breidenbach, R. W., Kahn, A. and Beevers, H. (1968). *Pl. Physiol.* **43**, 705–13.
Burg, S. P. and Thimann, K. V. (1961). *Archs Biochem. Biophys.* **95**, 450–7.
Chaplin, M. H. (1968). Ph.D. Thesis, Michigan State University.
Constantinides, S. M. (1966). Ph.D. Thesis, Michigan State University.
Constantinides, S. M. and Bedford, C. L. (1962). *J. Fd Sci.* **32**, 446–50.
Davies, J. W. and Cocking, E. C. (1965). *Planta* **67**, 242–53.
Davies, J. W. and Cocking, E. C. (1967). *Planta* **76**, 285–305.
de Duve, C. and Bandhuin, P. (1966). *Physiol. Rev.* **46**, 323–57.
de Duve, C., Wattiaux, R. and Wibo, M. (1962). *Biochem. Pharmac.* **9**, 97–116.
Dickinson, D. B. (1962). Ph.D. Thesis, University of Illinois.
Dilley, D. R. (1962). *Nature, Lond.* **196**, 387–8.
Dilley, D. R. (1966). *Pl. Physiol.* **41**, 214–20.
Dilley, D. R. (1969). *Hort. Science* **4**, 111–14.
Ezell, B. D. and Gerhardt, F. (1938). *J. agric. Res.* **56**, 365–86.
Ezell, B. D. and Gerhardt, F. (1942). *J. agric. Res.* **65**, 453–71.
Faust, M. (1965). *Proc. Am. Soc. hort. Sci.* **87**, 1–9.
Finkle, B. J. and Nelson, R. F. (1963). *Biochim. biophys. Acta* **78**, 747–9.
Foda, Y. H. (1957). Ph.D. Thesis, University of Illinois.
Frenkel, C., Klein, I. and Dilley, D. R. (1968). *Pl. Physiol.* **43**, 1146–53.
Frenkel, C., Klein, I. and Dilley, D. R. (1969). *Phytochem.* **8**, 945–55.
Galliard, T. (1968). *Phytochem.* **7**, 1915–22.
Galliard, T., Rhodes, M. J. C., Wooltorton, L. S. C. and Hulme, A. C. (1968). *Phytochem.* **7**, 1453–63.
Goldacre, P. B., Galston, H. W. and Weintraub, R. L. (1953). *Archs Biochem. Biophys.* **43**, 358–73.
Greenberg, D. M. and Winnick, T. (1945). *A. Rev. Biochem.* **14**, 31–68.
Grunwald, C. (1968). *Pl. Physiol.* **43**, 484–8.
Hall, C. B. (1964). *Bot. Gaz.* **125**, 156–7.
Hall, W. C. and Morgan, P. W. (1964). *Colloques Int. Cent. natn. Rech. scient.* 1963, **123**, 727–45.
Hansen, E. (1967). *Proc. Am. Soc. hort. Sci.* **91**, 863–7.
Harel, E. and Mayer, A. M. (1968). *Phytochem.* **7**, 199–204.
Hartmann, C. (1962). *Revue gén. Bot.* **69**, 26–30.
Hartmann, C. (1963). *Phytochem.* **2**, 408–11.
Henderson, R. W., Morton, R. K. and Rawlinson, W. A. (1959). *Biochem. J.* **72**, 340–4.

Hobson, G. E. (1962). *Nature, Lond.* **195**, 804.
Hobson, G. E. (1963). *Biochem. J.* **86**, 358–65.
Hobson, G. E. (1964). *Biochem. J.* **92**, 324–32.
Hobson, G. E. (1967). *J. Sci. Fd Agric.* **18**, 523–6.
Hobson, G. E. (1968). *J. Fd Sci.* **33**, 588–92.
Holden, M. (1965). *J. Sci. Fd Agric.* **16**, 312–15.
Holm, R. E. and Abeles, F. B. (1967). *Pl. Physiol.* **42**, 1094–1102.
Holman, R. T. (1960). *In* "Food Enzymes" (H. W. Schultz, ed.), pp. 75–83. The Avi Publishing Company, Westport, Connecticut.
Hulme, A. C. (1951). *J. Sci. Fd Agric.* **2**, 160–6.
Hulme, A. C. (1958). *Adv. Fd Res.* **8**, 297–412.
Hulme, A. C. and Wooltorton, L. S. C. (1962). *Nature, Lond.* **196**, 388–9.
Hulme, A. C., Jones, J. D. and Wooltorton, L. S. C. (1963). *Proc. Roy. Soc. B.* **158**, 514–35.
Hulme, A. C., Rhodes, M. J. C., Galliard, T. and Wooltorton, L. S. C. (1968). *Pl. Physiol.* **43**, 1154–61.
Hultin, H. O. and Levine, A. S. (1965). *J. Fd Sci.* **30**, 917–21.
Imaseki, H., Uchiyama, M. and Uritani, I. (1968). *Agric. Biol. Chem.* **32**, 387–9.
Jacobson, D. W. and Wang, C. H. (1968). *Pl. Physiol.* **43**, 1959–66.
Jermyn, M. A. and Isherwood, F. A. (1956). *Biochem. J.* **64**, 123–32.
Kay, E., Shannon, L. M. and Lew, J. Y. (1967). *J. Biol. Chem.* **242**, 2470–3.
Kertesz, Z. I. (1938). *J. Fd Sci.* **3**, 481–7.
Kertesz, Z. I., Eucare, M. and Fox, G. (1959). *J. Fd Sci.* **24**, 14–19.
Kidson, E. B. (1958). *N.Z. J. agric. Res.* **1**, 896–902.
Ku, H. S. and Romani, R. J. (1969). *Pl. Physiol.* **44** (in press).
Li, P. H. and Hansen, E. (1964). *Proc. Am. Soc. hort. Sci.* **85**, 100–11.
Lieberman, M. (1969). Personal communication.
Lieberman, M. and Kunishi, A. T. (1967). *Science, N.Y.* **158**, 938.
Lieberman, M. and Mapson, L. W. (1964). *Nature, Lond.* **204**, 243–345.
Looney, N. E. and Patterson, M. E. (1967a). *Nature, Lond.* **214**, 1245–6.
Looney, N. E. and Patterson, M. E. (1967b). *Phytochem.* **6**, 1517–20.
MacDonnell, L. R., Jang, R., Jansen, E. F. and Lineweaver, H. (1950). *Archs Biochem.* **28**, 260–73.
Mapson, L. W. and Wardale, D. A. (1968). *Biochem. J.* **107**, 433–42.
Maris McArthur-Hespe, G. W. F. (1956). *Acta bot. neerl.* **5**, 200–13.
Markakis, P. (1969). Personal communication.
Mason, H. S. (1955). *Adv. Enzymol.* **16**, 105–84.
Matile, P. (1968). *Planta* **79**, 181–96.
Mattoo, A. K. and Modi, V. V. (1969). *Pl. Physiol.* **44**, 308–10.
Maxie, E. L., Sommer, N. F., Muller, C. J. and Rae, H. L. (1966). *Pl. Physiol.* **41**, 437–42.
McCready, R. M. and McComb, E. A. (1954). *J. Fd Sci.* **19**, 530–5.
Meigh, D. F. and Hulme, A. C. (1965). *Phytochem.* **4**, 863–71.
Meister, H. (1960). *In* "The Enzymes" (P. D. Boyer, H. Lardy and K. Myrback, eds), pp. 193–217. Academic Press, New York and London.

Meynhardt, J. T., Maxie, E. C. and Romani, R. J. (1965a). *S. Afr. J. agric. Sci.* **8,** 291–2.

Meynhardt, J. T., Romani, R. J. and Maxie, R. C. (1965b). *S. Afr. J. agric. Sci.* **8,** 691–702.

Miller, L. A. and Romani, R. J. (1966). *Pl. Physiol.* **41,** 411–14.

Nagel, C. W. and Patterson, M. E. (1967). *J. Fd Sci.* **32,** 294–7.

Neal, G. E. and Hulme, A. C. (1958). *J. exp. Bot.* **9,** 142–57.

Nelson, R. F. and Finkle, B. J. (1964). *Phytochem.* **3,** 321–5.

Palmer, J. K. (1963). *Pl. Physiol.* **38,** 508–13.

Pithawala, H. R., Sovur, G. R. and Sreenivasan, A. (1948). *Archs Biochem.* **17,** 235–48.

Pollard, A. and Kieser, M. F. (1951). *J. Sci. Fd Agric.* **2,** 30–6.

Ponting, J. D. (1960). *In* "Food Enzymes" (H. W. Schultz, ed.), pp. 105–24. The Avi Publishing Company, Westport, Connecticut.

Pratt, H. K. and Goeschl, J. D. (1969). *A. Rev. Pl. Physiol.* **20,** (in press).

Rhodes, M. J. C. and Wooltorton, L. S. C. (1967). *Phytochem.* **6,** 1–12.

Rhodes, M. J. C., Wooltorton, L. S. C. and Hulme, A. C. (1969). *Qualitas Pl. Mater vég.* **19,** 167.

Richmond, A. and Biale, J. B. (1966a). *Pl. Physiol.* **41,** 1247–53.

Richmond, A. and Biale, J. B. (1966b). *Archs Biochem. Biophys.* **115,** 211–14.

Richmond, A. and Biale, J. B. (1967). *Biochim. biophys. Acta* **138,** 625–7.

Rior, J., Monselise, S. P. and Kahan, R. S. (1969). *Pl. Physiol., Lancaster* **44,** 631.

Romani, R. J. (1962). *Pl. Physiol.* **37,** 523–6.

Saunders, B. C., Holmes-Siedle, A. G. and Stark, B. P. (1964). "Peroxidase". Butterworths, Washington.

Schmidt, G. and Laskowski, M. (1961). *In* "The Enzymes" (P. D. Boyer, H. Lardy, K. Myrback, eds), Vol 5, pp. 3–35. Academic Press, New York and London.

Shannon, L. M., Kay, E. and Lew, J. Y. (1966). *J. Biol. Chem.* **241,** 2166–72.

Smillie, R. M., Palmer, J. K., Brady, C. J. and O'Connell, P. B. H. (1970). *Phytochem.* (in press).

Smith, E. L. and Kimmel, J. R. (1960). *In* "The Enzymes" (P. D. Boyer, H. Lardy and K. Myrback, eds), Vol 4, pp. 133–73. Academic Press, New York and London.

Sterling, C. (1961). *J. Fd Sci.* **26,** 95–8.

Stumpf, P. K. (1965). *In* "Plant Biochemistry" (J. Bonner and J. E. Varner, eds), pp. 323–45. Academic Press, New York and London.

Stumpf, P. K. and Barber, G. A. (1957). *J. Biol. Chem.* **227,** 407–17.

Tager, J. M. and Biale, J. B. (1957). *Physiologia Pl.* **10,** 79–85.

Tappel, H. L., Stewart, P. L. and Shibka, S. (1963). Ciba Fdn Symp. Lysosomes 1963, 78.

Thatcher, R. W. (1915). *J. agric. Res.* **5,** 103–16.

Tolbert, N. E., Oeser, A., Kisaki, T., Hageman, R. H. and Yamazaki, R. K. (1968). *J. biol. Chem.* **243,** 5179–84.

Walker, J. R. L. and Hulme, A. C. (1966). *Phytochem.* **5,** 259–62.

Wang, C. H., Doyle, W. P. and Ramsey, J. C. (1962). *Pl. Physiol.* **37,** 1–7.

Weissmann, G. (1964). *Fedn Proc.* **23,** 1038–44.

Weurman, C. (1954a). *Acta Bot. neerl.* **3,** 100–7.

Weurman, C. (1954b). *Acta Bot. neerl.* **3,** 108–13.

Wooltorton, L. S. C., Jones, J. D. and Hulme, A. C. (1965). *Nature, Lond.* **207,** 999–1000.

Yang, S. F. (1967). *Archs Biochem. Biophys.* **122,** 481–7.

Yang, S. F. and Stumpf, P. K. (1965). *Biochem. biophys. Acta* **98,** 19–26.

Young, R. E. (1965). *Archs Biochem. Biophys.* **111,** 174–80.

Chapter 9

Lipids

P. MAZLIAK

Faculté des Sciences, Sorbonne, Paris, France

I. INTRODUCTION

A great number of publications concerning fruit lipids have appeared in recent years. Interest in these constituents arose initially from the fact that the fruits of some plant species (palm, olive, avocados) accumulate large

TABLE I. Lipid content of some fruits

Common name	Taxonomic name	Lipid content expressed as % of the dry matter weight	Nature of reserve substances in the pericarp
Oleaginous			
Oil-palm trees	*Eleaeis guineensis*	74–81	Fats
Avocado	*Persea americana*	30–70	Oil
Olive	*Olea europea*	35–70	Oil
Laurel	*Laurus nobilis*	24–55	Fats
Non-oleaginous			
Apple	*Pirus malus*	0·06	Carbohydrates, organic acids
Banana	*Musa cavendishi*	0·1	Carbohydrates, organic acids
Grapes	*Vitis vinifera*	0·2	Carbohydrates, organic acids

oleaginous reserves during their development (Table I.) Consequently these fruits have always constituted an important source of fats for human nutrition. Secondly, the physiology of several non-oleaginous fruits (apples, pears, bananas), of great commercial value because of their carbohydrate reserves or their high vitamin content, has been studied recently in great detail, and it was unavoidable that interest developed in the lipid metabolism of these organs.

II. MAIN LIPID COMPONENTS OF FRUITS

There is no simple definition of lipids, grouping the properties common to all the molecular types ranged in the class of fatty substances.* However, lipids are generally defined as biochemical compounds which (a) contain one or more long-chain fatty acids and (b) are less soluble in water than in various organic solvents such as chloroform, ether, etc. Lipids are then hydrophobic compounds.

In living cells, however, many lipid compounds (particularly the *phospholipids*) are bound to proteins by non-covalent bonds (although these are not very strong, they are very numerous) and it is impossible to extract these complex lipids by simply extracting the fresh matter with apolar solvents. One must, on the contrary, employ polar solvent mixtures (that is, chloroform-methanol) (Folch *et al.*, 1957), or ether-isopropanol (Nichols, 1964) to break the bonds between proteins and lipids and extract the lipids integrated in cellular structures, such as living membranes. On the other hand, the reserve lipids (fats and oils) or the natural-coating lipids (waxes) may be directly extracted by extracting the dried biological matter with a very apolar solvent (petroleum ether, for instance) (Huelin and Gallop, 1951a).

A. Fatty Acids in Fruits

Fatty acids are aliphatic compounds bearing a carboxylic acid group at one end of their molecular chain. The main fatty acids identified so far in the pericarp lipids belong to the three following classes: (a) saturated normal fatty acids; (b) unsaturated normal fatty acids; (c) hydroxyacids. The principal fatty acids of each class found in fruits are listed in Table II.

Examples of the fatty acid composition of the pericarp lipids from some fruits are shown in Table III. Analyses of fatty acid compositions are conducted principally by means of gas chromatography of the methyl esters of

---

* Because of the lack of precise terminology, "lipids" and "fats" have been frequently used interchangeably in recent publications. Lipid chemists and biochemists now tend to define "lipids" as above and to reserve the term "fats" for the constituents of relatively large pools of lipid (usually triglycerides) which serve as reserves of carbon and energy, for example, in oil-rich seeds and fruits.

TABLE II. Main fatty acids of fruits

Abbreviation[a]	Systematic name	Common name	Examples of plants in which the fruit coat lipids contain a high proportion of the fatty acid[b]
1. Normal saturated fatty acids			
$C_{10:0}$	decanoic	capric	Palm
$C_{12:0}$	dodecanoic	lauric	Laurels
$C_{14:0}$	tetradecanoic	myristic	Capeberries (*Myristica cordifolia*)
$C_{16:0}$	hexadecanoic	palmitic	Palm (in fact all fruit-fats contain this acid)
$C_{18:0}$	octadecanoic	stearic	Sumac (*Rhus succedanea*)
$C_{26:0}$	hexacosanoic	cerotic	⎫ These acids are present in waxes
$C_{28:0}$	octacosanoic	montanic	⎬ from numerous fruits (apples,
$C_{30:0}$	triacontanoic	melissic	⎭ grapes, etc.)
2. Normal unsaturated fatty acids			
$C_{16:1}\Delta^9$	hexadecenoic	palmitoleic	Palm
$C_{18:1}\Delta^9$	octadecenoic	oleic	All fruit lipids contain this acid— abundant in avocado and olive
$C_{18:2}\Delta^{9,12}$	octadecadienoic	linoleic	Avocado, olive
$C_{18:3}\Delta^{9,12,15}$	octadecatrienoic	α-linolenic	Dukudu (*Celastrus paniculatus*) Ivy (*Laurus communis*)
3. Hydroxyacids			
10, 16-dihydroxy-hexadecanoic acid			⎫
10, 18-dihydroxy-octadecanoic acid			⎬ These acids are present in the cutin of fruit epidermis (for
9, 10, 18-trihydroxy-octadecanoic acid			⎬ example, apple cutin)
18-hydroxy-octadec-9 enoic acid			⎭

[a] The number immediately after C refers to the number of carbon atoms in the molecule; the number after the colon refers to the number of double bonds. The figures after Δ indicate the position in the chain of the first carbon atom of each double bond, numbering from the carboxyl carbon atom.

[b] Compiled from data of Eckey (1954), Hilditch and Williams (1964), and Mazliak (1963a).

fatty acids; positive identifications are best obtained by combining gas chromatography on several stationary phases with complementary methods such as thin-layer chromatography, mass spectrometry or ultra-violet and infra-red spectrophotometry.

It is important to point out that the fatty acid composition of pericarp tissues is generally different from the fatty acid composition of the seeds enclosed inside the fruit proper. This point is strikingly illustrated when the pericarps contain abundant oily reserves. Some examples of these differences in fatty acid composition are given in Table IV. Generally, fatty acids are not free in the cells but are esterified with hydroxyl groups of several different types of compounds. Some molecular types of fruit lipids are presented in Fig. 1.

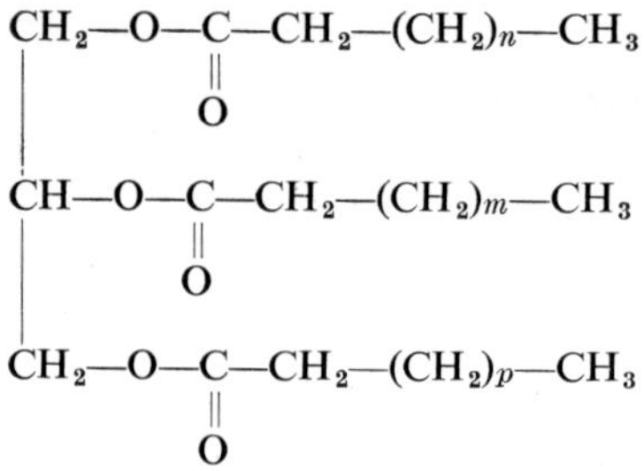

$$CH_2-O-C-CH_2-(CH_2)_n-CH_3$$
$$\underset{\displaystyle O}{\overset{\displaystyle \|}{}}$$

$$CH-O-C-CH_2-(CH_2)_m-CH_3$$
$$\underset{\displaystyle O}{\overset{\displaystyle \|}{}}$$

$$CH_2-O-C-CH_2-(CH_2)_p-CH_3$$
$$\underset{\displaystyle O}{\overset{\displaystyle \|}{}}$$

Triglycerides

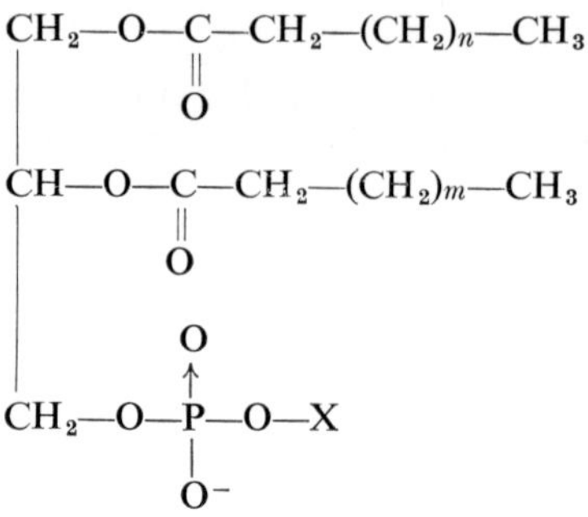

$$CH_2-O-C-CH_2-(CH_2)_n-CH_3$$
$$\underset{\displaystyle O}{\overset{\displaystyle \|}{}}$$

$$CH-O-C-CH_2-(CH_2)_m-CH_3$$
$$\underset{\displaystyle O}{\overset{\displaystyle \|}{}}$$

$$CH_2-O-P-O-X$$

Phospholipids

X = —H phosphatidic acid
= —CH_2—CH_2—NH_2
  phosphatidyléthanolamine
= —CH_2—CH_2—$N^+(CH_3)_3$
  phosphatidylcholine
etc.

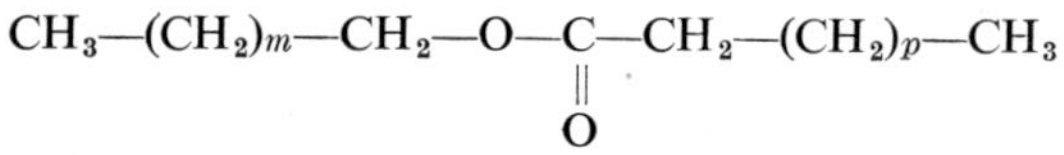

$$CH_3-(CH_2)_m-CH_2-O-C-CH_2-(CH_2)_p-CH_3$$
$$\underset{\displaystyle O}{\overset{\displaystyle \|}{}}$$

Wax Ester

$$CH_2-(CH_2)_m-CH-(CH_2)_p-C-O\ldots$$

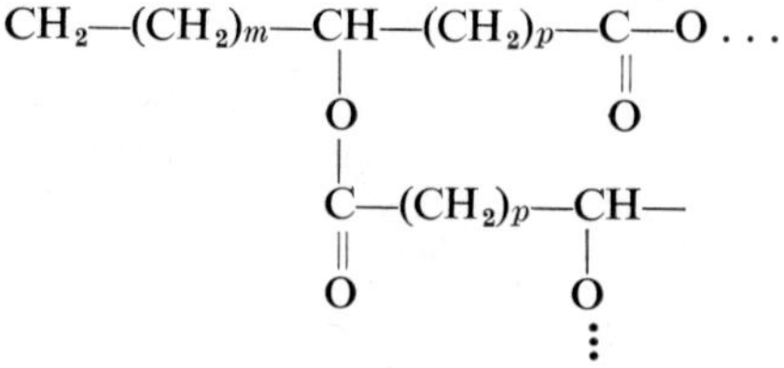

Cutin Estolide

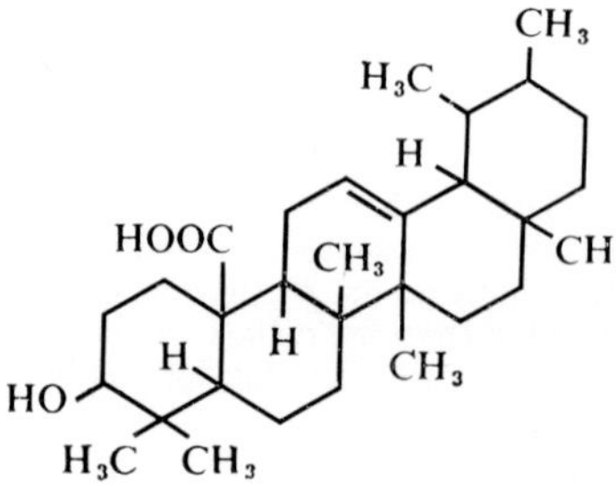

Ursolic Acid (triterpenoid compound)

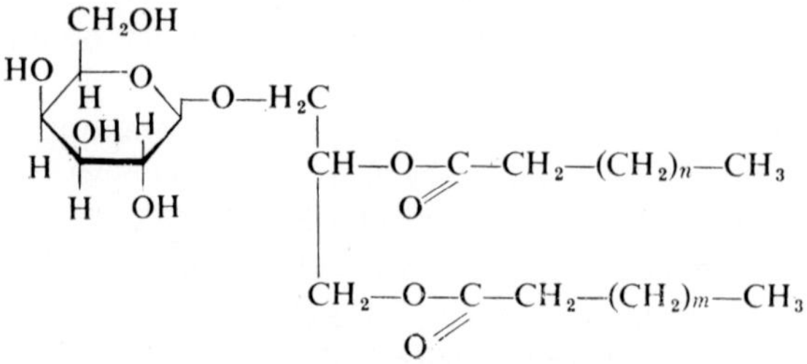

Galactolipid (monogalactosyldiglyceride)

FIG. 1. Some molecular types of fruit lipids.

TABLE III. Fatty acid composition of pericarp lipids from several fruits (expressed as % of the weight of total fatty acids)

Fatty acids	Palm[a]	Avocado[b] mesocarp	Olive[a]	Laurel[a]	Apple[c] pulp	Banana[d] pulp	Cape[a] berry wax	Dukudu[a]
$C_{12:0}$	trace	trace	—	0–2·7	0·6	trace	0·3	—
$C_{14:0}$	2·2	trace	1·2	—	0·9	0·6	47	2·7
$C_{16:0}$	39·2	13–16·7	15·6	20·3–24·3	30	57·8	51·8	23·8
$C_{16:1}$	1·1	3–5·1	1·6	—	0·5	8·3	—	—
$C_{18:0}$	4·3	trace	2·0	—	6·4	2·5	0·3	3·7
$C_{18:1}$	45·1	67–72	64·6	56–63	18·5	15	0·6	27·8
$C_{18:2}$	8	10·4–11·3	15·0	14–22	42·5	10·6	—	17·4
$C_{18:3}$	—	trace	—	—	1·0	3·6	—	15·7

[a] From the data listed in Eckey (1954).
[b] From Mazliak (1965a).
[c] From Mazliak and Pommier-Miard (1963).
[d] From Grosbois and Mazliak (1964).

TABLE IV. Differences in fatty acid compositions between pericarp and seed lipids from the same fruits

Fatty acids	Apple[a]		Avocado[b]		Oil-palm[c]		Ivy[d]	
	Pericarp	Seed	Mesocarp	Seed	Pericarp	Seed	Pericarp	Seed
$C_{12:0}$	—	—	—	—	trace	49·0	—	trace
$C_{14:0}$	0·9	trace	trace	0·8	1·0	16·3	—	trace
$C_{16:0}$	30	8–10	13–17	22·0	44·6	8·5	14·4	5·9
$C_{16:1}$	0·5	trace	3–5	3·2	0·4	trace	23	0·3
$C_{18:0}$	6·4	trace	trace	0·6	5·6	2·5	trace	trace
$C_{18:1}$	18·5	25–30	67–72	25·0	38·0	13·3	39·7	68·0
$C_{18:2}$	42·5	60–70	10–12	41·5	9·8	2·4	21·3	12
$C_{18:3}$	1·0	trace	trace	5·1	0·2	—	1·6	0·7

[a] From Mazliak and Pommier-Miard (1963).
[b] From Mazliak (1965a).
[c] From Eckey (1954).
[d] From Grosbois (1968).

B. Reserve Lipids of Fruits

Reserve lipids are mainly triglycerides, forming oily inclusions in the cells (Sorokin, 1967). The mixtures of natural triglycerides are very complex since a number of different fatty acids are present in the cell and each may be esterified with any one of the three hydroxyl groups of the glycerol molecule. For a mixture of n fatty acids present in the cell, one can distinguish theoretically $\dfrac{n^3 + 3n^2 + 2n}{6}$ triglycerides of different fatty acid composition or $\dfrac{n^3 + n^2}{2}$

species of triglycerides (including positional isomers) or n^3 species of triglycerides (including positional and optical isomers). For instance, a simple mixture of two fatty acids: palmitic acid (P) and oleic acid (O), could give the following six triglycerides:

$\begin{bmatrix} -P \\ -P \\ -P \end{bmatrix}$	$\begin{bmatrix} -P \\ -P \\ -O \end{bmatrix}$	$\begin{bmatrix} -P \\ -O \\ -P \end{bmatrix}$	$\begin{bmatrix} -P \\ -O \\ -O \end{bmatrix}$	$\begin{bmatrix} -O \\ -P \\ -O \end{bmatrix}$	$\begin{bmatrix} -O \\ -O \\ -O \end{bmatrix}$
tripalmitin	1-2-di-palmito 3-olein	1-3-di-palmito 2-olein	1-palmito 2-3-diolein	2-palmito 1-3-diolein	triolein

positional isomers   positional isomers

The complex mixtures of natural triglycerides are now analysed by means of fractional recrystallizations or, more directly, by means of chromatographic techniques, gas chromatography at very high temperatures (Kuksis and McCarthy, 1962) or column- or thin-layer chromatography on $AgNO_3$ impregnated adsorbents (Morris, 1964). As examples, the triglyceride compositions of two pericarp oils are given in Table V. The distribution of fatty

TABLE V. Triglyceride composition of two pericarp oils[a]

	Fatty acids	Triglyceride (moles %) molecular species	
Olive oil	S = 18·8%	SOO	57
	($C_{14:0}$, $C_{16:0}$, $C_{18:0}$)	SOL	4
	U = 81·2%	LOO	34
	$C_{16:1}$ = 1·6%	OOO	5
	$C_{18:1}$ = 64·6%		
	$C_{18:2}$ = 15 %		————
			100%
Palm oil	S = 47·4%	SSS	6·5
	($C_{14:0}$, $C_{16:0}$, $C_{18:0}$)	SSO	43
	U = 49·6%	SOO	44·5
	$C_{16:1}$ = 0·8%	SOL	
	$C_{18:1}$ = 38·6%	OOL	6
	$C_{18:2}$ = 10·3%	OOO	
			————
			100%

[a] From Hilditch and Williams, 1964.
Abbreviations used: S = saturated fatty acid; U = unsaturated fatty acid; L = linoleic acid; O = oleic acid.

acids between the various triglyceride molecular species follow the rules recently discussed by Hilditch and Williams (1964).

Diglycerides are intermediates in the metabolism of phospholipids and triglycerides. The presence of traces of diglycerides has been detected recently in apple parenchyma (Mazliak, 1967a).

C. Lipids of the Natural Coating of Fruits

The lipids which accumulate in the outer epidermal membranes of fruits form the cuticles and play a major role in the control of transpiration, in protecting the organs against weather inclemencies or against attacks from insects and parasites (Martin, 1964). The cuticle lipids form two classes— waxes and cutin.

1. *Fruit waxes*

Several reviews have recently been devoted to plant waxes (Kreger, 1958; Eglinton and Hamilton, 1967; Mazliak, 1968). In the restricted biochemical meaning of the term, waxes contain a particular kind of lipid which is an ester of high molecular weight resulting from the combination of a fatty acid with a long chain monoalcohol. In the broad and common meaning of the term, *natural* waxes contain not only wax esters but also hydrocarbons (paraffins, olefins), fatty acids (normal, hydroxylated, ethylenic), ketones, alcohols (primary and secondary), aldehydes, etc. All these compounds have high molecular weights and similar physical properties. They are water-repellent substances, insoluble in water, melting between 40 and 100°C and, at ordinary temperatures, are often crystalline or pseudo-crystalline. This last property allows the study of cuticular waxes by X-ray diffraction techniques (Kreger, 1948). The main compounds present in cuticular waxes have chain lengths ranging from C_{20} to C_{35}. The components possessing an oxygenated functional group on the terminal carbon atom (for example, primary alcohols, fatty acids, etc.) usually have an even number of carbon atoms. On the other hand, paraffins, secondary alcohols and ketones generally have an odd number of carbon atoms.

The detailed composition of fourteen waxes from fruits has been described by Mazliak (1963a). The results of two recent analyses of fruit wax components, by means of gas chromatography, are given in Table VI. Fruit waxes often contain cyclic compounds of triterpenoid type. Ursolic acid (Fig. 1) is widespread on the surface of apples, pears, grapes, etc.

2. *Fruit cutin*

Although cutin forms the major part of plant cuticles, its chemical nature has long remained obscure. The difficulty in analysing this substance lies in

TABLE VI. Chemical composition of two fruit waxes

% major constituents[a] in each fraction (columns C12–C35):

Fractions	% total waxes	C12	C14	C16	C18	C20	C22	C23	C24	C25	C26	C27	C28	C29	C30	C31	C32	C33	C34	C35
Apple fruits[b]																				
Paraffins	33							trace	trace	trace	trace	2	trace	96.5	trace	trace				
Alcohols	19											trace	28.8	trace	5.25					
Diols	2.5					trace	30		15.8		35		10							
Saturated fatty acid	14.4	trace	trace	62.5	13.9	3	1	trace	1	trace	2	trace	4.5	trace	8					
Unsaturated fatty acid	25			0.5	99.5															
Hydroxyacids	6	11.4	8.9	10	11	7.7	5													
Grapes[c]																				
Paraffins	1.2	trace	trace	trace	trace	trace	trace	5.7	3.5	17.2	3.8	19.5	2.6	22.1	2.4	14.8	1.1	1.9	—	0.4
Alcohols, free	51.4					0.1	1.3	1.2	14.2	5.7	42.6	5.3	21.3	4.4	3.3		trace			
Alcohols, esterified	11.5					0.2	1.7	1.7	11.6	6.2	44.4	6.6	20.7	2.5	1.2	0.5	trace			
Aldehydes, free	15.4			0.2	0.8	1.7	0.4	0.6	12.4	2.8	41.7	2.5	21.8	1.1	7.5		2.8		trace	
Acids, free	9		0.4	4.6	9.5	12.2	7.8	1.4	12.8	2.6	18.0	1.2	10.6	1.0	3.3	2.3	2.0			
Acids, esterified	11.5		0.4	5.3	18.1	31.7	18.0	1.5	9.8	1.4	3.9	0.7	2.3	0.7	1.2	0.3	1.2			

[a] These major constituents are defined by their respective chain lengths.
[b] From Mazliak, 1963b
[c] From Radler and Horn, 1965.

its poor solubility in most organic solvents. Since they are very rich in secondary oxygenated functions, the long chain constituents of cutin are firmly fixed by cross-polymerization in the membrane.

The chemical study of cutin can only commence after the depolymerization of the main components, usually by saponification. It has been shown that these components are hydroxyacids and that during the process of polymerization an acidic function from one molecular chain may esterify with an alcoholic function from another molecular chain to form "estolides".

In 1963, Baker and Martin isolated several hydroxyacids from apple cutin and *Euonymus* leaf cutin. These acids were used as standards to identify the ether-soluble acids of the cutin from different fruits, by means of reversed phase chromatography on castor oil impregnated paper. Their results are given in Table VII. It should be noted that ether-soluble acids form, in general,

TABLE VII. Ether-soluble acids in the cutin from some fruits[a]

Fruit	9, 10, 18 trihydroxy-octadecanoic acid	10, 16 dihydroxy-hexadecanoic acid	10, 18 dihydroxy-octadecanoic acid	18-hydroxy-octadecanoic acid
Gooseberry		+++		+
Blackcurrant		+++		+
Pear				
Conference	+++	+++	+	++
Gladfield	+++	+++	+	++
Apple				
Bramley	+++	+++		++
Cox	+++	+++	+	++
Worcester	+++	+++	+	++
Dove	+++	+++	+	+
Dabinett	+++	+++	+	+

[a] From Baker and Martin, 1963.

80% of the total cutin acids. The remaining acids in the cutin, from apple for instance, are hydroxy fatty acids with some degree of unsaturation.

A reinvestigation of the constituent acids of apple cuticle was undertaken recently by Eglinton and Hunneman (1968), using preparative thin-layer chromatography and mass spectrometry of trimethylsilyl ethers of the methyl-esters. The location of the double bonds was determined by a novel method involving hydroxylation followed by gas-chromatography-mass spectrometry of the trimethylsilyl ethers of the resulting vicinal dihydroxy compounds. The results of this study are presented in Table VIII. The results

TABLE VIII. Identified cutin-acids of apple cuticle[a,b]

Acid	% total cutin acids
Monobasic acids	
tetradecanoic	·01
palmitic	·29
oleic + linoleic	·64
stearic	·06
eicosanoic	·06
docosanoic	·10
methyl tetradecanoic	·02
Dibasic acids	
hexadecane-1,16-dioic	·22
heptadecadiene-1,17-dioic	} ·09
heptadec-9-ene-1,17-dioic	
octadeca-9,12-diene-1,18-dioic	·06
octadec-9-ene-1,18-dioic	·28
octadecane-1,18-dioic	·04
Monohydroxy monobasic acids	
16-hydroxyhexadecanoic	8·0
18-hydroxy-octadeca-9,12-dienoic	13·0
18-hydroxy-octadec-9-enoic	5·0
Vic-dihydroxy dibasic acids	
8,9-dihydroxyheptadecane-1,17-dioic	·18
9,10-dihydroxyoctadecane-1,18-dioic	·06
Dihydroxy monobasic acids	
10,16-dihydroxyhexadecanoic	24·0
Trihydroxy monobasic acids	
9,10,18-trihydroxyoctadecenoic	3·0
erythro-9,10,18-trihydroxyoctadecanoic	7·0
threo-9,10,18-trihydroxyoctadecanoic	17·0

[a] Non-identified acids are not quoted.
[b] From Eglinton and Hunneman, 1968.

of previous workers are partly confirmed but the presence of 18-hydroxy octadecanoic and 10,18-dihydroxy octadecanoic acids was not detected. Previous identification of these acids was based on TLC Rf values which do not give absolute identifications.

D. Living Membrane Lipids of Fruits (Phospholipids and Glycolipids)

Lipoprotein membranes of cells and subcellular organelles are very rich in polar lipids—phospholipids and glycolipids. Phospholipids also form microscopic inclusions (spherosomes) in the cytoplasms of many fruit cells (Sorokin, 1967).

These complex lipids are amphipathic and contain a polar "head" (ionizable or polarizable chemical groups) and a non-polar "tail" (hydrophobic long-chain fatty acids). Such amphipathic molecules accumulate at the boundaries of different cellular compartments as components of lipoprotein membranes (see Chapman, 1968).

The lipids of cytoplasmic or mitochondrial membranes are mainly phospholipids. The most commonly encountered molecular types are phosphatidylcholine, phosphatidylethanolamine, phosphatidylserine, phosphatidylinositol, phosphatidylglycerol, diphosphatidylglycerol and phosphatidic acid. Each molecule comprises the phosphatidyl root (that is, a phosphorylated 1,2-diglyceride) linked in a phosphate ester bond to a hydroxyl group of serine, ethanolamine, choline etc. (see also Fig. 1).

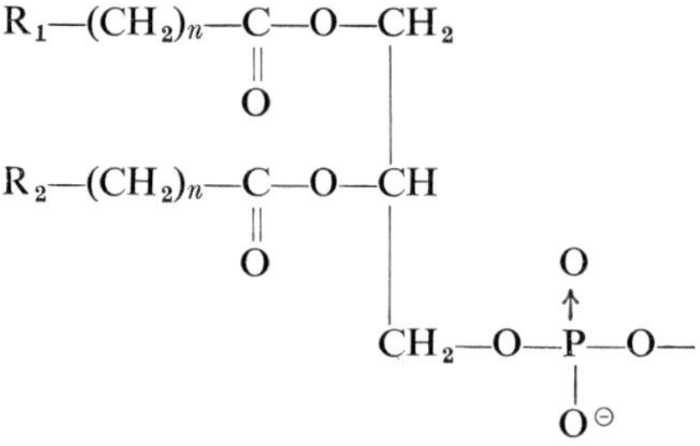

R_1—$(CH_2)_n$—C—O—CH_2
‖
O

R_2—$(CH_2)_n$—C—O—CH
‖
O

CH_2—O—P—O—
↑
O
|
$O^{\ominus}$

The phosphatidyl root
of phospholipids

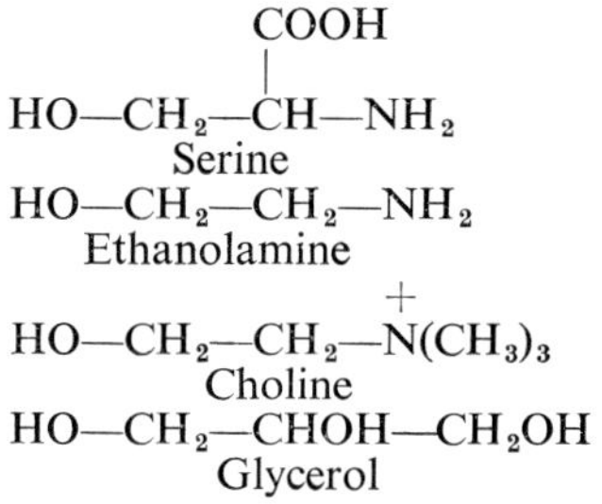

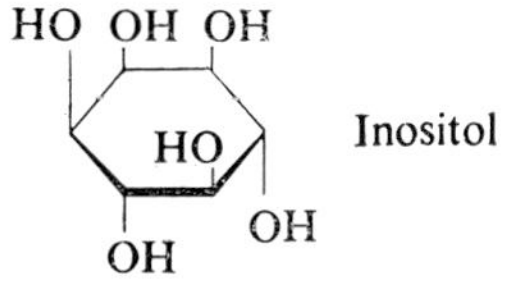

COOH
|
HO—CH_2—CH—NH_2
Serine

HO—CH_2—CH_2—NH_2
Ethanolamine

$\overset{+}{}$
HO—CH_2—CH_2—$N(CH_3)_3$
Choline

HO—CH_2—CHOH—CH_2OH
Glycerol

HO OH OH

HO

OH

OH

Inositol

Some alcoholic components
of phospholipids

If we consider a particular phospholipid, for example, dilinoleyl-phosphatidylglycerol:

H_3—$(CH_2)_4$—HC=CH—CH_2—HC=CH—$(CH_2)_7$—C—O—CH_2
‖
O

H_3—$(CH_2)_4$—HC=CH—CH_2—HC=CH—$(CH_2)_7$—C—O—CH
‖
O

CH_2—O—P—O—CH_2
↑
$^{\ominus}$O

CHOH

CH_2OH

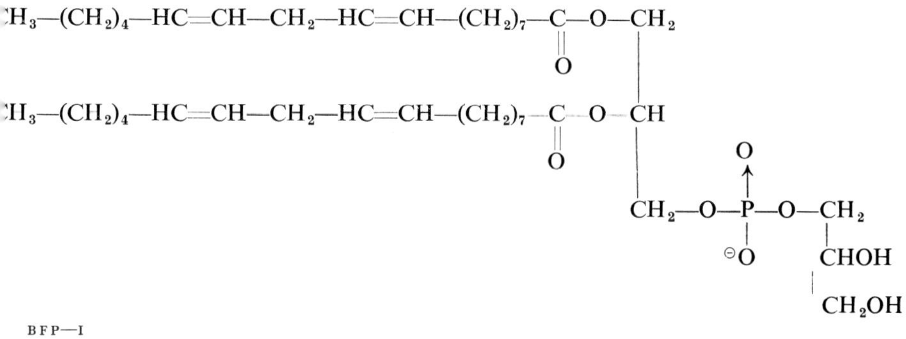

We see that the "polar head" is phosphorylglycerol and that the "non-polar tail" is the 1,2-dilinoleyl-diglyceride. Where the polar head is just limited to PO_4H_3, we get the simplest of all phospholipids, that is, phosphatidic acid:

$$R_1-(CH_2)_n-\underset{\underset{O}{\|}}{C}-O-CH_2$$

$$R_2-(CH_2)_n-\underset{\underset{O}{\|}}{C}-O-CH$$

$$CH_2-O-\underset{\underset{O^\ominus}{|}}{\overset{\overset{O}{\wedge}}{P}}-O^\ominus$$

Metabolic pathways involving the biosynthesis or the degradation of these complex lipids have been studied particularly in bacteria and in rat liver tissue (Ansell and Hawthorne, 1964). The main biosynthetic pathways can be summarized as follows. Starting with glycerol-3-phosphate derived by hydrogenation from dihydroxyacetonephosphate (a direct product from glycolysis), two successive esterifications give phosphatidic acid:

glycerol-3-phosphate + 2 acyl-CoA→phosphatidic acid + 2 CoA-SH

Phosphatidic acid loses its phosphoryl group to give a 1,2-diglyceride:

Phosphatidic acid→1,2-diglyceride + PO_4H_3

This diglyceride may then be engaged in one of the three following pathways:
    (i) it may be esterified by a third acyl-CoA to give a triglyceride:

1,2-diglyceride + acyl-CoA→triglyceride + CoA-SH

    (ii) it may receive a phosphorylated alcoholic complement from CDP*-choline, or CDP-ethanolamine or CDP-serine. For example,

1,2-diglyceride + CDP-choline→phosphatidylcholine + CMP

    (iii) it may combine with CTP to give CDP-diglyceride, the precursor of acidic phospholipids, namely phosphatidylglycerol or diphosphatidylglycerol:

1,2-diglyceride + CTP→CDP-diglyceride + PO_4H_3

CDP-diglyceride + glycerol-3-phosphate→phosphatidylglycerolphosphate + CMP

phosphatidylglycerolphosphate→phosphatidylglycerol + PO_4H_3

phosphatidylglycerol + CDP-diglyceride→diphosphatidylglycerol + CMP

* CTP, CDP, CMP equals, respectively, cytidine tri-, di-, mono-phosphate.

The structure of diphosphatidylglycerol has been recently established.

$$_1-(CH_2)_n-\underset{\underset{O}{\|}}{C}-O-CH_2$$

$$_2-(CH_2)_n-\underset{\underset{O}{\|}}{C}-O-CH$$

$$CH_2-O-\underset{\underset{O^\ominus}{|}}{\overset{\overset{O}{\wedge}}{P}}-O-CH_2-CHOH-CH_2-O-\underset{\underset{O^\ominus}{|}}{\overset{\overset{O}{\wedge}}{P}}-O-CH_2$$

$$CH_2-O-\underset{\underset{O}{\|}}{C}-(CH_2)_n-R_3$$

$$CH-O-\underset{\underset{O}{\|}}{C}-(CH_2)_n-R_4$$

The breakdown of phospholipids is catalysed by phospholipases, of which four types are known. Phospholipase A removes a fatty acid to give lyso-phospholipids:

Phosphatidylcholine $\xrightarrow{\text{H}_2\text{O, phospholipase A}}$ lysophosphatidylcholine + fatty acid

Phospholipase B (lysophospholipase) removes the remaining fatty acid of lysocompounds:

lysophosphatidylcholine $\xrightarrow{\text{H}_2\text{O, phospholipase B}}$ glycerylphosphorylcholine + fatty acid

Phospholipase C hydrolyses the ester bond between the carbon 3 of glycerol and phosphoric acid:

phosphatidylcholine $\xrightarrow{\text{H}_2\text{O, phospholipase C}}$ 1,2-diglyceride + phosphoryl-choline

Finally phospholipase D hydrolyses the ester bond between the phosphatidyl root of the molecules and the alcoholic complements:

phosphatidylcholine $\xrightarrow{\text{H}_2\text{O, phospholipase D}}$ phosphatidic acid + choline

Phosphalisase D may also catalyse some transphosphatidylation reactions:

phosphatidylcholine + glycerol $\xrightarrow{\text{phospholipase D}}$ phosphatidylglycerol + choline

The lamellae of chloroplasts are remarkable in containing only one kind of phospholipid, that is, phosphatidylglycerol in addition to three different glycolipids, which are also "polar lipids". These complex lipids comprise the same "non-polar tails" as phospholipids, that is, 1,2-diglycerides, but the "polar heads" are represented by one or two monosaccharide molecules. The three main glycolipids of chloroplasts are monogalactosyl-diglyceride, digalactosyl-diglyceride, and sulpholipid. A trigalactosyl-diglyceride has recently been isolated from potatoes (Galliard, 1969).

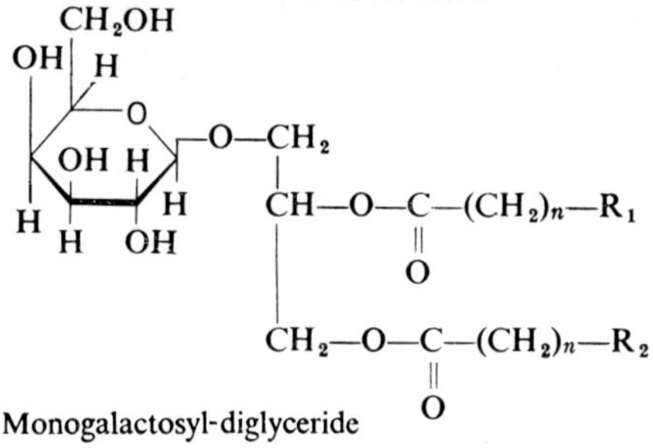

Monogalactosyl-diglyceride

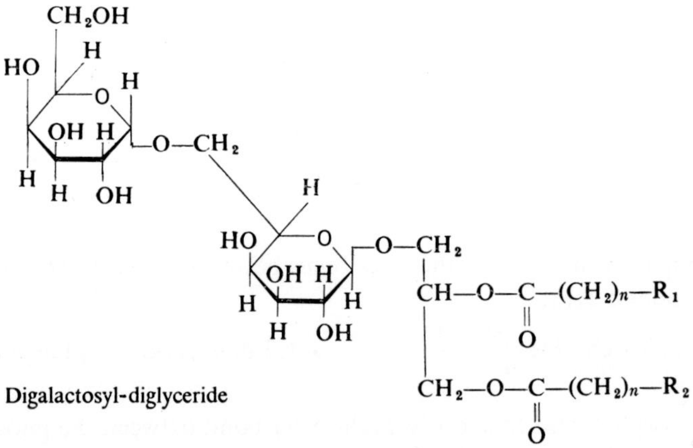

Digalactosyl-diglyceride

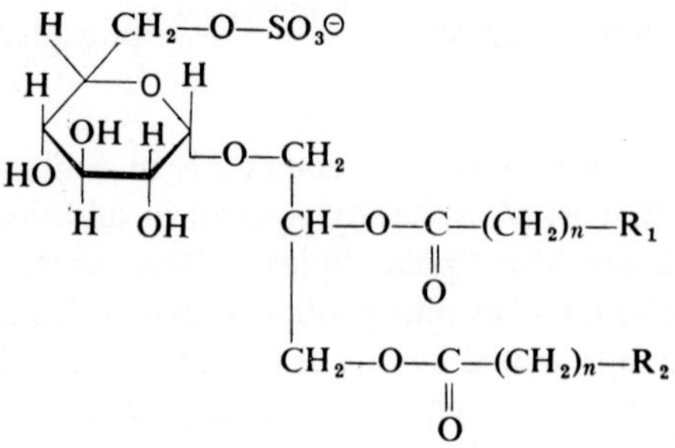

Sulpholipid (Sulphoquinovosyldiglyceride)

It should be emphasized that these pathways have been worked out by experiments with lower organisms and little direct information is yet available for the higher plants.

The preparation of pure lipoprotein membranes from plant cells still presents numerous technical problems. Consequently, the analysis of the membrane lipids of fruits is still conducted upon fractions of sub-cellular

TABLE IX. Phospholipid composition of some fractions of apple parenchyma[a]

Lipids	Internal parenchyma (pulp)			External pericarp (peel)
		Fractions		
	Whole tissue	Mitochondria	Microsomes	Whole tissue
	% Total lipids			
Neutral lipids	24	10	++	85
Glycolipids	trace	trace	trace	5·5
Phospholipids	75	90	++	9·5
	% Total phospholipids			
Lyso compounds	1	——	0·3	——
Phosphatidyl-inositol	1·6	5	14·7	18·2
Phosphatidyl-choline	32·6	45	39·5	33·8
Phosphatidyl-glycerol	trace	7	7·6	9·5
Phosphatidyl-serine	6·9	3	12·2	trace
Phosphatidyl-ethanolamine	38·7	35	25·6	18·2
Diphosphatidyl-glycerol	3·8	——	0·1	8·7
Phosphatidic acid	16·3	5	——	11·6

[a] Ben Abdelkader et al., 1968.

organelles prepared by differential centrifugation. Table IX shows some data recently obtained from experiments with apple pericarp.

The main phospholipids of plant lipoprotein membranes are characterized by a high linoleic acid content. However, the microsomal phospholipids of apple pulp parenchyma tissue are relatively less rich in linoleic acid than the mitochondrial phospholipids (Thibaudin et al., 1968). In apple peel parenchyma, the membrane phospholipids are markedly richer in linoleic acid than are the neutral lipids; the galactolipids which remain in the degenerated chloroplasts of the external pericarp of apple fruit do not contain much linolenic acid (in contrast with photosynthesizing chloroplasts) but contain relatively more saturated acids (Mazliak and Catesson, 1968). Various phospholipids and galactolipids have been identified in the pericarps of ivy fruits (Grosbois, 1968) and pepper fruits (Capsicum annuum) (McArthur et al., 1964).

Plant physiologists, after having explored the chemical composition of the fats found in pericarps, have also followed the metabolism of these products during the growing period, the maturation and the senescence of fruits.

III. LIPID METABOLISM IN FRUITS

A. Avocado

In a review which appeared in 1951, Schwob indicated that the oil stored in the pulp of the avocado represented 50–75% of the dry weight and from 4–20% of the fresh weight of the fruit, the values varying with different varieties. The author also showed that in the various varieties the lipid content of the pulp was inversely proportional to water content (see Table X).

TABLE X. Correlation between the lipid (fat) content and the water content of the pericarps of several varieties of avocado[a]

Varieties	Water content % Fresh matter weight	Lipid content	
		% Fresh matter weight	% Dry matter weight
Wagner	72·47	18·77	67·46
Lula	73·89	13·60	53·30
Taylor	76·89	12·81	53·38
Eagle Rock	78·06	12·18	55·12
Winslowson	78·08	13·02	58·31
Linda	78·74	12·32	58·66
Collinson	79·44	11·55	53·80
Waldin	82·37	6·34	35·37
Schmidt	82·55	7·21	39·97
Trapp	83·53	5·91	35·61
Simmondo	83·88	6·63	37·12
Pollock	85·05	4·77	31·39

[a] From Schwob, 1951.

The fatty acids contained in oils from American, Turkish, Asiatic or Israeli varieties have been analysed (Eckey, 1954; Mazliak, 1965a), and it has been found that in all these varieties only four acids represent more than 95% of the total weight of fatty acids. These are palmitic, palmitoleic, oleic (major constituent) and linoleic acids (see Table III). The pericarp has the same fatty acid composition in deep cellular layers (endocarp) as in superficial ones (mesocarp and exocarp). However, the fruit exocarp contains, in addition, very long chain fatty acids characteristic of epidermal waxes (Mazliak, 1965a). In the fruit pericarp phospholipids contain less oleic acid than do reserve triglycerides. The unsaponifiable part of the avocado oil contains hydrocarbons (20%) *n*-alcohols (3%), terpenoids (30%) and sterols (45%) (Paquot and Tassel, 1966). Recently, Kikuta (1968) separated the lipids extracted from avocado mesocarp by means of silicic acid column chromatography as well as thin layer chromatography. The following classes were found in the total lipids: hydrocarbons, triglycerides, free fatty acids, diglycerides, glycolipids, monoglycerides and various phospholipids (phosphatidic acid, phosphatidylglycerol, phosphatidylethanolamine, phosphatidylcholine and phosphatidyl inositol).

Davenport and Ellis (1959) have followed the appearance of lipids in the pericarp cells during development of the fruit. Microscopic examination revealed that oil droplets accumulate first in cell vacuoles. As the growing

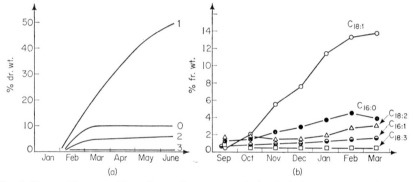

Fig. 2. Fatty acid composition of avocado mesocarp during fruit development (the months of the year have been put in abscissa). (a) The fatty acid compositions as determined spectroscopically on avocados grown in Australia. Redrawn from Davenport and Ellis, 1959; numbers on curves refer to degree of unsaturation. (b) The fatty acid compositions as determined by gas chromatography on avocados grown in Japan. Redrawn from Kikuta, 1968.

period of fruits is marked by a very important decline in the water content while triglycerides accumulate, the authors suggested that a true displacement of water by the oil droplets occurs "inside the vacuoles": oil droplets would form progressively, pushing away water molecules. The rate of appearance of the various kinds of fatty acids of the oil (differing in degree of unsaturation) has been followed spectrophotometrically. Saturated or polyunsaturated fatty acids are rapidly synthesized during the first weeks of the growing period; monounsaturated fatty acids (mainly oleic acid) are very actively synthesized all through the development (see Fig. 2a). The changes in lipid composition during the development of avocado have also been followed by Kikuta (1968) using mainly gas-liquid chromatography. During the phase of rapid lipid synthesis oleic acid was predominantly synthesized (see Fig. 2b), and eventually deposited in triglycerides in the mesocarp tissue of the fruit. An early rise in linoleic acid appeared to be associated both with glycolipids present in the chloroplasts of young fruit and with the phospholipids, which did not change in amount during the development of the fruit. This evidence supports the observation of an early establishment in the fruit of polyunsaturated fatty acids which then remain in fairly constant amounts throughout subsequent development.

Vogel (1958) and Dolendo *et al.* (1966) have found that there is no correlation between the oil content of the fruits and full maturity. Also, the qualitative composition of the oil does not change during the maturation or during the storage of the fruits after harvest. This fact would suggest that fat reserves do not play an important role in the metabolic changes which happen during the maturation. However, the lipid composition of avocados stored after harvest has been found to change slightly, according to the composition of the atmosphere surrounding the fruits (Mazliak, 1965b). The fruits have been subjected to various partial pressures of oxygen by means of polyethylene bags with varying numbers of perforations; it was found that the percentages of polyunsaturated fatty acids in the fruit fats were the highest in the more oxygenated atmospheres. These facts suggest that some slow turnover of reserve lipids does still take place during the post-harvest conservation of picked fruits.

The very existence of this slow turnover of lipids has permitted Stumpf and collaborators (at the University of California, Davis) to study numerous fundamental reactions of lipid metabolism, using enzymatic preparations extracted from avocado mesocarp. Barron *et al.* (1961) have demonstrated the presence of the enzyme acetyl-CoA carboxylase in avocado mesocarp; this enzyme catalyses the synthesis of malonyl-CoA, via the following reaction:

$$\text{Acetyl-CoA} + CO_2 + \text{ATP} \rightarrow \text{Malonyl-CoA} + \text{ADP} + \text{Pi}$$

The enzyme, which contains biotin, is located in subcellular particles sedimenting between 2000 and 15,500 g. Yang and Stumpf (1965) have shown that the malonyl-CoA is utilized for the total (*de novo*) biosynthesis of fatty acids by the fatty acid synthetase, a multi-enzymatic complex found in the soluble fraction of avocado cells. The *de novo* synthesis of palmitic acid by this cytoplasmic enzyme system is achieved according to the following overall reaction:

$$1 \text{ acetyl-CoA} + 7 \text{ malonyl-CoA} + 14 \text{ NADPH} + 14 \text{ H}^+ \rightarrow$$
$$\text{Palmityl-CoA} + 7 CO_2 + 14 \text{ NADP}^+$$

The successive cycles of condensation, permitting the bonding between the acyl-CoA intermediates and malonyl-CoA have been studied in great detail in the bacteria *Escherichia Coli* or *Clostridium kluyverii* by Vagelos (1964). By fractionating the fatty acid synthetase of these bacteria into its various constitutive proteins (by means of chromatography on sephadex or DEAE cellulose column), Vagelos *et al.* (1966) isolated a novel protein which was named ACP (Acyl-carrier protein); ACP in solution was not denatured by boiling for several minutes or by brief treatment with boiling 0·1N HCl. It possessed the same prosthetic group as co-enzyme A (that is, 4'-phospho-pantetheine). ACP was also found by Overath and Stumpf (1964) in the cytoplasm of avocado mesocarp cells, this being the first plant-ACP to be isolated. A comparison of the amino acid compositions of several ACPs from various origins has been recently described by Simoni *et al.* (1967) (Table XI).

TABLE XI. Amino acid composition of several Acyl carrier proteins (residues per mole of ACP)[a]

Amino acids	Avocado ACP	Spinach ACP	E. coli ACP
Cysteine	1·1	0·15	0·12
Taurine	0·92	0·89	0·97
Asparagine	0·95	0·93	1·0
Aspartic acid	12·0	12·0	10·8
Threonine	6·7	5·7	6·5
Serine	9·6	4·3	3·0
Glutamic acid	21·6	16·2	21·1
Proline	3·1	1·8	1·1
Glycine	7·1	4·2	4·9
Alanine	11·0	9·0	7·8
Valine	10·0	7·0	7·0
Methionine	0·89	0·92	0·9
Isoleucine	5·0	5·0	6·1
Leucine	9·0	7·0	6·0
Tyrosine	0·85	0·08	1·0
Phenylalanine	2·8	2·1	2·2
NH_4^+	10·4	8·3	9·6
Lysine	10·1	8·8	3·9
Histidine	0·93	1·0	1·2
Arginine	1·1	0·08	1·0
Total amino acids	117	88	88
—SH	1·6	0·83	0·65
Pantetheine	0·6	——	0·5
Molecular weight	11,900	9,500	9,350

[a] From Simoni *et al.*, 1967.

There are marked similarities in composition between plant and bacterial ACP, particularly a high content of glutamic and aspartic acids. Stumpf and co-workers obtained fatty acid biosynthesis by incubating malonyl-CoA in the presence of bacterial ACP and a fatty acid synthetase extracted from avocado or, conversely, in presence of avocado ACP and a bacterial synthetase. However, the products were different in the two experiments.

The condensation reactions in the *de novo* synthesis of saturated fatty acids are presumably the same in fruit cells as in bacteria. The following reactions are established in bacteria:

1. Acetyl-S-CoA + ACP-SH→Acetyl-S-ACP + CoA-SH
   Enzyme: Acyl transacylase
2. Malonyl-S-CoA + ACP-SH→Malonyl-S-ACP + CoA-SH
   Enzyme: Malonyl-transacylase
3. Acetyl-S-ACP + malonyl-S-ACP→acetoacetyl-S-ACP + CO_2
   $\qquad\qquad\qquad\qquad\qquad\qquad\qquad\qquad\qquad$ + ACP-SH
   Enzyme: β-Ketoacyl-ACP synthetase
4. Acetoacetyl-S-ACP + NADPH + H^+→
   $\qquad\qquad\qquad\qquad$ D-β-hydroxybutyryl-S-ACP + $NADP^+$
   Enzyme: β-Ketoacyl-ACP reductase
5. D-β-Hydroxybutyryl-S-ACP→crotonyl-S-ACP + H_2O
   Enzyme: Enoyl-ACP hydrase
6. Crotonyl-S-ACP + NADPH + H^+→butyryl-S-ACP + $NADP^+$
   Enzyme: Crotonyl-ACP reductase

This cycle continues until the long chain fatty acids are produced:

7. Butyryl-S-ACP + malonyl-S-ACP→
   $\qquad\qquad\qquad$ β-keto-hexanoyl-S-ACP + CO_2 + ACP-SH
   Enzyme: β-Keto-acyl-ACP synthetase

Thus slices of avocado mesocarp or cytoplasmic particles isolated from this tissue incorporate radioactive 1 or 2-^{14}C acetate into their constitutive fatty acids, as shown by Stumpf and Barber (1957) and Stumpf (1963). But these authors have found that the *in vitro* synthesis of fatty acids could not be simply ascribed to the natural *in vivo* syntheses. In reality, the fatty acids synthesized by enzyme systems *in vitro* are not formed in the same proportions as the natural fatty acids in the tissue. Stearic acid, for instance, was actively synthesized *in vitro*; polyunsaturated fatty acids, however, were not synthesized at all under the conditions used (Table XII).

Stumpf and co-workers have modified systematically different physico-chemical factors of the *in vitro* systems in an attempt to obtain products of lipid synthesis similar to those occurring by natural biosyntheses. The effects of pH variations have been studied; neutral pH's (7 to 8) are optimum for oleic acid synthesis; at higher pH values, saturated fatty acids are the most actively formed. The temperature of the medium also plays an important role: oleic acid synthesis is more active at 42°C than at 34°C. Oxygen is absolutely essential for oleic acid formation These results suggest that a

TABLE XII. *In vitro* synthesis of avocado pericarp fatty acids. Comparison with natural composition of the tissue[a]

	% Total fatty acids				
	$C_{16:0}$	$C_{16:1}$	$C_{18:0}$	$C_{18:1}$	$C_{18:2}$
Composition of natural fatty acids	12	2	0	74	12
% total radioactivity in fatty acids synthesized from ^{14}C-acetate *in vitro* (slices)	48·5	——	10·5	31·5	0
% total radioactivity in fatty acids synthesized from ^{14}C-acetate *in vitro* (particles)	42	——	21·5	23	0

[a] From Stumpf, 1963.

special enzyme (which may be a kind of oxygenase) functions in the biosynthesis of oleic acid by avocado mesocarp. However, this enzyme has not yet been isolated and it is not clear at present, whether stearic acid is a direct precursor of unsaturated fatty acids in higher plants.

A precursor–product relationship between oleic and linoleic acid (in apple parenchyma) has been suggested by Mazliak (1965c) following incorporation of labelled acetate into the tissues.

B. Olive

Studies concerning lipid metabolism in olive fruit are also numerous. The composition of the oils from several varieties has been examined in great detail by Greek (Katsoulis and Kaloxylos, 1966), American (Iverson *et al.*, 1965) and especially Italian workers (Montefredine and Laporta, 1963; Violante 1964; Lotti *et al.*, 1966; Losi and Pallotta, 1966).

Olives from European countries usually contain from 15–40% of the pulp fresh weight as fatty substances. The oil represents 35–70% of the dry weight. The fatty acid compositions of some olive oils from various origins are indicated in Table XIII. It may be seen that a high content of oleic acid is accompanied by low values for saturated and linoleic acids. The converse is true. Several authors (Montefredine and Laporta, 1963; Violante, 1964) have noticed that the proportion of unsaturated fatty acids in olive oil increases as the temperature of the environment diminishes. Thus the percentage of oleic acid is higher in the oils from the North of Italy than in the oils from the South. The same observation is made when comparing olives grown in the mountains with fruits grown in the plains. One finds also that

TABLE XIII. Fatty acid composition of olive oils from different countries[a]

| | % total fatty acids | | | | | |
| | Saturated | | | | Unsaturated | |
Origin	$C_{14:0}$	$C_{16:0}$	$C_{18:0}$	$C_{20:0}$	$C_{18:1}$	$C_{18:2}$
California	trace	7·0	2·3	0·1	85·8	4·7
Italy	trace	9·4	2·0	0·2	84·5	4·0
Spain	0·2	9·5	1·4	0·2	81·6	7·0
Tunisia	0·1	14·7	2·4	0·3	70·3	12·2
Israel	0·5	10·0	3·3	0·1	77·5	8·6

[a] From Eckey, 1954.

a late crop (November) gives an olive oil richer in oleic acid than an early crop (September).

Following early work by De Luca, Terroine (1920) has distinguished four periods in fat accumulation in olive pericarps (Fig. 3a). (a) a premonitory

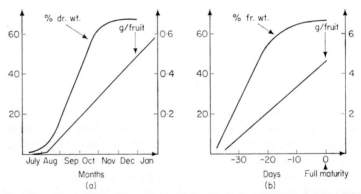

FIG. 3. Development of fatty substances in the pericarps of (a) olive fruit and (b) palm fruit, during fruit development. If the results are expressed relative to pericarp weight the increase in fat follows an S-shaped curve, but if the results are calculated for one fruit, the increase is linear during fruit development. Redrawn from Dessassis, 1961.

period, corresponding to maximum fruit growth upon the tree, without any noticeable fat accumulation; (b) a period of great accumulation of fats, during which the fat content of the pulp increases from 7·9 to 62·3%; (c) a stationary phase and (d) a regression period (from October to November).

Duran-Grande and Tamayo (1964) have made detailed histological studies of the different parts of olive oil fruit. These authors describe the progressive confluence of cytoplasmic oil droplets in the mesocarp. In mature fruits, fats form a large oily vacuole which occupies the greater part of the cell, pushing the cell nucleus and the cytoplasm against the walls.

C. Palm Fruit

Fat deposition in oil palm-fruits (*Eleaeis guineensis*) has been the object of wide quantitative studies by Desassis (1961). The qualitative aspects have been examined by Crombie and Hardman (1958). As seen previously for olive fruits, fats appear in great quantity in palm fruits only after a first phase of intense fruit growth. Crombie and Hardman have shown that fat accumulation in pericarps does not really begin before the nut (seed) has fully developed (about 19 weeks after pollination). After this time there follows a very rapid accumulation of lipids in fruits. The fat accumulation is marked by an abrupt increase in relative fat content (expressed in per cent of the fresh weight), but the increase in absolute fat weight, recorded for one fruit, is linear throughout the accumulation period (Fig. 3b). This fact has led Desassis to criticize Terroine's theory of four periods for fat accumulation. Desassis, distinguishes two phases in the process of fat accumulation in pericarps. (a) a phase of intense fruit growth without significant fat deposition in fruit cells and (b) a phase of linear accumulation of lipids during the entire final stage of development. Fat deposition stops only with the fall of fruits without attaining a definite limit. The iodine and saponification values of the fats do not change during the whole time of lipid accumulation in pericarps. Desassis insists on the following fact—at each time, the sum of the percentages of oil and water in the fresh fruit remains a constant. It seems that the oil progressively replaces water in the cell.

Considerable changes in the relative proportions of the various fatty acids present in fruit exocarps have been demonstrated during development of palm fruits by Crombie and Hardman (1958). At the beginning of the growing period, the fruits contain lipids which are rich in linoleic acid (24·4% of total fatty acids) and oleic acid forms only 4·2%. At the end of the development period, oleic acid represents 38·5% of total fatty acids and the percentage of linoleic acid has fallen. This shows that the reserve triglycerides which accumulate have a composition markedly different from the initial lipids (presumably constitutive phospholipids of the cells). These facts raise interesting questions. Do only *some* lipid synthesis enzymes show increases in activity at the period of fat accumulation in fruits? Or are there two fatty acid pools in the cells, one for reserve lipids (mainly triglycerides) and the other for membrane lipids? The answer awaits further research in this field.

D. Some Non-Oleaginous Fruits

The fatty acids of the lipids of banana have been analysed by means of gas liquid chromatography (Grosbois and Mazliak, 1964). In both the peel and pulp of the fruit the main fatty acids are the usual long-chain C_{16} and C_{18} molecules, palmitic acid being predominant. The maturation is accompanied by a partial disappearance of unsaturated fatty acids from fruit.

Lipid formation in fruit of *Cucurbita maxima* (pumpkin) has been studied by Mirac and Cupic (1964); the fruit oil is synthesized during a brief period of only 30 days. When the fruit is green, one finds linolenic and myristic acid in the lipids; however, in ripe fruit these acids have disappeared.

McArthur *et al.* (1964) have followed the progressive disappearance of lipids in the chloroplast of maturing fruits of pimento (*Capsicum annum*). These fruits, initially green, become red during maturation. The authors have observed an abrupt fall in the percentages of galactolipids and sulpholipids but no apparent change in the relative proportions of the remaining fatty acids.

A series of studies on apple lipids have been performed by Mazliak and co-workers. The following lipid classes have been distinguished in this fruit: cuticular waxes, neutral lipids (mainly triglycerides and diglycerides), galacto-lipids and phospholipids. Apple peel contains all these classes (Mazliak and Justin, 1967); the cells of the internal parenchyma contain mostly phospho-lipids (75% of total lipid weight).

A detailed analysis of cuticular waxes of Calville and Stayman cultivars has been made by Mazliak (1963b) and about sixty components have been detected by gas chromatography (see Section IIC). Similar results have been obtained for the fatty acids and hydrocarbons of waxes from the variety Edward VII by Meigh (1964). Mazliak (1963b) has carried out experiments with labelled acetate to follow the biosynthesis of the compounds present in waxes (fatty alcohols, diols, fatty acids, hydrocarbons, etc.) Only fatty acids and alcohols became intensively labelled after incubation of apple peels in a solution containing acetate-1-^{14}C. The experiments lasted from 1 to 48 hours. Apple peel was cut from fruits in full growth (upon trees) or from adult fruits stored in the cold after picking. The changes in the specific activity of each class with time, during labelling experiments, suggest a precursor-product relationship between fatty acids and alcohols (Fig. 4). During the growing period, fatty alcohols achieve, after several hours, higher specific radioactivities than fatty acids; during the maturation period, how-ever, fatty alcohols remain constantly less radioactive than fatty acids. In none of the experiments did the wax paraffins become significantly labelled; these paraffins however represent 33% by weight of total waxes. As other authors (for instance, Kolattukudy, 1967, 1968; Marekov *et al.*, 1968) have succeeded in labelling leaf or flower paraffins from acetate-1-^{14}C, as precursor, it must be assumed that incubation times, in Mazliak's experiments, were insufficient to allow termination of paraffin biosynthesis. Huelin and Gallop (1951b) and Mazliak (1963b) have followed the quantitative development of waxes during fruit development and subsequent storage. Waxes are synthesized after the initial stages of fruit formation and the total wax quantity

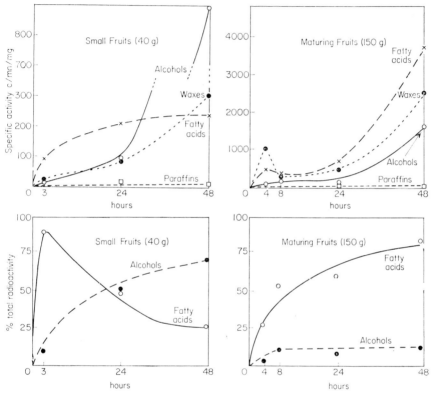

FIG. 4. Labelling of various fractions of apple-waxes, from 1-^{14}C-acetate given in solution to fragments of peel from small developing fruit or maturing fruits. (From Thibaudin and Mazliak, 1967.)

(per fruit) increases during the growing period, following an S-shaped curve. During storage after harvest, initially there is an accumulation of waxes at the surface of the epidermis up to a maximum level followed by a fall of the wax weight per unit area of surface. Similarly, the quantitative changes in fatty acids and waxes of apple peel have been followed. The growing period of fruits is accompanied by a preferential synthesis of saturated fatty acids in waxes; the maturation period is marked by an accumulation of unsaturated fatty acids in waxes (Thibaudin and Mazliak, 1967). The senescence of fruits, after the respiration climacteric, is accompanied by a decrease in unsaturated fatty acids in the waxes and it has been suggested that the short-chain compounds resulting from wax degradation could contribute to the volatile products emitted by the fruits (Mazliak, 1958). It should be noted that the analysis of volatile products from apples shows that many volatile components are similar to degradation products from fatty acids (Paillard, 1965).

Meigh et al. (1967) have shown that the rise in respiratory activity marking apple maturation (climacteric rise) is accompanied by a rapid accumulation of free and esterified fatty acids in apple peel. Subsequently, free fatty acids begin to disappear, followed later by a loss of esterified fatty acids. The fatty acid reserves inside and outside the cuticle appear to fluctuate in the same manner. When ripening begins a rise in lipoxidase activity precedes the evolution of ethylene, which in turn precedes the respiratory climacteric. These results suggest that the action of lipoxidase on unsaturated fatty acids in membrane structures would result in the formation of lipid peroxides which in turn might initiate the release of ethylene. (Mapson and Wardale (1967), have shown that the presence of hydrogen peroxide stimulates the production of ethylene from methionine by subcellular fractions from cauliflower florets). Ethylene has been shown to initiate the climacteric respiratory rise in fruits (see Chapter 16). Galliard et al. (1968a) have suggested that breakdown of linolenic acid is involved in the synthesis of ethylene.

The preferential synthesis of linoleic acid in apple parenchyma at the moment of climacteric rise has been found by Mazliak and Pommier-Miard (1963), Neubeller (1963), Meigh and Hulme (1965) and Meigh et al. (1967).

Phospholipid metabolism in cells of apple parenchyma has been recently studied by Mazliak (1967a, b, c) and Mazliak and Justin (1967). The principal phospholipids found are: phosphotidylethanolamine, phosphatidylcholine, phosphatidic acid, phosphatidylserine, phosphatidylinositol and several other minor components. These analytical results have been recently confirmed by Galliard (1968) who has also positively identified the following lipids in apple pulp: diphosphatidylglycerol, phosphatidylglycerol, two galactolipids, free and esterified steryl glucosides, sulpholipid and glucocerebroside. The turnover of the phospholipids has been followed by means of various labelled precursors ($^{32}PO_4HNa_2$, 1-^{14}C-acetate, 1-3-^{14}C-glycerol) (Mazliak, 1967a, b, c). Phospholipids are all synthesized or renewed in the cells both during growth and storage of the fruits. The rate of phospholipid synthesis was found to be similar for green and mature fruits, while the rate of glyceride synthesis has been found to be more important in ripe fruits (Fig. 5).

In apple pulp, the most labelling was obtained in phosphatidic acid, phosphatidylethanolamine and phosphatidylcholine. In apple peel the metabolic activity of phosphatidylcholine is much more important than that of other lipids. After short incubation periods, the greatest part of the radio-activity incorporated from acetate-1-^{14}C into lipids of apple pulp parenchyma was found in phosphatidic acid. This labelled compound was isolated by chromatography and subsequently re-administered to tissue fragments: most of the radioactivity was incorporated into the glycerides and the other phospholipids of the cells (Mazliak, 1967c), thus confirming the role of phosphatidic acid as a precursor of other lipids. Phospholipid metabolism in apple pulp mitochondria has been recently investigated by Mazliak *et al.* (1968).

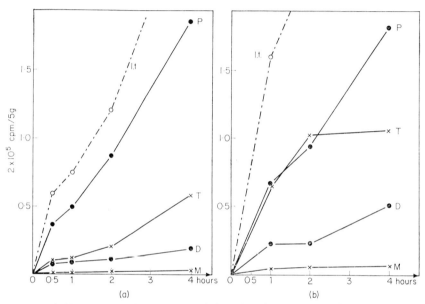

FIG. 5. Labelling of the various classes of lipids of apple parenchyma from 1-^{14}C-acetate, given in solution to parenchyma fragments during the times indicated in abscissa. (a) Experiment with green apple parenchyma. (b) Experiment with yellow ripe apple parenchyma (from Mazliak, 1967c). l.t. = total lipids; P = phospholipids; T = triglyceride; D = diglyceride; M = monoglyceride.

A positive turnover of the phospholipids has been found when mitochondria are *in situ* in the tissues. *In vitro* experiments revealed that phospholipid metabolism in subcellular organelles was altered following their isolation. Lipid metabolism in apple peel has recently been specially investigated. The biochemical changes of lipids in the peel during the growth of the fruits on the trees, has been compared with the morphological changes of chloroplasts in the tissues (Mazliak and Catesson, 1968). During the first phase of the growth of fruits on the tree (presumably during cell multiplication), linolenic acid forms 25% of the weight of total fatty acids in the peel. During the second phase (of cell enlargement), the percentage of linolenic acid drops;

linoleic acid first accumulates, then oleic acid. Electron microscopy shows that the lamellae of the chloroplast, initially present in an intact state in the cells, are progressively disorganized (see also Rhodes and Wooltorton, 1967). The organelles become loaded with osmiophilic globules and non-osmiophilic inclusions. These changes begin in the epidermis and progress towards the internal layers of the pericarp. Acetate-1-^{14}C is essentially incorporated in the phospholipids of the peel, notably in phosphatidylcholine. During the first phase of growth, incorporation of acetate is very active and does not markedly increase from 3 to 16 hours of incubation, *in vitro*. During the second phase of growth, the incorporation is weaker, but from 6 to 8 times more important after long incubation periods (the more important, the older the fruits are). These facts suggest that some process of ageing develops in mature tissues.

The influence of ageing on lipid synthesis in peel discs from pre-climacteric mature apples has recently been investigated by Galliard *et al.* (1968b). These authors found that the rate of incorporation of acetate-1-^{14}C into lipid reached a maximal rate within four hours of ageing of the discs and that the maximal rate was 2·5 times that in fresh discs (that is, assayed immediately without ageing). It is also indicated that the difference between the rate of synthesis in fresh discs and that in aged discs is greater in more immature fruit. As the fruit approaches the respiration climacteric, the rate in fresh discs approaches that of aged discs. Approximately 60% of the counts in fresh discs were recovered in phospholipids, phosphatidylcholine being most heavily labelled. The neutral lipids comprise about 30% of the counts. With aged discs, although there is an increase in the counts of most components, there is a large increase in the counts incorporated into free fatty acids.

Recently Grosbois (1968), reinvestigated the lipid metabolism in ivy fruits, following earlier work by Ulrich (1939). Ivy fruits (*Hedera helix* var. *Communis*) have three peculiarities: (a) fruit maturation happens during the cold season; (b) the pericarps become richer in phospholipids during fruit development; (c) the speed of fruit maturation is apparently controlled by the number of seeds enclosed inside the pericarps. The fruits containing two seeds ripen less quickly than fruits with four or six seeds. In all cases, fatty acid production during the process of maturation is the same: polyunsaturated fatty acids ($C_{18:2}$, $C_{18:3}$) progressively diminish in percentage while monounsaturated fatty acids ($C_{16:1}$, $C_{18:1}$) are actively produced. It is interesting to point out that ivy fruits contain petroselinic acid ($C_{18:1} \Delta$ ^6cis) and that the metabolism of this peculiar fatty acid appears to be very active in the fruits.

REFERENCES

Ansell, G. B. and Hawthorne, J. N. (1964). "Phospholipids". Elsevier.

Baker, E. A. and Martin, J. T. (1963). *Nature, Lond.* **199**, 1268–70.

Barron, R. J., Squires, C. and Stumpf, P. K. (1961). *J. biol. Chem.* **236**, 2610–14.

Ben Abdelkader, A., Catesson, A. M., Mazliak, P., Thibaudin, A. and Tremolières, A. (1968). *Bull. Soc. fr. Physiol. veg.* **14**, 323–49.

Chapman, D. (ed.) (1968). "Biological Membranes". Academic Press, London and New York.

Crombie, W. M. and Hardman, E. E. (1958). *J. exp. Bot.* **9**, 247–53.

Davenport, J. B. and Ellis, S. C. (1959). *Aust. J. biol. Sci.* **12**, 445–54.

Dessassis, A. (1961). "Sur les modalités de formation des matières grasses dans le fruit d'Eleaeis guineensis" (Jouve, ed.), p. 162. Thèse Fac. Sc. Paris.

Dolendo, A. L., Luth, B. S. and Pratt, H. K. (1966). *J. Fd Sci.* **31**, 332–6.

Duran-Grande, M. and Tamayo, A. I. (1964). *Grasas aceit.* **15**, 72–86.

Eckey, E. W. (1954). "Vegetable Fats and Oils", pp. 836. Reinhold Publishing Corp., New York.

Eglington, G. and Hamilton, R. J. (1967). *Science, N.Y.*, **156**, 1322–35.

Eglington, G. and Hunneman, D. H. (1968). *Phytochem.* **7**, 313–22.

Folch, J., Lees, M. and Sloane-Stanley, G. H. (1957). *J. biol. Chem.* **226**, 497–509.

Galliard, T. (1968). *Phytochem.* **7**, 1915–22.

Galliard, T. (1969). *Biochem. J.* **115**, 335.

Galliard, T., Hulme, A. C., Rhodes, M. J. C. and Wooltorton, L. S. C. (1968a). *F.E.B.S. Letters* **1**, 283.

Galliard, T., Rhodes, M. J. C., Wooltorton, L. S. C. and Hulme, A. C. (1968b). *Phytochem.* **7**, 1453–63.

Grosbois, M. (1968). *Revue gén. Bot.* **75**, 245–79.

Grosbois, M. and Mazliak, P. (1964). *Fruits* **19**, 55–9.

Hilditch, T. P. and Williams, P. N. (1964). "The Chemical Constitution of Natural Fats", 4th edition, pp. 745. John Wiley and Sons, New York.

Huelin, F. E. and Gallop, R. A. (1951a). *Aust. J. scient. Res.* **B4**, 526–32.

Huelin, F. E. and Gallop, R. A. (1951b). *Aust. J. scient Res.* **B4**, 533–43.

Iverson, J. L., Eisners J. and Firestone D. (1965). *J. Am. agric. Chem.* **48**, 1191–1203.

Katsoulis, P. and Kaloxylos, P. (1966). *Olii miner.* **43**, 352–6.

Kikuta, Y. (1968). *J. Fac. Agric. Hokkaido (imp.) Univ.* **55**, 469–5.

Kolattukudy, P. E. (1967). *Phytochem.* **6**, 963–75.

Kolattukudy, P. E. (1968). *Science, N.Y.* **159**, 498–505.

Kreger, D. R. (1948). *Recl Trav. bot. néerl.* **41**, 603–736.

Kreger, D. R. (1958). *In* "Encyclopedia of Plant Physiology" (W. Ruhland, ed.), Tome X, pp. 249–69. Springer Verlag, Berlin.

Kuksis, A. and McCarthy, J. M. (1962). *Can. J. Biochem. Physiol.* **40**, 679–86.

Losi, G. and Paliotta, U. (1966). *Olii miner.* **48**, 425–31.

Lotti, G., Bazan, E. and Averna, V. (1966). *Olii miner*, **48**, 438–49.

McArthur, J. M., Marsho, T. V. and Newman, D. W. (1964). *Pl. Physiol.* **39**, 551–4.

Mapson, L. W. and Wardale, D. A. (1967). *Biochem. J.* **102**, 574–85.

Marekov, N., Stoïanova-Ivanova, B., Mondeshky, L. and Zolotovitch, G. (1968). *Phytochem.* **7**, 231–4.

Martin, J. T. (1964). *A. Rev. Phytopathology* **2**, 81–100.

Mazliak, P. (1958). *C.r. hébd. Séanc. Acad. Sci., Paris* **246**, 3368–71.

Mazliak, P. (1963a). *Année biol.* **11**, 35–78.
Mazliak, P. (1963b). *Revue gén. Bot.* **70**, 437–553.
Mazliak, P. (1965a). *Fruits* **20**, 49–57.
Mazliak, P. (1965b). *Fruits* **20**, 117–22.
Mazliak, P. (1965c). *C.r. hébd. Séanc. Acad. Sci., Paris* **261**, 2716–19.
Mazliak, P. (1967a). *Phytochem.* **6**, 687–702.
Mazliak, P. (1967b). *Phytochem.* **6**, 941–56.
Mazliak, P. (1967c). *Phytochem.* **6**, 957–61.
Mazliak, P. (1968). *In* "Progress in Phytochemistry", Vol. I (L. Reinhold and Y. Liwschitz, eds.), pp. 49–111. J. Wiley and Sons, London.
Mazliak, P. and Catesson, A-M. (1968). *Fruits* **23**, 247–57.
Mazliak, P. and Justin, A.-M. (1967). *Fruits* **22**, 413–32.
Mazliak, P. and Pommier-Miard, J. (1963). *Fruits* **18**, 177–83.
Mazliak, P., Stoll, U. and Ben Abdelkader, A. (1968). *Biochim. biophys. Acta* **152**, 414–17.
Meigh, D. F. (1964). *J. Sci. Fd Agric.* **15**, 436–43.
Meigh, D. F. and Hulme, A. C. (1965). *Phytochem.* **4**, 863–71.
Meigh, D. F., Jones, J. D. and Hulme A. C. (1967). *Phytochem.* **6**, 1507–15.
Miric, M. and Cupic, Z. (1964). *Hrana Ishrana* **5**, 429–33.
Montefredine, A. and Laporta, L. (1963). *Olii miner.* **40**, 379–81.
Morris, L. J. (1964). In "New Biochemical Separations" (A. T. James and L. J. Morris, eds), pp. 295–319. Van Nostrand, New York.
Neubeller, J. (1963). *Gartenbauwissenschaft* **10**, 199–244.
Nichols, B. W. (1964). *In* "New Biochemical Separations" (A. T. James and L. J. Morris, eds), pp. 321–37. Van Nostrand, New York.
Overath, P. and Stumpf, P. K. (1964). *J. biol. Chem.* **239**, 4103–10.
Paillard, N. (1965). *Fruits* **20**, 189–97.
Paquot, C. and Tassel, M. (1966). *Oléagineux* **21**, 453–4.
Radler, F. and Horn, D. H. S. (1965). *Aust. J. Chem.* **18**, 1059–69.
Rhodes, N. J. C. and Wooltorton, L. S. C. (1967). *Phytochem.* **6**, 1–12.
Schwob, R. (1951). *Fruits* **6**, 177–83.
Simoni, R. D., Criddle, R. S. and Stumpf, P. K. (1967). *J. biol. Chem.* **242**, 573–81.
Sorokin, H. P. (1967). *Am. J. Bot.* **54**, 1008–16.
Stumpf, P. K. (1963). *In* "Biosynthesis of Lipids" (G. Popjak, ed.), pp. 74–84. Pergamon Press, London.
Stumpf, P. K. and Barber, G. A. (1957). *J. biol. Chem.* **227**, 407–17.
Terroine, E. F. (1920). *Annls Sci. nat. Bot.* **S10, 2**, 1–43.
Thibaudin, A. and Mazliak, P. (1967). *Fruits,* **22**, 3–18.
Thibaudin, A., Mayliak, P. and Catesson, A. M. (1968). *C.r. hébd. Séanc. Acad. Sci., Paris* **266**, 784–7.
Ulrich, R. (1939). *C.r. hébd. Séanc. Acad. Sci.* **208**, 664–7.
Vagelos, P. R. (1964). *A. Rev. Biochem.* **33**, 239–72.
Vagelos, P. R., Majerus, P. W., Alberts, A. W., Larrabee, A. R. and Ailhaud, G. P. (1966). *Fedn Proc.* **25**, 1485–94.
Violante, P. (1964). *Annali Fac. Sci. agr. Univ. Napoli* **29**, 119–40.
Vogel, R. (1958). *Fruits* **13**, 507–9.
Yang, S. F. and Stumpf, P. K. (1965). *Biochem. biophys. Acta,* **98**, 19–26.

Chapter 10

Volatile Compounds: The Aroma of Fruits

H. E. NURSTEN

Procter Department of Food and Leather Science,
The University, Leeds, England

I. INTRODUCTION

Aroma is only one component of flavour. Taste is the other major one, but appearance, behaviour on manipulation, feel in the mouth and even the sounds emitted on chewing, all play a part (see Amerine *et al.*, 1965). Aroma is the subjective sensation produced by smelling. The organs of smell are located in a small area, the olfactory epithelium, which is situated high up in the nasal cavity and therefore can be reached normally only by gases or vapours. For substances to possess a smell, it is necessary for them to be volatile, but, owing to the extraordinary sensitivity of the nose to some compounds, a very low degree of volatility may suffice.

For an understanding of the aroma of a fruit, it is therefore necessary to know (a) the nature of the constituents present; (b) the quality of the aroma of each, if any; (c) the quantity of each present; and (d) the intensity of the aroma of each. One would also wish to know how the pattern of the significant constituents changes in kind and quantity during the development of the fruit, and during its storage and processing; also, how each constituent arises and is in turn metabolized. Because of the complexity, the picture is not yet complete for any fruit.

In this chapter the way in which the nature of the volatile constituents has been investigated will first be described. Specific fruits will then be considered in turn from the point of view of the organoleptic significance (that is, significance by smell and taste) of the volatile constituents known to be present. Finally, the information currently available on the biosynthesis of each chemical class of volatile constituents will be reviewed.

II. NATURE OF THE VOLATILE CONSTITUENTS

A. General Considerations

The aroma-bearing constituents can be isolated from foods usually in yields of less than 100 p.p.m. Fruits, as might be guessed from the immediate impact of their aromas, occupy the upper end of this range. Thus, Valery bananas have given 65–338 p.p.m. of volatiles other than water; Gros Michel bananas 12–18 p.p.m. (Wick *et al.*, 1966, 1969); blackcurrants 1–22 p.p.m. (Andersson and von Sydow, 1964, 1966; Nursten and Williams, 1969b); cucumbers about 17 p.p.m. (Takei and Ono, 1939); strawberries 5–10 p.p.m. (Winter *et al.*, 1962); tomatoes 2–5 p.p.m. (Pyne and Wick, 1965); raspberries 2–3 p.p.m. (Winter *et al.*, 1962); American cranberries 1·1 p.p.m. (Anjou and von Sydow, 1967b) and mountain cranberries 0·8 p.p.m. (Anjou and von Sydow, 1967a).

The volatiles of most kinds of fruit have been found to comprise a large number of different compounds, 200 being the sort of number currently encountered, though with every refinement in technique additional components come into consideration. Individual, volatile substances are present generally in amounts of under a p.p.m. or even parts per thousand million and hence direct examination of fruits or fruit juices is only rarely useful in the elucidation of the composition of fruit volatiles, but may provide a successful means of following the changes occurring during, say, ripening (see, for example, McCarthy *et al.*, 1963). In most cases, the volatiles have to be concentrated, usually either by distillation and/or solvent extraction, followed by drying and concentration by fractionating off the solvent. The essence so obtained is then resolved into its components, usually by repeated gas chromatography, and the components are identified by infra-red, mass, and/or nuclear magnetic resonance spectrometry. For details, recent reviews and the references cited therein should be consulted (Wick, 1965; Chang, 1966; Ryder, 1966; Hornstein and Teranishi, 1967; Teranishi *et al.*, 1967; Weurman and van Lunteren, 1967; Weurman, 1969). Thin-layer chromatography is also often useful (Schmidt, 1967).

By means of such methods, knowledge of the nature of fruit volatiles has increased rapidly in recent years on the foundations laboriously laid by the earlier investigators, who were limited to the classical techniques of organic chemistry.

The classes of compound which have been found among fruit volatiles are not only esters, long characterized by their fruity aromas, but also lactones, alcohols, acids, aldehydes, ketones, acetals and hydrocarbons, together with examples of phenols, ethers and heterocyclic oxygen compounds.* Such a classification is to some extent arbitrary and often it can be more informative to draw together related compounds belonging to different classes, such as terpenoid hydrocarbons, alcohols and aldehydes, or compounds containing an aromatic ring, particularly when biogenetic origin comes into consideration.

Reviews listing the volatile constituents both by the variety of fruit (Nursten and Williams, 1967) and by chemical class (Gierschner and Baumann, 1967) have been published. As illustration, the lists of volatile compounds identified in four common fruits are given in Table I, but, otherwise attention will be focused on those constituents which have been shown to be organoleptically important. Unfortunately, in this respect current knowledge is much more meagre than on the chemical nature of the volatile constituents. However, it cannot be emphasized too strongly that, whereas in order to have an odour a compound must be volatile, odour is by no means a necessary consequence of volatility and, indeed, the detection threshold concentrations of substances vary widely, Guadagni (1968) quoting values ranging upwards from 0·007 μg/litre for aqueous solutions of β-ionone. Gas chromatography

TABLE I. Volatile compounds identified in four common fruits[a]

APPLES[b]

Acids

Formic	n-Pentenoic[e]	n-Octanoic
Acetic	n-Hexanoic	Octenoic[e]
n-Propionic	i-Hexanoic (from esters)	n-Nonanoic
n-Butyric	*trans*-2-Hexenoic	Nonenoic[e]
i-Butyric	n-Heptanoic	n-Decanoic
n-Pentanoic	Heptenoic[e]	Decenoic, etc.[e]
i-Pentanoic	Benzoic	

Alcohols

Methanol	2-Methylbutan-2-ol	n-Heptanol
Ethanol	2-Pentanol	2-Heptanol
n-Propanol	3-Pentanol[e]	n-Octanol
i-Propanol	n-Hexanol	2-Octanol
n-Butanol	2-Hexanol	n-Nonanol
i-Butanol	2-Methylpentan-2-ol	2-Nonanol
2-Butanol	*trans*-n-Hex-2-en-1-ol	n-Decanol, etc.
Pentanol	*cis*-n-Hex-3-en-1-ol	Geraniol
i-Pentanol	*trans*-n-Hex-3-en-1-ol	
2-Methylbutan-1-ol	n-Hex-1-en-3-ol[e]	

* The peppery and fragrant principle of the seeds (fruits) of *Dennetia tripetala* G. Baker has recently been shown to be 2-phenylnitroethane (Okogun and Ekong, 1969).

Esters

Methyl formate
Ethyl formate
Propyl formate
i-Propyl formate[e]
n-Butyl formate
n-Pentyl formate
i-Pentyl formate[e]
Methyl acetate
Ethyl acetate
Propyl acetate
i-Propyl acetate
n-Butyl acetate
i-Butyl acetate
t-Butyl acetate[e]
n-Pentyl acetate
i-Pentyl acetate
2-Methyl-1-butyl acetate
n-Hexyl acetate
trans-2-Hexen-1-yl acetate
cis-3-Hexen-1-yl acetate
Benzyl acetate
2-Phenethyl acetate
1-Octyl acetate
1-Nonyl acetate

1-Decyl acetate
Methyl propionate
Ethyl propionate
Propyl propionate
n-Butyl propionate
i-Butyl propionate
n-Hexyl propionate
Ethyl crotonate
Methyl i-butyrate[e]
Ethyl i-butyrate
i-Butyl i-butyrate[e]
Pentyl i-butyrate[e]
Methyl n-butyrate
Ethyl n-butyrate
Propyl n-butyrate
i-Propyl n-butyrate
n-Butyl n-butyrate
i-Butyl n-butyrate[e]
n-Pentyl n-butyrate
i-Pentyl n-butyrate[e]
n-Hexyl n-butyrate
Methyl 2-methylbutyrate
Ethyl 2-methylbutyrate
Propyl 2-methylbutyrate

n-Pentyl 2-methylbutyrate
Methyl i-pentanoate
i-Pentyl i-pentanoate
Methyl n-pentanoate
Ethyl n-pentanoate
Propyl n-pentanoate
n-Butyl n-pentanoate
Methyl n-hexanoate
Ethyl n-hexanoate
n-Butyl n-hexanoate
n-Pentyl n-hexanoate
n-Hexyl n-hexanoate
Ethyl phenacetate
Ethyl octanoate
n-Butyl octanoate
i-Butyl octanoate
n-Pentyl octanoate
n-Hexyl octanoate
Ethyl nonanoate
Ethyl decanoate
n-Butyl decanoate
n-Pentyl decanoate
Ethyl dodecanoate

Carbonyls

Formaldehyde
Acetaldehyde
Propanal
Acetone
Butanal
i-Butanal
2-Butanone
2,3-Butanedione
Pentanal

i-Pentanal
2-Methylbutanal
2-Pentanone
3-Pentanone
Hexanal
2-Hexenal
cis-3-Hexenal
Heptanal[e]
trans-2-Heptenal

Furfural
2-Hexanone
2-Heptanone
3-Heptanone
4-Heptanone
Acetophenone
Nonanal
7-Methyl-4-octanone

Ethers and acetals

1-Ethoxy-1-methoxyethane
1,1-Diethoxyethane
1-Ethoxy-1-propoxyethane
1,1-Diethoxypropane

1-Butoxy-1-ethoxyethane
1-Ethoxy-1-
 (2-methylbutoxy)ethane
1-Ethoxy-1-hexoxyethane

1,1-Diethoxypentane
2,4,5-Trimethyl-1,3-
 dioxolane

Hydrocarbons

Ethylene
Ethane[c]

Farnesene[d]
1-Methylnaphthalene[r]

2-Methylnaphthalene[r]

BANANAS

Acids

Acetic

Acids (from esters)[f]

Acetic
Propionic
n-Butyric

i-Butyric
n-Hexanoic
n-Hex-2-enoic

n-Hex-3-enoic
n-Octanoic

Alcohols

Methanol	2-Methylbutan-1-ol[g]	*trans*-4-Hexen-1-ol[f q, g]
Ethanol	2-Pentanol	2-Hexanol
n-Propanol	*cis*-2-Penten-1-ol[g]	2-Heptanol[f q, g]
n-Butanol	n-Hexanol	n-Octanol
i-Butanol	*cis*-3-Hexen-1-ol[g]	Two octen-1-ols[f q]
n-Pentanol[f q, g]	*trans*-3-Hexen-1-ol[g]	
i-Pentanol	*cis*-4-Hexen-1-ol[f q, g]	

Esters

Methyl acetate	2-Pentyl acetate	i-Butyl n-butyrate
Ethyl acetate	n-Hexyl acetate	n-Pentyl n-butyrate
n-Butyl acetate	i-Hexyl acetate	i-Pentyl n-butyrate
i-Butyl acetate	n-Pentyl n-propionate	2-Pentyl n-butyrate
n-Pentyl acetate	Ethyl n-butyrate[f]	n-Pentyl i-pentanoate
i-Pentyl acetate	n-Butyl n-butyrate	

Carbonyls

Acetaldehyde	i-Pentanal	2-Heptanone[f]
2-Butanone	2-Pentanone	2-Octanone
Butan-3-ol-2-one	*trans*-2-Hexenal	

Aromatics

Eugenol	Methyleugenol	Elemicin

ORANGES

Acids

Formic	n-Pentanoic	n-Octanoic
Acetic	i-Pentanoic	n-Decanoic
n-Propionic	n-Hexanoic	
n-Butyric	i-Hexanoic	

Alcohols

Methanol	i-Hexanol	i-Pulegol
Ethanol	n-Hex-x-en-1-ol	Neoisopulegol
n-Propanol	n-Hex-3-en-1-ol	Borneol
n-Butanol	*cis*-n-Hex-3-en-1-ol	*trans*-Carveol
i-Butanol	n-Hept-3-en-1-ol	Geraniol
2-Butanol[h]	n-Octanol	Nerol
n-Pentanol	Methylheptenol	Citronellol[j, h]
i-Pentanol	n-Nonanol	Farnesol
2-Pentanol[h]	2-Nonanol	Terpinen-4-ol
3-Methylbutan-1-ol	Decanol	Phenylethanol
2-Methylbut-3-en-2-ol	Linalool	
n-Hexanol	α-Terpineol	

Esters

Ethyl formate	Neryl acetate[j]	Methyl 3-hydroxyhexanoate
Geranyl formate	Ethyl propionate[h]	Ethyl 3-hydroxyhexanoate
Terpinyl formate[h]	Ethyl butyrate	Ethyl heptanoate[k]
Ethyl acetate	n-Octyl butyrate	Ethyl octanoate
n-Octyl acetate	Geranyl butyrate	Methyl 2-ethylhexanoate
n-Decyl acetate	Citronellyl butyrate[h]	Methyl anthranilate
Citronellyl acetate	Ethyl pentanoate[k]	Methyl *N*-methylanthranilate
Terpinyl acetate	Methyl i-pentanoate	Ethyl benzoate
Linalyl acetate	Ethyl i-pentanoate	
Bornyl acetate	n-Octyl i-pentanoate	
Geranyl acetate	Ethyl hexanoate	

Carbonyls
Acetaldehyde
Acetone
2-Butanone
Pentanal
n-Hexanal
2-Hexenal
2-Ethylbutyraldehyde[h]
4-Methyl-2-pentanone
Furfural
Heptanal[i]
n-Octanal
n-Octenal

6-Methyl-5-hepten-2-one[h,l]
n-Nonanal
n-Decanal
2-Decanone
2-Decenal
n-Undecanal
2-Dodecenal
Geranial
Citral
Neral
Citronellal
Carvone

Piperitenone[l]
Sinensal[m]
Nootkatone
α-Hexyl-β-heptylacrolein[n]
α-Hexyl-β-octylacrolein[n]
α-Hexyl-β-nonylacrolein[n]
α,β-Diheptylacrolein[n]
α-Heptyl-β-nonylacrolein[n]
α-Octyl-β-heptylacrolein[n]
α,β-Dioctylacrolein[n]

Hydrocarbons
Methane
3-Methylpentane
n-Hexane
Cyclohexane
Benzene
Toluene
o-Xylene
m-Xylene
p-Xylene
Limonene
p-Cymene
α-Thujene
Myrcene

α-Phellandrene
β-Phellandrene[h]
α-Terpinene
β-Terpinene
γ-Terpinene
Terpinolene
Sabinene
α-Pinene
β-Pinene
Car-3(4)-ene
Camphene
p-Methyl-i-
  propenylbenzene

2,4-p-Menthadiene
Farnesene
Ylangene
β-Elemene
α-Copaene
β-Copaene
Caryophyllene
α-Humulene
β-Humulene
Valencene
Cadinene

Miscellaneous
Ethyl-2-butyl ether
1,1-Diethoxyethane
1,8-Cineole[i]

cis-Limonene oxide[h]
trans-Limonene oxide[h]
cis-Linalool oxide[h]

trans-Linalool oxide[h]

STRAWBERRIES

Acids
Formic
Acetic
n-Propionic
n-Butyric

i-Butyric
n-Pentanoic
(+)-2-Methylbutyric[o]
n-Hexanoic

Cinnamic
Benzoic
Salicylic
Succinic

Alcohols
Methanol
Ethanol
n-Propanol
i-Propanol[p]
n-Butanol
i-Butanol
2-Butanol
n-Pentanol
i-Pentanol

2-Pentanol
2-Methyl-1-butanol
3-Methyl-2-butanol
2-Methyl-2-butanol
Pent-1-en-3-ol
n-Hexanol
Hex-2-en-1-ol
Hex-3-en-1-ol
2-Hexanol

2-Ethylhexanol
Benzyl alcohol
Phenylethanol
p-Hydroxyphenylethanol
Linalool
α-Terpineol
Borneol
Isofenchyl alcohol
Terpin

Esters
Ethyl formate[p]
n-Pentyl formate
i-Pentyl formate
Methyl acetate
Ethyl acetate

n-Propyl acetate
n-Butyl acetate
i-Butyl acetate[p]
i-Pentyl acetate
n-Hexyl acetate

2-Hexyl acetate
Hex-2-en-1-yl acetate
Benzyl acetate
Ethyl propionate
Methyl n-butyrate

Ethyl n-butyrate
i-Propyl n-butyrate
n-Hexyl n-butyrate
trans-2-Hexenyl n-butyrate
Methyl i-butyrate
Ethyl i-butyrate
Ethyl 2-butenoate
Ethyl acetoacetate
Ethyl n-pentanoate
Ethyl i-pentanoate
Methyl 2-methylbutyrate
Ethyl 2-methylbutyrate
Butyl 2-methylbutyrate
Methyl n-hexanoate

Ethyl n-hexanoate
i-Propyl n-hexanoate
n-Butyl n-hexanoate
n-Pentyl n-hexanoate
Pentenyl hexanoate
n-Hexyl n-hexanoate
cis-3-Hexen-1-yl
   n-hexanoate
trans-3-Hexen-1-yl
   n-hexanoate
2-Hexenyl n-hexanoate
Ethyl n-heptanoate
Methyl n-octanoate
Ethyl n-octanoate

n-Pentyl n-octanoate
n-Hexyl n-octanoate
Hexenyl n-octanoate
Methyl n-decanoate
Ethyl n-decanoate
Ethyl n-dodecanoate
Ethyl benzoate
Methyl *trans*-cinnamate
Methyl *cis*-cinnamate
Ethyl *trans*-cinnamate
Ethyl salicylate
γ-Decalactone[o]

Carbonyls
Acetaldehyde
Acetone
Propanal
2-Propenal
n-Butanal
2-Butenal
2-Butanone[p]

2,3-Butanedione
2-Pentenal
2-Pentanone
3-Methyl-2-butanone
Hexanal
2-Hexenal
cis-3-Hexenal

Heptanal
2-Heptanone
Benzaldehyde
Acetophenone
Furfural
Methylfurfural
2-Acetylfuran

Acetals
1,1-Dimethoxymethane
1,1-Dimethoxyethane
1-Ethoxy-1-methoxyethane
1,1-Diethoxyethane
1-Ethoxy-1-propoxyethane
1,1-Diethoxypropane
1-Butoxy-1-methoxyethane
1-Butoxy-1-ethoxyethane

1,1-Diethoxybutane
1-Methoxy-1-
   pentoxyethane
1,1-Diethoxypentane
1-Ethoxy-1-pentoxyethane
1-Hexoxy-1-methoxyethane
1,1-Diethoxyhexane
1-Ethoxy-1-hexoxyethane

1-Ethoxy-1-hex-3-
   enoxyethane
1,1-Diethoxypentane
1,1-Dihexoxyethane
1,1-Diethoxyoctane
1,1-Dihexenoxyethane

Hydrocarbons (probably from solvent)
i-Pentane
n-Hexane
Cyclohexane
Methylpentane

Methylcyclopentane
2-Methyl-1-pentene
Benzene
Naphthalene

1-Methylnaphthalene
2-Methylnaphthalene

[a] From Nursten and Williams (1967), with additions.
[b] Additions from Flath *et al.* (1969), unless indicated.
[c] Drawert *et al.*, 1968.
[d] Murray *et al.*, 1964.
[e] Gasco *et al.*, 1969.
[f] Wick *et al.*, 1969.
[g] Murray *et al.*, 1968.
[h] Wolford and Attaway, 1967.
[i] Teranishi *et al.*, 1966.
[j] Calvarano, 1966.
[k] Attaway and Oberbacher, 1968.
[l] Moshonas, 1967.
[m] Stevens *et al.*, 1965.
[n] Moshonas and Lund, 1969.
[o] Willhalm *et al.*, 1966.
[p] Popovskii *et al.*, 1965.
[q] Free or from esters.
[r] Possibly from solvent.

detectors vary in sensitivity according to design and to the nature of the substance detected. They can far exceed the human nose in sensitivity with compounds with little or no olfactory effect, but they can be up to 10,000 times less efficient than the nose for those compounds which the nose most readily senses.

B. Organoleptically Significant Components of Specific Fruits

The different kinds of fruit will now be reviewed in turn. Emphasis will be laid on those volatile constituents which have been shown to be organoleptically significant, but recent work and compounds of particular chemical interest will also be included.

1. *Apples*

Guadagni and his colleagues (Flath *et al.*, 1967; Guadagni, 1968) have recently shown that ethyl 2-methylbutyrate, although present in Delicious apples only in very small amount, has a quite disproportionate effect on the aroma, since it has an olfactory threshold of 0·0001 p.p.m. It provides the ripe note to the aroma, whereas hexanal and 2-hexenal, with thresholds of 0·005 and 0·017 p.p.m., respectively, are important as regards green, unripe odours.

2. *Apricots*

So far, only the volatiles of the Blenheim variety have been examined. Tang and Jennings (1967) have shown myrcene, limonene, *p*-cymene, terpinolene, *trans*-2-hexenol, α-terpineol, geranial, geraniol, 2-methylbutyric and acetic acids, linalool and its two oxides (cf. Felix *et al.*, 1963), γ-octalactone and γ-decalactone to be present, none of which, by themselves, have aromas suggestive of apricot. It seems that apricot aroma is due to an integrated response to these compounds when present in the proper proportions. Subsequently, Tang and Jennings (1968) added benzyl alcohol, caproic acid, an isomer of the linalool oxides, γ-caprolactone, δ-octalactone, δ-decalactone and γ-dodecalactone to the list of volatile compounds identified.

Canned whole apricots have been found to contain 0·13 p.p.m. HCN (Luh and Pinochet, 1959). Up to 33 p.p.m. HCN have been reported in canned, unstoned apricots (Gierschner and Baumann, 1969).

3. *Bananas*

Isopentyl acetate, long associated with banana odour by chemists, is indeed present, as is a whole range of other esters (Wick *et al.*, 1966, 1969). An important contribution to the full-bodied, mellow aroma of ripe bananas is made by eugenol (**I**), the related compounds, *O*-methyleugenol (**II**) and elemicin (**III**), being present also. Eugenol was added to synthetic banana essences long before its presence in bananas was proved chemically.

On the basis of comparisons between flavour profiles and gas chromatographic analyses, McCarthy *et al.* (1963) attributed the characteristic "banana-like" flavour to pentyl esters of acetic, propionic and butyric acids,

eugenol	*O*-methyleugenol	elemicin
I	**II**	**III**

distinctive "fruity" or "estery" notes to butyl acetate, butyl butyrate, hexyl acetate and pentyl butyrate, "green" notes to 2-hexenal, and "green, woody or musty" notes to methyl acetate, pentanone, butyl alcohol, pentyl alcohol and hexyl alcohol. Hultin and Proctor (1961) had already found 2-hexenal to contribute a green note and isopentyl alcohol to be significant as regards the rank odour of over-ripe fruit.

4. *Blackcurrants*

In spite of the identification of a wide range of volatile components, no "character impact compound" (Jennings, 1967) has yet been discovered (Andersson and von Sydow, 1964, 1966; Nursten and Williams, 1969a, b) and the aroma of a mixture of the known constituents does not closely resemble that of the fresh fruit. Kuusi *et al.* (1966) have made an extensive attempt to correlate gas chromatographic and organoleptic data as regards the effects of variables, such as season, growing locality, variety and ripeness.

5. *Cherries*

Canned whole cherries have been found to contain 0·048 p.p.m. HCN, whereas canned cherry juice contained 0·44 p.p.m. (Luh and Pinochet, 1959). A sample of commercial cherry juice gave 14·7 mg/litre HCN (Gierschner and Baumann, 1969). Montmorency cherry juice contains about 3 p.p.m. benzaldehyde (Nelson and Curl, 1939). Morello cherry volatiles are also dominated by benzaldehyde, but in addition 2-heptanone, linalool, and acetic, isovaleric and octanoic acids have been identified (Jorysch and Broderick, 1967).

6. *Cranberries*

Anjou and von Sydow (1967a, 1969) find that the acids make an important contribution to the aroma of mountain cranberries, particularly 2-methyl-butyric acid, the most abundant volatile next to benzyl alcohol, which has a fairly low specific odour intensity. Benzaldehyde, anisaldehyde, eugenol and a range of aliphatic aldehydes contribute; 94 components are known out of about 400 indicated. In the American cranberry, however, Anjou and von Sydow (1967b) could find little if any 2-methylbutyric acid, whereas α-ter-pineol (**IV**) constituted almost a quarter of the essential oil. The difference in aroma between the two kinds of berry may be explained by the difference in concentration of these two components, though other differences have also

α-terpineol
IV

been discovered. In the juice of the American cranberry, the components present in greatest concentration were benzoic acid, α-terpineol, benzyl benzoate, benzaldehyde and benzyl alcohol (Croteau and Fagerson, 1968). Interesting results have just been reported on bilberries (von Sydow and Anjou, 1969; von Sydow *et al.*, 1970).

7. *Cucumbers*

The characteristic odour of cucumbers has been shown to be due to un-saturated aldehydes, in particular, to *trans*-2,*cis*-6-nonadienal. Not only is this dienal the main aldehyde found (Takei and Ono, 1939; Forss *et al.*, 1962), but it also has an odour threshold of only 0·0001 p.p.m., at least 5 times lower than that of the *trans*-2-hexenal and 2-nonenal also present. In addition, saturated aldehydes and 2,6-nonadienol have been identified. In fermented, brined cucumbers only low-boiling saturated carbonyls have been found so far (Aurand *et al.*, 1965).

8. *Grapes*

Different species of grapes have different odours. Methyl anthranilate has long been known to be the major contributor to the characteristic aroma of the Concord grape, *Vitis labrusca* (Power and Chesnut, 1921), but at least 150 components are present in the essence (Stern *et al.*, 1967), including several other esters such as ethyl acetate, butyrate, crotonate, pentanoate and hexanoate and an interesting, pleasant-smelling ethyl alkylthioester. With Muscat of Alexandria and Grenache (*V. vinifera*), alcohols seem relatively much more important, but, whereas in the former linalool (**V**) and geraniol (**VI**) are major components, terpene alcohols represent a smaller percentage of the essence prepared from the latter (Stevens *et al.*, 1966, 1967). Changes in the volatiles of Muscat grapes on ripening and in Sultana grapes on drying have been studied recently (Hardy, 1970; Ramshaw and Hardy, 1969).

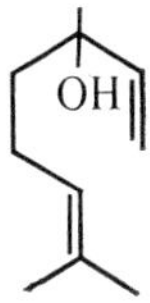

linalool
V

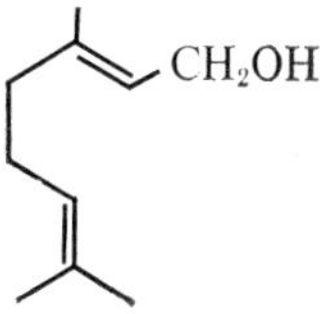

geraniol
VI

9. *Grapefruits*

The characteristic aroma of citrus fruits as a whole is ascribed to the relatively high-boiling, sparingly water-soluble oils. When these are isolated by steam-distillation, the distillate separates into two layers, the upper oily one containing almost all the aroma. The oils are a mixture mainly consisting of terpenes: hydrocarbons, mainly (+)-limonene (**VII**), constitute 80–90% of most citrus oils, but it is the oxygenated terpenes, representing about 5% of the oil, which provide the species-typical aroma (Stanley, 1958). Although a constituent of other citrus oils also, the amount of nootkatone (**VIII**) present in grapefruit oil is claimed to be a good indicator of flavour intensity (Mac-Leod, 1966; see also Berry *et al.*, 1967).

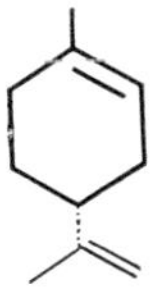

(+)-limonene
VII

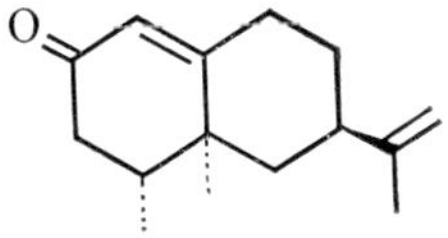

nootkatone
VIII

The composition of canned juice volatiles is similar to that of the fresh fruit, except that hex-3-en-1-ol is absent, that geraniol and some other compounds cannot be detected after storage (Kirchner *et al.*, 1953; Kirchner and Miller, 1953) and that furfural is only present in canned juice. There are other changes on storing canned juice: the limonene content decreases and there are increases in the relative amounts of linalool oxides, α-terpineol and furfural. The photolysis of nootkatone has been examined recently (Stevens and Scherer, 1968).

10. *Lemons*

Lemon oil consists of about 95% hydrocarbons and 5% oxygenated compounds. (+)-Limonene constitutes about 70% of the oil, but it is the content of citral (a mixture of the isomeric geranial (**IX**) and neral (**X**)) which is used commercially to assess lemon oils and is widely employed as a synthetic flavour ingredient. Over 60 constituents have been identified, nootkatone and a range of coumarins amongst them. On storage of lemon oil, γ-terpinene

geranial (*trans*)   neral (*cis*)   γ-terpinene   *p*-cymene   2-pinene   2(10)-pinene
      IX   **X**   **XI**   **XII**   **XIII**   **XIV**

(**XI**) is very liable to aromatization to *p*-cymene (**XII**), there are considerable losses of 2- and 2(10)-pinene (**XIII, XIV**) and terpinolene (**XV**) is oxidized to 4′-methylacetophenone (**XVI**) and limonene to carvone (**XVII**) (Rogers and Toth, 1968).

terpinolene   4′-methylacetophenone   carvone
   XV   **XVI**   **XVII**

11. Limes

Lime oil varies in composition with source (Slater, 1961a, b) and the method of preparation (Slater and Watkins, 1964). It contains almost 50% (+)-limonene. Citral, nootkatone, citropten (**XVIII**) and other coumarins are present. MacLeod (1968) has examined expressed lime oil by combined flow and temperature-programmed capillary gas chromatography.

citropten, limettin   thymol   carveol
      XVIII   **XIX**   **XX**

12. Mandarins (tangerines)

The peel oil has been thoroughly examined by Kugler and Kovats (1963), who have identified 48 components, constituting over 99% of the volatiles,

68% being (+)-limonene. Substantial amounts of other monoterpenoid hydrocarbons were also present. The amounts of the main oxygenated terpenes found were 1·1% (+)-α-terpineol and 0·24% (+)-linalool, but several aliphatic alcohols, aldehydes and acids were detected as well as a miscellaneous group of substances. No single compound was the sole carrier of the characteristic odour, but a mixture of the aliphatic, oxygen-containing terpenoid and miscellaneous compounds known to be present reproduced the odour almost completely. Mixtures of appropriate amounts of methyl N-methylanthranilate and thymol (**XIX**), present to the extent of 0·85 and 0·08% respectively, were already suggestive of mandarin.

13. *Oranges*

Orange oils contain some 90% (+)-limonene. Mainly as a result of much recent work, almost a hundred constituents are known. Varietal differences seem to be quantitative rather than qualitative (Wolford *et al.*, 1963). Canning and storage of orange juice leads to a loss of total volatiles with losses particularly of hydrocarbons, esters, aldehydes and linalool, but increases in α-terpineol, carveol (**XX**) and polyoxygenated compounds. Conversion of hydrocarbons to alcohols occurs, but the predominant off-flavour of stored

| valencene | sabinene | β-elemene | β-caryophyllene |
| **XXI** | **XXII** | **XXIII** | **XXIV** |

canned juice appears to be derived from non-volatile precursors (Kirschner and Miller, 1957). Canned orange juice differs from canned grapefruit juice in that no linalool oxides are formed (Stanley, 1958).

Boxes of Hamlin oranges, particularly early-maturing, ripe ones, give off a pleasant, fruity aroma when opened after storage. Attaway and Oberbacher (1968) showed that a series of ethyl esters was present, together with ethanol, (+)-limonene and an unidentified ketone or ester (molecular weight, 114). Butylcresol was also thought to be present.

Clean, fresh oranges possess a characteristic odour quite different from the above. The odour is very persistent and can be detected on hands up to an hour or more after handling. Attaway and Oberbacher (1968) rinsed the undamaged cuticle of Hamlin oranges with methylene chloride and showed the extract to consist of 90% valencene (**XXI**), together with sabinene

BFP—K

(XXII), β-elemene (XXIII), β-caryophyllene (XXIV), farnesene (XXV), humulene (XXVI) and δ-cadinene (XXVII).

farnesene	humulene	δ-cadinene
XXV	XXVI	XXVII

14. Passion fruits

Hui and Scheuer (1961) showed that the volatiles isolated by them contained the four esters identified by them, namely, ethyl n-butyrate and n-hexanoate and n-hexyl n-butyrate and n-hexanoate, to the extent of 1·4, 9·7, 13·9 and 69·6%, respectively.

15. Peaches

Esters are present as in all fruits. Alcohols and acids are present too. Benzaldehyde is noteworthy because of its associations with Prunus species, but the most striking feature is the discovery of a series of γ-lactones, the C_6, C_8, and C_{10}, together with δ-decalactone (Jennings, 1967). None of the compounds identified has a peach-like aroma by itself and peach aroma is an integration of all the above groups of compounds. It is worth pointing out that undecalactone has long been an ingredient of synthetic peach essences and is therefore known as "peach aldehyde". The lactones are in fact characterized by a coconut odour.

16. Pears

Here again esters are the most significant constituents. Heinz and Jennings (1966a) have shown that methyl and ethyl trans-2,cis-4-decadienoates are present in the Bartlett pear. They (and the esters of higher alcohols†) have remarkably pear-like odours and are character-impact compounds, though other esters, particularly, n-hexyl acetate, also make a contribution. It is noteworthy that a solution of ethyl trans-2,cis-4-decadienoate even produces the hoarse feel of pear juice in the gullet. Exposure of pear essence to both air and light for one week at room temperature produced changes in the gas chromatographic pattern, the main ones being explained by the degradation of the decadienoates to n-hexanal and the corresponding 4-hydroxycrotonates, minor constituents of the original essence (Heinz and Jennings, 1966b).

17. Pineapples

Pineapples are dealt with in Volume 2, Chapter 9b.

† Creveling and Jennings, 1970.

18. Raspberries

Both fresh raspberries and fresh strawberries have an odour which changes rapidly after crushing. Winter *et al.* (1962) therefore designed a special plant in which crushing and distilling are carried out in rapid succession under nitrogen. Many components have been identified, but 1-(*p*-hydroxyphenyl)-3-butanone (Schinz and Seidel, 1961), "raspberry ketone", is the nearest to a character impact compound that raspberries possess. An important contribution is made by *cis*-3-hexen-1-ol, which has a fresh, grassy odour, and the presence of α- and β-ionone (**XXVIII**, **XXIX**) (Winter and Sundt, 1962), as well as possibly of α-irone (**XXX**) (Schinz and Seidel, 1957) is of interest.

α ionone	β-ionone	α-irone
XXVIII	**XXIX**	**XXX**

Experiments, using head space vapour analysis to study the interaction of a raspberry substrate with a variety of enzyme preparations, allowed Weurman (1961) to conclude tentatively that fruit volatile formation is due to a complex system of several enzymes acting on several precursors.

19. Strawberries

In spite of much work and the detection of more than 150 volatile components (McFadden *et al.*, 1965), the source of strawberry aroma has not been discovered. For synthetic essences ethyl 1-methyl-2-phenylglycidate (**XXXI**), "strawberry aldehyde", is of key importance, but so far compounds of this type have not been found in nature.

ethyl 1-methyl-2-phenylglycidate
XXXI

Winter *et al.* (1958) showed that the 2-hexenal content of strawberry essence depends on the oxygen available at the time of crushing. Acidification of the distillate to pH 0·3 also seems to give rise to 2-hexenal, suggesting that a rearrangement, say, from 3-hexenal, may be involved (Winter and Sundt, 1962).

20. *Tomatoes*

The volatile constituents of tomatoes have been the subject of several studies, that of Pyne and Wick (1965) being the most comprehensive to date. The volatiles constitute only 2–5 p.p.m. in total, but comprise at least 50 compounds, among which n-hexanal, 2- and 3-methyl-1-butanol, *cis*-3-hexen-1-ol, an unsaturated aldehyde and another unsaturated carbonyl are the most important in amount. The origin of the characteristic tomato aroma remains unknown. In parallel work, Schormüller and Grosch (1964) provided evidence for the presence of several unusual components of fruit volatiles, namely, glyoxal, pyruvaldehyde, 2,3-butanedione, 2,3-pentanedione, cinnamaldehyde (**XXXII**), dihydrocinnamaldehyde and 2-methylhept-2-en-6-one. Very recently, Buttery and Seifert (1968) confirmed the presence of the last compound and identified the relatively high-boiling 2,6-dimethylundeca-2,6-dien-10-one as a major component (8%) of the essence, which also contains 2-heptenal, 2,4-decadienal and eugenol. A substantial proportion of 2,6,10-trimethylpentadeca-2,6,10-trien-14-one has been isolated subsequently (But-

cinnamaldehyde
XXXII

tery *et al.*, 1969). The amounts of the methylbutanols, pentanol and 3-hexen-1-ol have been compared quantitatively for varietal and harvest differences, as well as processing effects (Johnson *et al.*, 1968). Fruits harvested only a week apart differed considerably and processing always reduced the amounts of these volatiles found. The effects of variety, processing and storage on a wider range of volatiles have been quantitatively assessed by Nelson and Hoff (1969).

III. BIOSYNTHESIS OF THE VOLATILE CONSTITUENTS

A. General Considerations

Now that for almost every type of fruit the list of volatile constituents identified has become respectably long, emphasis in aroma research is moving in two directions. On the one hand, the significance of the components identified is being assessed and this can only be done by careful sensory evaluation (Amerine *et al.*, 1965). On the other hand, it is becoming increasingly important to understand the biochemical origin and fate of the organoleptically significant compounds in order that the implications for horticulture and the food industry can be fully worked out. It is therefore useful to survey the present, incomplete state of biochemical knowledge in this area as an encouragement to further advances. This will be done according to the chemical class.

There are very considerable difficulties in studying fruits biochemically. Weurman (1961) has already drawn the conclusion that a number of enzymes must be involved in the formation of the aromas of fruits. The extraction of active mitochondria from fruits, which usually contain high concentrations of acids and tannins, has been one of the main obstacles to progress. It is therefore worth noting that Haard and Hultin (1968) have developed a method which consists of freezing in liquid nitrogen, grinding and extracting under careful control of pH with a solution containing a protein capable of binding tannin, but otherwise inert. The method has been successful with green and ripe bananas, apples and potatoes. Jones *et al.* (1964) had already obtained mitochondrial preparations from apples; more recently, Romani and Yu (1967, 1968) have prepared active mitochondria from apples and pears.

Other sources of difficulty lie in the differences in permeability between various cellular membranes and in the great changes in metabolism observed on varying mildly the experimental conditions.

Because of these difficulties and because the subject is still new, direct experimental evidence is often lacking and it is necessary to argue by analogy from areas of biochemistry, sometimes fortunately close, but at others dangerously far removed. Much of what follows must therefore only be accepted with reservations.

B. The Biosynthesis of the Chemical Classes of Fruit Volatiles

1. *Alcohols*

The homologous series of normal alcohols, C_1 to C_6, followed by those containing an even number of carbon atoms up to about C_{12}, is, or is suspected to be, present in most fruits. The origin of methanol is certainly partly in pectin, the methoxy groups of which are significant for the production of volatiles in cooked vegetables (Casey *et al.*, 1963), and ethanol is expected to be formed by reactions analogous to anaerobic fermentation; that is, via pyruvic acid and acetaldehyde. It should be noted that there is considerable ethanol production in cut potato tubers on storage in cold water (Self, 1967). It is not obvious how higher straight chain alcohols are formed.

Branched alcohols, such as the fusel oil constituents, 3- and 2-methyl-1-butanol and 2-methyl-1-propanol, are likely to be formed from the appropriate amino acids, leucine, isoleucine and valine, via the corresponding aldehydes. Similarly, glycine and alanine could contribute to the methanol and ethanol found; phenylalanine and tyrosine can lead to 2-phenylethanol and its *p*-hydroxy derivative, tyrosol, a bitter-tasting compound (Senthe-Shanmuganathan and Elsden, 1958). There is direct evidence that L-leucine-

U-^{14}C is converted in part into isopentyl alcohol in banana slices (Myers *et al.*, 1968). However, the carbon skeleton of fermentation alcohols may also be derived from carbohydrates via the oxo acid, which can be decarboxylated and reduced to the alcohol or transaminated to the amino acid (see Webb, 1967). Genevois and Lafon (1957) have shown that wine yeast fermentation of sucrose in a synthetic medium containing a little [2-^{14}C] acetate produces radioactive pentyl and isopropyl alcohol, but inactive 2-methylbutanol.

Yeast mutants unable to synthesize particular amino acids are also largely incapable of producing the corresponding alcohol (Ingraham and Guymon, 1960). Recent model experiments by Drawert *et al.* (1967) on wine fermentation with *Saccharomyces cerevisiae* have shown that uniformly-labelled D-glucose, L-glutamic acid, L-aspartic acid and 3-^{14}C-DL-malic acid can give rise to radioactive ethanol, 1-propanol, 1- and 2-butanol, 2-methylpropanol, 1-pentanol and 2- and 3-methyl-1-butanol. Yeasts, at any rate, seem to possess such a multiplicity of inter-connected pathways that they can adjust to a wide variety of nutrients, and it is correspondingly difficult to work out which mechanisms are operative under particular conditions.

The reciprocal interconversion of alcohols and aldehydes has recently been emphasized by the work of Eriksson (1968) in studies of an alcohol; NAD oxidoreductase from peas. At neutral pH and not too high a ratio of NAD+ to NADH, most alcohols will predominate over the corresponding aldehydes, but the systems are sensitive to changes in either factor. The enzyme does not catalyse equally the backward and forward reactions. Alcohols unsaturated at position 2 are oxidized much more readily than the normal saturated ones, but alcohols with double bonds in other positions and alcohols with a methyl substituent are oxidized much less readily. Other types of alcohol, such as polyhydric, acetylenic, secondary, terpenoid, cyclic and aromatic ones (except cinnamyl alcohol) are oxidized slowly or not at all. The reverse reaction is more complex: whereas *trans*-2-hexenal is reduced more slowly than hexanal, the situation is the other way about for *trans*-6-nonenal and nonanal, *trans*-2-nonenal falling between them in rate of reduction.

1-Octen-3-ol has been found in blackcurrant fruit and in other plants. Hoffmann (1962) has shown it to be formed from methyl linoleate on mild oxidation and to be present in several oxidized vegetable oils. He postulated that it was derived via a hemiacetal of 2-octenal, capable of undergoing an intramolecular cyclic rearrangement.

On the origin of unsaturated alcohols, it is at present unprofitable to speculate. It is surprising that neither isopentenyl nor dimethylallyl alcohol have been found in fruits, particularly those producing large amounts of terpenes. 2-Methyl-3-buten-2-ol and its 3,2,1-isomer have been found and could well be closely connected with the mevalonate pathway. Genevois

(1961) has already stressed the relationship of isopentenyl pyrophosphate to isopentyl alcohol and has cited evidence for the formation of this alcohol by yeasts without intervention of leucine.

The fungus, *Neurospora crassa*, has recently been shown by Gross *et al.* (1968) to contain two distinct enzymes, an aryl-aldehyde: NADP oxidoreductase (ADP) as well as an aryl-alcohol reductase, which between them are capable of reducing aromatic acids, such as cinnamic and salicylic, to the corresponding alcohols. Benzyl alcohol could be formed in higher plants in this way via benzaldehyde, though the precursor is probably benzoyl-SCoA, rather than benzoic acid (Zenk, 1966).

An enzyme preparation has recently been obtained from tomatoes (Yu *et al.*, 1968a) and has been shown to be capable of converting amino acids into alcohols and aldehydes apparently by a pathway involving transamination. Leucine and valine gave mainly alcohols; alanine mainly aldehydes, particularly propanal, which was present in most reaction products (Yu *et al.*, 1968b).

2. Aldehydes

It is not clear yet whether alcohols are formed from aldehydes by intervention of the alcohol: NAD oxidoreductase or whether the reverse is the case. The former is more likely under physiological conditions (cf. Eriksson, 1968) and so for the origin of aldehydes one has to look elsewhere, although Meigh *et al.* (1966) have shown that sterile tomato tissue is capable of converting ethanol, propanol and isopropanol into acetaldehyde, propanal and acetone, respectively.

The amino acids are likely precursors via the α-oxo acids for a limited number of aldehydes, which are probably in turn the precursors of the corresponding alcohols, as mentioned above. The conversion of amino acids to aldehydes can also occur non-enzymically by the Strecker reaction with suitable α-dicarbonyl compounds, such as may be formed from sugars on heating.

Drawert *et al.* (1965, 1966) have presented evidence to show that linolenic and linoleic acids give rise to 2-hexenal and hexanal, respectively, by a pathway which differs substantially from autoxidation of unsaturated fatty acids and from pure lipoxidase activity (Heimann and Drawert, 1967).

Although 2-hexenal has been shown to be given off by whole trees (Schildknecht and Rauch, 1961), it appears that its production greatly increases on cell damage and consequently it has been regarded as a "wounding hormone". These facts correlate well with the work of Winter *et al.* (1958) on strawberries, the volatiles of which contain less and less 2-hexenal, the more carefully their isolation is carried out.

Benzaldehyde, a constituent of many fruits, is probably formed from cinnamic acid via benzoyl-SCoA by β-oxidation (Zenk, 1966).

3. Acetals

Acetals have so far been identified in essences from apples (Flath *et al.*, 1967), oranges (Schultz *et al.*, 1964) and strawberries (McFadden *et al.*, 1965). It would appear that these are artefacts of essence preparation, being formed from the aldehydes and alcohols present as their concentration increases. Greater amounts of acetals have in fact been found in apple essence after one year's storage (Flath *et al.*, 1967).

4. Ketones

2-Alkanones are the type of ketone most commonly found in fruits; they are prominent also in dairy products. Gehrig and Knight (1963) showed that *Penicillium roqueforti* spores, but not hyphal cells, can convert sodium n-octanoate in higher concentrations (20 μM) to 2-heptanone, probably by β-oxidation and decarboxylation. This and other 2-alkanones are probably formed similarly in higher plants. Acetone would be expected to be derived from acetoacetate, itself produced, not by β-oxidation, but rather by interaction of 2 molecules of acetyl-coenzyme A.

A few 3-alkanones have been isolated and it is possible that they are derived by β-oxidation of fatty acid groups, followed by complete reduction of the carbonyl C atom.

5. Acids

The biosynthesis of most organic acids relevant to the aroma of fruits has been dealt with in Chapter 4, which covered the homologous series of fatty acids, as well as the hydroxy acids.

Here it is only necessary to note that, as Jennings (1967) has pointed out, many of the compounds found in the Bartlett pear are methyl or ethyl esters of compounds which could be derived by β-oxidation of fatty acids, that is, *trans*-2-alkenoates, 3-hydroxyalkanoates and the fatty acids with 2 carbon atoms less.

James (1968), in a recent review of the biosynthesis of unsaturated acids by plants, has emphasized that they can introduce a 9,10-double bond into saturated acids, provided these are bound to the acyl carrier protein (ACP). Difficulties can arise in work with systems lacking a suitable acyl transferase to catalyse the transfer of the acyl group from acyl-S-CoA to acyl-S-ACP. The desaturation involves *cis*-hydrogens. In *Chlorella vulgaris* there is a desaturase acting on the 7,8-position, as well as a 9,10-desaturase. Since these enzymes appear to count from the carboxy group, they are likely to interact both with the carboxy groups and with the dehydrogenation centre; removal of an animo acid residue lying between the two sites from a 9,10-desaturase would shorten it by about the right amount to give a 7,8-desaturase. So far,

9- and 10-hydroxy-, 9,10-epoxy- and 9,10-dihydroxy-stearic acids have not been demonstrated to be convertible into the 9,10-unsaturated acid. *trans*-3-Hexadecenoic acid can be isolated from a variety of tissues, particularly photosynthetic ones, and Nichols *et al.* (1965) have shown that in *Chlorella vulgaris* it is formed from palmitic acid by a dehydrogenation requiring both light and oxygen.

6. Lactones

A whole range of γ- and δ-lactones has been isolated from certain fruits. Lactone formation is only likely with 5- and 6-membered rings, but aliphatic hydroxy acids, other than the 4- and 5-isomers corresponding to these lactones, have not been reported, except for esters of lactic, 4-hydroxycrotonic, 3-hydroxyhexanoic and 3-hydroxyoctanoic acids. 3-Hydroxy acid derivatives are intermediates in β-oxidation. It is worth noting that germinating castor bean extract appears to be able to convert 10-hydroxypalmitic into 4-hydroxydecanoic acid (Yamada and Stumpf, 1965).

Both types of lactones could be derived from 4-alkenoic acids by addition of water, but the only volatile derivatives of such an acid found so far are the methyl and ethyl esters of *cis*-4-decenoic acid in pears (Heinz and Jennings, 1966a). 4-Enoic acids could be formed from 3-hydroxy acids by dehydration and rehydration to the 4-hydroxy acids, followed by a further dehydration (Tang and Jennings, 1968) or by hydration and dehydration of 3-enoic acids (see above).

For the case of milk fat, Boldingh and Taylor (1962) speculated that lactonized 5-hydroxy acids could originate in two consecutive additions of acetate, the first occurring without the usual reduction to the 3-hydroxy acid-coenzyme A, thus leading to the 5-oxo acid, which then does undergo reduction and subsequent ring closure. The lactone precursors in milk fat have been shown to consist of hydroxy triglycerides (Wyatt *et al.*, 1967) and [1—^{14}C]acetate is incorporated into δ-lactones and saturated fatty acids up to C_{16} at comparable rates, implying that the δ-hydroxy acids are formed from acetate in parallel with these saturated fatty acids, rather than by a subsequent oxidation of C_{18} saturated or unsaturated acids (Walker *et al.*, 1968).

7. Esters

Every organic chemist would expect the esters of fruits to be formed by interaction of the corresponding alcohols and acids. The first point to settle is whether such an explanation suffices.

The formation of volatile esters in fermentation with brewer's yeast has been extensively studied by Nordström (1964). With *Saccharomyces* under not strictly anaerobic conditions, he found that the concentration of ethyl acetate formed exceeded the equilibrium concentration by over 100 times, *Hansenula* and *Pichia* leading aerobically to concentrations even greater (Peel, 1951; Tabachnik and Joslyn, 1953). For these and other reasons the straightforward reaction between ethanol and acetic acid is significant only under unusual conditions, such as low pH and high concentrations of the reactants. Several pieces of evidence pointed to the involvement of co-enzyme A in ester formation, leading Nordström (1964) to propose as the key equation:

$$RCOSCoA + R'OH \rightleftharpoons RCOOR' + CoASH$$

The acyl-coenzyme A can be formed in a variety of ways, for example, directly from the fatty acid, from the α-oxo acid by decarboxylation and as part of lipid synthesis. The C_4–C_{11} n-acids were able to act as substrates; propionic, isobutyric and isovaleric acids were not; formic acid very probably not; and isocaproic acid was a relatively poor substrate. Addition of acetic acid did not give rise to increased amounts of ethyl acetate, acetyl-coenzyme A being mainly formed from pyruvic acid. Ethyl acetate is thus in a somewhat special situation. Although α-oxo acids were also shown to be metabolized, they gave mainly the fusel alcohols and about 5% were converted into propionic, isobutyric and isovaleric acids, the corresponding esters not being formed directly.

Fatty acid synthesis proceeds via acyl-coenzyme A (or acyl-ACP) intermediates. These are very likely to be susceptible to alcoholysis to the corresponding ester as well as to the normal hydrolysis to the free acid. Leakage from lipid synthesis would readily explain the predominance of esters of even-numbered fatty acids and of ethanol, the alcohol invariably predominant in fruits.

One must be conscious of possible fallacies in drawing analogies between fermentation and fruit metabolism. In the absence of more appropriate data, it is worth noting, however, that Nordström (1964) found experimental support for his conclusion that, as ester formation requires acyl-coenzyme A, it is associated with the fundamental metabolism of the cell, and therefore it must correlate with yeast growth. This would seem to provide a direct explanation of the association of the climacteric in fruits with maximum rates of ester formation. It should be noted that Hultin's calculations (1962) show the concentration of esters in bananas to exceed greatly those expected on the basis of the equilibrium constants of the direct interactions of acids and alcohols.

The alcohols thus compete in ester synthesis as do the acids. Hultin and Proctor (1961) noted that, except for ethyl alcohol and ethyl acetate, the change in each ester of the banana during ripening followed the trend in the content of the corresponding alcohol. Nordström (1964) found methanol and propanol to be very good substrates, n-alcohols to be better than isoalcohols and isopentanol to be better than 2-methyl-1-butanol, but alcohols other than primary (2-butanol, t-butanol, t-pentanol) yielded no esters. However, a few esters of non-primary alcohols have been shown to be present in fruits, for example, 2-pentyl acetate in bananas, 2-hexyl acetate in strawberries and linalyl acetate in many citrus fruits.

In yeasts, ester formation is rather unspecific, being dependent only on the availability of alcohols and co-enzyme A derivatives. This probably holds also for fruits. In studying fruit volatiles, the practice of looking for compounds corresponding to all the combinations of alcohol and acid moieties already identified (Wick *et al.*, 1966) has, therefore, a more than purely empirical basis. The possibilities of genetic control of fruit aromas through ester composition seem good, but would lie in control of the formation of alcohols and/or the co-enzyme A derivatives.

Only the first, tentative steps have been taken in investigating the bio-synthesis of esters in fruits. Myers *et al.* (1969) have examined the incorporation of L-leucine-U-^{14}C into isopentyl alcohol and isopentyl acetate in banana slices. One to three per cent incorporation into volatiles was found, most radioactivity going into isopentyl alcohol, some into isopentyl acetate (both into the alcohol and the acetate moieties) and a significant proportion into a wide range of other compounds. The situation is thus complex, and this is in keeping with model experiments on wine fermentation with *S. cerevisiae*, in which Drawert *et al.* (1967) have shown that uniformly labelled D-glucose, L-glutamic acid and L-aspartic acid, and [3-^{14}C]-DL-malic acid can give rise to radioactive ethyl and isopentyl acetates.

8. *Phenols and phenol ethers*

The biosynthesis of these has been dealt with in Chapter 11 and will therefore not be considered further here.

9. *Heterocyclics*

Heterocyclics are becoming recognized as significant aroma components in a number of foodstuffs, for example, bread, potato crisps, roasted peanuts, coffee and cocoa.

However, except for the terpenoid 1,8-cineole, some terpene oxides, coumarins and other lactones, a furan from pineapple, and α- and γ-pyrone, all of which are oxygen heterocyclics, volatile heterocyclics have not yet been isolated from fruits.

10. *Hydrocarbons*

The volatile hydrocarbons isolated from fruits fall into three classes: terpenes, other aliphatic ones and aromatic ones. The terpenes are the most significant as far as aroma is concerned and will be dealt with in the next section along with other terpenoid compounds. The other aliphatic hydrocarbons include the important, but odourless ethylene, to which a separate chapter, Chapter 16, is devoted. The less volatile, longer chain hydrocarbons were treated together with the lipids in Chapter 9. Aromatic hydrocarbons, other than those with obvious terpenoid connections such as *p*-cymene, have only recently been recognized as natural components of various foodstuffs (Johnson *et al.*, 1969) and it would not be appropriate to give them further attention here.

11. *Terpenes*

The biosynthesis of volatile terpenoid compounds has been all too little studied, particularly in fruits such as the various species of berries and citrus, where their presence is of organoleptic significance. In his recent review of the biosynthesis and metabolism of monoterpenes, Loomis (1967) does not mention fruits and it is therefore necessary at present to argue by analogy without direct evidence.

Even with those parts of plants which have been examined directly, the study of terpenoid biosynthesis is made difficult by the physical isolation of its site. It is likely that only certain compounds, such as sugars and amino acids, are capable of entering the secretory cells and that the mevalonic acid, universally expected to be the key metabolite on analogy with sterol and carotenoid biosynthesis, needs to be produced locally. However, so far, incorporation of [2-^{14}C]mevalonate into a terpene has been achieved by Arigoni (see Loomis, 1967), but only at a level of 0·01% with complete randomization into the 1,8-cineole of *Eucalyptus globulus* Labill., by Nicholas (1962) into the steam-volatiles of *Ocimum basilicum* L. and by Hefendehl *et al.* (1967) into the volatile oil of *Mentha piperita* L. Recently, almost 11% incorporation has been achieved into the glucosides of geraniol, nerol and citronellol of rose petals (Francis and O'Connell, 1969).

Following Reitsema and Loomis (Loomis, 1967), one would picture the biosynthesis of terpenes in *Mentha* on p. 263.

There is evidence that the choice between steps (1) and (2) in the scheme is controlled by a single gene pair, the dominant allele leading to limonene.

Attaway and Buslig (1968, 1969) have shown that leaves of *Citrus jambhiri* Lush. and fruit of *C. reticulata* Blanco are able to convert 3-[^{14}C]linalool into radioactive α-terpineol and terpinen-4-ol. In the fruit significant labelling occurred also in (+)-limonene and other hydrocarbons. In the earlier study of the variation during a season of the percentage composition of peel oils of grapefruit, orange and tangerine, Attaway *et al.* (1967) showed that, particularly in the tangerine, the proportion of linalool decreased as that of limonene increased. In consequence, they drew attention to the possibility

Biosynthesis of terpenes in *Mentha*
(after Reitsema and Loomis)

that isopentenyl and dimethylallyl pyrophosphates could interact to form linalyl instead of neryl pyrophosphate.

12. Sulphur Compounds

Although sulphur compounds, particularly thiols, sulphides, disulphides and isothiocyanates play an important part in the aroma of vegetables, it is noteworthy that hardly any volatile sulphur compounds seem to have been isolated from fruits. The only examples appear to be hydrogen sulphide in grapefruits (Kirchner *et al.*, 1953) and oranges (Kirchner and Miller, 1957), hydrogen sulphide, methanethiol and dimethyl disulphide in strawberries (Winter, 1963), methyl and ethyl 3-methylthiopropionates in pineapple (Connell, 1964), an ethyl alkylthioester in grapes (Stern *et al.*, 1967) and benzothiazole and 2-hexyl- and 2-heptyl-thiophene in American cranberries (Anjou and von Sydow, 1967b).

On heating, tomatoes and tomato juice give rise to hydrogen sulphide and considerable amounts (0·4–10·9 p.p.m.) of dimethyl sulphide (Miers, 1966).

IV. SUMMARY

Chemically a great deal is known by now of the volatile constituents of fruits. From the psychological point of view, it is only just becoming clear which of these compounds are of significance and, it so happens, that the organoleptically important components are often present in such infinitesimally small amounts, that even present-day methods are stretched to their limits to enable them to be chemically identified. The biochemical aspect is probably the most difficult one to pursue and, partly because of that, it is the one which most needs further efforts at elucidation. Advances are not likely to be made in the various relevant disciplines working in isolation and future attacks on the problems of the aromas of fruits should be made on an integrated, fully multidisciplinary basis.

REFERENCES

Amerine, M. A., Pangborn, R. M. and Roessler, E. B. (1965). "Principles of Sensory Evaluation of Food". Academic Press, New York and London.
Andersson, J. and von Sydow, E. (1964). *Acta chem. scand.* **18**, 1105–14.
Andersson, J. and von Sydow, E. (1966). *Acta chem. scand.* **20**, 522–8.
Anjou, K. and von Sydow, E. (1967a). *Acta chem. scand.* **21**, 945–52.
Anjou, K. and von Sydow, E. (1967b). *Acta chem. scand.* **21**, 2076–82.
Anjou, K. and von Sydow, E. (1969). *Acta chem. scand.* **23**, 109–14.
Attaway, J. A. and Buslig, B. S. (1968). *Biochim. biophys. Acta* **164**, 609–10.
Attaway, J. A. and Buslig, B. S. (1969). *Phytochem.* **8**, 1671–3.
Attaway, J. A. and Oberbacher, M. F. (1968). *J. Fd Sci.* **33**, 287–9.
Attaway, J. A., Pieringer, A. P. and Barabas, L. J. (1967). *Phytochem.* **6**, 25–32.
Aurand, L. W., Singleton, J. A., Bell, T. A. and Etchells, J. L. (1965). *J. Fd Sci.* **30**, 288–95.
Berry, R. E., Wagner, Jr, C. J. and Moshonas, M. G. (1967). *J. Fd Sci.* **32**, 75–8.
Boldingh, J. and Taylor, R. J. (1962). *Nature, Lond.* **194**, 909–13.
Buttery, R. G. and Seifert, R. M. (1968). *J. agric. Fd Chem.* **16**, 1053.
Buttery, R. G., Seifert, R. M. and Ling, L. C. (1969). *Chemy Ind.* 238.
Calvarano, I. (1966). *Essenze Deriv. Agrumari* **36** (1), 5–25: *Chem. Abstr.*, 1966, **65**, 16785–6.
Casey, J. C., Self, R. and Swain, T. (1963). *Nature, Lond.* **200**, 885.
Chang, S. S. (1966). *In* "Encyclopedia of Chemical Technology" (A. Standen, ed.) 2nd Edn, Vol. 9. pp. 336–46. Interscience, New York.
Connell, D. W. (1964). *Aust. J. Chem.* **17**, 130–40.
Creveling, R. K. and Jennings, W. G. (1970), *J. agric. Fd chem.* **18**, 19–24.
Croteau, R. J. and Fagerson, I. S. (1968). *J. Fd Sci.* **33**, 386–9.
Drawert, F., Heimann, W., Emberger, R. and Tressl, R. (1965). *Z. Naturf.* **20b**, 497–8.
Drawert, F., Heimann, W., Emberger, R. and Tressl, R. (1966). *Liebigs Ann.* **694** 200–8.

Drawert, F., Heimann, W., Emberger, R. and Tressl, R. (1968). *Phytochem.* **7**, 881–3.

Drawert, F., Rapp, A. and Ullemeyer, H. (1967). *Vitis* **6**, 177–97.

Eriksson, C. E. (1968). *J. Fd Sci.* **33**, 525–32.

Felix, D., Melera, A., Seibl, J. and Kováts, E. sz. (1963). *Helv. chim. Acta* **46**, 1513–36.

Flath, R. A., Black, D. R., Guadagni, D. G., McFadden, W. H. and Schultz, T. H. (1967). *J. agric. Fd Chem.* **15**, 29–35.

Flath, R. A., Black, D. R., Forrey, R. R., McDonald, G. M., Mon, T. R. and Teranishi, R. (1969). *J. Chromat. Sci.* **7**, 508–12.

Forss, D. A., Dunnstone, E. A., Ramshaw, E. H. and Stark, W. (1962). *J. Fd Sci.* **27**, 90–3.

Francis, M. J. O. and O'Connell, M. (1969). *Phytochem.* **8**, 1705–8.

Gasco, L., Barrera, R. and de la Cruz, F. (1969). *J. Chromat. Sci.* **7**, 228–38.

Gehrig, R. F. and Knight, S. G. (1963). *Appl. Microbiol.* **11**, 166–70.

Genevois, L. (1961). *Brauwissenschaft* **14**, 52–5.

Genevois, L. and Lafon, M. (1957). *Chemy Ind.* **78**, 323–6.

Gierschner, K. and Baumann, G. (1967). *In* "Aroma und Geschmackstoffe in Lebensmitteln" (J. Solms and H. Neukom, eds), pp. 49–89. Forster Verlag, Zurich.

Gierschner, K. and Baumann, G. (1969). *Z. Lebensmittelunters. u.-Forsch.* **139**, 132–41.

Gross, G. G., Bolkart, K. H. and Zenk, M. H. (1968). *Biochem. biophys. Res. Commun.* **32**, 173–8.

Guadagni, D. G. (1968). *In* "Correlation of Subjective-Objective Methods in the Study of Odors and Taste", pp. 36–48. A.S.T.M. Special Publication No. 433, Philadelphia.

Haard, N. F. and Hultin, H. O. (1968). *Anal. Biochem.* **24**, 299–304.

Hardy, P. J. (1970). *Phytochem.* **9**, 709–15

Hefendehl, F. W., Underhill, E. W. and von Rudloff, E. (1967). *Phytochem.* **6**, 823–35.

Heimann, W. and Drawert, F. (1967). *In* "Bericht über die Getreidechemiker-Tagung, von 30. Mai bis 2. Juni 1967" (Arbeitsgemeinschaft Getreideforschung), pp. 199–205. Granum-Verlag, Detmold.

Heinz, D. E. and Jennings, W. G. (1966a). *J. Fd Sci.* **31**, 69–80.

Heinz, D. E. and Jennings, W. G. (1966b). *J. Am. Oil Chem. Soc.* **43**, 165–7.

Hoffmann, G. (1962). *J. Am. Oil Chem. Soc.* **39**, 439–44.

Hornstein, I. and Teranishi, R. (1967). *Chem. Engng News* **45**, No. 15, 93–108.

Hui, D. N. and Scheuer, P. J. (1961). *J. Fd Sci.* **26**, 557–63.

Hultin, H. O. (1962). *J. Fd Sci.* **27**, 426–9.

Hultin, H. O. and Proctor, B. E. (1961). *Fd Technol., Champaign* **15**, 440–4.

Ingraham, J. L. and Guymon, J. F. (1960). *Archs Biochem. Biophys.* **88**, 157–66.

James, A. T. (1968). *Chem. in Britain* **4**, 484–8.

Jennings, W. G. (1967). *In* "The Chemistry and Physiology of Flavors" (H. W. Schultz, E. A. Day and L. M. Libbey, eds), pp. 419–30. Avi, Westport.

Johnson, A. E., Nursten, H. E. and Self, R. (1969). *Chemy Ind.* 10–12.

Johnson, J. H., Gould, W. A., Badenhop, A. F. and Johnson, Jr, R. M. (1968). *J. agric. Fd Chem.* **16**, 255–8.

Jones, J. D., Hulme, A. C. and Wooltorton, L. S. C. (1964). *Phytochem.* **3**, 173–88.

Jorysch, D. and Broderick, J. J. (1967). *Cereal Sci. Today* **12**, 292–4, 312–13.

Kirchner, J. G. and Miller, J. M. (1953). *J. agric. Fd Chem.* **1**, 512–18.
Kirchner, J. G. and Miller, J. M. (1957). *J. agric. Fd Chem.* **5**, 283–91.
Kirchner, J. G., Miller, J. M., Rice, R. G., Keller, G. J. and Fox, M. M. (1953). *J. agric. Fd Chem.* **1**, 510–12.
Kugler, E. and Kováts, E. sz. (1963). *Helv. chim. Acta.* **46**, 1480–1513.
Kuusi, T., Siriiä, A. and Kuusi, T. (1966). *J. sci. agric. Soc., Finland* **38**, 162–79.
Loomis, W. D. (1967). *In* "Terpenoids in Plants" (J. B. Pridham, ed.), pp. 59–82. Academic Press, London and New York.
Luh, B. S. and Pinochet, M. F. (1959). *Fd Technol. Champaign* **24**, 423–7.
McCarthy, A. I., Palmer, J. K., Shaw, C. P. and Anderson E. E. (1963). *J. Fd Sci.*, **28**, 379–84.
McFadden, W. H., Teranishi, R., Corse, J., Black, D. R. and Mon, T. R. (1965). *J. Chromatography* **18**, 10–19.
MacLeod, Jr, W. D. (1966). *Calif. Citrogr.* **51**, 120–3.
MacLeod, Jr. W. D. (1968). *J. agric. Fd Chem.* **16**, 884–6.
Meigh, D. F., Pratt, H. K. and Cole, C. (1966). *Nature, Lond.* **211**, 419–20.
Miers, J. C. (1966). *J. agric. Fd Chem.* **14**, 419–23.
Moshonas, M. G. (1967). *J. Fd Sci.* **32**, 206–7.
Moshonas, M. G. and Lund, E. D. (1969). *J. agric. Fd Chem.* **17**, 802–4.
Murray, K. E., Huelin, F. E. and Davenport, J. B. (1964). *Nature, Lond.* **204**, 80.
Murray, K. E., Palmer, J. K., Whitfield, F. B., Kenneth, B. H. and Stanley, G. (1968). *J. Fd Sci.* **33**, 632–4.
Myers, M. J., Issenberg, P. and Wick, E. L. (1968). Personal communication. *Phytochem.* 1970. In press.
Nelson, E. K. and Curl, A. L. (1939). *J. Am. chem. Soc.* **61**, 667–8.
Nelson, P. E. and Hoff, J. E. (1969). *J. Fd Sci.* **34**, 53–7.
Nicholas, H. J. (1962). *J. biol. Chem.* **237**, 1485–8.
Nichols, B. W., Harris, P. and James, A. T. (1965). *Biochem. biophys. Res. Commun.* **21**, 473–9.
Nordström, K. (1964). *Svensk kem. Tidskr.* **76**, 510–43.
Nursten, H. E. and Williams, A. A. (1967). *Chemy Ind.* 486–97.
Nursten, H. E. and Williams, A. A. (1969a) *J. Sci. Fd Agric.* **20**, 91–8.
Nursten, H. E. and Williams, A. A. (1969b). *J. Sci. Fd Agric.* **20**, 613–19.
Okogun, J. I. and Ekong, D. E. V. (1969). *Chemy Ind.* 1272.
Peel, J. L. (1951). *Biochem. J.* **49**, 62–7.
Popovskii, V. G., Timofeeva, O. A. and Soboleva, I. M. (1965). *Tr. Moldavsk. Nauchn.-Issled. Inst. Pishchevoi Prom.* **6**, 126–38; *Chem. Abstr.*, 1966, **65**, 1307.
Power, F. B. and Chesnut, V. K. (1921). *J. Am. chem. Soc.* **43**, 1741–2.
Pyne, A. W. and Wick, E. L. (1965). *J. Fd Sci.* **30**, 192–200.
Ramshaw, E. H. and Hardy, P. J. (1969). *J. Sci. Fd Agric.* **20**, 619–21.
Rogers, J. and Toth, Z. (1968). *Cereal Sci. Today* **13**, 294, 296–8, 320.
Romani, R. J. and Yu, I. K. (1967). *Archs Biochem. Biophys.* **117**, 638–44.
Romani, R. J. and Yu, I. K. (1968). *Archs Biochem. Biophys.* **127**, 283–7.
Ryder, W. S. (1966). *Advances in Chem. Series* **56**, 70–93.
Schildknecht, H. and Rauch, G. (1961). *Z. Naturf.* **16b**, 422–9.
Schinz, H. and Seidel, C. F. (1957). *Helv. chim. Acta* **40**, 1839–59.
Schinz, H. and Seidel, C. F. (1961). *Helv. chim. Acta* **44**, 278.
Schmidt, H. W. H. (1967). *In* "Aroma und Geschmacksstoffe in Lebensmitteln" (J. Solms and H. Neukom, eds), pp. 35–46. Forster Verlag, Zurich.
Schormüller, J. and Grosch, W. (1964). *Z. Lebensmittelunters. u-Forsch.* **126**, 38–49.

Schultz, T. H., Teranishi, R., McFadden, W. H., Kilpatrick, P. W. and Corse, J. (1964). *J. Fd Sci.* **29**, 790–5.

Self, R. (1967). *In* "The Chemistry and Physiology of Flavors" (H. W. Schultz, E. A. Day and L. M. Libbey, eds), pp. 362–89. Avi, Westport.

SentheShanmuganathan, S. and Elsden, S. R. (1958). *Biochem. J.* **69**, 210–18.

Slater, C. A. (1961a). *J. Sci. Fd Agric.* **12**, 732–4.

Slater, C. A. (1961b). *Chemy Ind.* 833–5.

Slater, C. A. and Watkins, W. T. (1964). *J. Sci. Fd Agric.* **15**, 657–64.

Stanley, W. L. (1958). *In* "Flavor Research and Food Acceptance" (A. D. Little, Inc., sponsors), pp. 344–68. Reinhold, New York.

Stern, D. J., Lee, A., McFadden, W. H. and Stevens, K. L. (1967). *J. agric. Fd Chem.* **15**, 1100–3.

Stevens, K. L., Bomben, J., Lee, A. and McFadden, W. H. (1966). *J. agric. Fd Chem.* **14**, 249–52.

Stevens, K. L., Bomben, J. and McFadden, W. H. (1967). *J. agric. Fd Chem.* **15**, 378–80.

Stevens, K. L., Lundin, R. E. and Teranishi, R. (1965). *J. org. Chem.* **30**, 1690–2.

Stevens, K. L. and Scherer, J. R. (1968). *J. agric. Fd Chem.* **16**, 673–8.

Tabachnik, J. and Joslyn, M. A. (1953). *J. Bact.* **65**, 1–9.

Takei, S. and Ono, M. (1939). *J. agric. Chem. Soc. Japan* **15**, 193–5.

Tang, C. S. and Jennings, W. G. (1967). *J. agric. Fd Chem.* **15**, 24–8.

Tang, C. S. and Jennings, W. G. (1968). *J. agric. Fd Chem.* **16**, 252–4.

Teranishi, R., Lundin, R. E., McFadden, W. H., Mon, T. R., Schultz, T. H., Stevens, K. L. and Wasserman, J. (1966). *J. agric. Fd Chem.* **14**, 447.

Teranishi, R., Lundin, R. E. and Scherer, J. R. (1967). *In* "The Chemistry and Physiology of Flavors" (H. W. Schultz, E. A. Day and L. M. Libbey, eds), pp. 161–81. Avi, Westport.

von Sydow, E. and Anjou, K. (1969). *Lebensm.-Wiss. u. Technol.* **2**, 78–81.

von Sydow, E., Andersson, J., Anjou, K., Karlsson, G., Land, D. G. and Griffiths, N. (1970). *Lebensm.-Wiss. u. Technol.* **3**, 11–17.

Walker, N. J., Patton, S. and Dimick, P. S. (1968). *Biochim. biophys. Acta* **152**, 445–53.

Webb, A. D. (1967). *Biotech. Bioengng* **9**, 305–19.

Weurman, C. (1961). *Fd Technol. Campaign* **15**, 531–6.

Weurman, C. (1969). *J. agric. Fd Chem.* **17**, 370–84.

Weurman, C. and van Lunteren, G. (1967). *In* "Aroma-und Geschmacksstoffe in Lebensmitteln" (J. Solms and H. Neukom, eds), pp. 21–34. Forster Verlag, Zurich.

Wick, E. L. (1965). *Fd Technol. Champaign* **19**, 827–33.

Wick, E. L., McCarthy, A. I., Myers, M., Murray, E., Nursten, H. and Issenberg, P. (1966). *Advances in Chem. Series* **56**, 241–60.

Wick, E. L., Yamanishi, T., Kobayashi, A., Valenzuela, S. and Issenberg, P. (1969). *J. agric. Fd Chem.* **17**, 751–9.

Willhalm, B., Palluy, E. and Winter, M. (1966). *Helv. chim. Acta* **49**, 65–7.

Winter, M. (1963). *Mitt. Geb. Lebensmittelunters. u. Hyg.* **54**, 520–6.

Winter, M., Palluy, E., Hinder, M. and Willhalm, B. (1962). *Helv. chim. Acta* **45** 2186–95.

Winter, M. and Sundt, E. (1962). *Helv. chim. Acta* **45**, 2195–211.

Winter, M., Willhalm, B., Hinder, M., Palluy, E. and Sundt, E. (1958). *Perfum. essent. Oil Rec.* **49**, 250–5.

Wolford, R. W. and Attaway, J. A. (1967). *J. agric. Fd Chem.* **15,** 369–77.

Wolford, R. W., Attaway, J. A., Alberding, G. E. and Atkins, C. D. (1963). *J. Fd Sci.* **28,** 320–8.

Wyatt, C. J., Pereira, R. L. and Day, E. A. (1967). *J. Dairy Sci.* **50,** 1760–3.

Yamada, M. and Stumpf, P. K. (1965). *Pl. Physiol.* **40,** 659–64.

Yu, M.-H., Olsen, L. E. and Salunkhe, D. K. (1968a). *Phytochem.* **7,** 555–60.

Yu, M.-H., Olsen, L. E. and Salunkhe, D. K. (1968b). *Phytochem.* **7,** 560–5.

Zenk, M. H. (1966). *In* "Biosynthesis of Aromatic Compounds" (G. Billek, ed.), pp. 45–60. Pergamon Press, Oxford.

Chapter 11

Fruit Phenolics

J. VAN BUREN

New York State Agricultural Experiment Station (Cornell University),
Geneva, New York, U.S.A.

I. INTRODUCTION

Phenolic compounds enjoy a wide distribution in the plant kingdom, and they are particularly prominent in fruits where they are important in determining colour and flavour. Neish (1964) has suggested that they were originally by-products of the metabolism of aromatic amino acids. There exist elaborate biosynthetic pathways for their production in plants, and, perhaps because they are secondary products and apparently play no vital role in metabolism, these pathways lead, in different fruits and in the same fruit, to a wide variety of compounds. For instance, the lowbush blueberry (*Vaccinium angustifolium*) has at least fifteen anthocyanins (Francis *et al.*, 1966). Such diversity has caused much difficulty in studying these compounds, but the development of improved methods of isolation and identification, primarily through

TABLE I. Total phenolic compounds in ripe fruits

Fruit	Phenolic content	Reference
Apple (*Malus pumila*)		
Various varieties	0·11–0·34 g/100 g fr. wt.	Walker (1962)
Various varieties	0·1–1 g/100 g fr. wt.	Williams (1959)
Various varieties	Average of 0·05 g/100 g fr. wt.	Harel *et al.* (1966)
Cox's orange Pippin	5·5 g/100 g dr. wt.	Hulme and Edney (1960)
Cox's orange Pippin	2 g/100 g dr. wt.	Hulme and Jones (1963)
Baldwin	0·25 g/100 g fr. wt.	Caldwell (1934)
Cider apple juice	0·11–0·34 g/100 ml	Burroughs (1961)
Cider apple Launette	1·1 g/100 g fr. wt.	Caldwell (1934)
Cider apple Waldhöfler	0·45 g/100 g fr. wt.	Van Buren *et al.* (1966)
Banana (*Musa*)	0·53 g/100 g dr. wt.	Goldstein and Swain (1963)
Date (*Phoenix dactylifera*)	0·5 g/100 g fr. wt.	Maier and Metzler (1965a)
Cherry (*Prunus cerasus*)		
Montmorency	0·2 g/100 g fr. wt.	Caldwell (1934)
Grape (*Vitis* spp.)		
Red wine	0·15–0·5 g/100 ml	Ribéreau-Gayon (1964)
White wine	0·015–0·1 g/100 ml	Ribéreau-Gayon (1964)
Riesling, cluster	0·95 g/100 g fr. wt.	Cantarelli and Peri (1964)
Tokay, cluster	0·48 g/100 g fr. wt.	Cantarelli and Peri (1964)
Muscat, skin	0·35 g/100 g fr. wt.	Cantarelli and Peri (1964)
Muscat, pulp	0·10 g/100 g fr. wt.	Cantarelli and Peri (1964)
Muscat, seed	4·5 g/100 g fr. wt.	Cantarelli and Peri (1964)
Concord, wine	0·064 g/100 ml	Robinson *et al.* (1967)
Chelois N (S. 10878)		
wine	0·092 g/100 ml	Robinson *et al.* (1967)
Passion fruit (*Passiflora edulis*)	1·4 mg/100 g fr. wt.	Pruthi *et al.* (1961)
Peach (*Prunus persica*)		
Mixed varieties	0·028–0·141 g/100 g fr. wt.	Guadagni *et al.* (1949)
Elberta	0·069–0·180 g/100 g fr. wt.	Guadagni and Nimmo (1953)
Elberta	0·240 g/100 g fr. wt.	Craft (1961)
Unspecified	2 g/100 g dr. wt.	Goldstein and Swain (1963)
Pear (*Pyrus cummunis*)		
Muscachet	0·4 g/100 g fr. wt.	Jacquin and Cherel (1957)
Persimmon (*Diospyros*)	8·5 g/100 g dr. wt.	Goldstein and Swain (1963)
Plum (*Prunus domestica*)		
Victoria, flesh	2·1 g/100 g dr. wt.	Hillis and Swain (1959)
Victoria, skin	5·7 g/100 g dr. wt.	Hillis and Swain (1959)
Unknown, whole	2 g/100 g dr. wt.	Goldstein and Swain (1963)

chromatographic procedures, has stimulated a tremendous amount of work in this field in recent years.

The accumulation of phenols in fruits may be higher or lower than in other parts of the plant, such as bark, leaves or heart wood. The concentration of phenolics decreases as a fruit matures, but usually the amount per fruit increases (Williams, 1959; Craft, 1961). Fruits and flowers often contain considerable amounts of some types of phenolics, such as anthocyanins, while other parts of the same plants, that is, leaves or bark, have very little or none. Other phenolics, such as phloridzin of apples and arbutin of pears, are present in significant amounts in other organs but are virtually absent in the fruit. Comprehensive reviews of the phenolics in the fruit of the grape (*Vitis* spp.) (Ribéreau-Gayon, 1964) and of the apple (*Malus pumila*) (Monties, 1966) have been presented.

The levels of phenolics in fruits vary widely from species to species, variety to variety, season to season, and location to location. Disease also influences concentration. Despite this, it may be of value to see some representative values for total fruit phenolics (Table I). The class making up the largest contribution is normally either the cinnamic acid derivatives or the monomeric-polymeric flavans (Craft, 1961). These two classes are also more uniformly distributed throughout the tissues of the fruits than the other classes such as anthocyanins and flavonol glycosides.

In this account of fruit phenolics attention will be concentrated on the major classes found in fruits; however, the descriptions of metabolism and biosynthesis contain information derived largely from studies on other tissues, organs and species. For fuller information on phenolics that are quantitatively less important in fruit, but biochemically very interesting, such recent works as those by Harborne (1964a) and (1967) should be consulted.

II. THE COMMON PHENOLIC COMPOUNDS OF FRUITS

A. Cinnamic Acid Derivatives

The hydroxy cinnamic acids combine the characteristics of almost universal distribution and high concentration in higher plants. This may be due, in part, to the key role they play in the formation of other, more complicated phenolic compounds. Despite their widespread presence in angiosperms, those found consist almost entirely of the four *trans* acids shown in Fig. 1. They are rarely present in an uncombined form, but usually as esters (Harborne, 1964c); by far the most common combination is with quinic acid. Of the quinic esters the most frequently observed form involves the 3 position hydroxyl group of the quinic acid.

Accordingly, chlorogenic acid is the most important cinnamic acid derivative found in fruits and is found in large enough concentrations in apples to permit its isolation and characterization (Hulme, 1953). A second ester of importance is p-coumaryl quinic acid (Williams, 1958) which also involves the 3 position of quinic acid. Esterification of caffeic acid at other positions on quinic acid gives rise to a whole series of isomeric esters (Sondheimer, 1958; Corse et al., 1965). A general review of this class of compounds has been prepared by Sondheimer (1964).

In some fruits, such as dates (Maier and Metzler, 1965b), shikimic acid esters, dactyliferic acids, are formed in much the same pattern as seen for quinic acid (Harborne, 1964c) with the caffeic acid derivatives being presumably the 3 position ester. Malic and tartaric acids have also been found

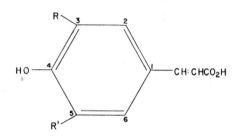

p-COUMARIC (R=R'=H)   FERULIC (R=OMe, R'=H)

CAFFEIC (R=OH, R'=H)   SINAPIC (R=R'=OMe)

FIG. 1. Cinnamic acids.

esterified by cinnamic acids in some plants. Sugar-cinnamic esters are frequently found in which one or, more rarely, two (shakuchirin, see Fig. 2) cinnamic acids are esterified on the sugar (Harborne, 1964c). Anthocyanin and flavonoid glycosides are also found acylated by cinnamic acids through their sugar hydroxyl groups. Here p-coumaric acid is most commonly the acylating agent. Besides forming esters, the hydroxylated cinnamic acids also form, to a lesser extent, O-glycosides with sugars (Harborne and Corner, 1961). While depsides predominate in fruits, derived fermentation products often contain considerable amounts of free cinnamic and quinic acids due to hydrolysis during fermentation and storage (Burkhardt, 1965).

Chlorogenic acid is sometimes the predominant single phenolic compound in fruits, its concentration being as high as 0·25% in the bilberry (*Vaccinium myrtillus*) (Swain, 1962). Isomers are also prominent (Cartwight, 1955; Sondheimer, 1958; Williams, 1958), and often occur together, as in the peach (*Prunus persica*) (Corse, 1953; Luh et al., 1967) and the apple (*Malus pumila*)

(Herrmann, 1958). In the sweet cherry (*Prunus avium*), and other *Prunus* species, the most prominent depside is neochlorogenic acid (Sondheimer, 1958; Swain, 1962). Several dicaffeoylquinic acids are found in coffee (Scarpati and Guiso, 1964).

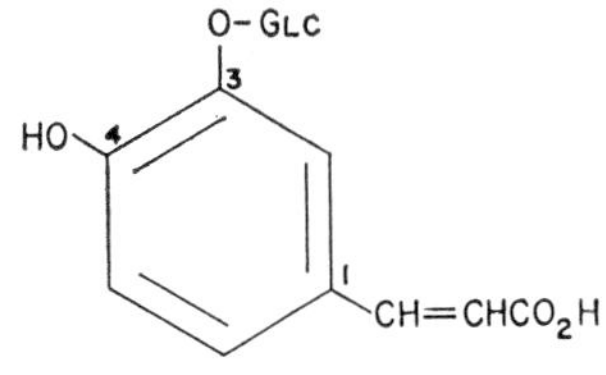

O‐GLC

HO

CH=CHCO₂H

CAFFEIC ACID   3‐GLUCOSIDE

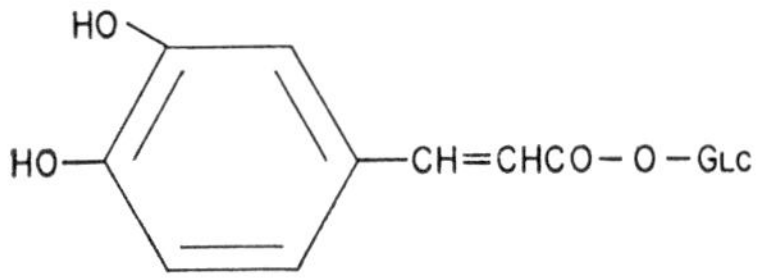

HO

HO

CH=CHCO‐O‐GLC

1‐CAFFEOYLGLUCOSE

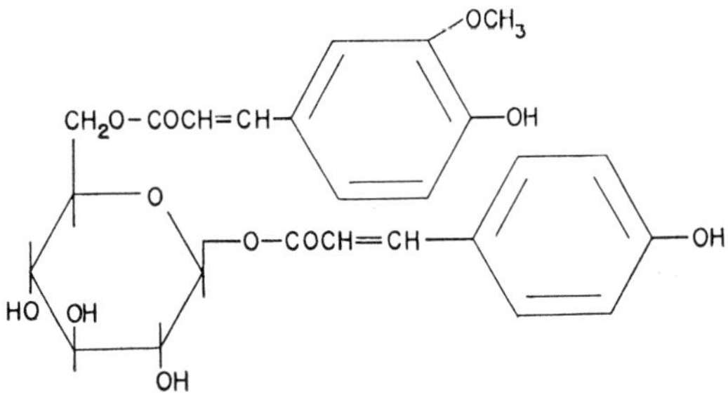

OCH₃

CH₂O‐COCH=CH

OH

O

O‐COCH=CH

OH

HO   OH

OH

SHAKUCHIRIN

FIG. 2. Cinnamic glycosides.

The concentration of cinnamic acid derivatives declines as fruit matures (Walker, 1963); however, the amount per fruit increases as the fruits enlarge during the growing season. An exception is found in the date (Maier and Metzler, 1965a) where the darkening accompanying ripening results from a condensation of dactyliferic acids to give insoluble polymeric products. As is the case for most fruit phenolics, the concentration of cinnamic acid derivatives is highest in the skin and peel. Some concentrations of these compounds are given in Table II.

TABLE II. Concentration of hydroxy-cinnamic acids esterified with quinic acid in fruits

Fruit	Concentration mg/100 g fr. wt.	Reference
Apple (*Malus pumila*)	134	Walker (1963)
	125	Sondheimer (1958)
Bilberry (*Vaccinium (myrtillus)*)	250	Sondheimer (1958)
Cherry, sweet (*Prunus avium*)	140	Sondheimer (1958)
Grape (*Vitis* hybrid) Steuben	185	Sondheimer (1958)
Peach (*Prunus persica*)	75	Sondheimer (1958)
Pear (*Pyrus communis*)	170	Sondheimer (1958)
Plum (*Prunus domestica*)	90	Sondheimer (1958)

B. Flavans

These phenolics are widely distributed, and they and their derivatives are present in particularly large amounts in higher plants. While there are a large number of types found in nature, those detected in fruits are rather restricted in composition. The presence of two or three asymmetric centres makes possible a great many isomers (Clarke-Lewis *et al.*, 1963; Brown and MacBride, 1964). (+)Catechin and (−)epicatechin are the most common forms (Herr-

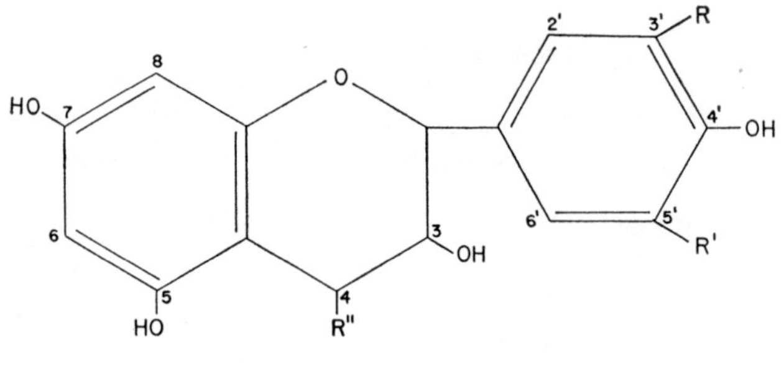

CATECHIN   OR EPI CATECHIN   (R=OH, R'= R"=H)

GALLOCATECHIN   OR EPI GALLOCATECHIN   (R= R'=OH, R"=H)

FLAVAN-3,4,-DIOL   (R=R"=OH, R'=H)

FIG. 3. Flavans.

mann, 1959; Weinges, 1964), but, although they often appear together in fruits, varieties of the same fruit can differ in their relative content of these compounds. An extreme case is the pear (*Pyrus communis*) where (+)catechin and (−)epicatechin are present in dessert types such as the Bartlett variety (Nortje, 1966) but are not present in detectable amounts in perry pears (Williams, 1957, 1959). In all cases of fruits where the flavans have not been found as monomers, polymeric materials are present which are unquestionably derived from them. Flavan-3,4-diols have not been found in fruits and only rarely in other plants. They are, however, suspected to be precursors of the very common polymeric proanthocyanidins. Table III shows the flavans detected in fruits.

TABLE III. Flavans in common fruits

Fruit	(+) catechin	(−) epicatechin	Other	Reference
Apple (*Malus pumila*)	+	+		Herrmann (1958, 1959)
Apricot (*Prunus armeniaca*)	+	+		Herrmann (1958, 1959)
Blackberry (*Rubus fruticosus*)	+	+		Herrmann (1958, 1959)
Cherry, sour (*Prunus cerasus*)	+	+		Herrmann (1958, 1959)
Cherry, sweet (*Prunus avium*)	+	+		Herrmann (1958, 1959)
Cowberry (*Vaccinium vitis-idaea*)	+			Weinges (1964)
Currant, red (*Ribes rubrum*)	+		(+)gallocatechin	Herrmann (1958, 1959)
Currant, black (*Ribes nigrum*)	+		(+)gallocatechin	Herrmann (1958, 1959)
Gooseberry (*Ribes uva-crispa*)	+		(+)gallocatechin	Herrmann (1958, 1959)
Grape (*Vitis* spp.)	+	+	(−)catechin (+)gallocatechin (−)gallocatechin (−)epigallocatechin 3-galloylepicatechin	Herrmann (1958, 1959); Ribéreau-Gayon (1964)
Peach (*Prunus persica*)	+			Herrmann (1958, 1959)
Pear (*Pyrus cummunis*)	+	+		Nortje (1966)
Plum (*Prunus domestica*)	+	+	(+)gallocatechin	Herrmann (1958, 1959)
Quince (*Cydonia oblonga*)		+		Herrmann (1958, 1959)
Raspberry, red (*Rubus idaeus*)	+	+		Herrmann (1958, 1959)
Strawberry (*Fragaria*)	+	+		Herrmann (1958, 1959)

Flavan monomers are not found in fruits as glycosides, nor are they esterified or methylated or in any other heterogeneous combinations except for the identification of (−)epicatechin-3-gallate in grapes (Tsai Su and Singleton, 1969). In tea (*Thea sinensis*), where large amounts of gallic acid accumulates, galloyl esters of (−)epicatechin and (−)epigallocatechin (Roberts *et al.*, 1957) are present.

The flavans are more prominent in the skin and peel of fruits, although they are also distributed throughout the flesh (Segal and Grager, 1967). The concentration is three times as high in apple peel as in apple flesh (Sal'kova and Bekbulatova, 1965). Their concentration in immature fruits is higher than in mature fruits.

C. Anthocyanidins and Anthocyanins

These compounds, largely because they are coloured and easily detected, have received considerable attention. The structure of common anthocyanidins is shown in Fig. 4.

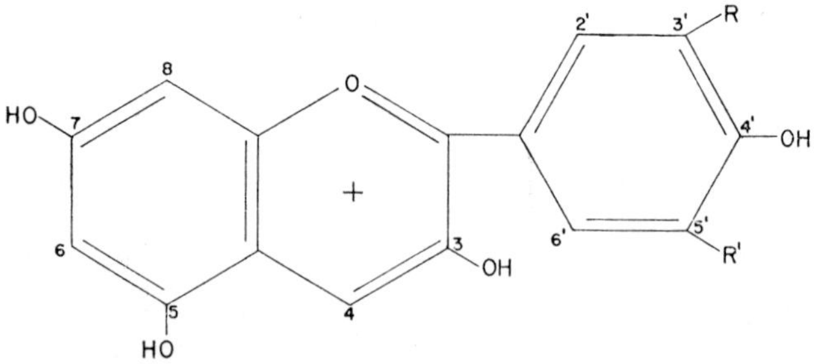

PELARGONIDIN (R=R'=H)	DELPHINIDIN (R=R'=OH)
CYANIDIN (R=OH, R'=H)	PETUNIDIN (R=OH, R'=OMe)
PEONIDIN (R=OMe, R'=H)	MALVIDIN (R=R'=OMe)

FIG. 4. Anthocyanidins.

The normal forms of these in fruits are as the β-glycosides with sugars at the 3 and 5 positions; only very rarely do the other anthocyanidin hydroxyls take part in a glycosidic bond. The sugars are normally present in the pyranose form. While a great variety of sugars have been found, the most frequently occurring mono- and di-saccharides are D-glucose, D-galactose,

L-rhamnose, L-arabinose, rutinose, sophorose and sambubiose. Branched tri-saccharides have also been reported (Harborne and Hall, 1964). The 3 position, with one exception (Sun and Francis, 1967), is always glycosylated. Di-saccharides and tri-saccharides examined so far contain at least one glucose. The linkages found are β 1→2, β 1→6, or α 1→6. At the 5 position, the substituent is always glucose.

The sugars, in turn, may be acylated with cinnamic acids, most commonly with p-coumaric acid followed in frequency by caffeic and ferulic acids. This acylation occurs on the sugar attached to the 3 position (Harborne, 1964b). Various positions of the sugar can take part in the formation of the ester. Birkofer (1965), Birkofer et al. (1965) and Watanabe et al. (1966) reported, for different anthocyanins, acylations on the 4 position of rhamnose, the 6 position of glucose and the 2 position of the terminal glucose of sophorose. The anthocyanins of many fruits are shown in Table IV. There can be considerable quantitative and qualitative variations in pigment content with variety.

There is evidence that anthocyanins may be combined with other cell constituents. Metal complexes are described by Hayashi (1962), and a metal-flavonoid complex was isolated from cornflower (Centaurea cyanus) by Asen and Jurd (1967). Such combinations may explain some of the colour effects in fruits.

The anthocyanins are typically located in the epidermal layers of a large number of fruits, such as apples (Malus pumila), plums (Prunus domestica) and pears (Pyrus communis) (Dayton, 1966), although with some apples, such as the Barry variety (McIntosh and Cox Orange), anthocyanin is also seen in the flesh. With sweet cherries (P. avium), if the epidermis contains significant amounts of anthocyanin, the flesh will generally have somewhat smaller concentrations of the same compound(s), but with the sour cherry (P. cerasus) there are some varieties, such as Montmorency, with anthocyanins only in the skin and others, such as Morello, having the pigment in the flesh as well. Berries have a more uniform distribution of anthocyanins than tree fruits. In contrast to the cinnamic acids and the flavans, the concentration of anthocyanins increases rapidly in fruits as they near maturity (Ribéreau-Gayon, 1964). The levels of anthocyanins found in a variety of fruits are shown in Table V.

Many fruits (Van Buren et al., 1960; Scheiner et al., 1960) possess an enzyme system that is capable of decolourizing anthocyanins. Some of these systems require trace amounts of catechol, catechin or other orthodihydroxyl phenols as well as oxygen. Sakamura et al. (1966) have described a similar system in eggplant (Solanum melongena) that differs in that a second, catechol-like phenol is not required. Still another variant, this time found in the apple, has been studied by Schmid (1967), which he believes first removes the sugar

TABLE IV. Anthocyanins of Common Fruits

Fruit	Anthocyanins	Reference
Apple (*Malus pumila*)	**Cy-3-galactoside**, Cy-3-arabinoside, Cy-7-arabinoside	Swain (1962); Sun and Francis (1967)
Banana (*Musa*)	Pel-3-monoside	Swain (1962)
Bilberry (*Vaccinium myrtillus*)	Pel-3-glycoside, Cy-3-glycoside, Pet-monoside, Dp-3-glucoside, Dp-3-galactoside, Mv-3-glucoside	Swain (1962)
Blackberry (*Rubus fruticosus*)	**Cy-3-glucoside**, Cy-3-rutinoside	Harborne and Hall (1964)
Blueberry (*Vaccinium angustifolium*)	Dp, Mv, Pet, Peon, Cy-3-glucosides, galactosides and arabinosides	Francis *et al.* (1966)
Cherry, sour (*Prunus cerasus*)	Cy-3-rutinoside, **Cy-3-sophoroside**, Cy-3-glucosylrutinoside, Cy-3-glucoside	Harborne and Hall (1964); Schaller and von Elbe (1968); Li and Wagenknecht (1956)
Cherry, sweet (*Prunus avium*)	Cy-3-glucoside, Cy-3-rutinoside	Swain (1962); Harborne (1967)
Cowberry (*Vaccinium vitis-idaea*)	Cy-3-galactoside	Swain (1962)
Cranberry (*Vaccinium macrocarpum*)	**Cy-3-galactoside, Cy-3-arabinoside, Peon-3-galactoside,** Peon-3-glucoside, Cy-3-glucoside, Peon-3-arabinoside	Swain (1962); Sakamura and Francis (1961); Zapsalis and Francis (1965); Fuleki and Francis (1967)
Currant, red (*Ribes sativum*)	Dp-3-glucoside, Cy-3-rutinoside, Cy-3-xylosylrutinoside, Cy-3-glucosylrutinoside, Cy-3-sophoroside, Cy-3-rutinoside, Cy-3-sambubioside	Swain (1962); Harborne and Hall (1964)
Currant, black (*Ribes nigrum*)	Cy-3-glucoside, Cy-3-rutinoside, Dp-3-glucoside	Harborne and Hall (1964)
Elderberry (*Sambucus nigra*)	Cy-3-glucoside, Cy-3-sambubioside, Cy-3-sambubioside-5-glucoside	Harborne (1967); Harborne (1963a)
Fig (*Ficus carica*)	Cy-3-monoside	Swain (1962)
Gooseberry (*Ribes uva-crispa*)	Cy-3-glucoside, Cy-3-rutinoside	Harborne and Hall (1964)

Fruit	Anthocyanins	Reference
Grape (*Vitis vinifera, V. riparia, V. labrusca* and hybrids)	Mv, Peon, Pet, Cy, Del-3-glucosides and 3,5-diglucosides, Mv-3-p-coumaroyl glucoside-5-glucoside, Mv-3-p-coumaroyl glucoside, Mv-3-caffeoyl glucoside-5-glucoside, Peon-3-p-coumaroyl glucoside, Peon-3-p-coumaroyl glucoside-5-glucoside	Ribéreau-Gayon (1964); Chen and Luh (1967)
Huckleberry (*Solanum nigrum guineese*)	Pet and Mv-3-p-coumaroyl rutinoside-5-glucoside, Pet-3-rutinoside-5-glucoside	Francis and Harborne (1966)
Mulberry (*Morus nigra*)	Cy-3-glucoside	Harborne (1967)
Orange (*Citrus sinensis*)	Cy-3-glucoside, Dp-3-glucoside	Harborne (1967)
Passion fruit (*Passiflora edulis*)	Dp-3-glucoside, Dp-3-glucosylglucoside	Harborne (1967)
Peach (*Prunus persica*)	Cy-3-glucoside	Hsia *et al.* (1965); Van Blaricom and Senn (1967)
Pear (*Pyrus cummunis*)	Cy-3-galactoside	Harborne and Hall (1964)
Plum (*Prunus domestica*)	**Cy-3-glucoside,** Cy-3-rutinoside, Peon-3-glucoside, Peon-3-rutinoside	Harborne (1967); Dickinson and Gawler (1956)
Pomegranate (*Punica granatum*)	Dp-3,5-diglucoside	Harborne (1967)
Raspberry, red (*Rubus idaeus*)	**Cy-3-glucoside,** Cy-3-glucosylrutinoside, Cy-3-rutinoside, Cy-3-sophoroside, Cy-3-glucosylsophoroside	Swain (1962); Harborne and Hall (1964); Nybom (1960)
Raspberry, black (*Rubus occidentalis*)	**Cy-3-glucoside,** Cy-3-rutinoside, Cy-3-sambubioside, Cy-3-xylosylrutinoside, Cy-3,5-diglucoside, Cy-3-rutinoside-5-glucoside	Harborne and Hall (1964); Daravingas and Cain (1966)
Sloe (*Prunus spinosa*)	Cy-3-glucoside, Cy-3-rutinoside, Peon-3-glucoside, Peon-3-rutinoside	Harborne (1967)
Strawberry (*Fragaria* spp.)	**Pg-3-glucoside,** Pg-3-galactoside, Cy-3-glucoside	Swain (1962)

Abbreviations used: Pg = pelargonidin; Cy = cyanidin; Peon = peonidin; Del = delphinidin; Pet = petunidin; Mv = malvidin. Bold anthocyanins are those most prominent.

TABLE V. Anthocyanin levels in fruits

Fruit	Anthocyanin level	Reference
Apple (*Malus pumila*)		
McIntosh, sunny side	0·030 mg/cm² peel	Faust (1965a, b)
shaded side	0·025 mg/cm² peel	Faust (1965a, b)
Various varieties	0·1–21·6 mg/g fr. wt. peel	Walker (1964)
Cranberry (*Vaccinium macrocarpus*)		
Howe variety	56–100 mg/100 g fr. wt.	Fuleki and Francis (1968)
Currant, black (*Ribes nigrum*)		
Juice	0·1–0·4 g/100 ml	Koch and Haase-Sajak (1967)
	0·145 g/100 ml	Morton (1968)
Grape (*Vitis* spp.)		
Merlot fruit	0·1–0·135 g/100 g fr. wt.	Ribéreau-Gayon (1964)
Red wine	Up to 0·05 g/100 ml[a]	Ribéreau-Gayon (1964)
Plum (*Prunus domestica*)		
Victoria fruit	0·0019–0·0053 g/100 g fr. wt.	Dickinson and Gawler (1956)
juice	0·0013–0·0026 g/100 ml	Dickinson and Gawler (1956)
skin	0·8 g/100 g dr. wt.	Hillis and Swain (1959)
Raspberry (*Rubus* spp.)		
Red	0·04 g/100 g fr. wt.	Daravingas and Cain (1965)
Black	0·345 g/100 g fr. wt.	Daravingas and Cain (1965)
Strawberry (*Fragaria chiloensis*)		
Dresden juice	0·023 mg/100 ml	Sondheimer and Kertesz (1952)

[a] Some teinturier wines have 10 times this level of pigment.

and then brings about an oxidative ring opening of the aglycone, but since activity increased on storage there is the possibility that micro-organisms may have been responsible for the enzymes observed. Peroxidase has also been associated with anthocyanin destruction (Grommeck and Markakis, 1964).

D. Flavonols and Flavonol Glycosides

The flavonols enjoy a wider distribution than the anthocyanins, although they are not so readily detected because of their faint or absent colour. The structure of the common flavonols bears some resemblance to that of the anthocyanidins, and, like the anthocyanidins, they are usually found as glycosides. Position 3 is almost always occupied, and when two positions are occupied the 7 position is the second one to become glycosylated. There are no known 5-glycosides in fruits. Perhaps the formation of a glycoside at this position is hindered by the strong hydrogen bond type interaction of this hydroxyl group with the carbonyl function at the 4 position. The sugars

TABLE VI. Flavonol glycosides of common fruits

Fruit	Flavonol glycosides	Reference
Apple (*Malus pumila*)	Qu-3-galactoside, arabinoside, glucoside, rutinoside, rhamnoside, xyloside, rhamnoglucoside, Km-glycosides	Siegelman (1955b); Harborne (1967)
Apricot (*Prunus armeniaca*)	Qu-3-glucoside	Harborne (1967)
Bilberry (*Vaccinium myrtillus*)	Qu-3-glucoside, rhamnoside, arabinoside	Harborne (1967)
Cherry, sweet (*Prunus avium*)	Qu-3-rutinoside	Harborne (1967); Swain (1962)
Cranberry (*Vaccinium macrocarpum*)	Qu-3-galactoside, arabinoside, rhamnoside, Myr-3-arabinoside, digalactoside	Harborne (1967); Puski and Francis (1967)
Currant, black (*Ribes nigrum*)	Qu-3-glucoside	Harborne (1967); Swain (1962)
Grape (*Vitis* spp.)	Km-3-glucoside, Qu-3-glucoside, rhamnoside, rutinoside, glucuronide, Myr-3-glucoside	Harborne (1967); Swain (1962)
Pear (*Pyrus cummunis*)	Isorhamnetin-3-glucoside, isorhamnetin-rutinoside, isorhamnetin-3-rhamnosylgalactoside, Qu-3-galactoside, glucoside, rutinoside	Harborne (1967); Nortje and Koeppen (1965); Wagenbreth (1959)
Plum (*Prunus domestica*)	Qu-3-arabinoside, glucoside, rhamnoside, rutinoside, Kaempferol	Siegelman (1955b); Harborne (1967); Bate-Smith (1961)
Strawberry (*Fragaria* spp.)	Qu-3-glucoside, Km-3-glucoside	Siegelman (1955b); Co and Markakis (1968)
Tomato (*Lycopersicum esculentum*)	Qu-3-rhamnoside, rutinoside	Rivas and Luh (1968); Wu and Burrell (1958)

Abbreviations used: Km = kaempferol; Qu = quercetin; Myr = Myricitin forming glycosides are usually D-glucose or L-rhamnose, with rutinose being the most common disaccharide. The types of flavonol glycosides in fruits (Table VI) show much less variety than was seen with the anthocyanins.

The amount of flavonol present in a fruit can vary considerably between varieties. In apple peel they range from 0·47 to 18·8 mg/g fresh weight (Walker, 1964); almost none is found in the flesh (Workman, 1963). Since the concentration in the peel decreases slightly as the fruit matures, it follows

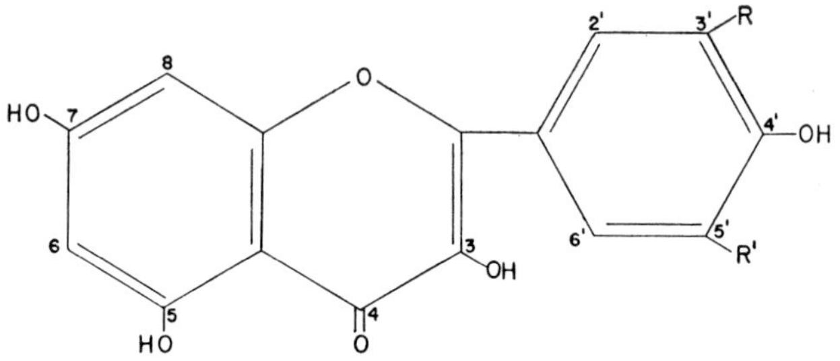

KAEMPFEROL (R = R' = H)

QUERCETIN (R = OH, R' = H)

ISORHAMNETIN (R = OMe, R' = H)

MYRICETIN (R = R' = OH)

FIG. 5. Flavonols.

that the formation of flavonol glycosides is not governed by the same factors as the synthesis of the anthocyanins. It appears that light is of some import-ance to flavonol production inasmuch as the concentration of flavonol glycosides on the sunny side of individual fruits is twice that on the shady side.

The relative amounts of the different types of flavonol glycosides are related to variety. For instance, in the grape, where there are wide differences with regard to anthocyanins, there are also differences in flavonol glycosides (Ribéreau-Gayon, 1964).

E. Condensed Polyphenols

These are extremely widespread compounds, both with regard to the type of fruit and the location within the fruit. The condensed materials are, like the monomeric flavans, more uniformly distributed in fruit tissue than the anthocyanins and the flavonol glycosides, but, even so, they are more concentrated in the peel than in the flesh. Flavans appear to be the precursors of these covalently linked polymers. The exact nature of the bonds involved in the condensation reaction is not known with certainty, but the mass of evidence points to a carbon–carbon bond between the 4 position of one flavan moiety and the 6 or 8 position of another (Geissman and Dittmar, 1965; Weinges *et al.*, 1968). Such a linkage would not reduce the number of

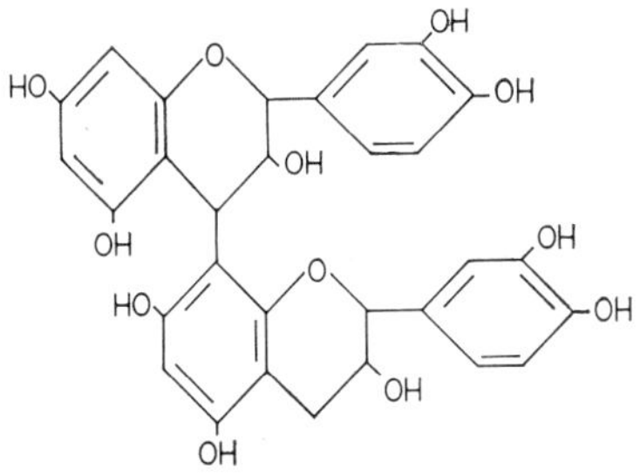

FIG. 6. Condensed flavans.

phenolic hydroxyl groups per flavan unit. Some of these condensed flavans yield anthocyanidins when heated with dilute mineral acids. This type of condensed flavan has been termed leucoanthocyanidin or proanthocyanidin (Freudenberg and Weinges, 1960) and is present in all fruits.

Condensed flavans having two flavan units have been isolated in pure form from strawberry leaves (Creasy and Swain, 1965), avocados (Geissman and Dittmar, 1965), apples (Van Buren *et al.*, 1966) and a number of other fruits (Weinges *et al.*, 1968), while the presence of such dimers is suspected in additional cases (Nortje, 1966). Those studied thus far have all yielded cyanidin on treatment with dilute acids. Some also produce (−)epicatechin. More highly condensed, less well characterized materials also form cyanidin and catechins (Ito and Joslyn, 1964, 1965), and others yield pelargonidin in addition (Van Buren *et al.*, 1966). Still more highly condensed materials have been found, verging on colloidal size, in perry pears (Kelhofer, 1908; Williams, 1957). The most striking change occurring with fruit maturation is an increase in the degree of condensation (Barnell and Barnell, 1945; Goldstein and Swain, 1963; Swardt, 1967).

F. Less Common Polyphenols

1. *Flavones*

These compounds are widely distributed in higher plants, but they are not prominent in fruits other than citrus, where they usually occur as glycosides with sugar attached at the 7 position or occasionally at the 5 position.

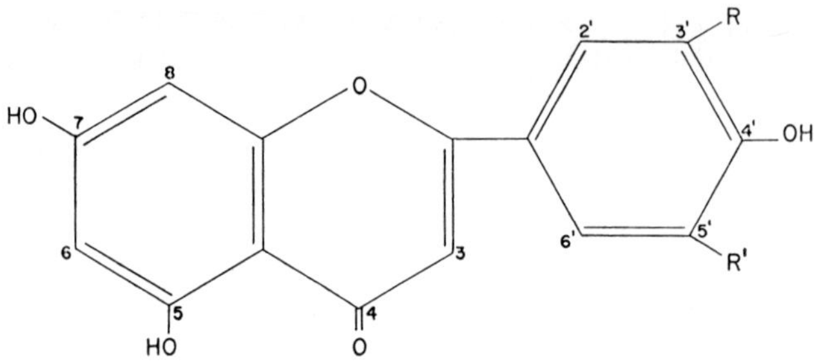

APIGENIN (R = R'= H)

LUTEOLIN (R=OH, R'=H)

TRICIN (R= R'= OME)

FIG. 7. Flavones.

2. *Flavanones*

These are also prominent only in citrus fruits where they are present as the 7-glycosides. Some of these are responsible for a bitter taste. An extensive presentation of the citrus flavanoids has been given by Horowitz (1961), and

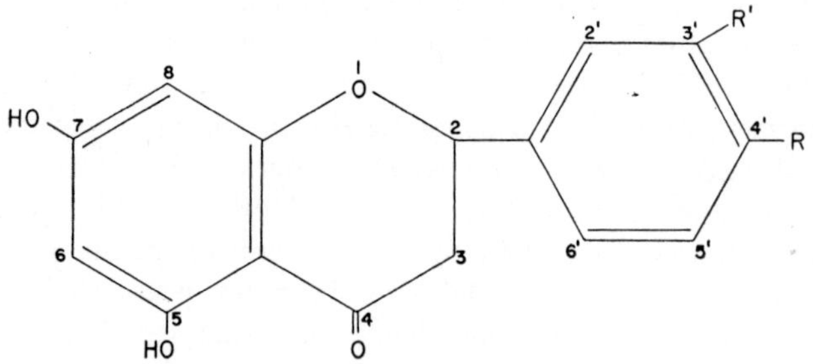

PINOCEMBRIN (R=R'=H)

NARINGENIN (R=OH, R'=H)

ERIODICTYOL (R=R'=OH)

FIG. 8. Flavanones.

considerable recent work has been carried out by Maier and his colleagues (Maier and Metzler, 1967a, b) on grapefruit phenolics. (See also Volume 2, chapter 3.)

3. *Isoflavones*

The isoflavones (Ollis, 1962) comprise a class of compounds showing wide diversity in structure, but as yet they have not been found to be significant in fruits. They frequently occur as the 7-glycoside.

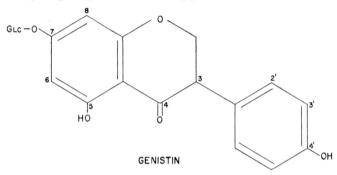

GENISTIN

FIG. 9. Isoflavones.

4. *C-glycosides*

This group is made up of those flavonoids, usually flavones, where a sugar is attached by a C–C bond at the 6 or 8 position (Harborne, 1967). While they have not been reported in commercial fruits, they have been found in

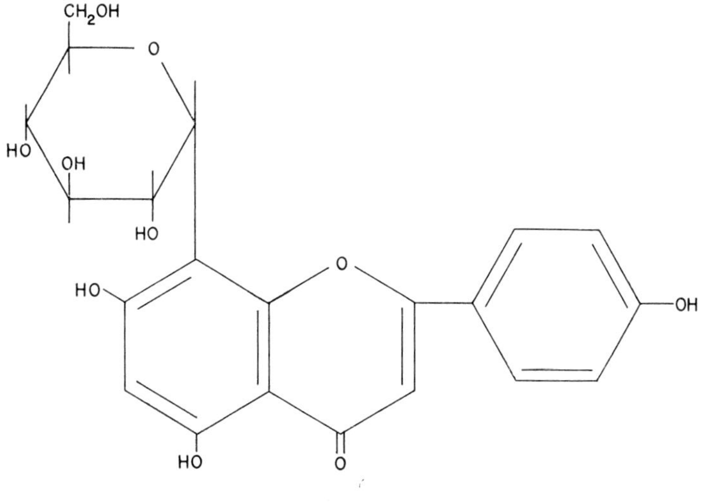

VITEXIN

FIG. 10. C-glycosides.

other parts of fruit-bearing plants, such as in the leaves of grapes (Wagner *et al.*, 1967).

III. BIOSYNTHESIS OF PHENOLIC COMPOUNDS

A. Pathways to Basic Structures

The biosynthesis of phenolic compounds takes place in a number of stages. First, there is the formation of cinnamic acids, then the condensation of acyl groups to build up the "A" phenyl ring, followed by transformations leading to the various flavonoids. These pathways have been worked out through the use of bacteria and fungi as well as higher plants. The physiological aspects of phenolic biosynthesis has recently been reviewed in detail by Siegelman (1964).

Steps leading to the formation of cinnamic acids (Fig. 11) (Neish, 1964) may be considered to start with the condensation of phosphoenolpyruvate with D-erythrose-4-phosphate to form a heptulosonic acid. This can be cyclized, in the presence of divalent cobalt, yielding 5-dehydroquinic acid, an intermediate in the formation of both shikimic acid and quinic acid (Gamborg, 1967). The conversion of shikimic acid to cinnamic acid in higher plants requires the intermediate formation of phenylalanine. The addition of acetyl and malonyl groups to the $C_6 : C_3$ structure of the cinnamic acids provides the carbons of the eventual "A" phenyl ring. This condensation undoubtedly requires the participation of co-enzyme A.

B. Stimulation of Synthesis

The stimulatory effect of light on the production of polyphenols can be expected in view of these pathways. Rapid photosynthesis makes available the carbohydrate and acyl building blocks for the polyphenols as well as providing the energy needed to force the reaction in the direction and at the rates observed. Sucrose can partially replace light and CO_2 (Creasy, 1968) as a promoter of general phenolic synthesis.

The stimulation of anthocyanin formation by light is particularly dramatic. It appears that the light is required to produce early precursors, available also for synthesis of other flavonoids (Faust, 1964, 1965b), as well as to initiate reactions concerned only with anthocyanin synthesis (Neish, 1964). Increased production of most flavonoids closely follows light exposure, but, in some important fruits, anthocyanin pigment synthesis is subject to a lag period (Siegelman, 1964).

Thimann and Radner (1962) found that anthocyanin formation was inhibited by purine and pyrimidine analogues and suggested, therefore, that polynucleotides may control anthocyanin synthesis. Faust (1965b), in

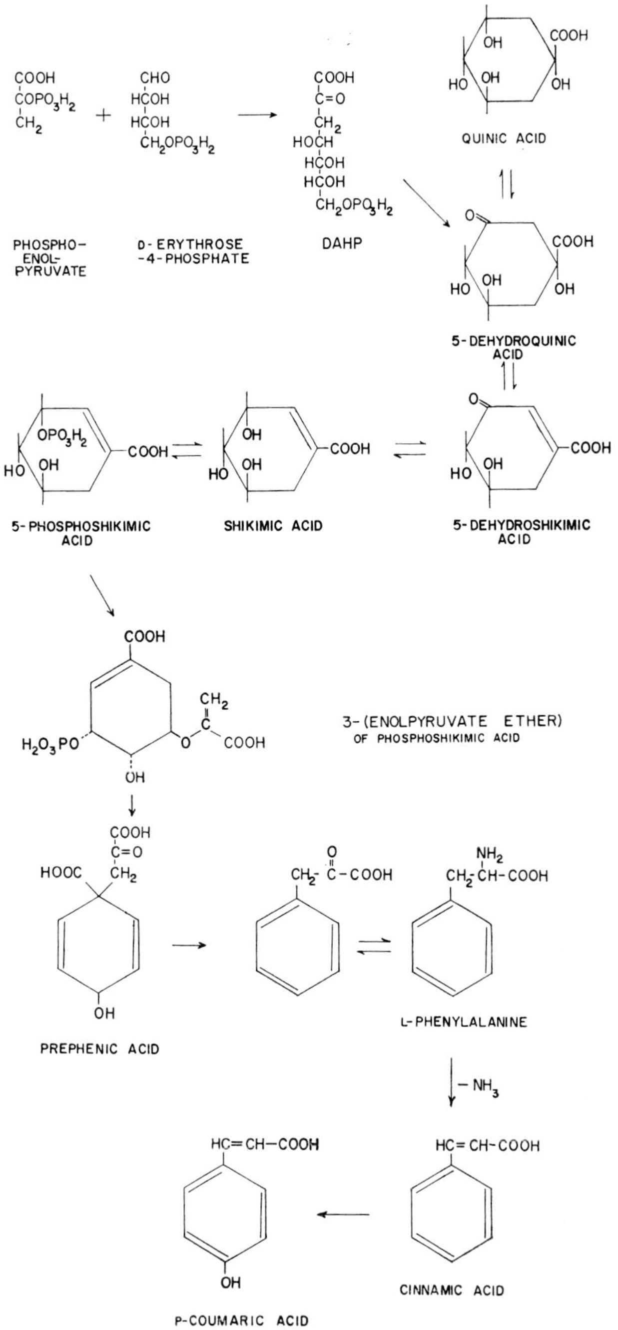

FIG. 11. Biosynthesis of cinnamic acids.

experiments with discs of apple peel, found that inhibitors of nucleic acid and protein synthesis prevented the formation of anthocyanin in the peel and also came to the conclusion that RNA metabolism is involved in the synthesis of anthocyanins.

The formation of anthocyanins in apple skins appears dependent upon carbohydrate availability and phytochrome activation and perhaps other influences. It has long been known that exposure to sunlight affects anthocyanin synthesis in apples to a greater degree than general phenolic synthesis (Walter, 1966). Two photoreactions control red coloration in apple skin (Siegelman and Hendricks, 1958). The first reaction has an action spectra similar to that found for photosynthesis (Downs et al., 1965), and the illumination intensities needed are quite high. Carbohydrates have been shown by Smock (1966) to enhance anthocyanin formation in illuminated floating apple skin discs. The second photo reaction has an action peak at 655 mμ, typical of the activation of phytochrome. Here the illumination can be brief and at relatively low intensities. The point of connection between the phytochrome system and anthocyanin synthesis is still obscure.

The colouring of tree-borne apples is enhanced by night-time temperatures of 7–10°C and day-time temperatures of 18–24°C. Creasy (1969) has suggested that low temperatures permit higher carbohydrate accumulation in the fruit epidermis. Hot day-time temperatures inhibit anthocyanin synthesis. The stimulatory effect of low night temperatures is most marked on the shaded sides of apples where lighting conditions are sufficient for phytochrome activation but not strong enough for significant photosynthesis.

The degree of phenolic formation can be controlled somewhat by selecting growing conditions. In Table VII it can be seen that decreasing the amount of fruit per vine and increasing exposure to sunlight raised the phenolic level in grapes. The use of sprays of B9 or Alar (N-dimethylaminosuccinamic acid), induces early formation of anthocyanin in cherries (Ryugo, 1966) but leaves the proanthocyanidins unaffected. The effect of Alar on anthocyanin synthesis is apparently indirect since it has no effect on isolated tissues.

The sequences of changes after the formation of the $C_6 : C_3 : C_6$ skeleton are not yet known with any great degree of certainty. Careful work by various researchers has led to the postulation of various pathways for the formation of the major flavonoids, usually on the basis of possible mechanisms that account for the observations. While there is general agreement that flavanonols probably precede flavonols and anthocyanins in the synthetic sequence (Grisebach, 1965; Harborne, 1967; Wong, 1968), there is no direct evidence that shows any class of flavonoid as a natural obligatory intermediate in the synthesis of any other class. The interconversion of many flavonoids and the dynamic state of these compounds in plant tissues makes it necessary to isolate and study individual steps before definite pathways can be conclusively established. Furthermore, since there exists such a diversity in relative amounts of flavonoids between species, there may be different major pathways in different species.

TABLE VII. Phenolic concentration and colour under different cultural conditions. Wine from Chelois Grapes (S. 10878),[a] 1965 New York State

Date of harvest	Growing location	Pruning or thinning	Total Phenolics mg/100 ml	Colour Density OD at 520 mμ
14 Sep.	Naples, exposed hillside	Normal	145	8·0
14 Sep.	Naples, valley bottom	Normal	66	3·8
21 Oct.	Geneva	Light pruning	68	3·6
21 Oct.	Geneva	Severe pruning	86	8·0
21 Oct.	Geneva	Cluster thinned	121	9·6

[a] Willard B. Robinson, Cornell University, unpublished data.

Genetic studies suggest that flavonols and anthocyanins are closely related biosynthetically since there are genes that control both of them together but do not affect other flavonoids (Harborne, 1967). However, they are probably not formed in a stepwise sequence from flavonol to anthocyanin because studies, for example, with *Primula sinensis*, have revealed genes that increase anthocyanins without affecting flavonols and other genes that can increase flavonol three to five fold with little effect on anthocyanins.

C. Introduction of Substituents

The initial hydroxylation of cinnamic acid can be brought about enzymatically by cinnamic acid hydroxylase, and the introduction of further hydroxyl groups may be accomplished by means of phenolases such as those described by Satô *et al.* (1968). Hanson and Zucker (1963) have shown that, in the potato, chlorogenic acid is formed by the hydroxylation of p-coumarylquinic acid, while the work of Steck (1968) suggests that caffeic acid may be formed in some plants apart from the quinic ester. Genetic evidence from *Antirrhinum majus* (Sherratt, 1958) indicates that hydroxylation takes place at the cinnamic acid stage, but the role of dihydrokaempferol as an efficient precursor in buckwheat (*Fagopyrum sagittatum*) for quercetin and cyanidin (Patschke *et al.*, 1966) shows that hydroxylation may occur after completion of the flavonoid structure. Interpretations of experimental data in support of specific sequences for the introduction of functional groups is complicated by the dynamic metabolic state of the flavonoids, as demonstrated by Grisebach and Bopp (1959).

The methylation of phenolic compounds is apparently carried out by enzymes that utilize S-adenosyl-methionine as the methyl donor (Nelson and Finkle, 1964). These enzymes methylate simple hydroxycinnamic acids as well as more complex esters.

Genetics also control the distribution of phenolic compounds between different tissues of a plant or fruit. In the sour cherry (*P. cerasus*) there are varieties such as Montmorency where all the anthocyanins are found in the skin and other varieties such as Morello that also have pigmented flesh. A similar situation occurs in apples and grapes.

Methylation is under complex genetic control in *Petunia* where separate genes control the sequences leading to petunidin and to malvidin (Hess, 1964). Since flavonols are rarely methylated, it appears that methylation of anthocyanins or their precursors takes place at a stage after the pathways to anthocyanin and flavonols have separated, or that methylated precursors are used only for anthocyanin synthesis (Hess, 1965).

It has been frequently shown (Pridham, 1964) that foreign phenols injected into higher plants are rapidly converted to β-D-glucopyranoside derivatives. The source of the glucose is probably uridine diphosphoglucose and its addition enzymatically mediated by UDPG: phenol glucosyltransferases. Somewhat similar reactions are likely with regard to the glycosylation of flavonoids. Such a system, capable of first glycosylating quercetin using thymidine diphosphoglucose to give the 3-glycoside, and then, in the presence of thymidine diphosphorhamnose, forming the rutinoside, was described by Barber (1962). ATP also enhanced the reaction. These results are in line with the suggestion, based on genetic evidence (Harborne, 1963a), that phenols are converted first to the β-monosides and then to di- and tri-saccharides. The lack of flavan glycosides indicates that sugar additions do not take place immediately after formation of the $C_6 : C_3 : C_6$ skeleton.

Anthocyanins and flavonol glycosylations may require different groups of enzymes since these pigments often show, as in the apple, different ratios of sugars and, as in *Antirrhinum majus*, different glycosylation patterns.

The close relation between acylation of anthocyanins and glycosylation at the 5 position can be related to the nearness of gene loci, since in some plants, for example, eggplant (Abe and Gotoh, 1959), it appears that the gene-controlling acylation is closely linked to the 5-O-glycosylating loci. There are now known, especially in *Vitis* species (Smith and Luh, 1965; Albach et al., 1965; Chen and Luh, 1967) a number of acylated anthocyanin monoglycosides, as well as the more common acylated 3,5-diglycosides. Mansell and Hagen (1966) and Miles and Hagen (1968) have shown that white petals of *Impatiens balsamina* possess enzyme systems capable of adding a 5-position glucose and acylating exogenous pelargonidin-3-glucoside. The mechanism of the acylation is obscure, but it may be similar to the acylation of UDP-glucose by leaf enzymes described by Corner and Swain (1965).

IV. PROPERTIES AND REACTIONS OF PHENOLICS

A. Effects of Hydroxyl Groups

The solubility of the phenolic compounds in water depends upon the presence of a sufficient proportion of polar or hydrophillic groups. The limited solubility of chlorogenic acid is increased under pH conditions where carboxyl ionization is possible; the solubility of flavonoids is increased as the number of phenolic hydroxyl groups is raised, and decreases when they are methylated. The presence of a 4 position carbonyl function that can effectively interact with a neighbouring 5 position hydroxyl group decreases water solubility. A large solubility increase accompanies the glycosylation of the flavonoids, for instance, cyanidin is virtually insoluble in water except in the presence of strong mineral acid, while the 3-glycosides are soluble at a concentration of several per cent at pH 2–4.

Any 3 position hydroxyl group behaves as a typical aliphatic hydroxyl. It is of interest that this hydroxyl group is almost always glycosylated in some classes of flavonoids, such as flavonols and anthocyanins, even though the aromatic hydroxyl groups can be considered more accessible and possibly more reactive. This glycosylation at the 3 position also greatly decreases the susceptibility of these flavonoids to oxidation at the pH levels found in fruits (Baruah and Swain, 1959; Roberts, 1960). In the case of the flavans the 3 and 4 position hydroxyls are rather unreactive, methylating or acetylating with difficulty.

However, the 4 position, in most flavonoids, interacts at the electron level with hydroxyl groups at the 5 and 7 positions. Such hydroxyls tend to donate electrons, increasing the electron density around the 4 position carbon. Thus, when there is a carbonyl function at the 4 position, the oxygen carries an enhanced negative charge and participates in very strong hydrogen-bonding with the hydrogen of the 5 position hydroxyl group. The reactivity at the 4 position also provides an explanation for its participation in condensation reactions of flavans leading to dimers and polymers (Creasy and Swain, 1965).

A 4 position carbonyl in conjunction with a 3 or 5 position hydroxyl group forms strong complexes with metals (Letan, 1966a). Ortho dihydroxy and vicinal trihydroxy phenols also chelate with many metals such as copper, iron, lead and aluminum (Timberlake, 1959; Swain, 1962). This property of fixing metals, together with the ability of polyphenols to terminate oxidations mediated by free radicals (Letan, 1966b), gives many flavonoids especially effective antioxidant properties.

B. Colour of Anthocyanins and their Complexes

The anthocyanins possess a particularly interesting chemistry involving their colour, the pH of their milieu and their structure. At low pH levels

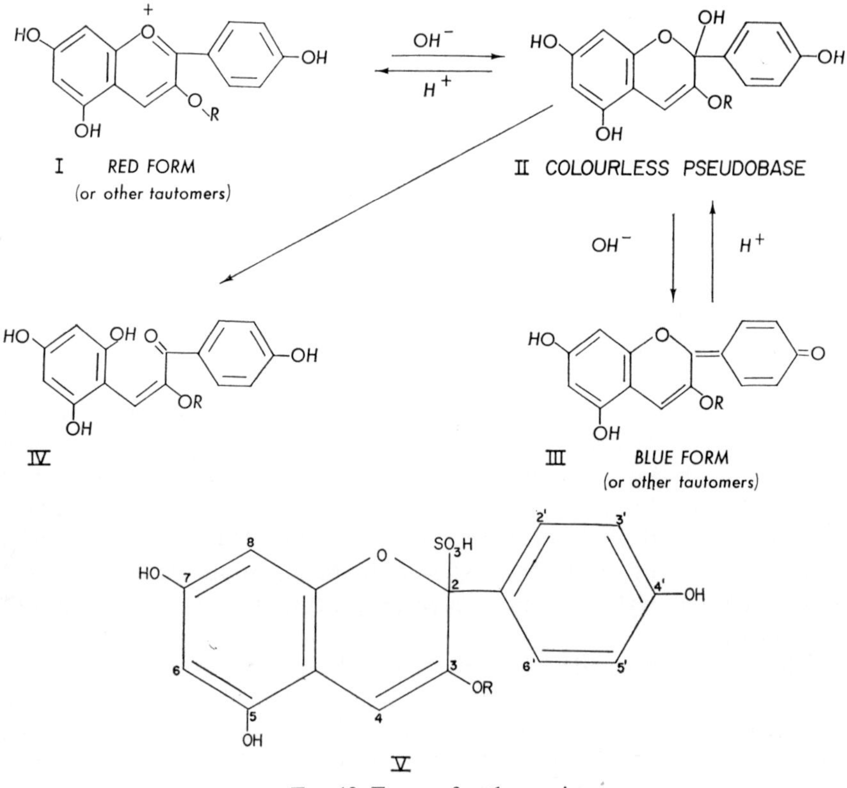

FIG. 12. Forms of anthocyanins.

the structure of anthocyanins can be represented by I, the solution being red coloured. As the pH is raised, the colour fades along with the formation of II (Jurd, 1963; Timberlake and Bridle, 1967). At still higher pH levels, near and above neutrality, a blue or greenish colour appears, due presumably to the formation of structures such as III. There are also indications that the pseudobase II can undergo ring splitting to yield IV or the like. Furthermore, under very high pH conditions ring cleavages and oxidations take place very readily, leading to irreversible loss of anthocyanins. A reaction similar to pseudobase formation occurs when anthocyanins are exposed to HSO_3^-, in which case the product is V (Jurd, 1964), a colourless material. Sodium hydrosulphite also causes anthocyanins to turn colourless (Trotter, 1962).

The greater the degree of β-ring hydroxylation the bluer the colour (Harborne, 1965). Thus, delphinidin glycosides are the bluest common anthocyanins. On the other hand, methylation of the hydroxyl groups, or glycosylation, leads to redder solutions with a lower wavelength for maximum light absorption. In the case of the monoglycosides the absorption spectrum shows a shoulder in the 440–460 mμ region that is absent in 3,5-diglycosides. The 3,5-diglycosides possess a fluorescence that is partially quenched if the 3 position sugar is acylated.

Co-pigmentation effects frequently have a more profound influence on anthocyanin colour than do substituents on the anthocyanin molecule. The increased blueness of anthocyanin solutions when other, colourless polyphenols are present has been known for a long time (Robinson and Robinson, 1931). This type of co-pigmentation is particularly important in accounting for blueness when malvidin and peonidin type anthocyanins are involved. Strong complexes of anthocyanins and tannins have been found in fresh grapes (Somers, 1968). While many fruits having a blue colour are at a pH suitable for redness, the pigment may be located in regions of the cells of higher than average pH. Most blue fruits, when crushed, yield red juice. The possibility is strong that a combination of local pH and co-pigmentation are both important in colour expression of anthocyanins. While the co-pigments are often flavonol glycosides (Harborne, 1963b) or tannins (Somers, 1966), other compounds have also been studied, such as the C-glucosidic xanthone, mangiferin, which interacts with acylated delphinidin 3,5-diglycoside to produce a spectrum of colours through red and mauve to blue (Bate-Smith and Harborne, 1963). Such extreme cases are rare; in general, the shift to a longer wavelength of maximum absorption associated with polyphenol co-pigmentation is in the order of 5 mμ.

When the hydroxylation pattern of flavonoids contains ortho-hydroxyl groups, they have the ability to form chelates with many metallic ions. Colourless flavonoids form yellow or brown complexes with aluminum, yellow complexes with tin, blue, green or brown products with iron. Chlorogenic acid forms dark complexes with iron. Iron-induced darkening is inhibited by citric acid. Lead and other metals result in a blue complex with anthocyanins.

Other, more complex metal-anthocyanin combinations have been found, all of which are blue. Bayer et al. (1960) obtained a preparation of cyanidin-3,5-diglucoside complexed with iron and aluminum. Hayashi (1962) describes complexes containing potassium and magnesium together with p-coumaric acid, and Jurd and Asen (1966) have prepared a complex containing anthocyanin, quercitrin, aluminum and chlorogenic acid. The participation of plant polysaccharides in some complexes has been shown by Bayer (1966).

C. Condensation of Flavans

The flavans have a pronounced tendency to condense with themselves, the flavan-3,4-diols undergoing self-condensations in hot water or cold mineral acids at a faster rate than catechins. While both types of flavans may react at the 6 or 8 position, due to neighbouring hydroxyl groups, the greater reactivity of the flavan-3,4-diols indicates that the 4 position hydroxyl group enhances condensation by increasing the ease with which the 4 position carbon becomes reactive. This idea is reinforced by the 6–4 carbon linkage found in natural dimeric flavans (Weinges et al., 1968). Furthermore, similar dimers have been prepared by Creasy and Swain (1965) from catechin and flavan-3,4-diol. Apparently the 5 position hydroxyl group is not required since condensations occur readily with 7,3,3′,4′hydroxyl flavans.

The ease of flavan condensation is reflected in the loss of low molecular weight flavans when fruits are heated. This can be readily seen with tissues such at those of the apple, containing a wide variety of flavans. Here there occurs also a condensation involving oxygen and enzymes which may be prevented by ascorbic acid, SO_2, or other reducing agents. Thus there are two common condensation mechanisms, one acid catalysed and heat sensitive, the other resulting from or accompanying oxidation. While there seems to be general agreement that flavan polymers are built up by the formation of carbon–carbon bonds between smaller units, these bonds are much more labile than the customary bond of this type. This may be because of the enhancement of reactivity at the 4 position by the 7 position para hydroxyl group.

As already stated, the ability of 3,4-diols and many condensed flavans to yield anthocyanidins upon treatment with hot dilute mineral acid has led to the designation of these substances as leucoanthocyanidins or proanthocyanidins. Work by Jurd (1966) has indicated that the reaction can involve the participation of benzoquinones.

D. Interaction of Condensed Polyphenols and Proteins

Condensed polyphenols have a general ability to form complexes with polypeptides and proteins; this is usually referred to as the tanning reaction. The dominating mechanism is the formation of hydrogen bonds between the phenolic hydroxyls of the condensed polyphenols and the carbonyl groups of the peptide linkages of the polypeptides (Gustavson, 1954). These hydrogen bonds are, individually, several times weaker than covalent bonds, but, since the total number of hydrogen bonds between a condensed polyphenol or tannin molecule and a peptide chain can be quite large, the total binding force becomes appreciable, and stable complexes are possible. The stability increases as the size of the participating molecules increases. Other polymeric materials, such as starch and cellulose, can form weaker complexes with condensed polyphenols. In some immature perry pears the amount of condensed polyphenol is so large that the juice, "scheidmoste", can be used as a source of tannins for the clarification of other fruit beverages (Kelhofer, 1908).

The ability of condensed polyphenols to complex with proteins (Gustavson, 1954) accounts in large part for the inhibitory effects of these polymers on enzymes. Pectolytic enzymes are easily inactivated by tannins such as those found in large quantities in cider apples and perry pears (Pollard et al., 1958). In the isolation of plant enzymes and plant enzyme systems, it has been found essential where appreciable amounts of phenolics are present in the tissue to incorporate into the extracting medium a reagent such as polyvinylpyrrolidone (Hulme and Jones, 1963; Loomis and Battaile, 1966) to combine with the phenolics and so prevent them inactivating the enzymes.

This property of condensed tannins to inactivate enzymes was utilized by Barnell and Barnell (1945) to study changes in tannins in the banana. Their work showed that the inhibitory ability per unit weight of tannin decreased as the fruit ripened. This was due to a continued condensation of the tannins beyond the size for optimum efficiency of enzyme inhibition.

V. METABOLISM OF PHENOLICS

A. Oxidation and Respiration

The possible participation of plant phenolics in respiration has been a subject of investigation and speculation for some time. On one hand, it is evident that plant tissues possess enzyme systems that can include phenols as terminal participants in electron transfer chains. On the other hand, newer evidence continually decreases the likelihood that they play a significant respiratory role in normal tissue.

Crucial in any respiratory pathway involving phenols is polyphenol oxidase, a copper containing enzyme present in virtually all vegetable tissue (Herrmann, 1958). The polyphenol–polyphenol oxidase system can take part in coupled oxidations of cell components in addition to providing a possible pathway to oxygen for electrons from a respiratory intermediate.

It is certain that in all respiring plant cells the phenolic compound of much greater importance than the ones involved in the polyphenol–polyphenol oxidase system is ubiquinone. Ubiquinone(s) is an essential intermediate in the electron transport chain of mitochondria, its position lying between flavo-protein and the cytochrome systems (Trebst, 1963). The formula of ubiquinone is shown in Figure 13.

Polyphenoloxidase is found in many forms. Active and latent enzymes are described by Drawert and Gebbing (1967), while Harel *et al.* (1964) reported on enzymes with different inhibitor susceptibilities derived from different tissues and different parts of the cells. These inhibitors are of several types, those that combine with copper, such as KCN or thiocarbamates, competitive types resembling substrates, such as benzoic acid and napthalene-2,3-diol (Mayer *et al.*, 1964), or general protein denaturants. Walker and Hulme (1966) separated several types on DEAE cellulose, some of which may have been allosteric forms resulting from preparative methods (Harel and Mayer, 1968). The action of the enzyme is easily reversed in the presence of compounds, such as ascorbic acid and phenylenediamine, that will reduce orthoquinones. The substrates for this enzyme are, in general, dihydroxy ortho-phenols. There are many preparations that are also capable of

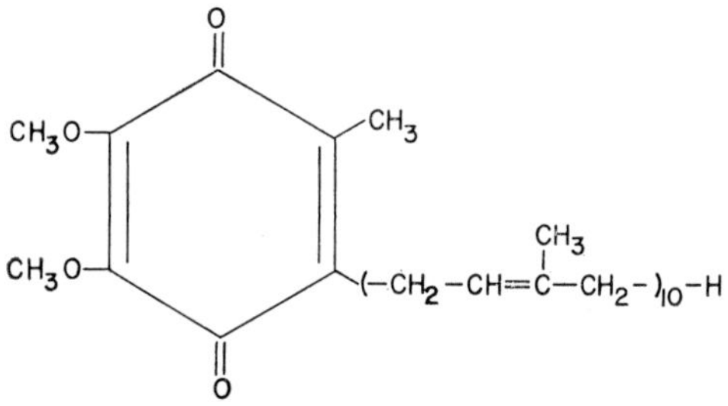

UBIQUINONE

FIG. 13.

hydroxylating monohydric phenols. The major natural substrates for the enzymes are hydroxycinnamic acid esters and monomeric and dimeric flavans. Flavonol glycosides and anthocyanins are not directly attacked.

Although chlorogenic acid and p-coumaryl-quinic acid (Walker, 1962) are the major substrates for polyphenoloxidase in most fruits, their oxidation products are not so dark as those derived from flavans, and this fact led Siegelman (1955a) to conclude that flavan oxidation caused most of the browning in apples. The enzymatic oxidation of hydroxycinnamic acid derivatives and flavans gives rise to products that can oxidize other fruit components such as anthocyanins (Peng and Markakis, 1963), flavonol glycosides (Heimann and Heinrich, 1960) and ascorbic acid.

B. Substitution

The methylation of polyphenols can be brought about by the enzyme *O*-methyltransferase. It requires S-adenosyl-methionine, a divalent ion such as Mg^{2+} or Co^{2+} and a pH around 8. Its action has been reported in apple (Nelson and Finkle, 1964) and in other plant tissue (Finkle and Masri, 1964). In apple juice it tends to reduce enzymic browning.

Esterification reactions are largely confined to the lower molecular weight aromatic compounds such as the hydroxy cinnamic acids which then serve as the acylating agent. Furthermore, the reactions take place almost entirely with shikimic or quinic acids or with sugars, either free or combined. It appears that when a large excess of hydroxy cinnamic acids is present, acylation of sugars by the cinnamic acid proceeds in preference to glycosidation of the cinnamic acid through the phenolic hydroxyl group (Harborne and Corner, 1961).

C. Lignin Formation

Hydroxylated cinnamic acids are believed to be important precursors of lignin. One line of evidence presented by Stafford (1960) showed that lignin-like polymers were formed by incubating p-coumaric, ferulic, or sinapic acid, or coniferol alcohol with an enzyme system from *Phleum pratense*. The polymer from ferulic acid most closely resembled natural lignin. Other evidence derives from the application of radioactive compounds; for instance, Higuchi (1962) demonstrated that p-coumaric and ferulic acids were efficiently incorporated into coniferyl lignin by cambial tissue cultures of *Pinus strobus*. Coniferin, a β-D-glucoside of coniferyl alcohol, has been found in conifers and a few other plants. This compound can serve as a precursor lignin in spruce and has the ability to greatly stimulate lignin formation in carrots. However, it has not been shown to be an obligatory intermediate in lignin biosynthesis.

VI. TASTE CHARACTERISTICS OF PHENOLICS

The great majority of the phenolic compounds found in fruits have no particular taste characteristics when tested at low concentrations in the pure form. The exceptions to this general rule are the sourness associated with phenolic acids, the astringency of condensed flavans and the bitterness associated with some of the citrus flavonoids.

A. Astringency

For several decades there has been steadily mounting evidence that astringency is due to phenolics of a certain degree of polymerization, and this has come to mean molecular weights roughly between 500 and 3000. Simple phenolics, such as hydroxy cinnamic acids, catechins and anthocyanins, are not astringent, but dimers of the flavans show this character (Van Buren *et al.*, 1966), as do other carefully purified condensed fruit phenolics. Varieties of fruits high in phenolics are more astringent than varieties low in phenolics, for example, perry pears compared with dessert pears and red grapes compared with white grapes. During maturation the condensation of phenolics continually increases (Goldstein and Swain, 1963), and at the same time the astringency decreases, perhaps because the highly condensed flavans are less soluble and tightly bound to other cell components. Furthermore, there may be an optimum size of the polymer for maximum astringency per unit weight of phenolic. The question of the relation between astringency and phenolics has been comprehensively reviewed by Joslyn and Goldstein (1964). Astringency is closely connected to the tanning reaction of condensed tannins (Rossi and Singleton, 1966a, b) and the ability of tannins to inhibit enzymes. Thus it is dependent upon the number of phenolic hydroxyl groups per molecule.

The astringency of fruit juices may be reduced by removing tannins through adsorption on substances containing peptide groups such as gelatin, other proteins, or artificial peptide polymers such as nylon. In some cases, as with apple juice, the addition of pectolytic enzyme decreases the stabilizing effect of pectin and thus allows the precipitation of pectin–tannin–protein complexes (Zitko and Rosik, 1962).

B. Bitterness

The pronounced bitterness of some citrus flavonoids should be mentioned, despite their somewhat restricted distribution. One of them, naringin, is the chief flavonoid constituent of the grapefruit (*Citrus paradisi*) and the pummelo (*C. grandis*) and also occurs in several types of oranges. It is exceedingly bitter and is easily detectable in 10^{-5} to 10^{-4} molar solutions. It is composed of the aglycone naringenin and the disaccharide neohesperidose (2-*O*-α-L-rhamnopyranosyl-D-glucopyranose). Another flavanone glycoside with about one-tenth the bitterness of naringin is neohesperidin. It also contains neohesperidose. The aglycones are not bitter, nor is neohesperidose in the free form. The type of sugar at the 7 position is crucial, since neohesperidose imparts strong bitterness, glucose gives much less, while rutinose imparts no bitterness at all. A derivative of neohesperidin, its dihydro-chalcone, readily formed by ring splitting in alkali followed by hydrogenation, has 20 times the sweet taste, on a molar basis, of saccharin.

VII. PHARMACOLOGY

Fruits are particularly rich in polyphenolic compounds that possess considerable reactivity toward body constituents and might alter metabolic processes. The ability of condensed phenolics to complex with proteins, the metal complexing ability of many flavonoids, the antioxidant properties of phenolics, all suggest possible pharmacological effects. Despite this, fruit phenolics have very little effect on the animal body, largely because of permeability barriers to many of the plant phenolics in the alimentary tract and detoxification mechanisms in other body organs such as the liver.

Such barriers are seen to be particularly effective against those plant phenolics having the greatest potential effect on the animal body. 5-Hydroxy-tryptamine, a powerful vasoconstrictor present in many fruits (Strong, 1966), is totally excluded from the blood stream when taken by ingestion. Some undesirable plant phenolics, such as the glucosuria-inducing phloridzin, are virtually absent in cultivated fruits, although they are present in appreciable amounts in other parts of the plant.

Much interest has been given to rutin, quercetin, hesperidin and eriodictyol because their action in decreasing the fragility of guinea pig capillaries sug-gested a therapeutic value for these flavonoids. However, such a possibility has never been fully established. These flavonoids, in large doses, act as anti-oxidants, protecting adrenaline and ascorbic acid, and help to relax smooth muscle. The relatively mild action of large amounts of these phenolics had led to considerable dispute about the practical value of taking advantage, in medicine, of the metabolic activity of the flavonoids (DeEds, 1959).

There are a number of phenolic materials that can pass into the blood stream, among these are flavonols, their glycosides and hydroxy cinnamic acid esters (DeEds, 1959). Quercetin is metabolized to give 3,4-dihydroxy-phenylacetic acid and benzoic acid derivatives which are then excreted. Caffeic acid undergoes a variety of transformations including dehydration, methylation, hydrogenation of the side chain, B-oxidation and the formation of conjugates.

In the opinion of Harborne (1967) the only really important pharmaco-logically active group of flavonoids are the isoflavones, some of which have weak oestrogen-like activity and can be converted in the animal to much more active substances such as equol. These isoflavones are widespread in legumes but as yet have not been found to be important in fruits.

Finally, plant phenolics have long been suspected of playing a role in the disease resistance of plants (Farkas and Kiraly, 1962; Cruickshank and Perrin, 1964), and this function has been accounted for in a number of ways. While there are correlations between levels of phenolics and disease resistance in fruits such as the apple, only a few cases have been presented where per-formed phenolics are definitely identified as protective substances. Perhaps more important than normal phenolics is the rapid rise in polyphenol con-centration that takes place after infection. Together with this rise there is often a considerable amount of phenolic oxidation mediated by both host and parasite polyphenol oxidase (Akinrefon, 1968). The oxidized phenolics are more potent anti-fungal agents than the non-oxidized materials (McNew and Burchfield, 1951), and they may also play a role in the hypersensitivity reaction which consists of the rapid death of a few cells resulting in the confinement of the pathogen to a restricted area of high polyphenol oxidase and oxidized phenol content. Oxidized polyphenols are potent inhibitors of pectolytic enzymes commonly necessary for the invasive ability of fungal pathogens. It has also been suggested that the susceptibility of plant tissues to pathogens is dependent upon the oxidation–reduction balance of the tissue and the action of polyphenol oxidase upsets this balance, creating a less favourable environment for the pathogen. It appears that, although phenolics are important in disease resistance, specific diseases and hosts must be individually evaluated for significance and mechanism.

REFERENCES

Abe, Y. and Gotoh, K. (1959). *Bot. Mag., Tokyo* **72**, 432–7.
Akinrefon, O. A. (1968). *Phytopath. Z.* **63**, 153–64.
Albach, R. F., Kepner, R. E. and Webb, A. D. (1965). *J. Fd Sci.* **30**, 69–76.
Asen, S. and Jurd, L. (1967). *Phytochem.* **6**, 577–84.
Barber, G. A. (1962). *Biochemistry* **1**, 463–8.
Barnell, H. R. and Barnell, E. (1945). *Ann. Bot.* **9**, 77–99.
Baruah, P. and Swain, T. (1959). *J. Sci. Fd Agric.* **10**, 125–9.
Bate-Smith, E. C. (1961). *J. Linn. Soc., Bot.* **58**, 39–54.
Bate-Smith, E. C. and Harborne, J. B. (1963). *Nature, Lond.* **198**, 1307–8.
Bayer, E. (1966). Angew. Chem. International edition **5**, 791–7.
Bayer, E., Nether, K. and Egeter, H. (1960). *Chem. Ber.* **93**, 2871–9.
Birkofer, L. (1965). *Planta Med.* **13**, 445–52.
Birkofer, L., Kaiser, C. and Kosmol, H. (1965). *Z. Naturf.* **20b**, 605–6.
Brown, B. R. and MacBride, J. A. H. (1964). *J. chem. Soc., London*, 3822–31.
Burkhardt, R. (1965). *Mitt. Reb. Wein.* **15**, Series A 2, 80–6.
Burroughs, L. F. (1961). *Ann. Rept. Agr. Hort. Res. Sta.*, Long Ashton, Bristol, pp. 173–5.
Caldwell, J. S. (1934). U.S.D.A. Agr. Tech. Bull. **403**, 53.
Cantarelli, C. and Peri, C. (1964). *Am. J. Enol. Vitic.* **15**, 146–53.
Cartwight, R. A. (1955). *Chemy Ind.* 1062–3.
Chen, L. F. and Luh, B. S. (1967). *J. Fd Sci.* **32**, 66–74.
Clarke-Lewis, J. W., Spotswood, T. M. and Williams, L. R. (1963). *Aust. J. Chem.* **16**, 107–11.
Co, H. and Markakis, P. (1968). *J. Fd Sci.* **33**, 281–3.
Corner, J. J. and Swain, T. (1965). *Nature, Lond.* **207**, 634–5.
Corse, J. W. (1953). *Nature, Lond.* **172**, 771–2.
Corse, J., Lundin, R. E. and Waiss, A. C., Jr. (1965). *Phytochem.* **4**, 527–9.
Craft, C. C. (1961). *Proc. Am. Soc. hort. Sci.* **78**, 119–31.
Creasy, L. L. (1968). *Phytochem.* **7**, 1743–9.
Creasy, L. L. (1969). *Proc. Am. Soc. hort. Sci.* **93**, 716–24.

Creasy, L. L. and Swain, T. (1965). *Nature, Lond.* **208**, 151–3.
Cruickshank, I. A. M. and Perrin, D. R. (1964). *In* "Biochemistry of Phenolic Compounds" (J. B. Harborne, ed.), pp. 511–44. Academic Press, New York and London.
Daravingas, G. and Cain, R. F. (1965). *J. Fd Sci.* **30**, 400–5.
Daravingas, G. and Cain, R. F. (1966). *J. Fd Sci.* **31**, 927–36.
Dayton, D. F. (1966). *Proc. Am. Soc. hort. Sci.* **89**, 110–16.
DeEds, F. (1959). *In* "The Pharmacology of Plant Phenolics" (J. W. Fairbairn, ed.), pp. 91–102. Academic Press, London and New York.
Dickinson, D. and Gawler, J. H. (1956). *J. Sci. Fd Agric.* **7**, 699–705.
Downs, R. J., Siegelman, H. W., Butler, W. L. and Hendricks, S. W. (1965). *Nature, Lond.* **205**, 909–10.
Drawert, F. and Gebbing, H. (1967). *Naturwissenschaften* **54**, 226–7.
Farkas, G. L. and Kiraly, Z. (1962). *Phytopath. Z.* **44**, 105–50.
Faust, M. (1964). *Proc. Am. Soc. hort. Sci.* **85**, 85–90.
Faust, M. (1965a). *Proc. Am. Soc. hort. Sci.* **87**, 1–10.
Faust, M. (1965b). *Proc. Am. Soc. hort. Sci.* **87**, 10–20.
Finkle, B. J. and Masri, M. S. (1964). *Biochim. Biophys. Acta* **85**, 167–9.
Francis, F. J. and Harborne, J. B. (1966). *J. Fd Sci.* **31**, 524–8.
Francis, F. J., Harborne, J. B. and Barker, W. B. (1966). *J. Fd Sci.* **31**, 583–7.
Freudenberg, K. and Weinges, K. (1960). *Tetrahedron* **8**, 336–9.
Fuleki, T. and Francis, F. J. (1967). *Phytochem.* **6**, 1705–8.
Fuleki, T. and Francis, F. J. (1968). *J. Fd Sci.* **33**, 72–7.
Gamborg, O. F. (1967). *Phytochem.* **6**, 1067–73.
Geissman, T. A. and Dittmar, H. K. F. (1965). *Phytochem.* **4**, 359–68.
Goldstein, J. L. and Swain, T. (1963). *Phytochem.* **2**, 371–83.
Grisebach, H. (1965). *In* "Biosynthetic Pathways in Higher Plants" (J. B. Pridham and T. Swain, eds), pp. 159–61. Academic Press, London and New York.
Grisebach, H. and Bopp, M. (1959). *Z. Naturf.* **14b**, 485–90.
Grommeck, R. and Markakis, P. (1964). *J. Fd Sci.* **29**, 53–7.
Guadagni, D. G. and Nimmo, C. C. (1953). *Fd Technol.* **7**, 59–61.
Guadagni, D. G., Sorber, D. G. and Wilbur, J. S. (1949). *Fd Technol.* **3**, 359–64.
Gustavson, K. H. (1954). *J. Polym. Sci.* **12**, 317–24.
Hanson, K. R. and Zucker, M. (1963). *J. biol. Chem.* **238**, 1105–15.
Harborne, J. B. (1963a). *Phytochem.* **2**, 85–97.
Harborne, J. B. (1963b). *Phytochem.* **2**, 327–34.
Harborne, J. B. (1964a). "Biochemistry of Phenolic Compounds". Academic Press, London and New York.
Harborne, J. B. (1964b). *Phytochem.* **3**, 151–60.
Harborne, J. B. (1964c). *In* "Biochemistry of Phenolic Compounds" (J. B. Harborne, ed.), pp. 129–69. Academic Press, London and New York.
Harborne, J. B. (1965). *In* "Chemistry and Biochemistry of Plant Pigments" (T. W. Goodwin, ed.), pp. 247–78. Academic Press, London and New York.
Harborne, J. B. (1967). "Comparative Biochemistry of the Flavonoids". Academic Press, London and New York.
Harborne, J. B. and Corner, J. J. (1961). *Biochem. J.* **81**, 242–50.
Harborne, J. B. and Hall, E. (1964). *Phytochem.* **3**, 453–63.
Harel, E. and Mayer, A. M. (1968). *Phytochem.* **7**, 199–207.
Harel, E., Mayer, A. M. and Shain, Y. (1964). *Physiologia Pl.* **17**, 921–30.
Harel, E., Mayer, A. M. and Shain, Y. (1966). *J. Sci. Fd Agric.* **17**, 389–92.

302 J. VAN BUREN

Hayashi, K. (1962). *In* "The Chemistry of Flavonoid Compounds" (T. A. Geissman, ed.), pp. 248–85. Pergamon Press, New York.
Heimann, W. and Heinrich, B. (1960). *Archs Pharm.* **293**, 598–609.
Herrmann, K. (1958). *Z. Lebensmittelunters. u.-Forsch.* **108**, 152–7.
Herrmann, K. (1959). *Z. Lebensmittelunters. u.-Forsch.* **109**, 487–507.
Hess, D. (1964). *Planta* **61**, 73–89.
Hess, D. (1965). *Z. Pflanzenphysiol.* **53**, 1–18.
Higuchi, T. (1962). *Canad. J. Biochem. Physiol.* **40**, 31–4.
Hillis, W. E. and Swain, T. (1959). *J. Sci. Fd Agric.* **10**, 135–44.
Horowitz, R. M. (1961). *In* "The Orange; Its Biochemistry and Physiology" (W. B. Sinclair, ed.), pp. 334–72. University of California, Davis.
Hsia, C. L., Luh, B. S. and Chichester, C. O. (1965). *J. Fd Sci.* **30**, 5–12.
Hulme, A. C. (1953). *Biochem. J.* **53**, 337–40.
Hulme, A. C. and Edney, K. L. (1960). *In* "Phenolics in Plants in Health and Disease" (J. B. Pridham, ed.), pp. 87–94. Pergamon Press, New York.
Hulme, A. C. and Jones, J. D. (1963). *In* "Enzyme Chemistry of Phenolic Compounds" (J. B. Pridham, ed.), pp. 97–120. Pergamon Press, New York.
Ito, S. and Joslyn, M. A. (1964). *Nature, Lond.* **204**, 475–6.
Ito, S. and Joslyn, M. A. (1965). *J. Fd Sci.* **30**, 44–51.
Jacquin, P. and Cherel, J. (1957). *Annls Technol. agric.* (*Paris*) **6**, 429–60.
Joslyn, M. A. and Goldstein, J. L. (1964). *Adv. Fd Res.* **13**, 179–217.
Jurd, L. (1963). *J. org. Chem.* **28**, 987–91.
Jurd, L. (1964). *J. Fd Sci.* **29**, 16–19.
Jurd, L. (1966). *Chemy Ind.* 1683–4.
Jurd, L. and Asen, S. (1966). *Phytochem.* **5**, 1263–71.
Kelhofer, W. (1908). *Landw. Jb. Schweiz* **22**, 340–408.
Koch, J. and Haase-Sajak, E. (1967). *Z. Lebensmittelunters. u.-Forsch.* **131**, 347–351.
Letan, A. (1966a). *J. Fd Sci.* **31**, 395–9.
Letan, A. (1966b). *J. Fd Sci.* **31**, 518–23.
Li, K. C. and Wagenknecht, A. C. (1956). *J. Am. chem. Soc.* **78**, 979–80.
Loomis, W. D. and Battaile, J. (1966). *Phytochem.* **5**, 423–38.
Luh, B. S., Hsu, E. T. and Stachowicz, K. (1967). *J. Fd Sci.* **32**, 251–8.
Maier, V. P. and Metzler, D. M. (1965a). *J. Fd Sci.* **30**, 80–4.
Maier, V. P. and Metzler, D. M. (1965b). *J. Fd Sci.* **30**, 747–52.
Maier, V. P. and Metzler, D. M. (1967a). *Phytochem.* **6**, 763–5.
Maier, V. P. and Metzler, D. M. (1967b). *Phytochem.* **6**, 1127–35.
Mansell, R. L. and Hagen, C. W., Jr. (1966). *Amer. J. Bot.* **53**, 875–82.
Mayer, A. M., Harel, E. and Shain, Y. (1964). *Phytochem.* **3**, 447–51.
McNew, G. L. and Burchfield, H. P. (1951). *Contr. Boyce Thompson Inst. Pl. Res.* **16**, 357–74.
Miles, C. D. and Hagen, C. W., Jr. (1968). *Pl. Physiol.* **43**, 1347–54.
Monties, B. (1966). *Ann. Physiol. Veg.* **8**, 49–73, 101–35.
Morton, A. D. (1968). *J. Fd Technol.* **3**, 269–75.
Neish, A. C. (1964). *In* "Biochemistry of Phenolic Compounds" (J. B. Harborne, ed.), pp. 295–359. Academic Press, London.
Nelson, R. F. and Finkle, B. J. (1964). *Phytochem.* **3**, 321–5.
Nortje, B. K. (1966). *J. Fd Sci.* **31**, 733–5.
Nortje, B. K. and Koeppen, B. H. (1965). *Biochem. J.* **97**, 209–13.
Nybom, N. (1960). *Ann. Rep. Balsgård Fruit Inst.* (Sweden), 8–16.

Ollis, W. D. (1962). *In* "Chemistry of Flavonoid Compounds" (T. A. Geissman, ed.), pp. 353–405. Pergamon Press, New York.

Patschke, L., Barz, W. and Grisebach, H. (1966). *Z. Naturf.* **21b**, 45–7.

Peng, C. Y. and Markakis, P. (1963). *Nature, Lond.* **199**, 597–8.

Pollard, A., Kieser, M. E. and Sissons, D. J. (1958). *Chemy Ind.* 952.

Pridham, J. B. (1964). *Phytochem.* **3**, 493–7.

Pruthi, J. S., Susheela, R. and Lal, G. (1961). *J. Fd Sci.* **26**, 385–8.

Puski, G. and Francis, F. J. (1967). *J. Fd Sci.* **32**, 527–30.

Ribéreau-Gayon, P. (1964). *Ann. Physiol. Veg.* **6**, 119–39, 211–42, 259–82.

Rivas, N. and Luh, B. S. (1968). *J. Fd Sci.* **33**, 358–63.

Roberts, E. A. H. (1960). *Nature, Lond.* **185**, 536–7.

Roberts, E. A. H., Cartwright, R. A. and Oldschool, M. (1957). *J. Sci. Fd Agric.* **8**, 72–80.

Robinson, G. M. and Robinson, R. (1931). *Biochem. J.* **25**, 1687–1705.

Robinson, W. B., Einset, J., Kimball, K. H. and Bertino, J. J. (1967). *N.Y. St. Agric. Exp. Sta. Res. Circ.* 9.

Rossi, J. A., Jr. and Singleton, V. L. (1966a). *Am. J. Enol. Vitic.* **17**, 231–9.

Rossi, J. A., Jr. and Singleton, V. L. (1966b). *Am. J. Enol. Vitic.* **17**, 240–6.

Ryugo, K. (1966). *Proc. Am. Soc. hort. Sci.* **88**, 160–6.

Sakamura, S. and Francis, F. J. (1961). *J. Fd Sci.* **26**, 318–21.

Sakamura, S., Shibusa, S. and Obata, Y. (1966). *J. Fd Sci.* **31**, 317–19.

Sal'kova, E. G. and Bekbulatova, R. I. (1965). *Appl. Biochem. Microbiol.* **1**, 355–7.

Satô, M., Katô, N. and Hasegawa, M. (1968). *Bot. Mag., Tokyo* **81**, 356–61.

Scarpati, M. L. and Guiso, M. (1964). *Tetrahedron Lett.* **39**, 3851–3.

Schaller, D. R. and von Elbe, J. H. (1968). *J. Fd Sci.* **33**, 442–3.

Scheiner, D. M., Van Buren, J. P. and Wagenknecht, A. C. (1960). *Fedn Proc.* **19**, No. 1, Pt. 1.

Schmid, P. (1967). *Z. Lebensmittelunters. u.-Forsch.* **133**, 304–10.

Segal, B. and Grager, W. (1967). *Nahrung* **11**, 223–8.

Sherratt, H. S. A. (1958). *J. Genet.* **56**, 28–36.

Siegelman, H. W. (1955a). *Archs Biochem. Biophys.* **56**, 97–102.

Siegelman, H. W. (1955b). *J. biol. Chem.* **213**, 647–54.

Siegelman, H. W. (1964). *In* "Biochemistry of Phenolic Compounds" (J. B. Harborne, ed.), pp. 437–56. Academic Press, New York and London.

Siegelman, H. W. and Hendricks, S. B. (1958). *Pl. Physiol.* **33**, 185–90.

Smith, R. M. and Luh, B. S. (1965). *J. Fd Sci.* **30**, 995–1005.

Smock, R. M. (1966). *Proc. Am. Soc. hort. Sci.* **88**, 80–8.

Somers, T. C. (1966). *Nature, Lond.* **209**, 368–70.

Somers, T. C. (1968). *Vitis* **7**, 303–20.

Sondheimer, E. (1958). *Archs Biochem. Biophys.* **74**, 131–8.

Sondheimer, E. (1964). *Bot. Rev.* **30**, 667–712.

Sondheimer, E. and Kertesz, Z. I. (1952). *Fd Res.* **17**, 288–98.

Stafford, H. A. (1960). *Pl. Physiol.* **35**, 612–18.

Steck, W. (1968). *Phytochem.* **7**, 1711–17.

Strong, F. M. (1966). *In* "Toxicants Occurring Naturally in Foods", pp. 94–7. National Academy of Sciences (U.S.A.), NRC Publ. 1354, Washington, D.C.

Sun, B. H. and Francis, F. J. (1967). *J. Fd Sci.* **32**, 647–9.

Swain, T. (1962). *In* "The Chemistry of Flavonoid Compounds" (T. A. Geissman, ed.), pp. 513–52. Pergamon Press, New York.

Swardt, G. H. De. (1967). *Diss. Abstr.* Sect. B 27 (9), 2984B–2985B.

Thimann, K. V. and Radner, B. S. (1962). *Archs Biochem. Biophys.* **96**, 270–9.
Timberlake, C. F. (1959). *J. chem. Soc.*, 2795–8.
Timberlake, C. F. and Bridle, P. (1967). *J. Sci. Fd Agric.* **18**, 473–8.
Trebst, A. (1963). *Proc. Roy. Soc. B* **157**, 355–66.
Trotter, P. C. (1962). *Tappi* **45**, 449–53.
Tsai Su, C. and Singleton, V. L. *Phytochem.* **8**, 1553–9.
Van Blaricom, L. O. and Senn, T. L. (1967). *Proc. Am. Soc. hort. Sci.* **90**, 541–5.
Van Buren, J. P., Scheiner, D. M. and Wagenknecht, A. C. (1960). *Nature, Lond.* **185**, 165–6.
Van Buren, J. P., Senn, G. and Neukom, H. (1966). *J. Fd Sci.* **31**, 964–70.
Wagenbreth, A. (1959). *Flora* **147**, 164–6.
Wagner, H., Patel, J., Hörhammer, L., Yap, F. and Reichardt, A. (1967). *Z. Natursf.* **22b**, 988–9.
Walker, J. R. L. (1962). *N.Z. Jl Sci.* **5**, 316–24.
Walker, J. R. L. (1963). *N.Z. Jl Sci.* **6**, 492–4.
Walker, J. R. L. (1964). *N.Z. Jl Sci.* **7**, 585–8.
Walker, J. R. L. and Hulme, A. C. (1966). *Phytochem.* **5**, 259–62.
Walter, T. E. (1966). Rep. E. Malling Res. Stn, 70–82.
Watanabe, S., Sakamura, S. and Obata, Y. (1966). *Agr. Biol. Chem.* (Japan) **30**, 420–2.
Weinges, K. (1964). *Phytochem.* **3**, 263–6.
Weinges, K., Kaltenhäuser, W., Marx, H.-D., Nader, E., Nader, F., Perner, J. and Seiler, D. (1968). *Justus Liebigs Annln Chem.* **711**, 184–204.
Williams, A. H. (1957). *J. Sci. Fd Agric.* **8**, 385–9.
Williams, A. H. (1958). *Chemy Ind.* 1200.
Williams, A. H. (1959). *Bericht der wissenschaftlichtechnischen Kommission der Internationalen Fruchtsaft-Union*, 259–63. (Symposium Fruchtsaftkonzentrate, Bristol, 1958.)
Wong, E. (1968). *Phytochem.* **7**, 1751–8.
Workman, M. (1963). *Proc. Am. Soc. hort. Sci.* **83**, 149–61.
Wu, M. and Burrell, R. C. (1958). *Archs Biochem. Biophys.* **74**, 114–18.
Zapsalis, C. and Francis, F. J. (1965). *J. Fd Sci.* **30**, 396–9.
Zitko, V. and Rosik, J. (1962). *Nahrung* **6**, 561–77.

Chapter 12

Carotenoids and Triterpenoids

T. W. GOODWIN AND L. J. GOAD

*Department of Biochemistry, University of Liverpool,
Liverpool, England*

I. CAROTENOIDS

A. Introduction

During the last thirty to forty years there have been many investigations on the nature and distribution of carotenoids in fruit. Inevitably, advances in techniques and in knowledge of carotenoid chemistry have caught up with some earlier investigations, and later work has revealed additional pigments and

TABLE I. Carotenoids in fruit

Species	Pigments	Major pattern discernible	Comment	Reference
Actinophloeus angustifolia	5	III	Only lycopene reported	Lubimenko (1914)
Actinophloeus macarthurii	5	III	Only lycopene reported	Lubimenko (1914)
Aglaeonema nitidum	5	III	Only lycopene reported	Lubimenko (1914)
Aglaeonema oblongifolium	5	III	Only lycopene reported	Lubimenko (1914)
Aglaeonema simplex	5	III	Only lycopene reported	Lubimenko (1914)
Ananas sativus	7, 19	II?	Only lycopene reported	Mogistad (1935); Schön (1935)
Arbutus unedo	5, 6, 7, 15, 19, 20, 32	III, IV		
Archontophoenix alexandrae	5	III	Only lycopene reported	Lubimenko (1914)
Area alicae	5	III	Only lycopene reported	Lubimenko (1914)
Arum italicum	5	III, VII	"Lycopin erster ordnung"	Lubimenko (1914); Kylin (1927);
Arum maculatum	1, 2, 3, 5, 5A, 7, 8	III, VII	and Arumin are mixtures of	Karrer and Wherli (1930);
Arum orientale	5, 7, 19	III, VII	prolycopenes	Goodwin (1956); Kylin (1927)
Asparagus officinalis	15	IV	Only cryptoxanthin reported	Karrer and Wherli (1930)
Atropa belladonna	7, 15	IV		Goodwin (1956)
Attalea gomphococca	7	IV	Only β-carotene reported	Blackie and Cowgill (1939)
Berberis barbarossa	30	II, IV, VI		Goodwin (1956)
Berberis vulgaris	30	II, IV, VI	Capsanthin present in most	Wierzchowski and Bubicz (1961)
Berberis spp. (34)	2, 6, 7, 19, 20, 25, 27, 28, 30	II, IV, VI	varieties	Bubicz and Wierzchowski (1960); Bubicz (1965)
Bixa orellana		VI	Unique C-25 pigment	Karrer and Jucker (1950)
Brachychilum horsfieldi	5, 15	VI	Lycopene in seeds; cryptoxanthin in pericarp	Egger and Kleinig (1966)
Bryonia dioica	5	III	Only lycopene reported	Lubimenko (1914); Winterstein and Ehrenberg (1932)
Butia capitata		VII		Zechmeister and Schroeder (1942)
Caliptocalyx spicatus	5	III	Only lycopene reported	Lubimenko (1914)
Capsicum annuum	1, 2, 7, 15, 20, 25, 26, 27, 28, 30, 32, 36	III	Unique pigments capsanthin, capsorubin	Zechmeister and Cholnoky(1936); Cholnoky et al. (1956); Goodwin (1956);Curl(1962a);Egger(1968a)
v.*lycopersiciforme rubrum*		IV, VI		

Species	Compounds	Groups	Notes	References
Capsicum annum v. *lycopersiciforme flavum*	6, 7, 14, 15, 16, 19, 25, 32, 35, 37	IV	No unique pigments	Cholnoky et al. (1956)
Capsicum annum (green)	14, 19, 20, 30, 32, 33, 34, 35, 36, 37	II	No unique pigments	Curl (1964)
Capsicum frutescens	30	IV, VI		Zechmeister and Cholnoky (1931); Kuhn and Grundmann (1933)
Capsicum japonicum	7	IV	No unique pigments	Zechmeister and Cholnoky (1934) Yamamoto and Tin (1933);
Carica papaya	1, 2, 3, 4, 7, 15, 16, 17, 21, 24, 25, 28, 33, 35	IV	Lycopene in red mutant	Yamamoto (1964); Subbaraya and Cama (1964)
Celastrus scandens	47	IV, VI	Unique pigment celaxanthin	Le Rosen and Zechmeister (1942)
Citrullus vulgaris (red)	5, 6, 7, 8	III, IV	Similar to normal tomatoes	Zechmeister and Tuzson (1930); Zechmeister and Polgar (1941); Tomes et al. (1963)
Citrullus vulgaris (yellow)		VII	Similar to tangerine tomatoes	Tomes and Johnson (1965)
Citrus aurantium	5, 6, 15, 17, 19 20, 32	IV, V, VI	Unique apocarotenoids	Zechmeister and Tuzson (1934); Karrer and Jucker (1947a, b)
Citrus grandis	5, 6	III, IV, V		Matlock (1934)
Citrus limonia		IV		Curl (1962a, b)
Citrus madurensis	5, 15, 19, 32	III, IV		Zechmeister and Tuzson (1936)
Citrus paradisi	1, 2, 3, 5, 6, 7, 14, 15, 19, 24, 25, 27, 32, 33, 34	III, IV	Xanthophylls minor components: phytoene major components of peel	Khan and Mackinney (1953); Curl and Bailey (1957); Yokoyama and White (1967)
Citrus poonensis	7, 15, 19	IV		Yamamoto and Tin (1933)
Citrus reticulata	1, 2, 3, 5, 6, 7, 15, 19, 20, 25, 27, 32, 33, 34, 38, 40, 43	IV, V, VI	Unique apocarotenoids	Curl and Bailey (1957)
Citrus sinensis	1, 2, 3, 5A, 7, 15, 16, 17, 21, 25, 28, 29, 32, 33, 34	IV, V, VI	Unique apocarotenoids	Curl and Bailey (1954; 1961)
Citrus spp. (Nagpur)	5, 6, 7, 8, 19	IV, V	Peel different from pulp (see p. 322).	Subbrarayan and Cama (1965)
Convallaria majalis	7, 15, 17	III, IV		Winterstein and Ehrenberg (1932)
Cotoneaster bullata	7, 15, 17, 20, 28	IV, V		Goodwin (1956)
Cotoneaster frigida	7, 15, 17, 28	IV, V		
Cotoneaster hebephylla	19, 32	IV, V		
Cotoneaster occidentalis	15, 17, 19, 34	I (traces)		Karrer and Rutschmann (1945)
Crataegus oxacantha	7, 15, 17	IV, V		Goodwin (1956)
Crataegus pratensis		IV, V		Goodwin (1956)

Species	Pigments	Major pattern discernible	Comment	Reference
Cucumis citrullus	5	III	Only lycopene reported	Winterstein and Ehrenberg (1932)
Cucumis melo	1, 2, 3, 6, 7, 19, 20, 32, 33	IV		Curl (1966)
Cucurbita maxima	6, 7, 19, 20	II		Zechmeister and Tuzson (1934)
Cuscuta salina	13	VI		Schön (1938)
Cuscuta subinclusa	13	IV	Unique rubixanthin	Zechmeister and Schroder (1943)
Cycas revoluta	20	IV	Only zeaxanthin reported	Manunta (1939)
Cyphomandra betaceae	15	IV	Cryptoxanthin main pigment	Unpublished observations
Diospyros costata	1, 2, 3, 4, 6, 7, 8, 17, 14, 15, 21, 19, 20, 25, 26, 27, 32, 33, 34, 35, 37, 38, 40	III, IV		Schön (1935)
Diospyros kaki	2, 3, 5, 6, 7, 8, 14, 15, 19, 20, 25, 29, 32, 33, 35	III, IV	Lycopene(s) vary from 0–40% of total according to variety	Karrer *et al.* (1932); Curl (1960a, 1960b); Brossard and Mackinney (1963)
Dura nigrescens / *Dura virescens*	1, 2, 3, 5, 6, 7	III, IV, VII	Also prolycopenes	Argoud (1958) / Argoud (1958)
Elaeagnus longipes		III		Geiger-Vifian and Muller (1945)
Elaeis guineensis	5, 7	III, IV		Gill (1918); Brash (1926)
Elaeis melasiococca	5, 7	III, IV		Gill (1918)
Erythroxylon coca	5	III		Lubimenko (1914)
Erythroxylon novogranatense	5	III	Only lycopene reported	Hilbert and Jansen (1934)
Euonymus europaeus	5, 15, 47	III, IV, VI	Unique celaxanthin	Zechmeister and Escue (1942); Karrer and Jucker (1947b)
Euonymus fortunei		VII		Zechmeister and Escue (1942)
Euonymus japonicus	5	III	Only lycopene reported	Zechmeister and Schroeder (1942)
Ficus cerica	1, 2, 6, 7, 19, 20, 32, 33, 35, 38, 39	II		Curl (1964)
Fragaria chiloensis	traces	II		Curl (1964)
Gardinia grandiflora	31	VI	Unique crocetin	Kuhn *et al.* (1928)
Gonocaryum obovatum	5, 6, 7, 8	III, IV		Winterstein (1933)
Gonocaryum pyriforme	5, 6, 7, 8	III, IV		Winterstein (1933)
Gossypium spp.	7, 19	II		Gill and Greenup (1929)

Guava spp.	6, 7	III	Only α- and β-carotene reported	Suarez and Cadavieco (1956)
Hippophae rhamnoides	3, 5, 7, 8, 19, 20, 24	III		Karrer and Wehrli (1930); Winterstein and Ehrenberg (1932); Bielig (1944); Goodwin (1956)
Iris pseudacorus	32	?	Only violaxanthin reported	Drumm and O'Connor (1945)
Lathyrus sativus	7	IV	Only β-carotene reported	Kemmerer et al. (1942)
Lonicera japonica	2, 3, 5, 7, 8, 15, 20, 34	III, IV		Goodwin (1956)
Lonicera periclymenum	7, 15, 20, 34	III, IV		Goodwin (1956)
Luffa spp.	7, 19	II		Godnew and Korschenewsky (1930)
Lycium barbaratum	15	IV	Only zeaxanthin reported	Winterstein and Ehrenberg (1932)
Lycium hamimifolium	15	IV	Only zeaxanthin reported	Zechmeister and Cholnoky (1930)
Lycopersicum esculentum	1, 2, 3, 4, 5, 6, 7, 12, 18	III, IV		Numerous, see text
Lycopersicum hirsutum	3, 5, 7, 8	III, IV		Zechmeister et al. (1941)
Lycopersicum peruvianum	3, 5, 7, 8	III, IV		Zechmeister et al. (1941)
Malpighia punicifolia	1, 2, 3, 7, 8, 19, 20	II, (?III)	Mainly β-carotene	Baraud (1958)
Mangifera indica	1, 2, 7, 8, 15, 16, 17, 19, 20, 25, 27, 32, 33, 34	IV		Jungalwala and Cama (1963)
Momordica balsamina	5, 19	III		Duggar (1913)
Momordica charantia	5, 7	III, IV		Duggar (1913)
Murraya exotica	45, 46	VI	Major pigment semi-β-carotenone	Yokoyama and White (1967b); Yokoyama and White (1968a)
Musa paradisiaca	7, 19	II		Loesecke, H. von (1929)
Nenga polycephalus	5	III	Only lycopene reported	Lubimenko (1914)
Palisota barteri	3, 5, 7, 15, 20, 49, 50	VI		Egger and Kleinig-Voigt (1968)
Pandanus polycephalus	5	III	Only lycopene reported	Lubimenko (1914)
Passiflora coerulea	5	III	Only lycopene reported	Karrer et al. (1935)
Physalis alkekengi	1, 2, 3, 6, 7, 14, 15, 17, 19, 20, 33	IV		Kuhn and Grundmann (1933); Baraud (1958); Bodea and Nicoara (1959)
Prunus armeniaca	1, 2, 3, 5, 6, 7, 8, 13, 14, 15, 19, 20, 21, 25, 26, 27, 28, 32, 33, 34, 40, 41	III, IV	Also poly *cis* isomers	Brockmann (1933); Curl (1960a)

Species	Pigments	Major pattern discernible	Comment	Reference
Prunus domestica	1, 2, 3, 6, 7, 14, 15, 17, 20, 21, 25, 26, 27, 28, 32, 33, 35, 41	IV		Curl (1963)
Prunus persica	1, 2, 3, 6, 7, 14, 15, 19, 20, 25, 26, 27, 32, 33, 34, 41	III, IV	Also poly *cis* isomers	Mackinney (1937); Raborn and Quackenbush (1953); Curl (1959)
Ptychandra elegans	5	III	Only lycopene reported	Lubimenko (1914)
Ptychandra glauca	5	III	Only lycopene reported	Lubimenko (1914)
Punica granatum	in traces	II		Curl (1964)
Pyracantha angustifolia	5, 7	IV, VIII	Only *cis* lycopenes, γ-carotenes and neurosporene present	Zechmeister and Schroeder (1942); Zechmeister and Pinckard (1947); Magoon and Zechmeister (1957)
Pyracantha coccinea	trace	I		Karrer and Rutschmann (1945)
Pyracantha flava	7, 17, 19, 20, 28	III		Goodwin (1956)
Pyracantha rogersiana	7	I		Goodwin (1956)
Pyracantha yunanensis		IV, VII		Zechmeister and Pinckard (1947)
Pyrus (eating)	2, 3, 7, 11, 12, 16, 17, 19, 20, 23, 26, 28, 34, 35	IV, V	Major pigment varies with variety	Francis *et al.* (1955); Valadon and Mummery (1967)
Pyrus aucaparia	7	IV	Only β-carotene reported	Kuhn and Lederer (1931)
Pyrus baccata	2, 3, 7, 11, 15, 16, 19, 20, 23, 26, 28, 34	IV, V		Valadon and Mummery (1967)
Pyrus prunifolia	2, 7, 16, 19, 20, 23, 34	IV, V		Valadon and Mummery (1967)
Rosa canina	1, 2, 3, 5, 7, 6, 8, 13, 15, 19, 28	III, IV, VI, VII	4-oxo-3-hydroxy-carotene, also prolycopenes	Karrer and Widmer (1928); Kuhn and Grundmann (1934); Goodwin (1956); Neamtu *et al.* (1968); Baraud (1958)
Rosa damascena	5, 7, 8, 13, 19, 20	III, VI, VII	Also prolycopenes	Kuhn and Grundmann (1934)
Rosa moyesi	1, 2, 3, 5, 7, 13, 14, 19, 20	III, IV, VI, VII	Unique carotenoid rubixanthin	Goodwin (1956)
Rosa rubiginosa	5, 7, 8, 13, 19, 20	III, IV, VI		Kuhn and Grundmann (1934)
Rosa rubrifolia	1, 2, 5, 7, 12, 13, 20, 28	III, IV, VI		Goodwin (1956)
Rosa rugosa	5, 6, 7, 8, 13	III, IV, V		Willstaedt (1935)
Rubus chamaemorus	5, 6, 7, 13, 20	III, IV, VI		Willstaedt (1936a)

Species	Numbers	Roman	Comment	Reference
Rubus procerus	1, 2, 3, 6, 7, 19, 20	II	Also some epoxides	Curl (1964)
Sabal serrulatum	7	IV	Only β-carotene reported	Griebel and Barnes (1916)
Sambucus nigra	7, 19, 28, 35	II		Goodwin (1956)
Seaforta elegans	5	III	Only lycopene reported	Zechmeister (1950)
Shepherdia canadensis	1, 2, 5, 7, 12, 28	III		Stabursvik (1954)
Solanum balbisii	5	III	Only lycopene reported	Lubimenko (1914)
Solanum decasepalum	5	III	Only lycopene reported	Lubimenko (1920)
Solanum dulcamara	5, 12, 18, 19	III		Zechmeister and Cholnoky(1936); Goodwin (1956)
Solanum esculentum	5, 13, 18	III		Zechmeister and Schroeder (1942)
Solanum hendersonii	20	IV	Only zeaxanthin reported	Winterstein and Ehrenberg (1932)
Solanum lycopersicum	5, 7, 19	II, III		Brass *et al.* (1937)
Sorbus aucuparia	6, 7, 17, 19	II, IV		Kuhn and Lederer (1931); Goodwin (1956)
Synaspadix petrichiana	5	III	Only lycopene reported	Lubimenko (1914)
Tabernae montana pentasticta	5	III	Only lycopene reported	Lubimenko (1914)
Tamus communis	1, 2, 3, 5, 7, 8, 12, 14, 17, 20, 33,	III, IV		Zechmeister and Cholnoky(1936); Goodwin (1956); Baraud (1958)
Taxus baccata	1, 2, 7, 12, 17, 22, 44	II, IV	Unique pigments rhodoxanthin, eschscholtzsanthone	Kuhn and Brockmann (1933); Goodwin (1956); Bodea *et al.* (1964)
Trichosanthes spp.	5	III	Only lycopene reported	Monteverde and Lubimenko (1913)
Triphasia trifolia	45, 46	IV	Unique β-carotenone	Yokoyama and White (1968b)
Vaccinium spp. (blueberry)	Complex mixture	II		Curl (1964)
Vaccinium macrocarpon (cranberry)	1, 2, 3, 6, 12, 14, 15, 17, 19, 20, 25, 26, 27, 28, 32, 33, 35, 38, 40	II		Curl (1964)
Vaccinium vitis-idaea	5, 19, 20	IV		Willstaedt (1936b)
Viburnum opulus	2, 3, 5, 7, 8, 17	IV, V		Goodwin (1956)
Vigna sinensis	7, 15	II		Hilbert and Jansen (1934)
Vitis vinifera	1, 2, 5, 6, 19, 20, 32, 33	II	Other epoxides also present	Curl (1964)

TABLE II. Carotenoids found in fruit

Number[a]	Name	Structure
1	Phytoene[b]	
2	Phytofluene[b]	
3	ζ-Carotene	
4	Neurosporene	
5	Lycopene	
6	α-Carotene[c]	
7	β-Carotene	
8	γ-Carotene	

Number[a]	Name	Structure
9	δ-Carotene	
10	ε-Carotene	
11	β-Zeacarotene	
12	Lycoxanthin	16-hydroxylycopene
13	Rubixanthin	3-hydroxy-γ-carotene
14	α-Cryptoxanthin	3'-hydroxy-α-carotene
15	β-Cryptoxanthin	3-hydroxy-β-carotene
16	β-Carotene- 5,6-epoxide	
17	Mutatochrome (= citroxanthin) (5,8-epoxy-β-carotene)	
18	Lycophyll	16,16'-dihydroxylycopene
19	Lutein	3,3'-dihydroxy-α-carotene
20	Zeaxanthin	3,3'-dihydroxy-β-carotene
21	Cryptoflavin	5,8-epoxy-α-cryptoxanthin
22	Rhodoxanthin (3,3'-diketo-retro-β-carotene)	

Number[a]	Name	Structure
23	β-Carotene,5,6,5′,6′-diepoxide	——
24	Aurochrome	5,8,5′,8′-diepoxy-β-carotene
25	Antheraxanthin	5,6-epoxyzeaxanthin
26	Lutein-5,6-epoxide	——
27	Mutatoxanthin	5,8-epoxyzeaxanthin
28	Flavoxanthin Chrysanthemaxanthin }	5,8-epoxylutein
29	Cryptochrome	5,8,5′,8′-diepoxycryptoxanthin
30	Capsanthin	
31	Trollixanthin	
32	Violaxanthin	5,6,5,6-diepoxyzeaxanthin
33	Luteoxanthin	5,6,5′,8′-diepoxyzeaxanthin
34	Auroxanthin	5,8,5′,8′-diepoxyzeaxanthin
35	Neoxanthin	
36	Capsorubin	
37	Neochrome	5,8-epoxide of neoxanthin (isomer)
38	Valenciaxanthin	?
39	Valenciachrome	?
40	Sinenisiaxanthin	?
41	Persicaxanthin	?

Number[a]	Name	Structure
42	Crocetin	HOOC⌇⌇⌇⌇COOH
43	Trollein	?
44	Eschscholtzxanthone	?
45	Semi-β-carotenone	(structure)
46	β-Carotenone	(structure)
47	Celaxanthin	? rubixanthin derivative
48	Luteochrome	
49	β-Citraurin	(see Table VI)
50	β-Apo-8′-carotinal	(see Table VI)

[a] These numbers refer to Table I.

[b] Note the *cis* configuration around the central double bonds in these polyenes.

[c] The carotenoid molecule is numbered in two halves. The plain numerals take precedence over the prime numerals according to the nature of the end grouping in the order β-ionone residue, α-ionone residue, φ-ionone residue (open chain).

occasionally mis-identifications. This makes assessment of some early literature difficult if the fruit examined has not been re-investigated recently. The problem is further complicated by the aims of the original experiments which were usually carried out by organic chemists interested only in the major carotenoid components, whereas today biochemists are frequently concerned with minor components. These limitations should be borne in mind when the following section is considered.

B. Distribution of Carotenoids in Fruits

The distribution of various carotenoids in fruit is summarized in Table I and the structures of the various pigments are given in Table II. Within the limitations indicated in the introduction, seven main patterns of carotenoid distribution can be discerned although it should be emphasized that in many cases patterns merge into one another: (I) insignificant amounts of carotenoids; (II) small amounts of the carotenoids usually found in chloroplasts, mainly β-carotene, lutein, violaxanthin and neoxanthin; (III) comparatively large amounts of the acyclic lycopene and its partly saturated congeners phytoene, phytofluene, ζ-carotene and neurosporene; (IV) relatively large amounts of β-carotene and its derivatives, cryptoxanthin and zeaxanthin; (V) unusually large amounts of epoxides including furanoid epoxides; (VI) unique carotenoids, for example, capsanthin, and (VII) poly *cis* carotenoids such as prolycopene.

Apart from the fact that many fruits produce far more pigments than do the chloroplasts of green leaves, fruit xanthopylls differ from chloroplast xanthophylls in that they are mainly esterified, while the chloroplast xanthophylls are not. For example, physalein from *Physalis alkekengi* is zeaxanthin dipalmitate (Karrer *et al.*, 1948) whilst a pigment from *Carica papya* and *Citrus pooensis* first called caricaxanthin (Tamamoto and Tin, 1933) is cryptoxanthin palmitate (Karrer and Schlientz, 1934).

C. Taxonomic Significance of Carotenoid Distribution in Fruits

An attempt was recently made to assess the chemotaxonomic significance of fruit carotenoids (Goodwin, 1966) but the situation is not clear and more data are needed. In three *Rosa* spp. examined (Table III) (Goodwin, 1956) there is a qualitatively similar pattern of distribution with the rather specific rubixanthin predominating. If an extract were found to contain substantial amounts of rubixanthin then one could say with some confidence that it arose from the fruit of a species of *Rosa*. This generalization could not be extended to embrace the family Rosaceae because other genera such as *Cotoneaster*, *Crataegus*, *Pyracantha* and *Sorbus* do not synthesize rubixanthin.

Similar interspecies patterns have been obtained in *Cotoneaster* spp. (although aurochrome is found only in *C. bullala*), *Lonicera* spp. (Goodwin, 1956) and *Berberis* spp. (Bubicz, 1965), but none of these is sufficiently specialized to be taxonomically useful. A somewhat constant pattern is found amongst three members of the family Elaeagnaceae, *Hippophae rhamnoides* (Goodwin, 1956), *Shepherdia canadensis* (Stabursvik, 1954) and *Elaeagnus longpipes*, (Geiger-Vifian and Muller, 1945). However, wide divergences are observed amongst the Caprifoliaceae (Table IV). Furthermore, similar divergences can be observed in different species of the same genus; for example, *Pyracantha rogeriana* (Goodwin, 1956) and *P. coccinea* (Karrer and Rutschmann, 1945) produce insignificant amounts of carotenoids whilst *P. flava* synthesizes large amounts of β-carotene derivatives (Goodwin, 1956) and

TABLE III. Quantitative carotenoid distribution in *Rosa* spp.[a]

Polyene	% of total pigments[b]		
	R. canina	R. moyesii	R. rubrifolia
Phytoene	trace	4·5	2·5
Phytofluene	0·3	3·0	2·7
β-Carotene	16·5	14·5	28·5
α-Carotene	0·2	3·5	trace
γ-Carotene	1·4	——	trace
Prolycopenes	0·5	12·5	——
Lycopene	6·0	21·0	16·5
Mutatochrome	——	2·0	——
Cryptoxanthin	1·8	11·0	4·0
Zeaxanthin	6·0	4·5	2·5
Rubixanthin	42·0	14·0	41·0

[a] Goodwin (1956).
[b] Trace pigments not recorded.

TABLE IV. Major carotenoids in some Caprifoliaceae[a]

Polyene	Lonicera japonica	L. periclymenum	Sambucus nigra	Viburnum opulus
Phytofluene	+	?	—	+
β-Carotene	+	+	+	+
α-Carotene	+	+	—	+
γ-Carotene	+	—	—	+
Lycopene	+	+	—	+
Mutachrome	—	—	—	+
Cryptoxanthin	+	—	trace	—
Zeaxanthin	+	+	—	—
Lutein	+	—	+	—
Flavoxanthin	—	—	+	—
Chrysanthemaxanthin	—	—	+	—
Auroxanthin	+	+	—	—

[a] Goodwin (1956).

P. angustifolia, grown in California, produces poly *cis* carotenes (Magoon and Zechmeister, 1957).

Even capsanthin, long considered the characteristic pigment of red peppers, has lost its uniqueness for it is now reported in some *Berberis* spp. (Bubicz, 1965). Furthermore only β-carotene derivatives are present in the yellow (*flavum*) strain of *Capsicum annuum* and no unique pigments are present in the green strain (see Table I). The *rubrum* variety has probably evolved an enzyme which will carry out a pinacol rearrangement on violaxanthin.

In relation to tomato pigments discussed in detail in the next section, MacKinney (1966) has concluded that lycopene arose as the result of a single recessive mutation and "the unpredictable and spasmodic appearance of the acyclic members [carotenoids] becomes merely a question of whether a mutation has occurred and if so whether it has survival value and has persisted in its natural habitat or was considered worth keeping by man".

D. Mutants and Crosses

1. *Tomatoes*

By far the most important mutant studies have been carried out on tomatoes and the general pattern of distribution is given in Table V. The generally accepted pathway of synthesis from phytoene is given in Fig. 7 which should be referred to in conjunction with Table V for the ensuing discussion.

Normal (red) tomatoes possess the dominant allele r^+ whilst yellow

TABLE V. Carotenoid distribution in various tomato phenotypes

Genotypes	Pigments and colourless polyenes	Total concentration (μg/g fr. wt.)		Reference
		Total polyenes	Pigments only	
Red (normal)	1,2,3,4,5	87	50 ⎫	
High pigment (r^+r^+)	1,2,3,4,5	88	69 ⎬	Tomes (1963)
Tangerine (r^+r^+tt)	2,3,4,5,6	158	90 ⎭	
Yellow (*rrtt*)	1,2,4,5	4	2	Mackinney and Jenkins (1952)
Yellow Tangerine (*rrtt*)	1,2,4,5,7	24	14	Jenkins and Mackinney (1955)
Apricot (*atat*)	1,2,4,5	13	11	Mackinney and Jenkins (1952)
Yellow-⎫ Apricot⎭(*rrtt atat*)	2,4,5 (trace)	2	1	Jenkins and Mackinney (1955)
Tangerine-⎫ Apricot⎭(*tt atat*)	1,2,4,5,6,7	29	16	Jenkins and Mackinney (1955)
Yellow-⎫ Tangerine-⎬(*rrtt atat*) Apricot⎭	4,5	10	0	Jenkins and Mackinney (1955)
Ghost (*ghgh*)	1,4,5	295	1	Mackinney et al. (1956)
Intermediate β (b^+b^+)	1,2,3,4,5	50	46 ⎫	
High β ($b^+b^+mo_Bmo_B$)	1,2,3,4,5	80	70 ⎬	Tomes (1963)
Delta (*del*$^+$*del*$^+$)	1,2,3,4,5,7,8,9,10	84	68 ⎪	
High-delta (*del*$^+$*del*$^+$*hphp*)	1,2,3,4,5,8,9,10	55	46 ⎭	

Abbreviations used: 1. Lycopene; 2. β-Carotene; 3. γ-Carotene; 4. Phytoene; 5. Phytofluene; 6. Prolycopene; 7 ζ-Carotene; 8. α-Carotene; 9. δ-Carotene; 10. Neurosporene.

tomatoes are homozygous for the recessive allele r. The r^+/r gene controls the total amount of pigment formed; the rr genotype synthesizes only about 5% (4 μg/g wet weight) of that formed by the r^+r^+ genotype (Le Rosen et al., 1941). Apricot-coloured fruit homozygous for the recessive allele at have the synthesis of the acyclic series considerably inhibited, while β-carotene (cyclic) synthesis is unaffected (Jenkins and MacKinney, 1955). A third recessive gene, hp, increases the content of all components by about 100% (Tomes et al., 1958).

Qualitative changes are observed in tangerine tomatoes which are homozygous for the recessive t, whilst red fruit carry the dominant allele t^+ (MacArthur, 1934). The poly cis isomers prolycopene and pro-γ-carotene, of unknown structures accumulate at the expense of lycopene in tangerine tomatoes (Zechmeister and Went, 1948; Porter and Lincoln, 1950).

The effects of r and t are both reinforced by at (apricot), for, in the yellow-apricot phenotype, lycopene synthesis is completely suppressed and β-carotene synthesis reduced, while, in the tangerine-apricot phenotype, at enhances the channelling of synthesis into the prolycopene pathway (Jenkins and MacKinney, 1955).

An orange phenotype obtained by back-crossing a $L.$ $esculentum$ and a $L.$ $hirsutum$ hybrid has β-carotene and not lycopene as its major carotenoid (Lincoln and Porter, 1950). These fruit (high β) are either homozygous or heterozygous for the dominant allele b^+, whilst normal red fruit are homozygous for the recessive b. The expression of the b^+/b gene is partly regulated by an independently inherited modifier mo_B^+/mo_B (Tomes et al., 1954). In the presence of mo_B^+ in either the homozygous or heterozygous form, β-carotene, which represents over 90% of the total carotenes in the presence of b^+, is reduced whilst that of lycopene is increased so that they are about equal. On the other hand mo_B^+ has no effect on the allele b, for bb fruit still produce mainly lycopene in the presence of mo_B^+. A similar, if not identical, gene to b^+/b, which is tightly linked to the self-pruning locus has been described in an orange-fruited $L.$ $pimpinellifolium$ from the Galapagos islands (MacKinney et al., 1954).

A strain (delta) of tomatoes with a high concentration of δ-carotene, produced, apparently, at the expense of lycopene, possesses the high delta allele del^+ (Kargl et al., 1960) which is either incompletely dominant, or dominant but affected by a modifier gene (Tomes, 1963).

The ghost phenotype appears spontaneously in tomato lines carrying red fruit. The seedlings homozygous for the recessive allele gh germinate with green cotyledons which rapidly lose chlorophyll as they grow. Grafting of normal scions on to ghost stock results in plants which produce fruit which are milky white when unripe and yellowish when mature. Phytoene is present in amounts comparable to the lycopene levels observed in red fruit. The yellow colour of the mature fruit is due to the presence of an alkali-soluble pigment. The *gh* gene also affects the carotenoid pattern in leaves which also produce no coloured carotenoids but only phytoene (MacKinney *et al.*, 1956). Thus gh^+/gh must control synthesis of an enzyme or enzymes converting phytoene into lycopene. The effect on chlorophyll synthesis is probably a secondary result of the absence of carotenoids which are known to protect chlorophyll against photosensitized destruction (Krinsky, 1968).

A lutescent gene causes a delay of up to two weeks in the appearance of lycopene in ripening fruit. During this period the fruits behave like an *r* segregant but suddenly within 24–30 hours they rapidly turn red, due to the sudden onset of lycopene synthesis (Kargl *et al.*, 1960). The mode of action of this "timing" gene is quite unknown.

In a dirty red mutant the presence of both chlorophylls and carotenoids imparts the characteristic colour to the ripe fruit. This is controlled by a single recessive gene allelic to the green flesh mutant (*gf*). The carotenoid levels are normal but the chlorophyll levels instead of being zero are around 30% of those in green unripe fruit (Ramirez and Tomes, 1964).

A dwarf mutant gene (*d*) has no consistent effect on the carotenoid content of tomatoes (Baker and Tomes, 1964).

A recessive mutation, sherry (*sh*) produces fruit closely resembling yellow (*rr*) fruit but with rather more carotenoids. It is, however, non-allellic to yellow, apricot and tangerine (Zscheile and Lesley, 1967).

The variety ES_{24} (*uu* = uniform ripening) contained less lycopene than strain Tecumseh (u^+u^+), but F^2 studies indicated that pigment loss could not be assigned to the *u* gene. The uniform grey-green gene (*ug*) behaves similarly (Ayers and Tomes, 1966).

2. Peppers

A mutant of *Capsicum annuum* produces orange-yellow instead of bright red fruit; this character is probably due to a single recessive mendelian factor (Smith, 1950). Mutants are also known with no carotenoids in their fruit although the leaf carotenoids are normal (Kirk and Tilney-Bassett, 1967). It has been suggested that the mutations produce a faulty regulator gene which cannot combine with the inducer, thus some or all of the structural genes concerned with carotenogensis remain permanently repressed (Kirk and Juniper, 1966).

3. Papaya

The red-flushed *Carica papaya* differs from the normal yellow-fleshed types by a single gene; it produces considerable amounts of lycopene which is absent from the yellow variety (Yamamoto, 1964).

4. *Watermelons*

The orange-fleshed watermelon differs from the normal red type in the same way as the tangerine tomato differs from the red variety (see Section 1) (Tomes and Johnson, 1965). It is probable that the genetic difference is the same as in the tomato, which is homozygous for a recessive gene *t*.

A new colour type, crimson, contains more lycopene, phytoene and phytofluene than the standard varieties but less than the high pigment strains, while the β-carotene level is lower than in the standard variety; γ-carotene is the same as in the standard variety (Thompson *et al.*, 1965).

5. *Citrus fruit*

A series of important investigations on citrus hybrids has revealed a number of new naturally occurring apo-carotenoids in considerable quantity. Their structures are summarized in Table VI. Sintaxanthin, citranaxanthin

TABLE VI. Apocarotenoids present in citrus fruit

Name	Structure
β-Apo-10′-carotenal	
β-Apo-8′-carotenal	
Sintaxanthin	
Citranaxanthin	
β-Citraurin	3-Hydroxy-β-apo-8′-carotenal
8′-Hydroxy-7′,8′-dihydrocitranaxanthin	——
3-Hydroxysintaxanthin	——
Reticulataxanthin	3-Hydroxycitranaxanthin
8′-Hydroxy-7′,8′-dihydrocitranaxanthin	——

and reticulataxanthin occur in large amounts in the Sinton citrangequat, a trigeneric hybrid of the oval kumquat (*Fortunella margarita*) with the Rusk citrange (*Poncirus trifoliata* and *Citrus sinensis*), and are mainly responsible for the deep red colour of the flavedo of the fruit (Yokoyama and White, 1966). These pigments are not species-specific, although they are apparently restricted to the Rutaceae. However, they appear in significant amounts only on hybridization. For example, reticulataxanthin constitutes over 49% of the carotenoids in the Sinton citrangequat while it occurs only in traces, if at all, in the Rusk citrange (Yokoyama and White, 1966). It is only a minor component of the peel of *Citrus sinensis* (Curl and Bailey, 1954, 1956, 1961) and *C. reticulata* (Curl and Bailey, 1957; Curl, 1962a), but occurs in greater amounts in the peel of the hybrid Minneola tangor (*Citrus reticulata* and *Citrus sinensis*) (Yokoyama and White, 1965).

The biosynthetic significance of the formation of these methyl ketones is still not clear, because the apo-carotenoids normally present in citrus fruit β-apo-10'-carotenal, β-apo-8'-carotenal and β-citraurin (Table VI), are also present in the Sinton citrangequat, and this suggests that the usually accepted pathways of degradation of β-carotene and zeaxanthin are also functioning in the hybrid (Goodwin, 1958).

E. Ripening of Fruit

Most published reports have been concerned with tomato ripening, but in all fruit with carotenoids in chromoplasts there is a rapid synthesis during ripening which is accompanied by a simultaneous loss of chlorophyll as chloroplasts change into chromoplasts (Goodwin, 1958). Apart from the well known case of tomatoes (see, for example, Porter and Zscheile, 1946) this has been demonstrated in orange rind (Miller *et al.*, 1940), juice (Quinones *et al.*, 1944) and pulp (Stahl and Cain, 1939); pumpkins (Holmes and Spelman, 1947); rose hips of various species (Stamberg, 1947; Lassen *et al.*, 1944), mangoes (Ramasarma *et al.*, 1943) and various citrus fruit (Gonzalez-Silita, 1949).

It has been claimed that banana skins maintain a constant carotenoid level during ripening (Loesecke, 1929), as do certain apples (Valadon and Mummery, 1967).

Rind or peel of fruit is frequently the region of higher carotenoid concentration (Miller *et al.*, 1940; Steffen and Walter, 1958); the concentration in apple peel, for example, is five times that of the flesh, and 50–75% of the total carotenoids of oranges exist in the peel (Gonzalez-Silita, 1949; Curl and Bailey, 1956). In early season Valencia oranges there is a qualitative difference between carotenoids in pulp and peel, the latter containing relatively much more violaxanthin (Curl and Bailey, 1956) (see Table VII). The qualitative

TABLE VII. The quantitative and qualitative distribution of
carotenoids in orange pulp and peel[a]

Carotenoid	% of total pigments[b] Pulp	Peel
Phytoene	4·0	3·1
Phytofluene	1·3	6·1
α-Carotene	0·5	0·1
β-Carotene	1·1	0·3
δ-Carotene	5·4	3·5
OH-α-Carotene-like	1·5	0·3
Cryptoxanthin epoxide-like	——	0·4
Cryptoxanthin	5·3	1·2
Cryptoflavin-like	0·5	1·2
Cryptochrome-like	——	0·8
Lutein	2·9	1·2
Zeaxanthin	4·5	0·8
Capsanthin-like	——	0·3
Antheraxanthin	5·8	6·3
Mutatoxanthins	6·2	1·7
Violaxanthins	7·4	44·0
Luteoxanthins	17·0	16·0
Auroxanthins	12·0	2·3
Valenciaxanthin	2·8	2·2
Sinensiaxanthin	2·0	3·5
Trollixanthin-like	2·9	0·5
Valenciachrome	1·0	0·7
Sinensiachrome-like	——	0·2
Trollichrome-like	3·0	0·8

[a] Curl and Bailey (1956).
[b] Specific extinction values are assumed to be the same for all components.

and quantitative changes which ripening peppers undergo are given in Table VIII. The change from a chloroplast pattern to a chromoplast pattern with a surge of synthesis of unique carotenoids is made clear by these data. The morphological changes accompanying these pigment changes have been described in *Sambucus racemosa*, *Physalis alkekengi* and *Sorbus aucuparia* (Zurzycki, 1954), *Solanum capsicastrum* (Steffen and Walter, 1958), *Capsicum annuum* (Frey-Wyssling and Kreutzer, 1957; Kirk and Juniper, 1966), and in the rind of navel oranges (Thompson, 1965).

The disappearance of chlorophyll is not, however, essential for the development of chromoplasts with the synthesis of additional carotenoids (see Section 1 D1); there are tomato and pepper mutants in which considerable amounts of chlorophyll are present in mature fruit. Furthermore, in grapefruit, active carotenoid synthesis occurs before chlorophyll begins to disappear (Purcell, 1959; Yokoyama and White, 1967). In particular, in the flavedo of marsh seedless grapefruit there is no further synthesis of coloured carotenoids during ripening after all the chlorophyll has disappeared but there is a marked synthesis of phytoene (Yamamoto and White, 1967).

Many fruit are autonomous from the point of view of carotenoid synthesis as indicated by the common practice of ripening tomatoes off the vine. A stored tomato can synthesize as much as 1·2 mg of lycopene per day (Sadana and Ahmad, 1948). Isolated discs from the pericarp of *Capsicum annuum* will ripen and form characteristic red carotenoids when cultured aseptically in aerated liquid media (Abrams and Pratt, 1964). Ripening is insensitive to pH changes between 6·0 and 8·0, is inhibited by indolylacetic acid and

TABLE VIII. The major carotenoids of leaves, unripe and ripe fruit of *Capsicum annuum* v. *lycopersiciforme rubrum*[a]

| | Amount mg/100 g fr. wt. | | |
Pigment	Leaves	Unripe fruit	Ripe fruit
β-Carotene	7·92	0·095	2·35
Cryptoxanthin	0·45	0·027	1·10
Lutein	13·99	0·276	——
Zeaxanthin	——	——	1·75
Antheraxanthin	1·14	0·031	0·99
Violaxanthin	8·27	0·042	0·70
Foliaxanthin[b]	5·66	0·058	——
Capsanthin	——	——	9·60
Capsorubin	——	——	1·46

[a] From Cholnoky *et al.*, 1956.
[b] 5,6-epoxide of unknown structure.

gibberellins, but unaffected by kinetin or benzyladenine; it is only very slightly stimulated by ethylene.

There is no clear evidence that vine-ripened fruit produce significantly more carotenoids than do those ripened in storage (Ellis and Hamner, 1943; Sadana and Ahmad, 1946).

In fruit such as the tomato in which the chromoplasts normally develop from chloroplasts, the chromoplasts, and thus carotenoids, are still formed if chlorophyll formation is prevented by allowing the fruit to develop in complete darkness; the fruit is first white and then becomes red as it matures (Smith and Smith, 1931). Furthermore, carotenoid-rich chromoplasts can be formed from organelles (colourless vesicles or proplastids) other than chloroplasts as in *Asparagus officinalis* (Guilliermond, 1941) and *Convallaria majalis* (Steffen, 1964), and, of course, carrot root chromoplasts have not developed from chloroplasts.

F. General Factors Governing Carotenoid Formation in Ripening Fruits

1. *Oxygen*

Ripening in the absence of oxygen but in the presence of N_2, CO_2 or ethylene inhibits pigment formation in tomatoes, *Physalis alkekengi* (Vogele, 1937), and various citrus fruit (Miller, 1938). As carotenogenesis is an endergonic process as well as in the later stages an oxidative process, these observations are not unexpected. However, ethylene at physiological levels (1 in 4300 or less) stimulates carotenogenesis (Rosa, 1952) as does increasing the oxygen content of the atmosphere (Denisen, 1951).

2. *Light*

As indicated in Section IE light is not necessary for carotenoid synthesis in tomatoes, indeed, more pigment appears to be synthesized in the dark in the case of Albino and Golden tomatoes, Elberta peaches, Humbolt nectarines and Royal apricots (Smith and Smith, 1931). It is sometimes difficult to dissociate photo-effects from thermal effects, and the possible differential effect of light on different components has not been studied in detail under controlled conditions. Lack of control of these factors has probably led to the apparently contradictory results reported in the early literature (see Goodwin, 1952 for details).

3. *Temperature*

It has been known for some time that the temperatures above 30°C inhibit ripening in tomatoes, but only more recently was it shown that the effect was confined to lycopene and its congeners and not to β-carotene (Goodwin and Jamikorn, 1952; Tomes *et al.*, 1956; Czygan and Willuhn, 1968). The optimal temperature for lycopene synthesis is 16–21°C. Exposure of fruit to elevated temperatures has no permanent deleterious effect on lycopene synthesis because fruits held at a high temperature and subsequently transferred to a lower temperature rapidly begin to synthesize the pigment (Went *et al.*, 1942). This explains why tomatoes exposed to wide temperature fluctuations on the vine ripen normally as long as the night temperature drops below about 30°C (Sayre *et al.*, 1953).

In the red watermelon on the other hand, increasing the ripening temperature from 20°C to 37°C does not inhibit lycopene formation (Vogele, 1937).

4. *General*

A fully documented report indicates that variation in mineral nutrients of the soil has no effect on the carotenoid content of tomatoes (Ellis and Hamner, 1943). Similarly β-naphthoxyacetic acid treatment produces no alteration in carotenoid content of tomato fruit (Holmes *et al.*, 1947).

TABLE IX. Total carotenoid and β-carotene content of some fruits

		Carotenoid (mg/kg (fr. wt.))	β-Carotene (mg/kg (fr. wt.))	Reference
Arum maculatum		200	22·7	Goodwin (1956)
Atropa belladonna		18	4·1	Goodwin (1956)
Avocado		5·6	0·4–0·5	Lassen et al. (1944)
Berberis spp.	berries		0·17–5·9	Bubicz and Wierzchowski (1960)
Berberis barbarossa		0·25	trace	Bubicz (1965); Goodwin (1956)
Carica papaya	pulp	13·8	4·1	Subbrarayan and Cama (1964)
Capsicum annuum				
Pepper (green)		9·0–11·2	1·2–1·5	Curl (1964)
			0·1–377	Lanz (1943)
Pepper (red)		127–248	11·6–33	Curl (1962); Goodwin (1956)
Pepper (yellow)		234	31	Cholnoky et al. (1955)
Citrus paradisi	pulp	62·6	4·3	Cholnoky et al. (1958)
		8·2	2·2	Curl and Bailey (1957)
			trace–2·07	Curl and Bailey (1953)
ruby red	peel	10·4	0·75	Khan and Mackinney (1953)
Navel oranges	pulp	23	0·115 }	
	peel	67	0·11 }	Curl and Bailey (1961)
Nagpur oranges	pulp	14·4	0·01 }	
	peel	38·5	0·45 }	Subbrarayan and Cama (1965)
Tangerines	peel	186	0·74	Curl and Bailey (1965)
	pulp	27	1·11	Curl (1964)
Valencia oranges	peel	98	0·29 }	
	pulp	24	0·26 }	Curl and Bailey (1957)
Cotoneaster spp.		1·5–16	1·2	Goodwin (1956)
Crataegus spp		4–25	2·8–5·8	Goodwin (1956)
Musk melons (Cantaloups) (*Cucumis melo*)	(edible portion)	20·9–61·7	0·41–5·96	Tomes et al. (1963)
Watermelons (orange)		20·2	17·1	Curl (1966)
(red)		33·7	1·4	Tomes and Johnson (1965)
		20·9–61·7	0·41–5·96	Tomes et al. (1963)
Japanese persimmons (*Diospyros kaki*)		21·6–97·9		Brossard and Mackinney (1963)
		54	3·9	Curl (1960, 1964)
Dura nigrescens	oil	3900	3800 }	
Dura virescens	oil	930	871 }	Argoud (1958)

Species	Part			Reference
Ficus carica (figs)		8·5		Curl (1964)
Fragaria chiloensis (strawberry)			0·49	Galler and Mackinney (1965)
Hippophae rhamnoides			1·5	Goodwin (1956)
Lonicera spp.			1·6	Goodwin (1956)
Malpighia punicifolia			1·3	Baraud (1958)
Mangifera indica	pulp	13-62	26·2	Jungalwala and Cama (1963)
Mango spp.	pulp	108-154, 52	7·5	Sadana and Ahmad (1946)
Badami		21·8-25·7, 18	4·77-39·9	Ramasarma and Banerjee (1941)
Malgoa		57·9, 12·5	294	Ramasarma *et al.* (1946)
Physalis alkekengi	sepals	8683	86·5	Baraud (1958)
	berries	573	3·85	
Prunus spp. (Cherry)			0·64	Curl (1964)
Prunus (Cling peaches)		27	5-11	Galler and Mackinney (1965)
Prunus armenica (apricots)		35	2·7	Curl (1964)
Prunus domestica (prunes)			21, 3·9	Curl (1962)
Pyracantha spp.	whole fruit	1-15	trace-4·95	Goodwin (1956)
Pyrus spp. (apples)		54·9-126·1	1·98-76·3	Valadon and Mummery (1967)
	peeled mesocarp	0·9-5·4		Galler and Mackinney (1965)
	peel (Golden Delicious)	5·6		Galler and Mackinney (1965)
Pyrus spp. (pears)	peeled mesocarp	0·3-1·28		Valadon and Mummery (1967)
	peel (Comice)	5·6		
Pyrus baccata / *Pyrus prunifolia* (crab apples)		19·8, 2·3	4·2, 0·12	Galler and Mackinney (1965)
Punica granatum		0·16		Valadon and Mummery (1967)
Rosa spp.		25-224	4·3-24·6	Curl (1964)
Rubus procerus (blackberries)		5·9	0·56	Goodwin (1956)
Sambucus nigra		16	3·0	Curl (1964)
Solanum dulcamara		90	55	Goodwin (1956)
Sorbus aucuparia		120	46·8	Goodwin (1956)
Taxus baccata	whole berry	10	0·4	Goodwin (1956)
Viburnum opulus		607	8·1	Goodwin (1956)
Vaccinium macrocarpon (cranberries)		5·8	0·3	Curl (1964)
Vaccinium spp. (blueberries)		2·7		Curl (1964)
Vitis vinifera (grapes)	berries	1·8	0·58	Curl (1964)
Tamus communis		529	25	Baraud (1958)
		96	3·8	Goodwin (1956)

G. Quantitative Distribution

The more recent quantitative figures for total carotenoid and β-carotene content of fruit are assembled in Table IX. The β-carotene values are nutritionally important because of the vitamin A activity of this carotenoid. Earlier values for the β-carotene levels in many fruit have been summarized by Goodwin (1952).

II. TRITERPENOIDS

A. Introduction

For the purposes of this review the triterpenoids may be divided into four groups: (i) tetracyclic triterpenes and sterols; (ii) pentacyclic triterpenes and their derivatives; (iii) steroidal hormones, and (iv) bitter principle triterpenoids which may be further subdivided into the cucurbitacins and the limonoids. Information concerning the distribution of sterols and tetra- and penta-cyclic triterpenes in fruit is fragmentary and few generalizations seem possible at present; by contrast the cucurbitacins and limonoids, because of their commercial importance and structural complexity, have been more intensively studied. The physiological or biochemical roles of the various triterpenes in fruit have received very little attention and the literature is therefore mainly restricted to structural elucidation and distribution of the various compounds. The steroidal alkaloids found in the fruits of the Solanaceae family will not be considered in this review (see for example Schreiber et al., 1961; Willuhn, 1966; Fayez and Salih, 1968).

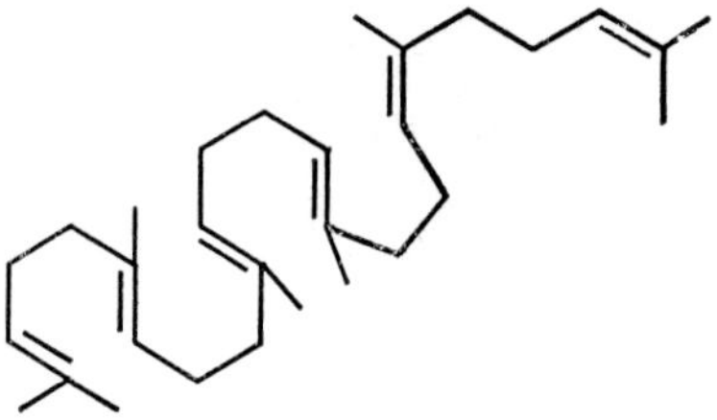

I Squalene

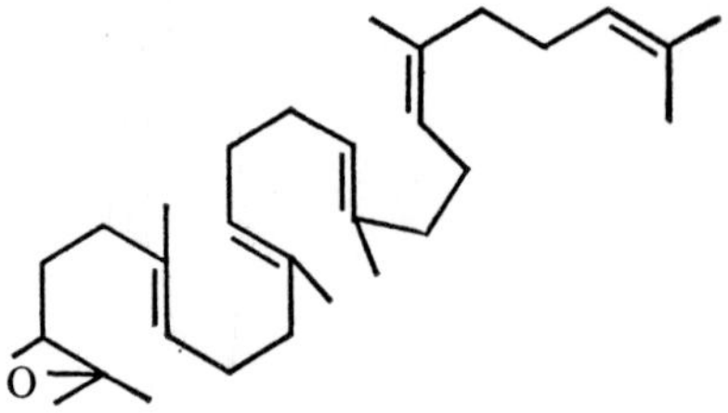

II Squalene-2,3-oxide

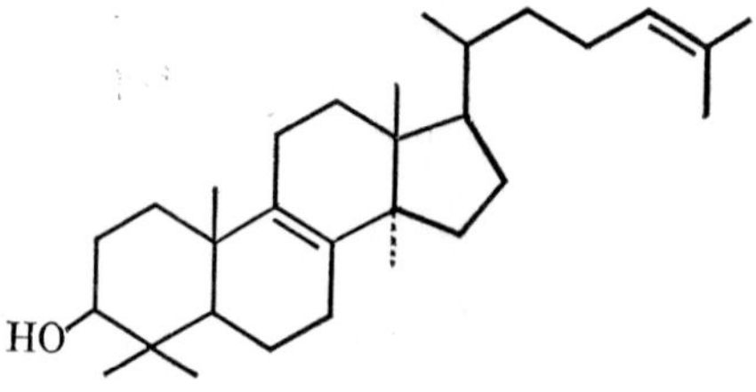

III Lanosterol

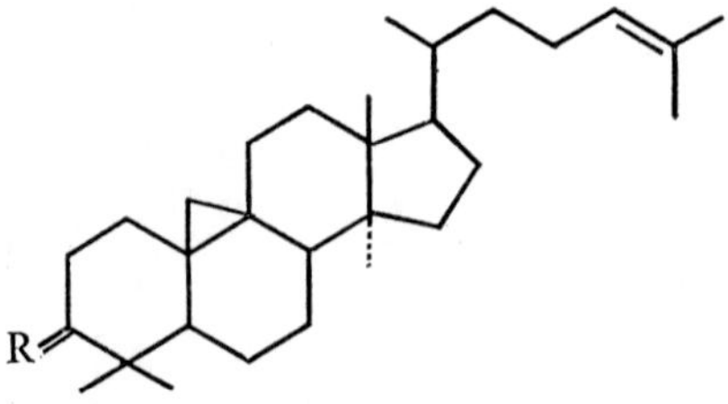

IV R = —H, —OH, cycloartenol
V R = O, cycloartenone

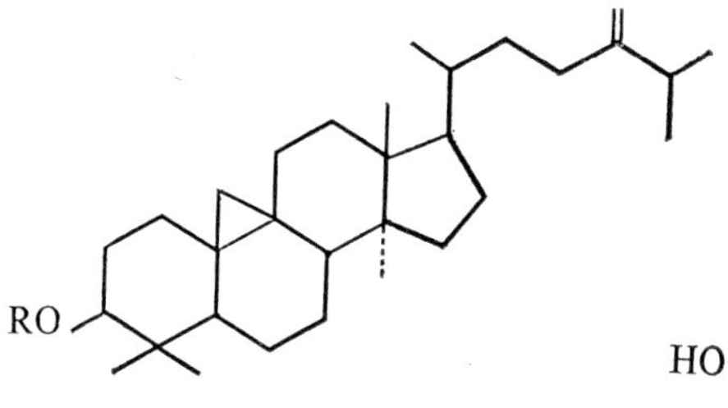

VI R = H, 24-methylene cycloartanol
VIa R = Palmitate

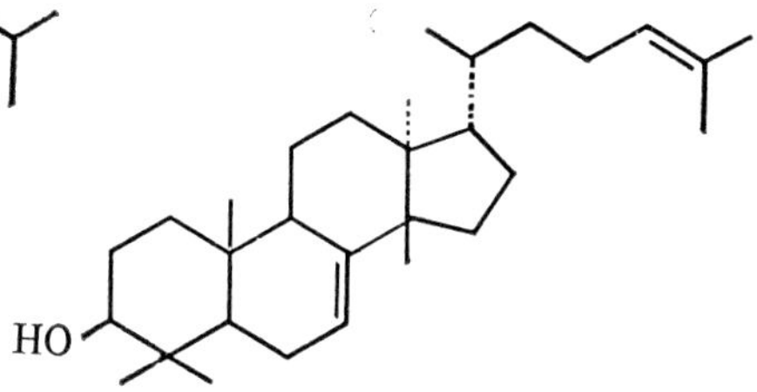

VII Butyrospermol

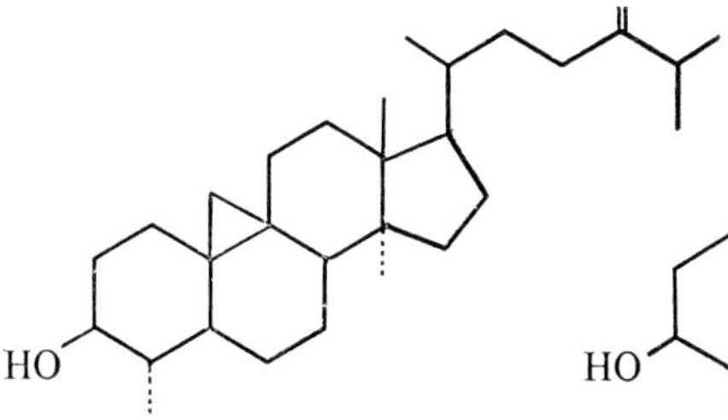

VIII Cycloeucalenol

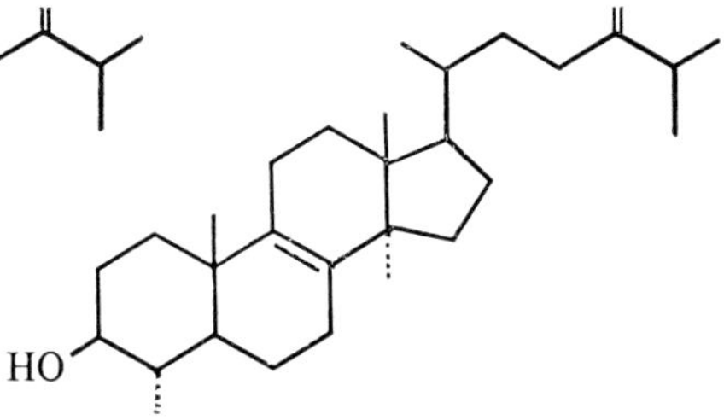

IX Obtusifoliol

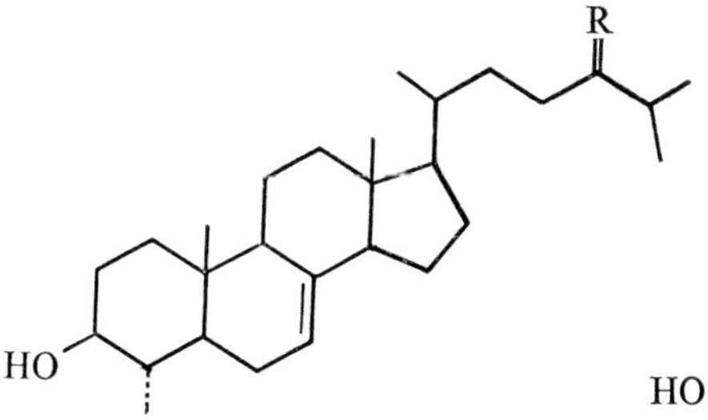

X R = CH$_2$, 24-methylene lophenol
XI R = CHCH$_3$, 24-ethylidene lophenol

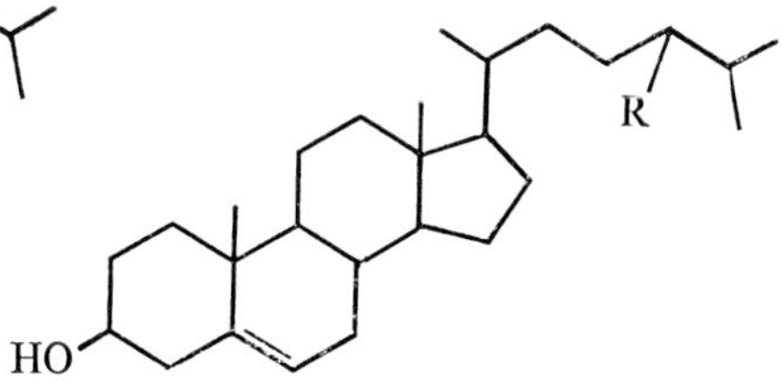

XII R = H, cholesterol
XIII R = CH$_3$, campesterol
XIV R = CH$_2$CH$_3$, β-sitosterol
XV   R = CH$_2$CH$_3$, Δ^{22}, stigmasterol

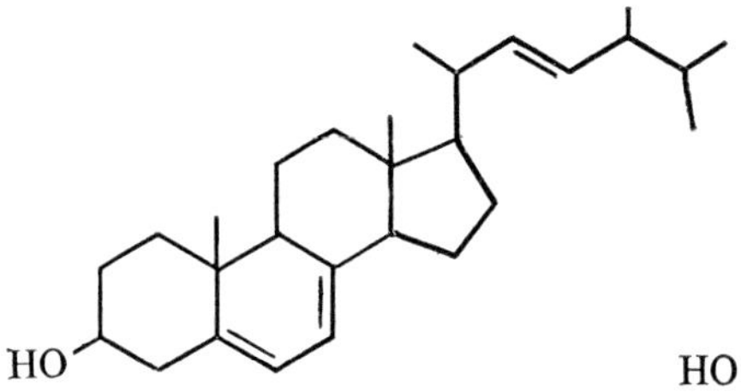

XVI Ergosterol

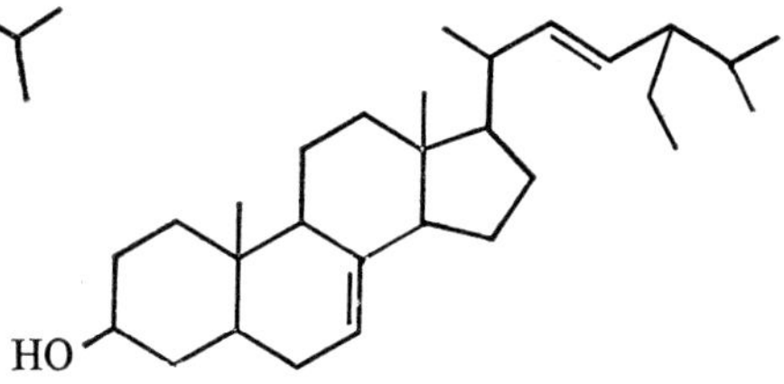

XVII α-Spinasterol

XVIII Stigmasta-5,25-dien-3β-ol

XIX Stigmasta-7,25-dien-3β-ol

XX Stigmasta-7,22,25-trien-3β-ol

XXI Stigmasta-7,24(28)-dien-3β-ol

B. Sterols and Tetracyclic Triterpenes

The sterol and tetracyclic triterpene components of various fruit are indicated in Table X. The most widely distributed sterol is β-sitosterol (**XIV**) which also occurs as the β-D-glucoside in many fruits. Citrus fruits have been fairly extensively examined and a number of 4-dimethyl and 4-monomethyl

TABLE X. Occurrence of sterols and triterpenoids in fruits

	Composition	Reference
Afraegle paniculata	γ-sitosterol	Quartey (1961)
Artocarpus integrifolia	cycloartenone (**V**)	Nath (1937); Barton (1951)
Aristolochia bracteata	β-sitosterol (**XIV**)	Sastry (1965)
Brynopsis laciniosa	β-sitosterol (**XIV**)	Paul *et al.* (1960)
Citrullus vulgaris	α-spinasterol (**XVII**); stigmasta-7,25-dien-3β-ol (**XIX**); stigmasta-7,22,25-trien-3β-ol (**XX**)	Sucrow and Reimerdes (1968)
Citrus limonia	β-sitosterol (**XIV**); γ-sitosterol β-sitosterol-D-glucoside	Chaliha *et al.* (1964) Vandercook and Yokoyama (1965)
Citrus mitis	β-sitosterol-D-glucoside	Row and Sastry (1962)
Citrus paradisi	Friedelin (**XXII**); cycloartenol (**IV**); 24-methylene cycloartanol (**VI**); cycloeucalenol (**VIII**); obtusifoliol (**IX**); 24-methylene lophenol (**X**); 24-ethylidenelophenol (citrostadienol) (**XI**); β-sitosterol (**XIV**); stigmasterol (**XV**); campesterol (**XIII**); β-sitosterol-D-glucoside	Ma and Shaffer (1953); Weizmann *et al.* (1955); Weizmann and Mazur (1958); Mazur and Sondheimer(1958); Mazur *et al.* (1958); Williams *et al.* (1967a); Goad *et al.* (1967)

	Composition	Reference
Citrus sinensis	β-sitosterol-D-glucoside	Swift (1952); Matlock (1929, 1940); Nolte and von Loesecke (1940)
Citrus hybrid		
Rangpur lime	ergosterol (**XVI**)	Yokoyama and White (1968)
Citrullus colocynthis	α-spinasterol (**XVII**)	Hamilton and Kermack (1952); Misra *et al.* (1962)
Cleistanthus collinus	β-sitosterol (**XIV**); lupeol (**XXIII**)	Maiti and Das (1965)
Coccinia indica	β-amyrin (**XXVI**); β-amyrin acetate (**XXVIa**); lupeol (**XXIII**)	Bhakuni *et al.* (1962)
Coriandrum sativum	unidentified sterol	Vaghani and Thakor (1958)
Cucumis melo	α-spinasterol (**XVII**); stigmasta-7,25-dien-3β-ol (**XIX**); stigmasta-7,22,25-trien-3β-ol (**XX**)	Sucrow and Reimerdes (1968)
Cucumis sativis	α-spinasterol (**XVII**); stigmasta-7,25-dien-3β-ol (**XIX**); stigmasta-7,22,25-trien-3β-ol (**XX**)	Sucrow and Reimerdes (1968)
Cucurbita pepo	α-spinasterol (**XVII**); stigmasta-7,25-dien-3β-ol (**XIX**); stigmasta-7,22,25-trien-3β-ol (**XX**); stigmasta-7,24(28)-dien-3β-ol (**XXI**)	Copius-Peerebohm (1964); Abdul-Alim *et al.* (1966); Sucrow and Reimerdes (1968); Sucrow (1968)
Diospyros chloroxylan	β-sitosterol (**XIV**)	Row *et al.* (1964)
Diospyros discolour	betulin (**XXVII**); betulinic acid (**XXVIII**); β-sitosterol (**XIV**)	Row *et al.* (1964)
Duranta repens	ursolic acid (**XXIX**); β-sitosterol (**XIV**)	Kapil (1960)
Feronia elephantum	stigmasterol (**XV**)	Chakraborty (1959)
Gladitschia australis	saponin of β-amyrin type	Ciulei *et al.* (1966)
Lansium domesticum	lansic acid (**XXXIII**); onoceradiendione (**XXXIV**)	Kiang *et al.* (1967); Habaguchi *et al.* (1968)
Lycopersicon species	stigmasterol (**XV**); β-sitosterol (**XIV**); α-amyrin (**XXV**); β-amyrin (**XXVI**)	Bennett *et al.* (1961); Brieskorn and Reinartz (1967)
Lyonia ovalifolia	oleanic acid (**XXX**); β-sitosterol (**XIV**)	Yasue and Kato (1959)
Maclura pomifera	butyrospermol (**VII**); lupeol (**XXIII**); lupan-3β, 20-diol (**XXIV**)	Lewis (1959)
Madhuca butyracea	α-amyrin acetate (**XXVa**); β-amyrin acetate (**XXVIa**); erythrodiol monopalmitate (**XXXIa**); oleanic acid palmitate (**XXXa**); α-spinasterol (**XVII**); β-sitosterol-D-glucoside	Awasthi and Mitra (1968)
Madhuca latifolia	α-amyrin acetate (**XXVa**); β-amyrin acetate (**XXVIa**); erythrodiol-3β-caprylate (**XXXIb**); 3β(capryloxy) oleanic acid (**XXXb**); β-sitosterol; β-sitosterol-D-glucoside	Awasthi and Mitra (1967)
Malus species	squalene (**I**); β-sitosterol (**XIV**); ursolic acid (**XXIX**); oleanic acid (**XXX**); 19α-hydroxyursolic acid; 19α-hydroxyursonic acid;	Brieskorn and Klinger (1963); Mazliak and Pommier-Miard (1963); Bock, *et al.* (1966); Brieskorn and Wunderer

	Composition	Reference
Malus species—cont.	2,20β-dihydroxyursonic acid	(1966, 1967); Lawrie *et al.* (1967)
Mimusops hexandra	α-amyrin acetate (**XXVa**); β-amyrin acetate (**XXVIa**); α-spinasterol (**XVII**); β-sitosterol-D-glucoside; ursolic acid (**XXIX**)	Mitra and Misra (1965); Misra and Mitra (1968)
Mimusops manilkara	Caprylic acid esters and acetates of α- and β-amyrin (**XXVa, XXVb, XXVIa, XXVIb**); α-spinasterol (**XVII**); β-sitosterol-D-glucoside	Misra and Mitra (1969)
Momordica charantia	β-sitosterol (**XIV**); β-sitosterol-D-glucoside; stigmasta-5,25-dien-3β-ol (**XVIII**); stigmasta-7,25-dien-3β-ol (**XIX**); stigmasta-7,22,25-trien-3β-ol (**XX**); α-spinasterol (**XVII**)	Sucrow (1966a, b)
Musa sapientum	cycloartenol (**IV**); 24-methylene cycloartanol (**VI**); cycloeucalenol (**VIII**); cycloeucalenone (?); β-sitosterol (**XIV**); stigmasterol (**XV**); campesterol (**XIII**); 24-methylene cycloartanyl palmitate (**VIa**)	Rao and Rao (1965); Knapp and Nicholas (1969)
Olea europaea	Campesterol (**XIII**); β-sitosterol (**XIV**); cycloartenol (**IV**); 24-methylene cycloartanol (**VI**)	Eisner *et al.* (1965); Fedeli *et al.* (1966)
Persia americana	cholesterol (**XII**); campesterol (**XIII**); β-sitosterol (**XIV**); stigmasterol (**XV**); cycloartenol (**IV**); 24-methylene cycloartanol (**VI**); butyrospermol (**VII**); β-amyrin (**XXVI**)	Paquot and Tassel (1966); Fedeli *et al.* (1967)
Prunus armeniaca	β-sitosterol (**XIV**)	Dhar and Chauhan (1963)
Prunus mahaleb	β-sitosterol (**XIV**)	El-Dakhakhny and Feyez (1962)
Prunus spinosa	β-sitosterol (**XIV**)	Kaminska-Theil and Ludwiczak (1967)
Punica granatum	β-sitosterol (**XIV**); ursolic acid (**XXIX**)	Fayez *et al.* (1963)
Santalum album	β-sitosterol (**XIV**); betulinic acid (**XXVIII**)	Singh *et al.* (1964)
Scindapsus officinalis	unidentified sterol	Bhakuni and Tewari (1959)
Seronoa repens	β-sitosterol (**XIV**); β-sitosterol-D-glucoside	Schöpflin *et al.* (1966)
Stemmadenia donnell-smithii	ψ-taraxasteryl acetate? (**XXXII**)	Estrada *et al.* (1962)
Verbascum thapsus	β-sitosterol (**XIV**)	Pande and Tewari (1961)
Viburnum opulus	β-sitosterol (**XIV**); ursolic acid (**XXIX**)	Bobbitt and Rao (1965)
Withania coagulans	β-sitosterol (**XIV**)	Atal and Sethi (1963)

sterols identified in addition to β-sitosterol. In particular, 24-ethylidene lophenol (citrostadienol) (**XI**), which is now suggested as an important phytosterol precursor, was first isolated from *Citrus* oils (Mazur *et al.*, 1958a, b). The co-occurrence of various 4-methyl compounds in grapefruit peel (Williams *et al.*, 1967a; Goad *et al.*, 1967) and also in banana peel (Knapp and Nicholas, 1969) provides circumstantial evidence for the possible phytosterol biosynthetic route now under consideration (see Section III). In banana peel 24-methylene cycloartanol (**VI**) is present predominantly as the palmityl ester (Knapp and Nicholas, 1969) whilst the 4-methyl triterpenes of grapefruit peel also appear to be extensively esterified (Williams, 1966). The possible role of steryl esters in phytosterol biosynthesis has been discussed (Goad, 1967; Kemp *et al.*, 1968; Knapp and Nicholas, 1969) and the formation of esters of potential phytosterol precursors in fruit therefore seems to warrant further investigation. However, it is also possible that steryl ester accumulation may be a reflection of a more general esterification process occurring during fruit development and is similar to the situation regarding the xanthophylls (see above) and the pentacyclic triterpenes such as α- and β-amyrin (**XXV, XXVI**) which also occur as esters in various fruits (see Table X).

Fruits and seeds of a few Cucurbitaceae species have been examined and found to contain sterols which are interesting biosynthetically. Stigmasta-5,25-dien-3β-ol (**XVIII**), stigmasta-7,25-dien-3β-ol (**XIX**) and stigmasta-7,22,25-trien-3β-ol (**XX**), isolated from the fruit of *Momordica charantia* (Sucrow, 1966a,b) and some other Cucurbitaceae species (Sucrow and Reimerdes, 1968), represent a possible alternative way in which the intermediate carbonium ion produced during C24 alkylation may be stabilized (see Fig. 4). In this case the co-occurrence of stigmasta-7,24(28)-dien-3β-ol (**XXI**), with sterols (**XIX**) and (**XX**) in the pumpkin (Sucrow, 1968) presumably means that the mechanism of C24 alkylation originally proposed by Castle *et al.* (1963) (see Fig. 4) is also operative in this species. It is interesting to speculate whether the β-sitosterol (**XIV**) present in *M. charantia* or the α-spinasterol (**XVII**) of the other cucurbits are derived by enzymic reduction of a 25-methylene precursor or from a 24-ethylidene intermediate. An interesting observation on sterol biosynthesis in fruit was made by Bennett *et al.*

XXII Friedelin   **XXIII** Lupeol

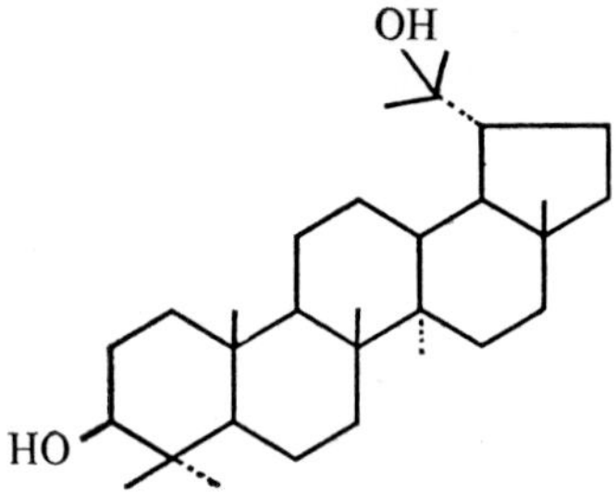

XXIV Lupan-3β,20-diol

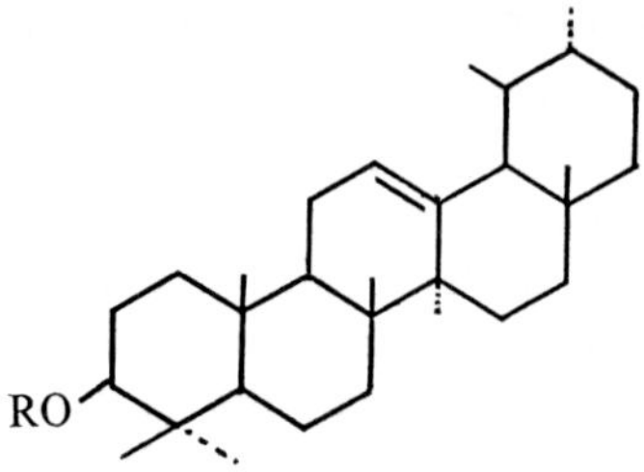

XXV R = H, α-amyrin
XXVa R = acetate
XXVb R = caprylate

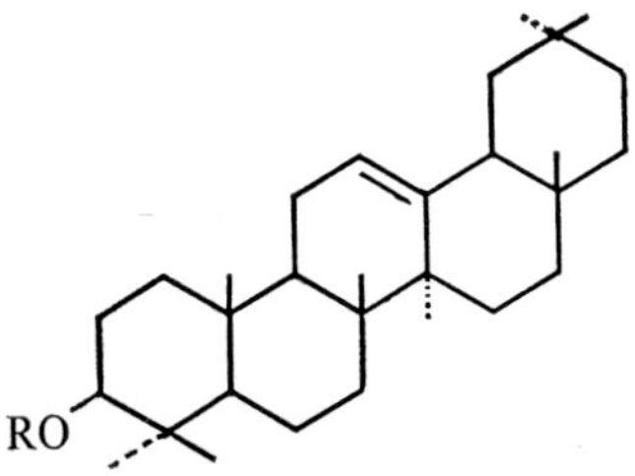

XXVI R = H, β-amyrin
XXVIa R = acetate
XXVIb R = caprylate

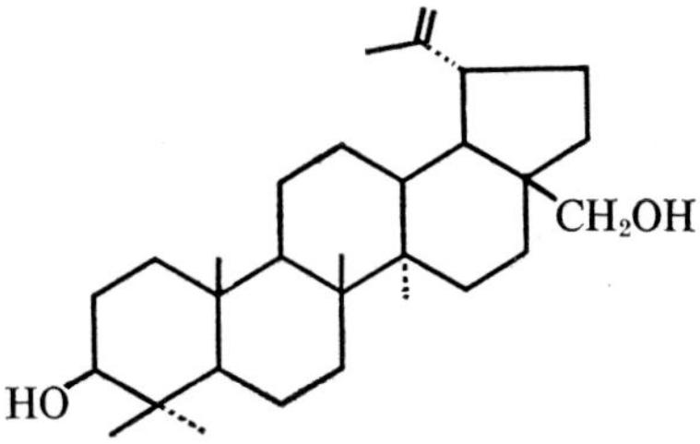

XXVII Betulin

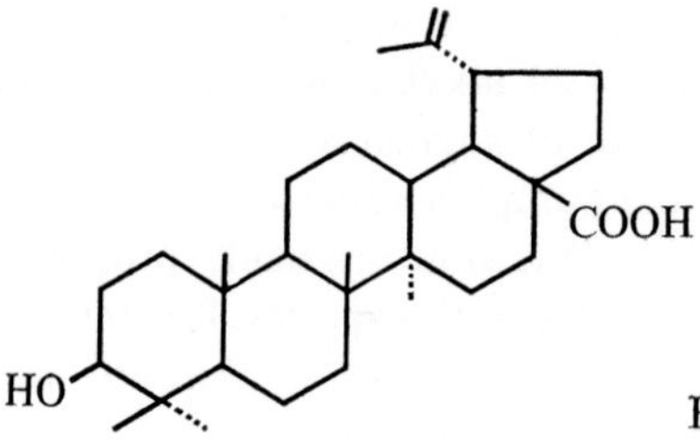

XXVIII Betulinic acid

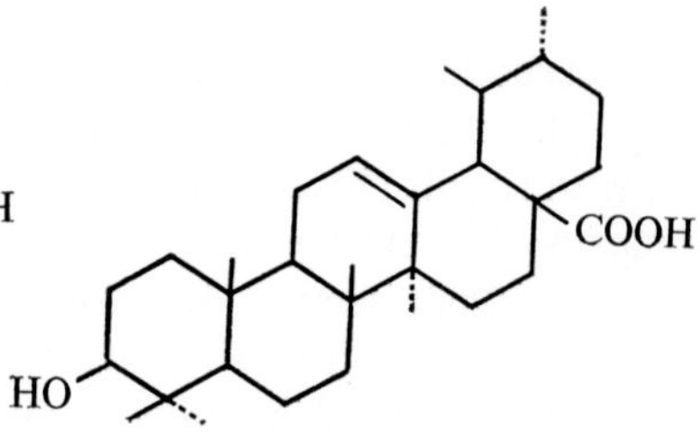

XXIX Ursolic acid

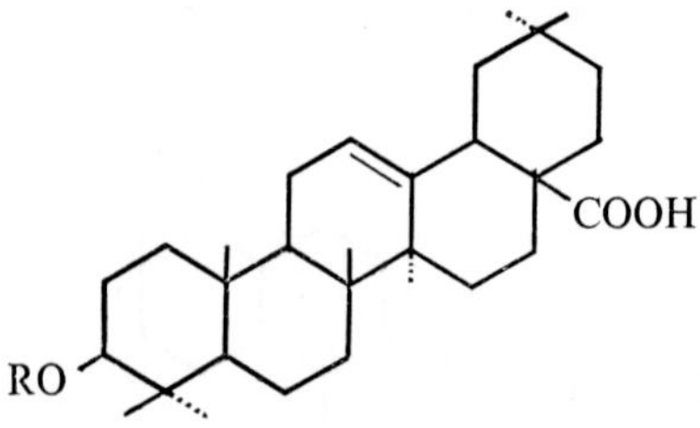

XXX   R = H, oleanic acid
XXXa R = palmitate
XXXb R = caprylate

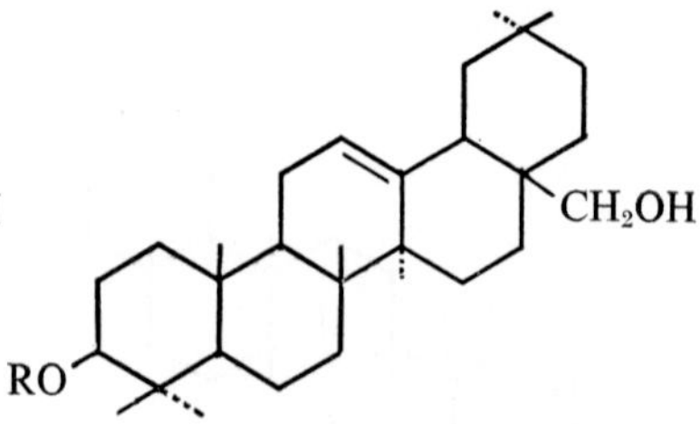

XXXI   R = H, erythrodiol
XXXIa R = palmitate
XXXIb R = caprylate

XXXII Ψ-Taraxasterol   **XXXIII** Lansic acid

(1961) who found that [2⁻¹⁴C] mevalonic acid but not [2⁻¹⁴C] acetate was incorporated into stigmasterol (**XV**) by tomatoes.

C. Pentacyclic Triterpenes

Recent reports of pentacyclic triterpenes in fruit are given in Table X; earlier references are documented by Boiteau *et al.* (1964). The most frequently encountered pentacyclic triterpenes are α- and β-amyrin (**XXV** and **XXVI**) and their esters, but ursolic acid (**XXIX**), oleanic acid (**XXX**) and other more oxidized derivatives are now being reported as fruit constituents.

XXXIV Onoceradiendione   **XXXV** Oestrone

XXXVI Progesterone

D. Steroidal Hormones

Recently there have been a few reports of the isolation of steroidal hormones from plant sources and in particular from fruit seeds. The original isolation of oestrone (**XXXV**) from a palm kernel preparation by Butenandt and Jacobi (1933) and subsequent reports (El Ridi and Wafa, 1947; Hassan and Wafa, 1947) were questioned by Jacobsohn *et al.*, (1965) who apparently found no evidence for oestrone (**XXXV**). However, in a re-examination of the seeds and pollen of the date palm (*Phoenix dactylifera*) oestrone (**XXXV**) was again identified (Heftmann *et al.*, 1965; Bennett *et al.*, 1966; Amin *et al.*, 1969). In view of the reported oestrogenic activity of pomegranate seed oil when injected into ovariectomized mice (Sharaf and Nigm, 1964) pomegranate seeds (*Punica granatum v. nana*) were analysed and oestrone (**XXXV**) identified by thin layer chromatography (Heftmann *et al.*, 1966). A second steroidal hormone, progesterone (**XXXVI**), has more recently been reported as a constituent of apple seeds which also contain cholesterol (**XII**) as a major sterol constituent (Gawienowski and Gibbs, 1968).

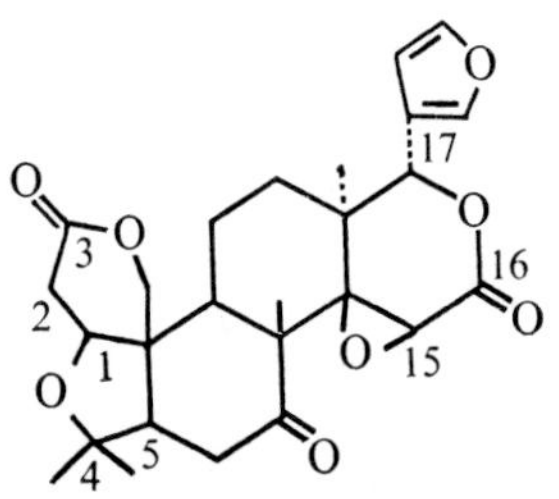

XXXVII Limonin

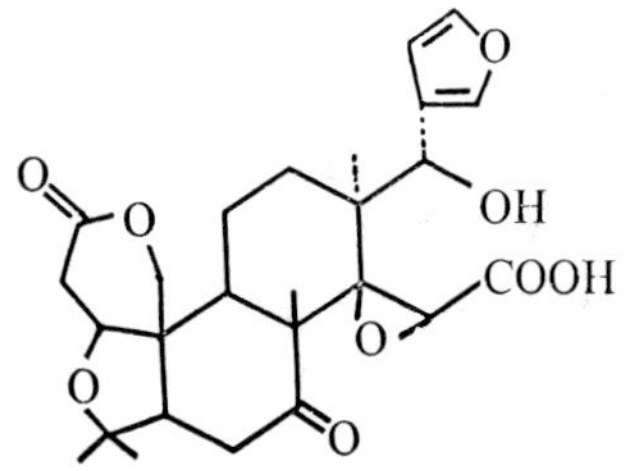

XXXVIII Limonoic acid A ring lactone

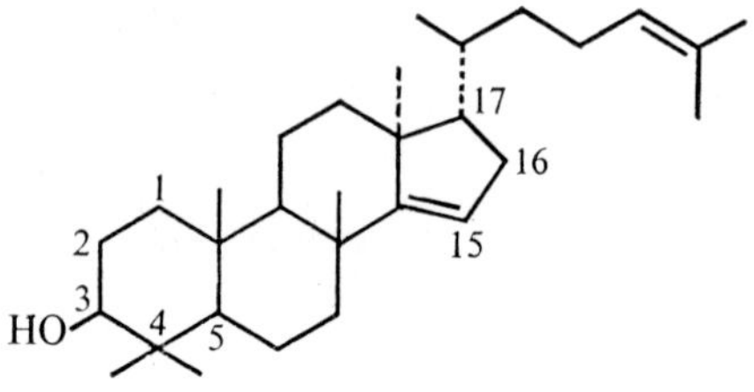

XXXIX

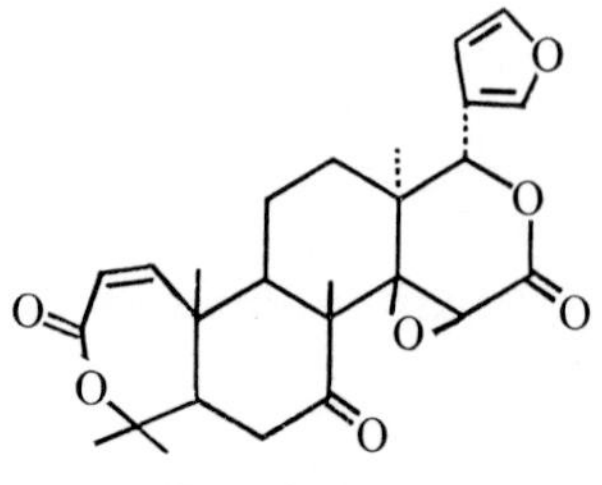

XL Obacunone

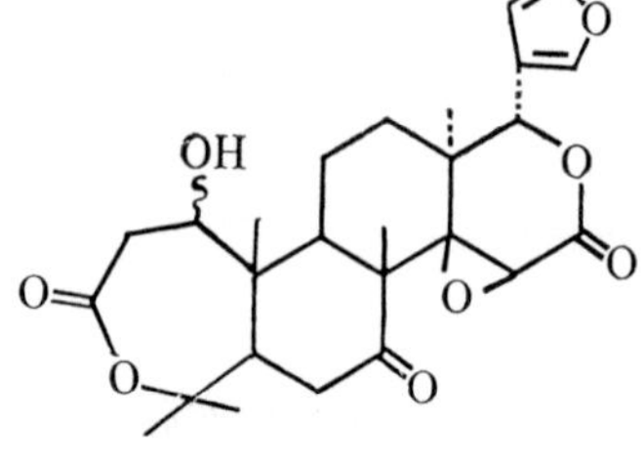

XLI Deacetylnomilin

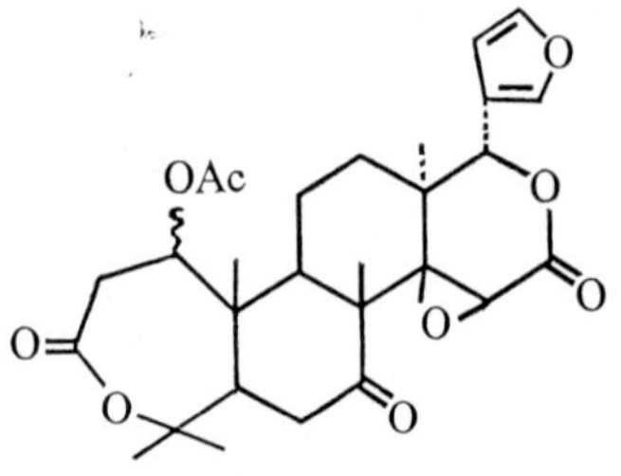

XLII Nomilin

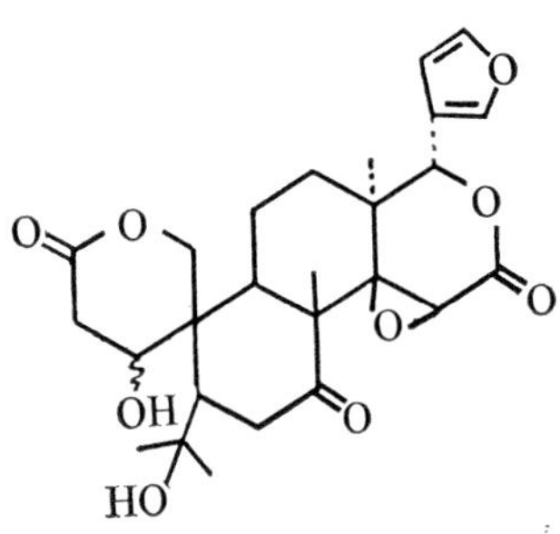

XLIII Ichangin

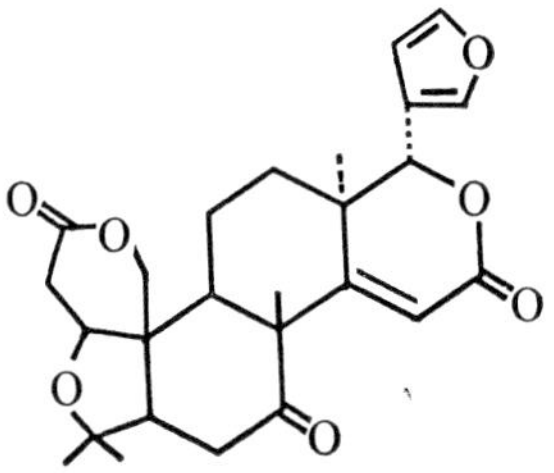

XLIV Deoxylimonin

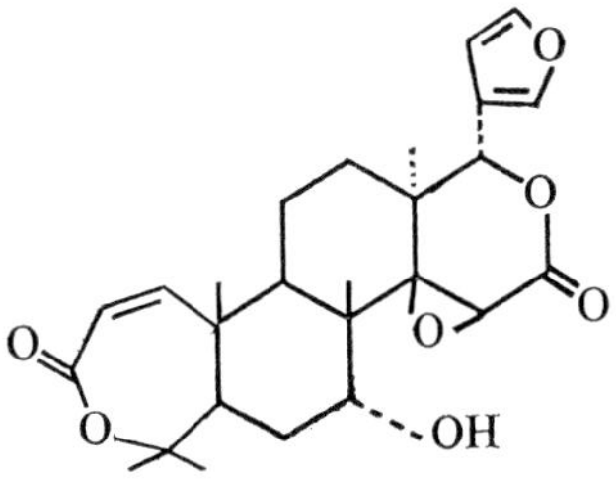

XLV 7α-Obacunol

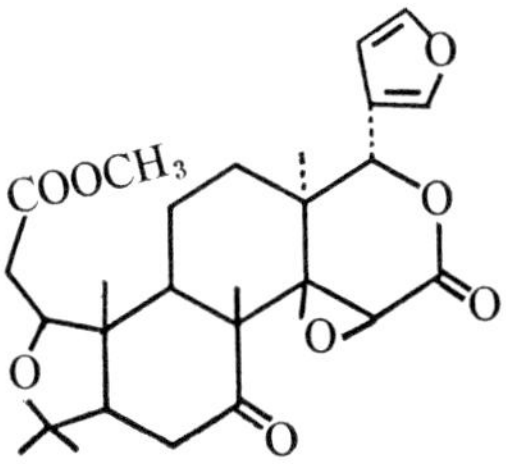

XLVI Veprisone

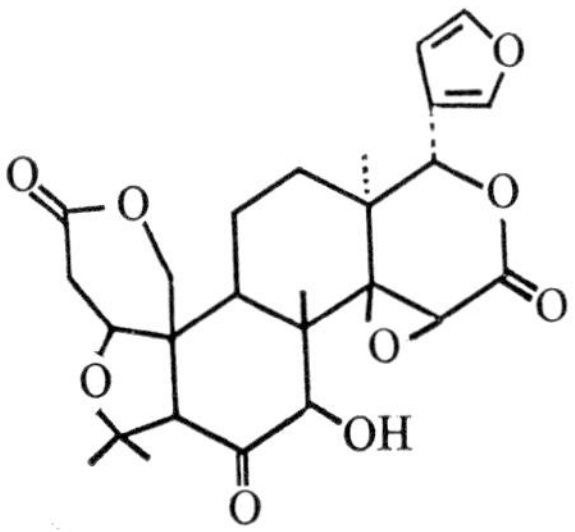

XLVII Rutaevin

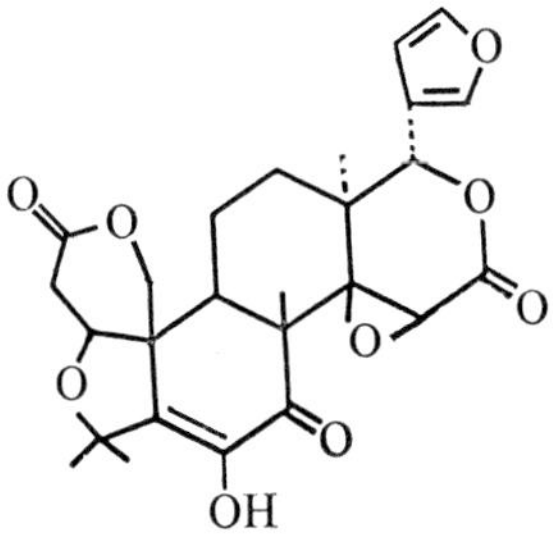

XLVIII Limonin diosphenol

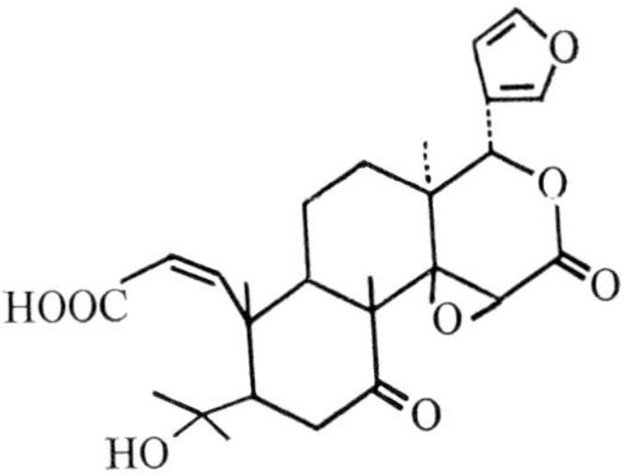

XLIX Obacunoic acid

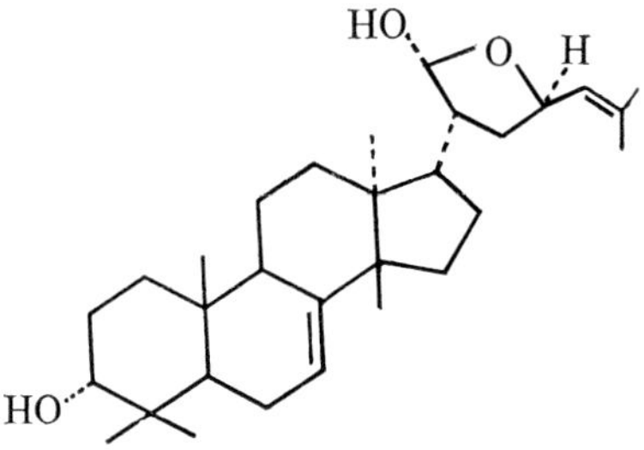

L Flindissol

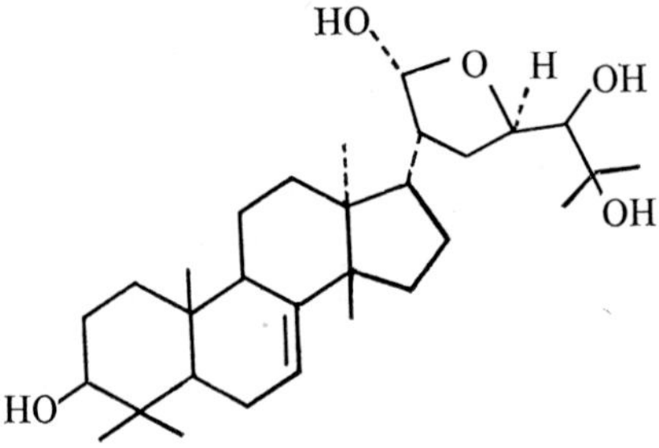

LI Meliantriol

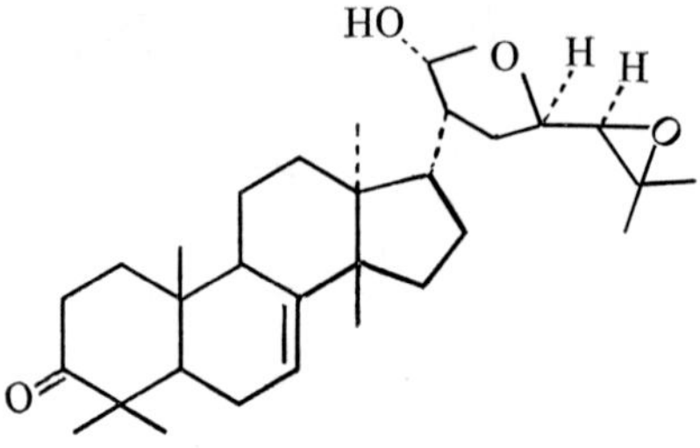

LII Melianone

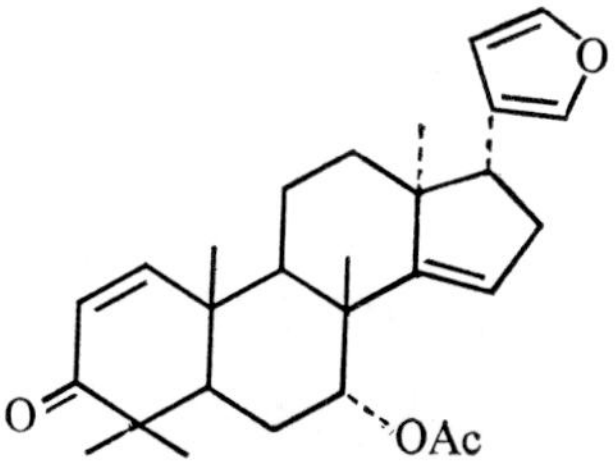

LIII Azadirone

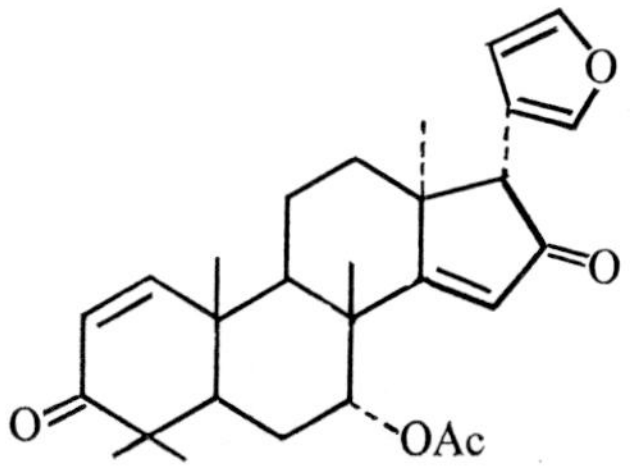

LIV Azadiradione

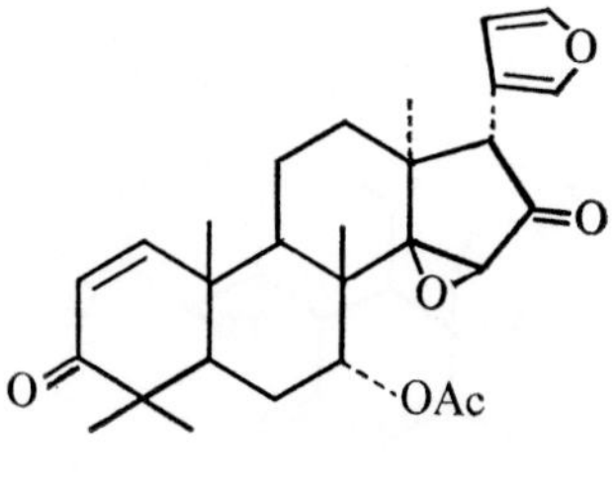

LV Epoxyazadiradione

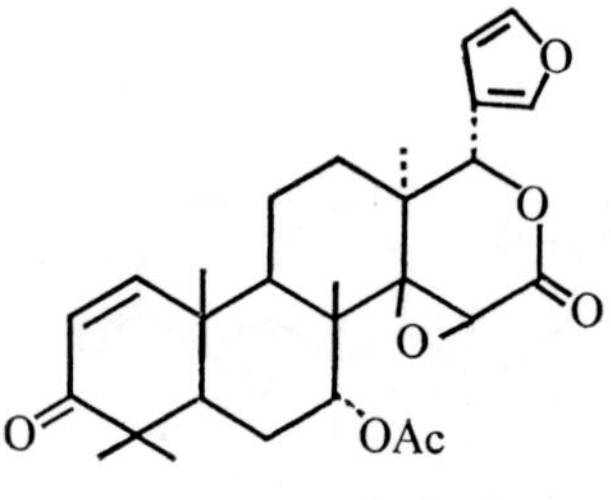

LVI Gedunin

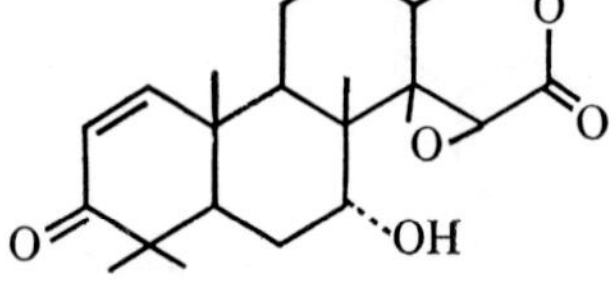

LVII 7-Deacetylgedunin

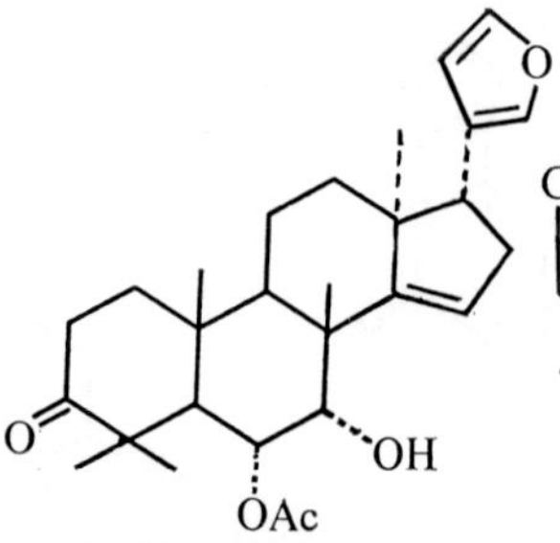

LVIII Meldenin

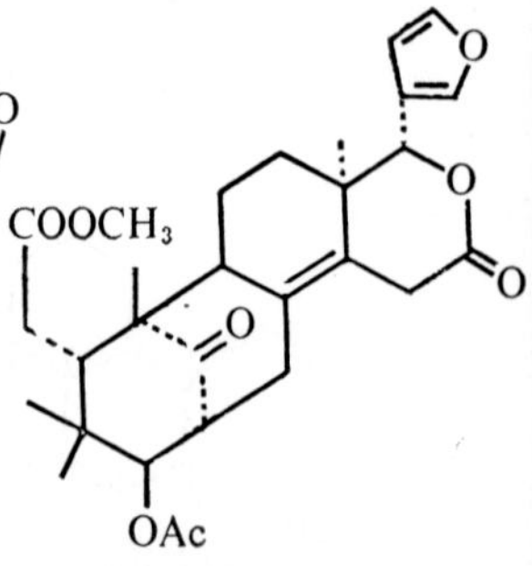

LIX Fissinolide

E. Fruit Bitter Principles

1. *The limonoids*

The bitter principles found in the fruit and seeds of various plants belonging to the Rutaceae and Meliaceae families are a group of C_{26} oxidized triterpenes known collectively as limonoids (Ourisson *et al.*, 1964; Dreyer, 1968b). This group includes a wide range of compounds, many of which have so far been reported only in the timbers or seeds of one particular plant species and are not therefore strictly within the scope of the present review. However, since many of these compounds are important in any consideration of limonoid biosynthesis some will be mentioned where relevant in the present article. A very detailed review of the distribution and chemistry of the limonoids is available elsewhere (Dreyer, 1968b).

(a) *The Rutaceae family.* The most widely distributed limonoid in the Rutaceae family is limonin (**XXXVII**) (Arigoni *et al.*, 1960; Arnott *et al.*, 1960; Barton *et al.*, 1961), which can be considered as arising from the basic triterpene structure (for example **XXXIX**) by shortening of the side chain with formation of a furan ring and cleavage of rings A and D accompanied by suitable oxidations and lactone formation. Limonin (**XXXVII**) is widely distributed in the members of the sub-family Awantoideae. In a survey of the limonoid content of various seeds Dreyer (1966b) found that thirteen *Citrus* species, a further thirteen *Citrus* hybrids and representatives of the closely related genera *Poncirus, Microcitrus* and *Fortunella* all contained limonin (**XXXVII**) and the closely related compounds obacunone (**XL**) and deacetylnomilin (**XLI**) (see below). In addition to the occurrence of limonin (**XXXVII**) in the seeds of *Citrus* species this compound is also present in other parts of the fruit and has been isolated from the pulp and juice of Navel and Valencia oranges (Higby, 1938; Emerson, 1948; Kefford, 1959 and references cited therein). With grapefruit (*C. paradisi*) limonin (**XXXVII**) was present in freshly extracted juice, commercially canned juice, frozen concentrate and dried powder (Maier and Dreyer, 1965). In contrast to Navel orange, where the limonin (**XXXVII**) content decreases as the fruit ripens, Maier and Dreyer (1965) reported that both mid- and late-season grapefruit contain limonin which is located in the peel, endocarp and seeds. With late-season fruit the limonin (**XXXVII**) content of the endocarp was greatest in the carpellary membranes and central vascular bundle. A problem of commercial interest is the development of bitterness in *Citrus* juices after standing for several hours or upon heating. It was originally suggested that this phenomenon may be due to either slow diffusion of limonoids from the damaged tissues into the juice (Kefford, 1959) or conversion of a non-bitter limonoid into the bitter limonin (Higby, 1938). More recently Maier and Beverly (1968) re-examined the problem using early season Navel oranges and grapefruits and showed that limonin monolactone, which is non-bitter and stable at neutral pH, was present in the albedo and endocarp tissues of the fruits but there was little or no limonin present. Maier and Beverly (1968) consider that disruption of the fruit tissues during juice production results in the release of the limonin monolactone which is then converted slowly by the acidic juice into the bitter dilactone, limonin (**XXXVII**). Extracts of late-season Navel oranges and grapefruits (cf. Maier and Dreyer, 1965) did not contain limonin monolactone and did not develop bitterness upon acidification or heating. It was therefore concluded that as the fruit matures limonin monolactone is removed from the tissues. In a continuation of these studies Maier and Margileth (1969) have characterized the monolactone and proposed the name limonoic acid A ring lactone (**XXXVIII**). Moreover, these authors have also obtained some evidence for an enzyme in extracts of orange and grapefruit carpellary membranes which converts limonoic acid A ring lactone (**XXXVIII**) into limonin (**XXXVII**). The rate at which bitter principles disappear as *Citrus* fruits mature is apparently affected by the rootstock on which the scion is grafted (Marsh, 1953; Kefford, 1959; Kefford and Chandler, 1961).

In addition to limonin (**XXXVII**), the seeds of Valencia oranges and lemons contain a second bitter principle nomilin (**XLII**) (Emerson, 1948) which was subsequently correlated with limonin (**XXXVII**) (Barton *et al.*, 1961). In a further study of Florida citrus seed oil Emerson (1951) isolated a third bitter principle, obacunone (**XL**) (Barton *et al.*, 1961; Kubota *et al.*, 1961) together with limonin (**XXXVII**) and nomilin (**XLII**). Deacetyl-nomilin (**XLI**) has been obtained from the seeds of a number of *Citrus* species (Dreyer, 1965b, 1966b). In a study of *Citrus ichangensis* seeds Dreyer (1966a) isolated a new limonoid, ichangin (**XLIII**), while examination of grapefruit seeds (*Citrus paradisi*) resulted in the isolation of small amounts of deoxylimonin (**XLIV**) (Dreyer, 1965b).

Limonoids have also been obtained from other sub-families of the Rutaceae (Dreyer, 1966b, 1968b). In the Toddalioideae, obacunone (**XL**) has been observed in three species of the genus *Phellodendron* (Kubota and Tokoroyama, 1957; Tokoroyama, 1958), and obacunone (**XL**) and limonin (**XXXVII**) have been obtained from the bark of *Phellodendron amurense* (Dreyer, 1966b). In the genus *Casimiroa* the presence of obacunone (**XL**) and nomilin (**XLII**) has been shown in the seeds of *Casimiroa tetrameria* (Dreyer, 1966b). Obacunone (**XL**) has been identified in the seeds of *Casimiroa edulis* (Kincl *et al.*, 1956; Sondheimer *et al.*, 1959), and more recently nomilin (**XLII**) (Dreyer, 1966b) and 7α-obacunol (**XLV**) (Dreyer, 1968a, b) have been isolated from the same source. In the genus *Vepris* the methyl ester of epi-isoobacunoic acid, veprisone (**XLVI**) has been identified in the one member, *Vepris bilocularis*, so far examined (Govindachari *et al.*, 1964).

The genera *Calodendrum*, *Evodia* and *Dictamnus* of the sub-family Rutoideae have been examined for their limonoid content (Dreyer, 1966b, 1968b). Rutaevin (**XLVII**) first isolated from the dried fruit of *Evodia rutaecarpa* (Fujita *et al.*, 1935; Fujita and Akatsuka, 1949) was subsequently isolated from *Calodendrum capense* and the structure determined (Dreyer 1967). Limonin diosphenol (**XLVIII**) has been identified as a naturally occurring limonoid in the seeds of *Calodendrum capense* and *Evodia rutaecarpa* (Hirose, 1963; Dreyer, 1966b, 1967). Limonin (**XXXVII**) has also been demonstrated in the seeds of *Evodia danielli hensel*, *E. rutaecarpa*, *E. hypenhensis* and *E. meliaefolia* (Dreyer, 1966b). Finally obacunoic acid (**XLIX**) has been isolated from *Dictamnus dasycarpus* (Nokinov, 1964) whilst Dreyer (1966b) indicates that limonin (**XXXVII**), limonin diosphenol (**XLVIII**) and rutaevin (**XLVII**) also occur in the genus *Dictamnus*.

Highly oxidized limonoids of the limonin type have not been reported in the sub-family Flindersioideae (Dreyer, 1966b). Flindissol (**L**) (Brown *et al.*, 1954; Birch *et al.*, 1963) may be regarded as representative of the type of triterpene so far isolated from *Flindersia* species (Breen *et al.*, 1966) and which may be pertinent to a consideration of limonoid biosynthesis (Moss, 1966; see below).

The chemical taxonomic value of the limonoids in the Rutaceae has been considered by Dreyer (1966b) with the conclusion that whilst the limonoid content may be useful at the generic level it is of little use at the species level. In general, when limonoids occur in one member of a genus they are likely to be found in all other species of that genus, and moreover the oxidation level tends to be approximately the same within a genus or sub-family. Thus the sub-families Flindersioideae, Toddalioideae, Awantioideae and Rutoideae contain increasingly oxidized limonoids (Dreyer, 1966b).

(*b*) *The Meliaceae family*. A wide variety of limonoids at various oxidation levels have been isolated from species of the Meliaceae family and the chemistry of these compounds is reviewed by Dreyer (1968b). In many cases these compounds have only been obtained from the timbers, but in some species the fruit or seed oils have served as good sources. *Melia azadarach* is not eaten by the desert locust and extracts of various parts of the plant were found to have anti-feeding properties against locusts (Schpan-Gabrielith, 1965). Subsequently the active principle was isolated from freshly crushed fruit of *M. azadarach* and from the seed oil of *M. azadarachta* (Lavie *et al.*, 1967b) and identified as meliantriol (**LI**). In addition melianone (**LII**) was obtained from the fruits of *M. azadarach* (Lavie *et al.*, 1966, 1967a). Other compounds isolated from the seed oil (nim oil) of *M. azaderachta* include azadirone (**LIII**), azadiradione (**LIV**), epoxyazadiradione (**LV**), gedunin (**LVI**) (Lavie and Jain, 1967) and meldenin (**LVIII**) (Connolly *et al.*, 1968). A possible limonoid precursor, aphanamixin (**LXIb**), reported to be the

21-epimer of turraeanthin (**LXIa**), has been isolated from the fruit shell of *Aphanomixis polystacha* (Chatterjee and Kundu, 1967). A representative of a complex group of tetranortriterpenoids termed bicyclononanolides (Connolly *et al.*, 1968) has been isolated from the fruit of *Cedrela fissilis* and *Guarea trichiloides* and identified as fissinolide (**LIX**) (Zelnik and Rosito, 1966). A possible route for the biosynthesis of this type of compound has been briefly discussed by Dreyer (1968b).

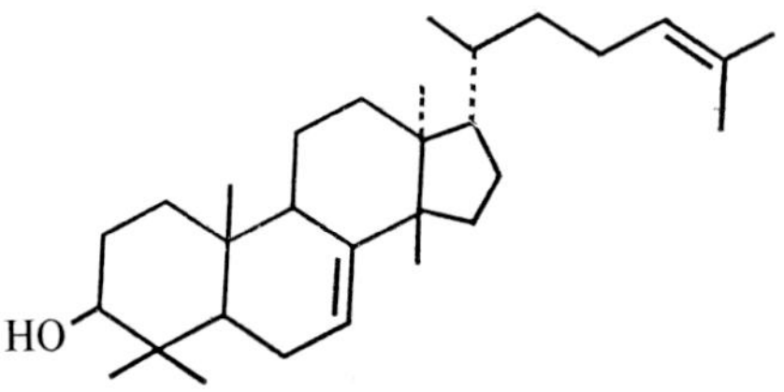

LX

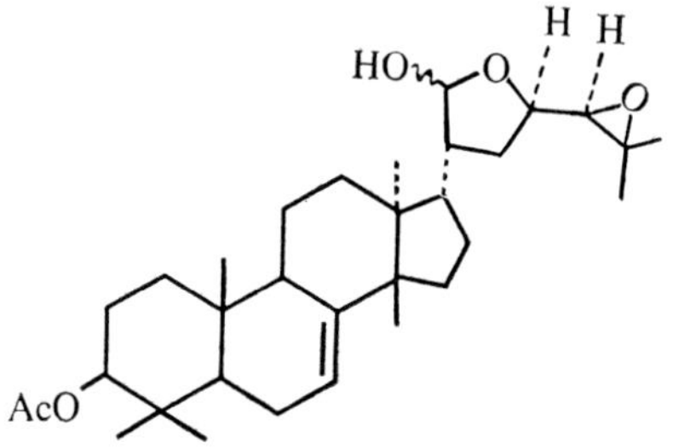

LXIa Turraeanthin
LXIb Aphanamixin

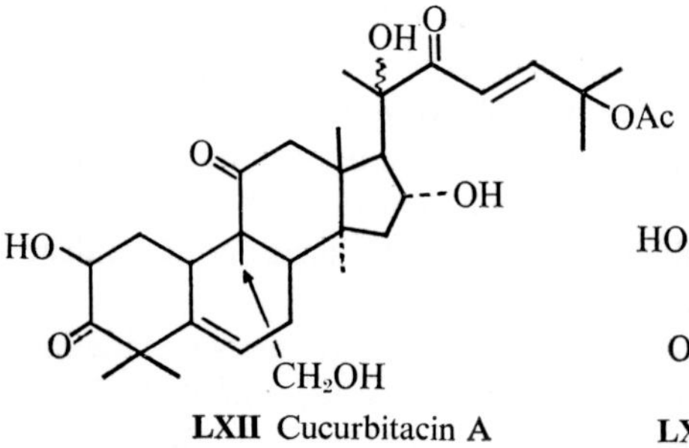

LXII Cucurbitacin A

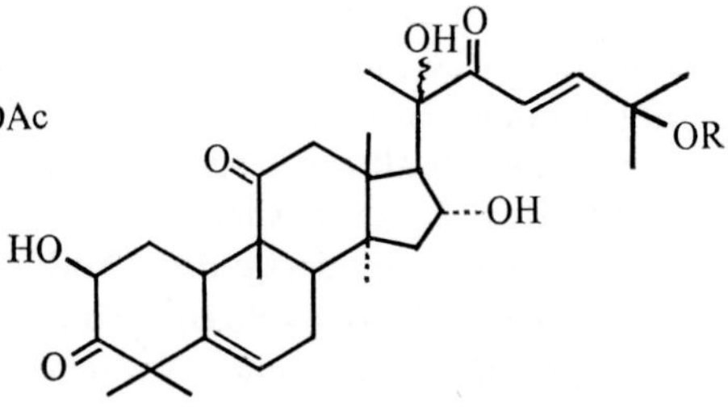

LXIII R = Ac, Cucurbitacin B
LXIV R = H, Cucurbitacin D (Elatericin A)

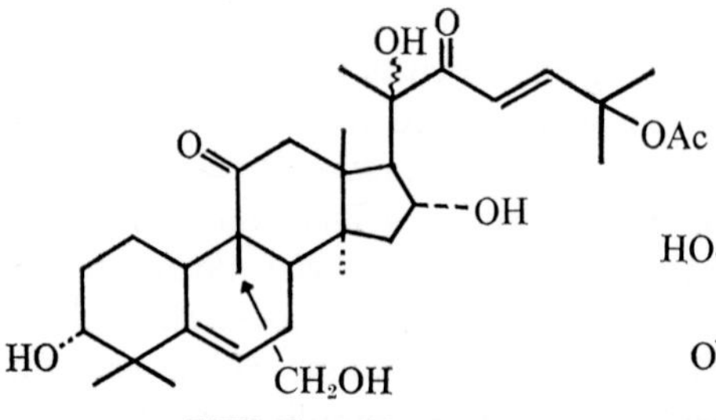

LXV Cucurbitacin C

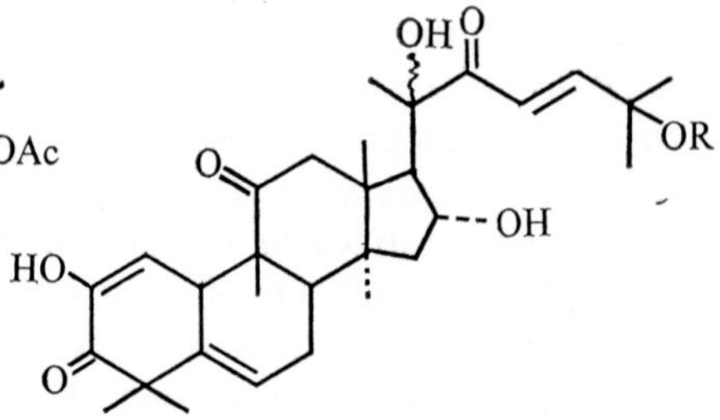

LXVI R = Ac, Cucurbitacin E (Elaterin)
LXVII R = H, Cucurbitacin I (Elatericin B)

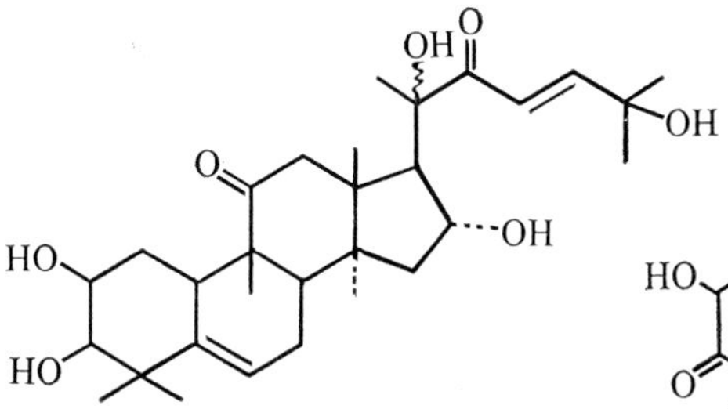

LXVIII Cucurbitacin F

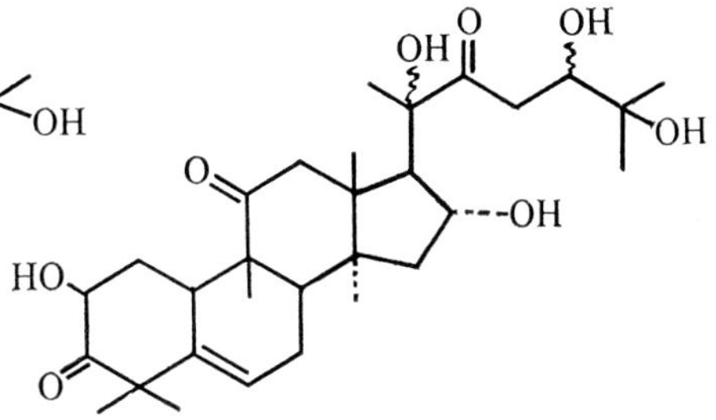

LXIXa Cucurbitacin G
LXIXb Cucurbitacin H (C24 epimers)

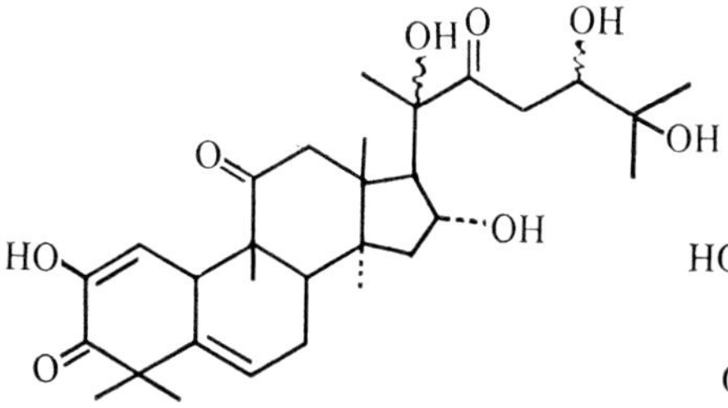

LXXa Cucurbitacin J
LXXb Cucurbitacin K (C24 epimers)

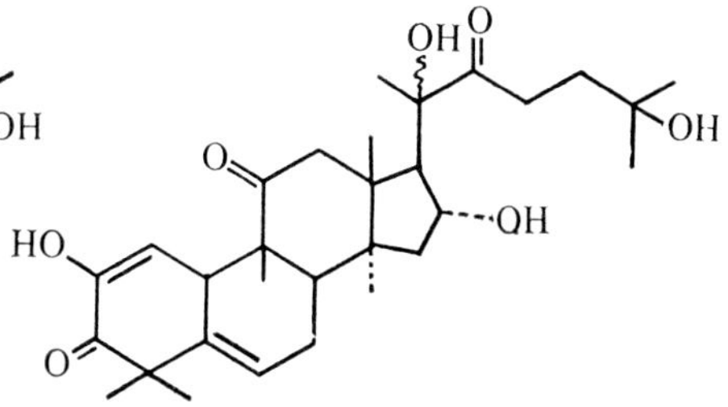

LXXI Cucurbitacin L

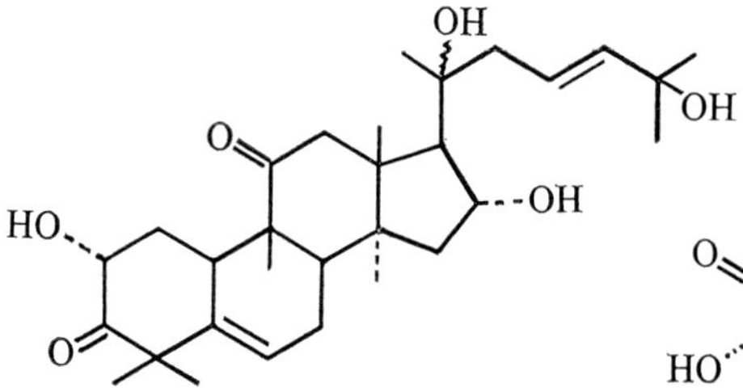

LXXII 22-Deoxocucurbitacin D

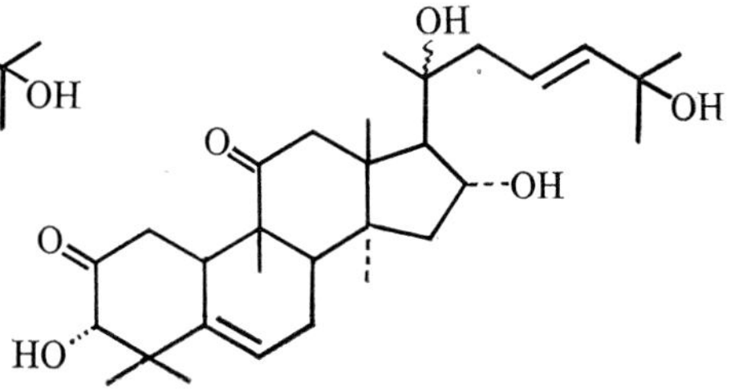

LXXIII 22-Deoxoisocucurbitacin D

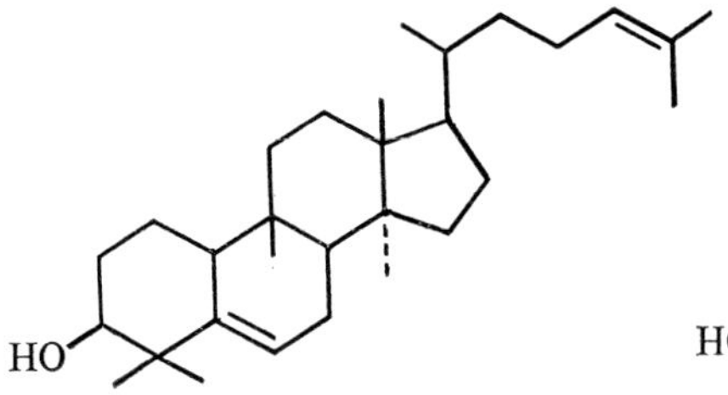

LXXIV Cucurbita-5,24-dien-3β-ol

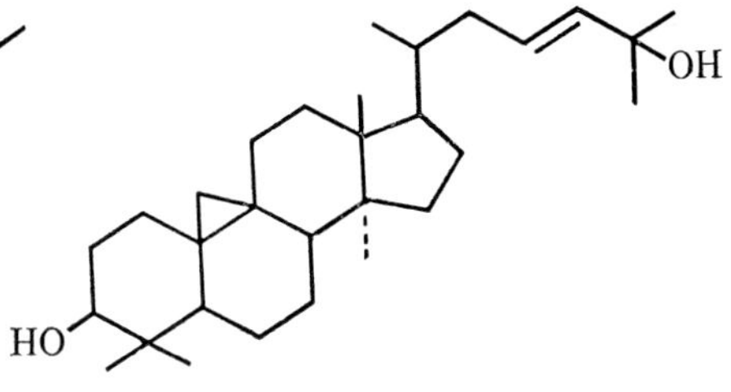

LXXV Cycloart-23-en-3β,25-diol

2. The Cucurbitacins

Plants belonging to the Cucurbitaceae family contain a number of structurally related triterpene bitter principles known collectively as the cucurbitacins (Lavie et al., 1962a; Ourisson et al., 1964; Moss, 1966). In mature plants the cucurbitacin content is usually highest in the fruits and roots. Leaves and stems often contain only very low levels of cucurbitacins although there are exceptions, for example, Cucumis angolensis and Cucumis foetidissima have very bitter leaves (Rehm et al., 1957). Also cucurbitacins are produced in the radicles and cotyledons of germinating Cucurbitaceae seedlings (Rehm and Wessels, 1957). The cucurbitacins have aroused considerable interest because of their toxicity and consequent commercial importance (Rehm, 1960) and also because of their reported antitumour activity (Belkin et al., 1952; Gitter et al., 1961; Gallily et al., 1962; Konopa et al., 1966, 1967; Kupchan et al., 1967; Farnsworth, 1966; Lavie et al., 1959).

The different cucurbitacins (structures **LXII–LXXIII**) have been designated cucurbitacins A to L (Enslin, 1954; Enslin et al., 1957). The alternative names for some of the cucurbitacins, for example, elaterin, elatericins A and B, were derived from Ecballium elaterium, the plant from which the compounds were originally isolated (Power and Moore, 1909; Lavie and Szinai, 1958; Lavie et al., 1962a, c). The structural elucidation of the cucurbitacins follow from the work of several laboratories (Lavie et al., 1962a and references therein; Ourisson et al., 1964 and references therein; Lavie et al., 1962c; de Kock et al., 1963; Biglino et al., 1963; Lavie et al., 1963; Enslin and Norton, 1964; Lavie and Benjaminov, 1964; van der Merwe et al., 1963; Melera and Noller, 1961; Holzapfel and Enslin, 1964; Lavie and Benjaminov, 1965; Enslin et al., 1967; Snatzke, et al., 1967; Audier and Das, 1966).

The distribution of the cucurbitacins in the Cucurbitaceae family has been discussed by Rehm et al. (1957). Forty-five species belonging to eighteen genera were examined and whilst this represented only a very small cross-sample of the Cucurbitaceae family a number of features of biochemical and physiological interest became apparent (see also Rehm, 1960). Cucurbitacin A (**LXII**) was only found in the fruit of three species of the genus Cucumis (C. hookeri, C. leptidermis and C. myriocarpus) whilst cucurbitacin C (**LXV**) occurred only in the fruit of Cucumis sativa but has more recently been reported in Cucumis prophetarum (Rao and Row, 1968). Cucurbitacin B (**LXIII**) was found by Rehm et al. (1957) in the fruits of a number of genera (Acanthosicyos, Coccinia, Cucumis, Cucurbita, Ecballium, Echinocystis and Lagenaria). Similarly, Cucurbitacin D (**LXIV**) is fairly widespread in fruits of Acanthosicyos, Citrullus, Cucumis, Cucurbita, Ecballium and Lagenaria species. Cucurbitacin E (**LXVI**) is a major component of the bitter principles of the fruits of the genera Citrullus and Cucurbita and also occurs in lesser amounts in *Ecballium elatarium*, *Echinocystis lobata*, *E. wrighti* and *Peponium mackenii*. Cucurbitacin F (**LXVIII**) was observed only in fruits of *Cucumis angolensis*. Small amounts of cucurbitacins G (**LXIXa**) and H (**LXIXb**) were found in the fruits of *Acanthosicyos horrida*, *Citrullus naudinianus*, *Cucumis* spp., *Cucurbita pepo* var. *ovifera*, *Lagenaria mascarena* and *L. siceraria*. Cucurbitacin I (**LXVII**) was present in fruit of *Ecballium elaterium*, *Lagenaria mascarena* and *Cucurbita pepo* var. *ovifera*, whilst the latter species also contained traces of cucurbitacins J (**LXXa**) and K (**LXXb**). In general cucurbitacins G, H, J, K and L were found in large amounts only in the roots of a few cucurbitaceae. Cucurbitacin L (**LXXI**) has only been reported in the fruits of one species, *Citrullus colocynthis*, where it accompanies cucurbitacins E (**LXVI**) and I (**LXVII**) (Lavie *et al.*, 1964). Lavie *et al.* (1962b) have isolated cucurbitacin E (**LXVI**) and 2-epicucurbitacin B from the fruit of *Luffa echinata* whilst cucurbitacins B (**LXIII**) and E (**LXVI**) have been reported in *L. echinata* var. *longistyla* and *L. graveolens* (Bhakuni *et al.*, 1961a,b; Sehgal *et al.*, 1961). More recently two new cucurbitacins, 22-deoxocurbitacin D (**LXXII**) and 22-deoxoisocucurbitacin D (**LXXIII**) have been identified in the fruits of a hybrid of *Lagenaria siceraria* (Enslin *et al.*, 1967).

Rehm *et al.* (1957) noted that cucurbitacins A, D, G and H are apparently only found in association with cucurbitacin B whilst cucurbitacins E, J, K and I also appear to occur together; these associations are probably explicable on biosynthetic grounds. The cucurbitacin composition of some fruit was observed to differ from that of the roots of the same plant; thus in *Citrullus naudinianus* the fruit contained cucurbitacins B, D, G and H but cucurbitacins B, D, E, G, H, I, J and K were found in the roots (Rehm *et al.* 1957). It has also been reported (Rehm *et al.*, 1957) that the cucurbitacin composition of some species is inconsistent, for example forms of *Cucurbita pepo* var. *ovifera* were found which contained the following: cucurbitacin E only; cucurbitacins E and B; cucurbitacins E and I; cucurbitacins B, D, E and I; and finally cucurbitacins B, D, E, G, H, I, J and K. Such variability indicates that caution may be required before the cucurbitacins are used for taxonomic purposes (Rehm *et al.*, 1957).

In some species (*Acanthosicyos horrida* and *Coccinia adoensis*) the green fruits are bitter but rapidly loose their bitterness as they ripen. In other species the opposite occurs. For example, ripe fruit of *Cucumis longipes* contains five times the concentration of cucurbitacin B (**LXIII**) found in very young fruits. The proportions of the various cucurbitacins also change in some fruits during development, young fruits of *Cucumis myriocarpus* contain more cucurbitacin B (**LXIII**) than A (**LXII**), but the reverse is found in ripened fruits (Rehm *et al.*, 1957). The location of the cucurbitacins within the fruit can vary with different species (Rehm *et al.*, 1957). Bitter principles are concentrated mainly in the outer layers of *Cucumis humifructus* fruit but in contrast the fruit of *Cucurbita mixta* contains the highest level in the inner spongy tissue while yet other species (for example, *Luffa acutangula* and *Sicyos angulata*) contain cucurbitacins in the seeds (Rehm *et al.*, 1957).

Some cucurbitaceae species which are bitter also occur in non-bitter forms which contain no cucurbitacins in the fruit (Rehm *et al.*, 1957; Rehm, 1960). It was originally concluded that a single dominant gene controlled bitterness (Pathak and Singh, 1950; Grebenscikov, 1954, 1955). However, the observation that some sweet fruited varieties either contain cucurbitacins in the roots (Rehm *et al.*, 1957) or in the seedlings (Rehm and Wessels, 1957) shows that these forms must possess the gene for bitterness. Rehm and Wessels (1957) conclude that in this case cucurbitacin formation in the fruit must be under control by a second genetic mechanism.

In some genera (*Citrullus, Coccinia, Cucurbita*) the cucurbitacins occur predominantly as glycosides whereas in others (*Acanthosicyos, Cucumis, Lagenaria*) only the free cucurbitacins (aglycones) are found (Rehm *et al.*, 1957). In general the aglycones are found in fruits which contain high levels of the enzyme elaterase, a glycosidase fairly specific for the hydrolysis of cucurbitacin glycosides (Enslin *et al.*, 1956; Joubert, 1960). Most fruits which contain cucurbitacin glycosides have no elaterase activity, but the fruits of *Ecballium elaterium* are apparently an exception since they contain high elaterase activity and also cucurbitacin glycosides (Rehm *et al.*, 1957; Gonzalez and Panizo, 1966). Ripe fruits seem to contain lower elaterase activity than unripe fruits (Enslin *et al.*, 1956).

The possible importance of cucurbitacins as feeding attractants for some insects has been reported by Chambliss and Jones (1966). Using sweet and bitter fruits of *Citrullus vulgaris* and *Cucurbita maxima*, they found that the bitter fruits were preferred by the cucumber beetle, *Diabrotica undecimpunctata howardi* Barb. The beetle attractants were identified as the cucurbitacins; cucurbitacin B **(LXIII)** had the greatest activity followed by E **(LXVI)** and D **(LXIV)**, but cucurbitacin I **(LXVII)** apparently had no biological activity.

III. BIOSYNTHESIS

A. Introduction

There is not space here to consider the biosynthesis of plant sterols and carotenoids in full detail, but an outline of the processes, as far as they are known, will be given with some details specially concerned with their formation in fruit.

B. Formation of Isopentenyl, Farnesyl and Geranylgeranyl Pyrophosphates

The formation of isopentenyl pyrophosphate, IPP, the universal biological isoprenoid precursor, from acetyl CoA via mevalonic acid is now well established and is outlined in Fig. 1. To produce higher terpenes IPP is

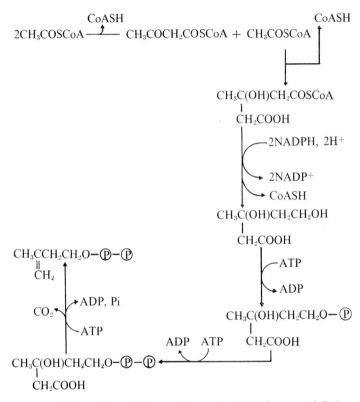

FIG. 1. Formation of isopentenyl pyrophosphate from acetyl-CoA.

isomerized to dimethylallyl pyrophosphate (Eq. 1) which acts as starter for

$$\underset{CH_2}{\overset{CH_3}{>}}CCH_2CH_2O-\textcircled{P}-\textcircled{P} \rightleftharpoons \underset{CH_3}{\overset{CH_3}{>}}C=CHCH_2O-\textcircled{P}-\textcircled{P} \qquad (1)$$

chain elongation. This process proceeds by sequential addition of molecules of IPP to form geranyl pyrophosphate (C-10), farnesyl pyrophosphate (C-15) and geranylgeranyl pyrophosphate (C-20). The mechanism involved is indicated in Eq. 2. In the first step in the formation of a triterpene two molecules

BFP—N

$$\underset{CH_3}{\overset{CH_3}{>}}C=CHCH_2 \quad \overset{\overset{O-\textcircled{P}-\textcircled{P}}{\frown}}{\overset{|}{C}} \quad CH_2=CCH_2CH_2O-\textcircled{P}-\textcircled{P} \qquad \underset{CH_3}{\overset{CH_3}{>}}C=CHCH_2CH_2-\overset{\overset{CH_3}{|}}{\underset{+}{C}}CH_2CH_2O$$

$$\textcircled{P}-\textcircled{P} \qquad \downarrow H^+ \tag{2}$$

$$\underset{CH_3}{\overset{CH_3}{>}}C=CHCH_2CH_2\overset{\overset{CH_3}{|}}{C}=CHCH_2O-\textcircled{P}-\textcircled{P}$$

of farnesyl pyrophosphate condense to form squalene (C-30). Similarly, to form the tetraterpenes two molecules of geranylgeranyl pyrophosphate condense to form phytoene (C-40).

C. Formation of Squalene and Sterols

The full details of squalene (**I**) formation including the stereochemistry of the reactions have been discussed by Popják and Cornforth (1966). In contrast to phytoene formation, NADPH is required for squalene synthesis.

The first demonstration that squalene (**I**) was a sterol precursor in animals was made by Langdon and Bloch (1953) but it was not until 1965 that this was confirmed for higher plants (Capstack et al., 1965; Bennett and Heftmann, 1965). The next step is the formation of squalene 2,3-oxide (**II**) (Corey et al., 1966; van Tamelen et al., 1966; Dean et al., 1967) which undergoes concerted cyclization. It is clear in animals that the first product formed is lanosterol (**III**) and that the mechanism involved is as illustrated in Fig. 2 (see, for example, Clayton, 1965; Nicholas, 1968). The changes which lanosterol (**III**) undergoes in its transformation into cholesterol (**XII**) involve (i) loss of three methyl groups; (ii) movement of a double bond from Δ^8 to Δ^5 and (iii) the saturation of the side chain (C-24). There is no compelling evidence to conclude that one specific biosynthetic sequence from lanosterol (**III**) to cholesterol (**XII**) is mandatory and it would appear that a number of enzymes involved in these changes have a rather wide specificity.

Although cholesterol (**XII**) is widely distributed in small amounts in higher plants (Nicholas, 1968) the major plant sterols contain alkyl groups at C-24 and many contain a double bond at C-22; these variations add additional complications in attempting to define experimentally biosynthetic sequences. But before this problem is discussed it must be pointed out that apart from *Euphorbia* latex, which is a special case (Ponsinet and Ourisson, 1968), lanosterol (**III**) has not been unequivocally demonstrated as a naturally occurring product in higher plants; cycloartenol (**IV**) appears to take its place (see, for example, Goad, 1967). It is clear from experiments of Rees et al. (1967) that cycloartenol (**IV**) is a primary product of cyclization of squalene oxide (**II**) (Fig. 2) and is not formed from lanosterol (**III**). Furthermore,

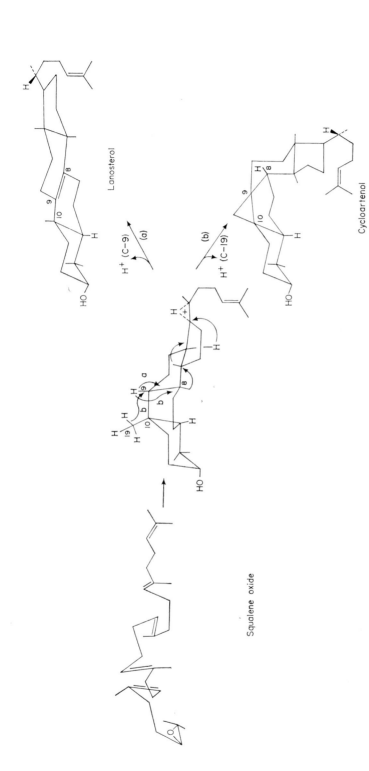

Squalene oxide

Lanosterol

Cycloartenol

H^+ (C-9)

(a)

(b)

H^+ (C-19)

FIG. 2. Mechanism for lanosterol and cycloartenol formation from squalene oxide.

enzyme preparations from French beans (*Phaseolus vulgaris*) and the alga *Ochromonas malhamensis* will convert [^{14}C]squalene-2,3-oxide (II) anaerobically into cycloartenol (IV) with no detectable production of lanosterol (III) (Rees *et al.*, 1968, 1969). The question then arises whether cycloartenol (IV) and not lanosterol (III) is the first cyclic precursor of sterols in plants. Evidence additional to that already quoted includes the detection of

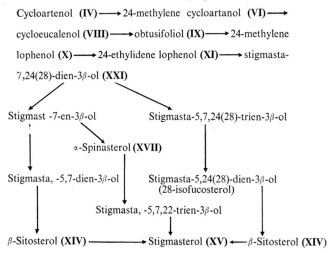

FIG. 3. A possible pathway from cycloartenol to phytosterols.

24-methylene cycloartanol (VI) and cycloeucalenol (VIII) in widely different higher plants. Obtusifoliol (IX), originally isolated from the latex of *Euphorbia obtusifolia* (Barrera *et al.*, 1967), has also now been found in other plants (Goad *et al.*, 1967; Benveniste, 1968). A logical biogenetic pathway to phytosterols is indicated in Fig. 3 but remains to be verified at the enzyme level. Furthermore, labelled cycloartenol (IV) and 24-methylene cycloartanol (VI) are very efficiently converted into poriferasterol (the C-24 epimer of stigmasterol (XV)) in *Ochromonas malhamensis* (Hall *et al.*, 1969). In the same organism lanosterol (III) is also active, similarly lanosterol (III) and 24-methylene dihydrolanosterol are converted into β-sitosterol (XIV) in plant tissues (Alcaide *et al.*, 1968; Baisted *et al.*, 1968); these conversions are possibly due to the fact that the enzymes concerned in plant sterol biosynthesis following the primary cyclization have only limited substrate specificity, as in the case with the enzymes concerned with cholesterol (XII) formation from lanosterol (III) in animals.

D. Mechanism of Alkylation of Plant Sterols

The methyl group at C-24 of ergosterol (XVI) arises by transmethylation from methionine (see Lederer, 1964) with loss of one of the hydrogens from the methyl group during transfer (Jaureguiberry *et al.*, 1965). Similarly the 24-ethylidene and ethyl groups of phytosterols arise by two successive trans-methylations (Castle *et al.*, 1963; Bader *et al.*, 1964; Villaneuva *et al.*, 1964). Two mechanisms appear to be involved because in poriferasterol synthesized by *Ochromonas malhamensis* only four hydrogens of the entering methyl groups appear in the sterol (Smith *et al.*, 1967) whilst in the slime mould *Dictyostelium discoideum* five hydrogens appear in the major sterol, Δ^{22}-stigmasten-3β-ol (Lenfant *et al.*, 1969). Mechanisms to explain these possibilities are given in Fig. 4. The reality of the proposed hydrogen shift

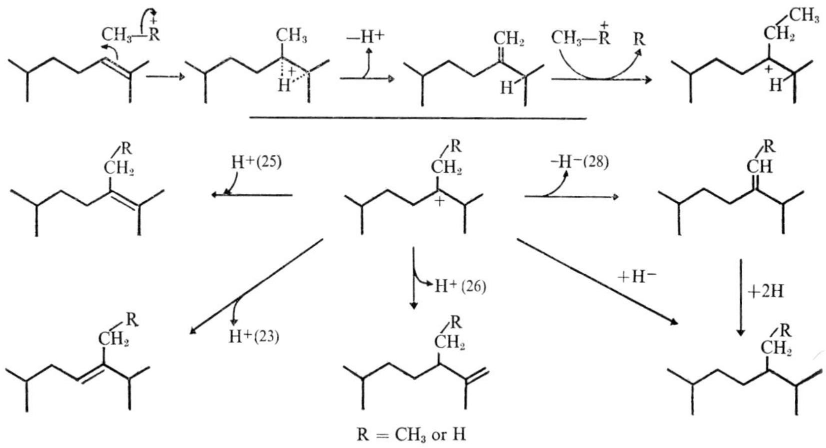

R = CH₃ or H

FIG. 4. Proposed mechanisms for alkylation of the phytosterol side chain.

from C-24 to C-25 has been demonstrated in the case of ergosterol (Stone and Hemming, 1967; Akhtar *et al.*, 1967), fucosterol (Goad and Goodwin, 1969) and 28-isofucosterol (Raab *et al.*, 1968).

E. Limonoid Biosynthesis

The biosynthesis of limonin has been discussed by a number of authors (Arigoni *et al.*, 1960; Barton *et al.*, 1961; Dreyer, 1965b, 1966a, 1968b; Moss, 1966). A possible route for the latter stages of biosynthesis has been suggested (Dreyer, 1966a, 1968b):

deacetylnomilin (**XLI**) → nomilin (**XLII**) → obacunone (**XL**) → obacunoic acid (**XLIX**) → isoobacunoic acid → limonin (**XXXVII**).

Dreyer (1965b, 1968b) has speculated that the isolation of deoxylimonin (**XLIV**) and ichangin (**XLIII**), from certain *Citrus* species (*loc cit.*), is an indication that enzymes involved in the latter stages of limonin biosynthesis may not have a high substrate specificity. A triterpene of the type (**XXXIX**) has been suggested as a likely primary precursor of the limonoids (Moss,

1966) and would presumably arise by a suitable cyclization of 2,3-oxido-squalene (**II**), the recently demonstrated precursor of lanosterol (**III**) in animals and of cycloartenol (**IV**) in plants (Rees *et al.*, 1968; Benveniste and Massy-Westrop, 1967). A triterpene such as tirucalla-7,24-dien-3β-ol (**LX**) has been suggested as a precursor of such compounds as turraeanthin (**LXIa**), flindissol (**L**) or melianone (**LII**) (Bevan *et al.*, 1965, 1967) and could also serve as a precursor of the more oxidized limonoids (Arigoni *et al.*, 1960; Barton *et al.*, 1961). Epoxidation of the Δ^7 bond followed by opening of the epoxide could result in a rearrangement of the C-14 methyl group to C-8 with C-15 proton elimination (Cotterrell *et al.*, 1967), to produce a 7α-hydroxy Δ^{14} compound as typified by the limonoids azadirone (**LIII**), azadiradione (**LIV**) and meldenin (**LVIII**). Epoxidation of the Δ^{14} bond could then lead to such limonoids as gedunin (**LVI**) and epoxyazadiradione (**LV**) and ultimately by further oxidations to limonin (**XXXVII**). The side chain furan ring is considered to arise by a sequence of reactions suggested by the side chain structures of flindissol (**L**), melianone (**LII**) and turraeanthin (**LXIa**) (Moss, 1966; Bevan *et al.*, 1965, 1967; Buchanan and Halsall, 1969) and resulting in the elimination of the four terminal carbon atoms.

So far there appears to have been only one communication describing experimental work using radioisotopes to investigate limonin biosynthesis. Datta and Nicholas (1968) have reported a low incorporation (0·03–0·05%) of [2-^{14}C]mevalonic acid into limonin (**XXXVII**) by germinating seeds of Valencia oranges. Injection of [2-^{14}C]mevalonic acid into orange fruit or uptake of [2-^{14}C]mevalonic acid by stems carrying orange fruit were reported to give extremely low incorporation of radioactivity into the limonin of the seeds.

F. Biosynthesis and Interconversion of Cucurbitacins

The cucurbitacins are considered to arise from a triterpene, cucurbita-5,24-dien-3β-ol (**LXXIV**) by suitable oxidation reactions. This triterpene (**LXXIV**) which has not been isolated from natural sources could be formed by cyclization of 2,3-oxidosqualene (**II**) followed by extensive rearrangement of the intermediate carbonium ion beyond the lanosterol (**III**) or cycloartenol (**IV**) stage (Lavie *et al.*, 1963; de Kock *et al.*, 1963; Moss, 1966) and possibly involving a transitory triterpene-enzyme intermediate (Rees *et al.*, 1968). The biogenesis of the various cucurbitacins has been discussed by Rehm (1960). Possible mechanisms for the modification of the side chain have been indicated by Moss (1966) and are shown in Fig. 5. A modified route which gains some support from the natural occurrence of cycloart-23-en-3β, 25-diol (**LXXV**) (McCrindle and Djerassi, 1961; Djerassi and McCrindle, 1962) and 22-deoxocucurbitacin D (**LXXII**) (Enslin *et al.*, 1967) is given in Fig. 6.

Enzymic interconversions of some cucurbitacins have been demonstrated. Juices from a number of cucurbit fruit contain an esterase which will convert cucurbitacin B (**LXIII**) into D (**LXIV**) and cucurbitacin E (**LXVI**) into I (**LXVII**) (Rehm, 1956; Schwartz et al., 1964). A Δ^{23} reductase has been isolated from the fruit of *Cucurbita maxima* (Schabort et al., 1968) and its role in cucurbitacin breakdown discussed (Schabort and Teijema, 1968).

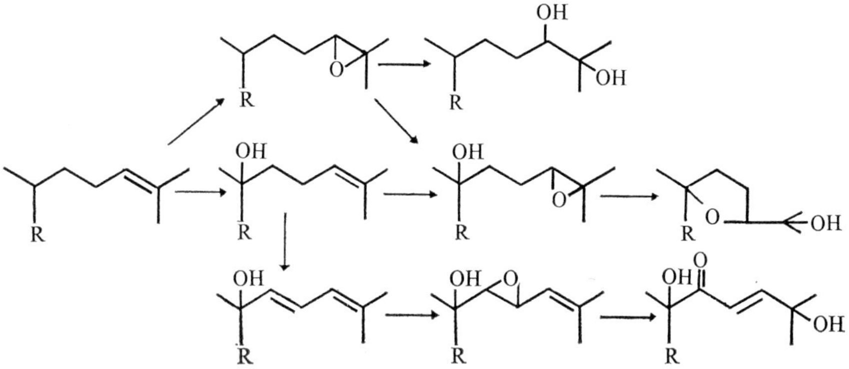

FIG. 5. Possible mechanisms for the formation of the cucurbitacin side chain (Moss, 1966).

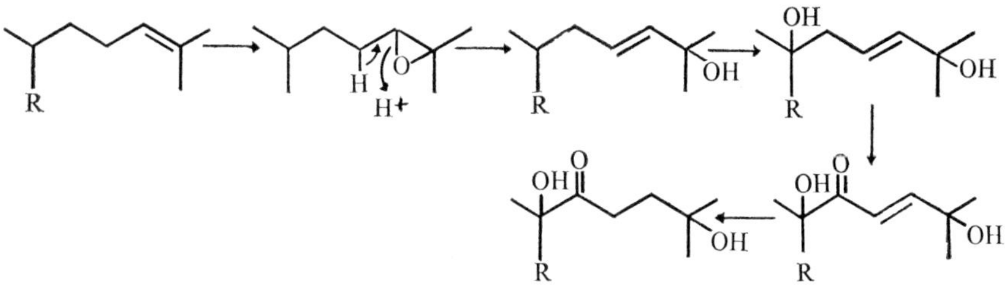

FIG. 6. Alternative mechanism for cucurbitacin side chain formation.

G. Biosynthesis of Carotenoids

More information on carotenoid biosynthesis has come from studies with fruit than in the case of sterols, but many key observations have been made with other tissues or with micro-organisms.

1. *Formation of acyclic carotenes*

Geranylgeranyl pyrophosphate is converted into phytoene by preparations from carrot roots (Jungalwala and Porter, 1968) and from a mutant of *Phycomyces blakesleeanus* (Lee and Chichester, 1969). No NADPH is required in contrast to its role in squalene biosynthesis (see Section IIIC) (Charlton et al., 1967; Graebe, 1968). The stepwise desaturation of phytoene to lycopene (Fig. 7) has considerable circumstantial support although no direct conversions have been clearly demonstrated. Evidence for this sequence includes (i) the series of compounds occur together in many tissues, particularly fruit, and were first noted in tomatoes (Porter and Lincoln, 1950); (ii) their chemical structures allow them to be arranged in a logical biogenetic sequence; (iii) intermediates such as phytoene accumulate in various mutants

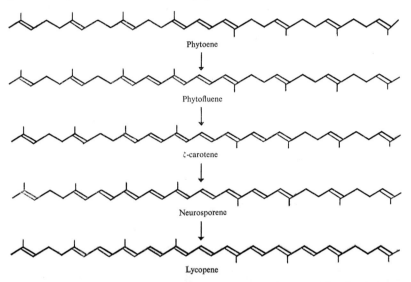

Fɪɢ. 7. Pathway of conversion of phytoene into lycopene. The central bonds of phytoene and phytofluene are indicated as *trans* for representational convenience.

of algae, fungi, as well as higher plants, and in cultures in which carotenogenesis has been inhibited by compounds such as diphenylamine; and (iv) kinetic studies of synthesis of the fully unsaturated carotenes and disappearance of the most saturated compounds compatible with a precursor/product relationship.

2. *Formation of cyclic carotenes*

Cyclization of the acyclic precursor apparently takes place either at the neurosporene level or at the lycopene level (Fig. 8). Again the evidence is mainly circumstantial, but recently experimental demonstration of lycopene to cyclic carotenes has been made (Hill and Rogers, 1969). The neurosporene pathway requires that α- and β-zeacarotenes are intermediates. They have been isolated from maize (Rabourn and Quackenbush, 1959), and β-zeacarotene is present in certain *Rhodotorula* spp. (Simpson *et al.*, 1964), *Chlorella* mutants (Claes, 1958) and diphenylamine-inhibited micro-organisms (Williams *et al.*, 1965), as well as in a few fruits (see Table I).

Support for the neurosporene pathway comes from the observation that

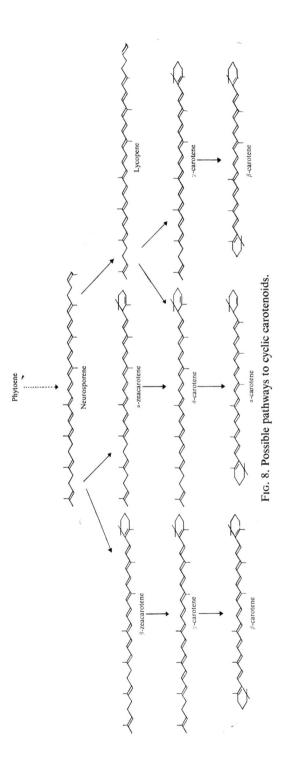

FIG. 8. Possible pathways to cyclic carotenoids.

whilst lycopene synthesis in red tomatoes is inhibited above 30°C, that of β-carotene is not (see Section IF), and that DMSO (dimethylsulphoxide) inhibits synthesis of the acyclic carotenes but not of β-carotene (Raymundo et al., 1967). However, in the orange tomato phenotype, lycopene is replaced by β-carotene and this synthesis is temperature-sensitive (IF). There thus appears to be two distinct (? compartmentalized) pathways of carotenoid biosynthesis in tomatoes, but none of the observations yet reported allows a decision to be made as to whether lycopene or neurosporene is the substrate for the cyclization enzymes.

Recent investigations with various stereospecific species of mevalonic acid appear to rule out any inter-conversion of the α- and β-ionone ring of the carotenes in green tissues, carrot roots, tomato fruit and *Physalis* fruit (Williams et al., 1967b; Walton et al., 1969). The mechanism proposed for the formation of the two rings is indicated in Fig. 9. It is supported by genetic evidence on tomatoes (Tomes, 1967). If *B* mediates the conversion of acyclic carotenes to carotenes containing β-ionone residues (β-carotene) and *del* controls the conversion of β-ionone derivatives to α-ionone derivatives

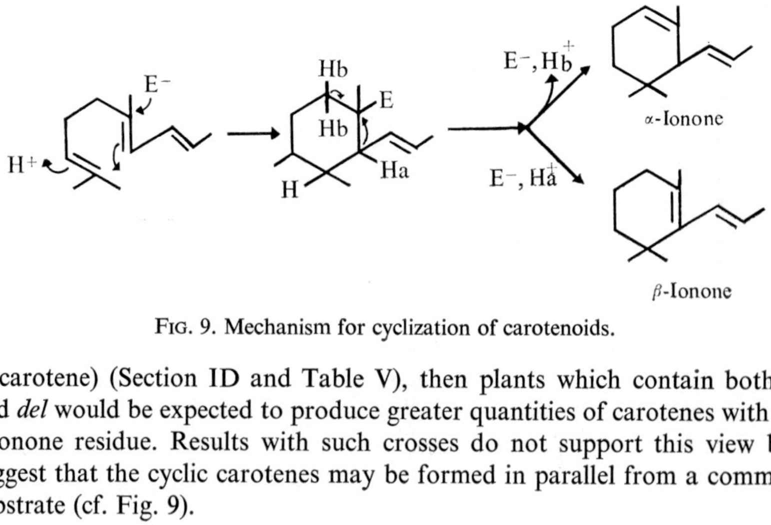

Fig. 9. Mechanism for cyclization of carotenoids.

(δ-carotene) (Section ID and Table V), then plants which contain both *B* and *del* would be expected to produce greater quantities of carotenes with an α-ionone residue. Results with such crosses do not support this view but suggest that the cyclic carotenes may be formed in parallel from a common substrate (cf. Fig. 9).

3. Formation of xanthophylls—insertion of oxygen

The weight of evidence indicates that insertion of oxygen into xanthophylls is a late step in the biosynthetic sequence, but again little direct evidence is available in support of this view. A mutant (5/520) of *Chlorella vulgaris* which synthesizes mainly phytoene when grown heterotrophically in the dark will on anaerobic illumination form coloured carotenoids at the expense of phytoene. If the cultures are then returned to darkness and allowed access to oxygen, then xanthophylls are formed with the simultaneous disappearance of carotenes (Claes, 1957, 1958). Anaerobic cultures of the non-sulphur purple photosynthetic bacterium *Rhodopseudomonas* are yellowish brown owing to the presence of spheroidene; on exposing the cultures to air they rapidly turn purplish-red owing to the conversion of spheroidene into spheroidenone (Fig. 10) (van Niel, 1949; Goodwin *et al.*, 1956; Davis *et al.*, 1961).

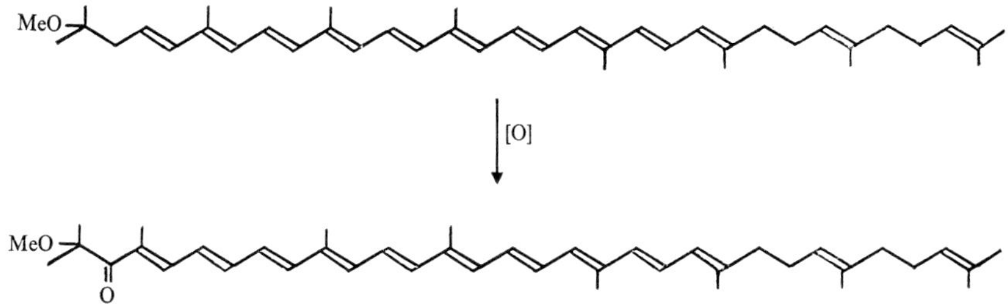

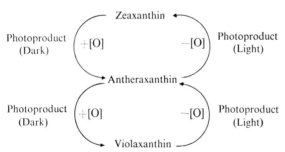

FIG. 10. The conversion of spheroidene into spheroidenone.

Zeaxanthin can be stepwise oxidized to violaxanthin via antheraxanthin and, in higher plants the reactions are considered to be photo-stimulated in both directions (Fig. 11) (Lee and Yamamoto, 1968).

Photoproduct (Dark) Zeaxanthin Photoproduct (Light)
+[O] −[O]
Antheraxanthin
Photoproduct (Dark) Photoproduct (Light)
+[O] −[O]
Violaxanthin

FIG. 11. The Violaxanthin cycle in higher plants.

In all cases examined experiments with $^{18}O_2$ and $H_2^{18}O$ have shown that gaseous oxygen is the source of the oxygen in the carotenoid; for example, in lutein and zeaxanthin in *Chlorella* (Yamamoto *et al.*, 1962), in antheraxanthin in higher plants (Yamamoto and Chichester, 1965) and spheroidenone in *Rsp. spheroides* (Shneour, 1962).

Experiments with stereospecifically labelled mevalonic acids have shown that lutein and zeaxanthin are not interconvertible in maize seedlings (Goodwin *et al.*, 1968). They also show that the process involves a direct stereospecific replacement of one hydrogen by a hydroxyl group and that a keto derivative is not involved (Walton *et al.*, 1969).

5,6-Epoxides (for example, violaxanthin or antheraxanthin) are easily isomerized to 5,8-epoxides and the accumulation of acids in ripening fruit may account for some of the 5,8-epoxides which also accumulate during ripening. This accumulation is specially marked in citrus fruit (see Table I and Goodwin, 1966). The conversion may also be partly enzymic.

Plausible mechanisms for the formation of neoxanthin and capsanthin are indicated in Fig. 12 but they await experimental verification.

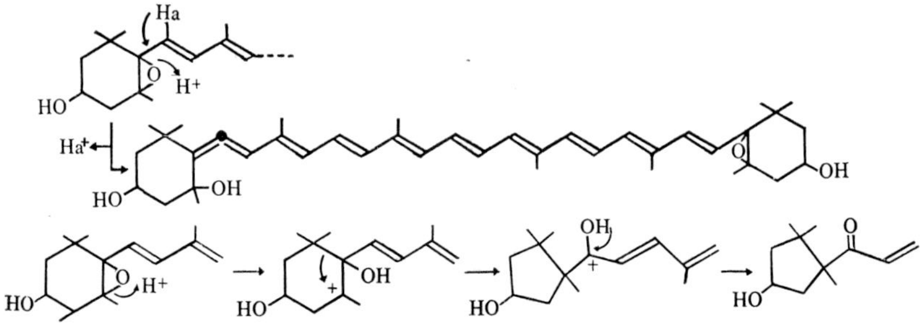

FIG. 12. Possible mechanism for the biosynthesis of neoxanthin and capsanthin.

REFERENCES

Abdul-Alim, M. A., Aboulezs, A. F., Fayez, M. B. E. and Seedhom, A. E. (1966). *Z. analyc. Chem.* **217**, 268.

Abrams, G. J. von and Pratt, H. K. (1964). *Pl. Physiol.* **39**, lxv.

Akhtar, M., Hunt, P. F. and Parvez, M. A. (1967). *Biochem. J.* **103**, 616.

Alcaide, A., Devys, M., Bottin, J., Fetizon, M., Barbier, M. and Lederer, E. (1968). *Phytochem.* **7**, 1773.

Amin, E. S., Awad, O., Samad, M. A. E. and Iskander, M. N. (1969). *Phytochem.* **8**, 295.

Argoud, S. (1958). *Oleagineaux* **13**, 249.

Arigoni, D., Barton, D. H. R., Corey, E. J., Jeger, O., Caglioti, L., Dev. S., Ferrini, P. G., Glazier, E. R., Melera, A., Pradhan, S. K., Schaffner, K., Sternhell, S., Templeton, J. F. and Tobinaga, S. (1960). *Experientia* **16**, 41.

Arnott, S. A., Davie, A. W., Robertson, J. M., Sim, G. A. and Watson, D. G. (1960). *Experientia* **16**, 49.

Atal, C. K. and Sethi, P. D. (1963). *Indian J. Pharm.* **25**, 163; Chem. Abst. **59**, 1438a.

Audier, H. and Das, B. C. (1966). *Tetrahedron Lett.* p. 2205.

Awasthi, Y. C. and Mitra, C. R. (1967). *Phytochem.* **6**, 121.

Awasthi, Y. C. and Mitra, C. R. (1968). *Phytochem.* **7**, 637.

Ayers, J. E. and Tomes, M. L. (1966). *Proc. Am. Soc. hort. Sci.* **88**, 550.

Bader, S., Guglielmetti, L. and Arigoni, D. (1964). *Proc. chem. Soc.* p. 16.

Baisted, D. J., Gardner, R. L. and McReynolds, L. A. (1968). *Phytochem.* **7**, 945.

Baker, L. R. and Tomes, M. L. (1964). *Proc. Am. Soc. hort. Sci.* **85**, 507.

Baraud, J. (1958). *Revue gén. Bot.* **65**, 221.

Barrera, J. B., Bréton, J. L., Delgado, M. J. and Gonzalez, A. G. (1967). *An. R. Soc. esp. Fís. Quím.* **B62**, 191.

Barton, D. H. R. (1951). *J. chem. Soc.* p. 1444.

Barton, D. H. R., Pradhan, S. K., Sternhell, S. and Templeton, J. F. (1961). *J. chem. Soc.* p. 255.

Belkin, M., Fitzgerald, D. B. and Cogan, G. W. (1952). *J. natn. Cancer Inst.* **13,** 139.

Bennett, R. D. and Heftmann, E. (1965) *Phytochem.* **4,** 475.

Bennett, R. D., Heftmann, E., Purcell, A. E. and Bonner, J. (1961). *Science, N. Y.* **134,** 671.

Bennett, R. D., Ko, S. T. and Heftmann, E. (1966). *Phytochem.* **5,** 231.

Benveniste, P. (1968). *Phytochem.* **7,** 951.

Benveniste, P. and Massy-Westropp, R. A. (1967). *Tetrahedron Lett.* p. 3553.

Bevan, C. W. L., Ekong, D. E. U., Halsall, T. G. and Toft, P. (1965). *Chem. Comm.* p. 636.

Bevan, C. W. L., Ekong, D. E. U., Halsall, T. G. and Toft, P. (1967). *J. chem. Soc.* (C), p. 820.

Bhakuni, D. S. and Tewari, J. D. (1959). *J. scient. ind. Res.* (*India*) **18B,** 427.

Bhakuni, D. S., Sharma, V. N. and Kaul, K. N. (1961a). *J. scient. ind. Res.* (*India*) **20B,** 232; *Chem. Abst.* (1962) **56,** 1773b.

Bhakuni, D. S., Sharma, V. N. and Kaul, K. N. (1961b). *J. scient. ind. Res.* (*India*) **20B,** 360.

Bhakuni, D. S., Srivastava, S. N., Sharma, V. N. and Kaul, K. N. (1962). *J. scient. ind. Res.* (*India*) **21B,** 237.

Bielig, H. J. (1944). *Ber. dt. chem. Ges.* **77B,** 748,

Biglino, G., Lehn, J. M. and Ourisson, G. (1963). *Tetrahedron Lett.* p. 1651.

Birch, A. J. D., Collins, D. J., Muhammad, S. and Turnbull, J. P. (1963). *J. chem. Soc.* p. 2762.

Blackie, W. J. and Cowgill, G. R. (1939). *J. Fd Sci.* **4,** 129.

Bobbitt, J. M. and Rao K. V. (1965). *J. Pharm. Sci.* **54,** 924.

Bock, W., Matz, J. and Taufel, K. (1966). *Nahrung Smittelindustrie* **10,** 409.

Bodea, C. and Nicoara, E. (1959) *Justus Liebigs Annln. chem.* **622,** 188.

Bodea, C., Nicoara, E. and Salontai, T. (1964). *Revue Roum. Chim.* **9,** 517.

Boiteau, P., Pasich, B. and Ratsimamanga, A. R. (1964). "Les Triterpenoids en physiologie vegetale et animale." Gauthier-Villars, Paris.

Brass, K., Bajrodt, A. and Mattsusch, J. (1937). *Naturwissenschaften* **25,** 60.

Breen, G. J. W., Ritchie, E., Sidwell, W. T. L. and Taylor, W. C. (1966). *Aust. J. Chem.* **19,** 455.

Brieskorn, C. H. and Klinger, H. (1963). *Z. Lebensmittelunters u.-Forsch,* **120,** 269.

Brieskorn, C. H. and Reinartz, H. (1967). *Z. Lebensmittelunters u.-Forsch.* **133,** 137.

Brieskorn, C. H. and Wunderer, H. (1966). *Z. Naturf.* **21B,** 1005.

Brieskorn, C. H. and Wunderer, H. (1967). *Chem. Ber.* **100,** 1252.

Brockmann, H. (1933). *Hoppe-Seyler's Z. physiol.* **216,** 45.

Brossard, J. and Mackinney, G. (1963). *Agric. Fd Chem.* **11,** 501.

Brown, R. F. C., Gilham, P. T., Hughes, G. K. and Ritchie, E. (1954). *Aust. J. Chem.* **7,** 181.

Bubicz, M. and Wierzchowski, Z. (1960). *Bull. Acad. pol. Sci. Sér. Sci. tech.* **8,** 323.

Bubicz, M. (1965). *Bull. Acad. pol. Sci. Sér. Sci. tech.* **13,** 251.

Buchanan, J. G. St. and Halsall, T. G. (1969). *Chem. Commun.* p. 48.

Butenandt, A. and Jacobi, H. (1933). *Hoppe-Seyler's Z. physiol. Chem.* **218,** 104.

Capstack, E., Rosin, N. L., Blondin, G. A. and Nes, W. R. (1965). *J. biol. Chem.* **240,** 3258.

Castle, M., Blondin, G. A. and Nes, W. R. (1963). *J. Am. Chem. Soc.* **85,** 3306.

Chakraborty, D. P. (1959). *J. scient. ind. Res.* (*India*) **18B**, 90.
Chaliha, B. P., Sastry, G. P. and Rao, P. R. (1964). *Indian J. Chem.* **2**, 40.
Chambliss, O. L. and Jones, C. M. (1966). *Science, N.Y.* **153**, 1392.
Charlton, J. M., Treharne, K. J. and Goodwin, T. W. (1967). *Biochem. J.* **105**, 205.
Chatterjee, A. and Kundu, A. B. (1967). *Tetrahedron Lett. p.* 1471.
Cholnoky, L., Györgyfy, K., Nagy, E. and Panczel, M. (1955). *Acta chim. hung.* **6**, 143.
Cholnoky, L., Györgyfy, K., Nagy, E. and Panczel, M. (1956). *Nature, Lond.* **178**, 410.
Cholnoky, L., Györgyfy, K., Nagy, E. and Panczel, M. (1958). *Acta chim. hung.* **16**, 227.
Ciulei, I., Mateescu, Gh. and Herman Ch. (1966). *Farmacia* **14**, 663; *Chem. Abst.* (1967). **66**, 52924m.
Claes, H. (1957). *Z. Naturf.* **12B**, 401.
Claes, H. (1958). *Z. Naturf.* **13B**, 222.
Clayton, R. B. (1965). *Q. Rev.* **19**, 168, 201.
Connolly, J. D., Handa, K. C. and McCrindle, R. (1968). *Tetrahedron Lett.* p. 437.
Connolly, J. D., Henderson, R., McCrindle, R., Overton, K. H. and Bhacca, N. S. (1965). *J. chem. Soc.* 6935.
Copius-Peereboom, J. W. (1964). *Z. analyt. Chem.* **205**, 325.
Corey, E. J., Russey, W. E. and Ortiz de Montellano, V. R. (1966). *J. Am. chem. Soc.* **88**, 4750.
Cotterrell, G. P., Halsall, T. G. and Wriglesworth, M. J. (1967). *Chem. Commun.* p. 1121.
Curl, A. L. (1959). *J. Fd Sci.* **24**, 413.
Curl, A. L. (1960a). *J. Fd Sci.* **25**, 190.
Curl, A. L. (1960b). *J. Fd Sci.* **25**, 670.
Curl, A. L. (1962a), *Agric. Fd Chem.* **10**, 504.
Curl, A. L. (1962b). *J. Fd Sci.* **27**, 171.
Curl, A. L. (1963). *J. Fd Sci.* **28**, 623.
Curl, A. L. (1964). *J. Fd Sci.* **29**, 241.
Curl, A. L. (1966). *J. Fd Sci.* **31**, 759.
Curl, A. L. and Bailey, G. F. (1954), *J. agric. Fd Chem.* **2**, 685.
Curl, A. L. and Bailey, G. F. (1956), *J. agric. Fd Chem.* **4**, 156.
Curl, A. L. and Bailey, G. F. (1957). *J. agric. Fd Chem.* **5**, 605.
Curl, A. L. and Bailey, G. F. (1957). *J. agric. Fd Chem.* **5**, 605.
Curl, A. L. and Bailey, G. F. (1961). *J. Fd Sci.* **26**, 424.
Czygan, F. C. and Willuhn, G. (1967). *Planta med.* **15**, 404.
Datta, S. and Nicholas H. J. (1968). *Phytochem.* **7**, 955.
Davis, J. B., Jackman, L. M., Siddons, P. T. and Weedon, B. C. L. (1961). *Proc. chem. Soc.* p. 261.
Dean, P. D. G., Ortiz de Montellano, P. R., Bloch, K. and Corey, E. J. (1967). *J. biol. Chem.* **242**, 3014.
Denison, E. L. (1951). *Oowa St, Coll. J. Sci.* **25**, 549.
Dhar, K. L. and Chauhan, R. N. S. (1963). *Agra Univ. J. Res.* **12**, 9; *Chem. Abst.* (1964). **60**, 4349a.
Djerassi, C. and McCrindle, R. (1962). *J. chem. Soc.* p. 4034.
Dreyer, D. L. (1965a). *Tetrahedron* **21**, 75.
Dreyer, D. L. (1965b). *J. org. Chem.* **30**, 749.
Dreyer, D. L. (1966a). *J. org. Chem.* **31**, 2279.

Dreyer, D. L. (1966b). *Phytochem.* **5**, 367.
Dreyer, D. L. (1967). *J. org. Chem.* **32**, 3442.
Dreyer, D. L. (1968a). *J. org. Chem.* **33**, 3577.
Dreyer, D. L. (1968b). *Fortschr. Chem. org. Natstoffe* **26**, 190.
Drumm, P. J. and O'Connor, W. F. (1945). *Biochem. J.* **39**, 211.
Duggar, B. M. (1913). *Wash. Univ. Stud. scient. Ser.* **1**, 22.
Egger, K. (1968). *Ber. Dt. bot. Ges.* **81**, 153.
Egger, K. and Kleinig, H. (1966). *Z. Pflanzenphysiol.* **55**, 224.
Egger, K. and Kleinig-Voigt, H. (1968). *Z. Naturf.* **23b**, 1105.
Eisner, J., Mozingo, A. K. and Firestone, D. (1965). *J. Ass. off. agric. Chem.* **48**, 417; *Chem. Abst.* (1965). **63**, 810e.
El-Dakhakhny, M. and Fayez, M. B. E. (1962). *Planta med.* **10**, 455.
El-Ridi, M. S. and Wafa, M. A. (1947). *J. Egypt. med. Ass.* **30**, 124.
Ellis, G. H. and Hamner, K. C. (1943). *J. Nut.* **25**, 539.
Emerson, O. H. (1948). *J. Am. chem. Soc.* **70**, 545.
Emerson, O. H. (1951). *J. Am. chem. Soc.* **73**, 2621.
Enslin, P. R. (1954). *J. Sci. Fd Agric.* **5**, 410.
Enslin, P. R. and Norton, K. B. (1964). *J. chem. Soc.* p. 529.
Enslin, P. R., Joubert, T. G. and Rehm, S. (1956). *J. Sci. Fd Agric.* **7**, 646.
Enslin, P. R., Rehm, S. and Rivett, D. E. A. (1957). *J. Sci. Fd Agric.* **8**, 673.
Enslin, P. R., Holzapfel, C. W., Norton, K. B. and Rehm, S. (1967). *J. chem. Soc.* (C), p. 964.
Estrada, H., Walls, F., Santos, E., Garcia, F. and Flores, S. E. (1962). *Bot. Inst. Quim Univ. Nacl. Auton. Mex.* **14**, 19; *Chem. Abst.* (1963) **59**, 902e.
Farnsworth, N. R. (1966). *J. Am. pharm. Ass.* **55**, 225.
Fayez, M. B. E. and Salih, A. A. (1968). *Acta Chimica*, **55**, 303.
Fayez, M. B. E., Negm, S. A. R. and Sharaf, A. (1963). *Planta med.* **11**, 439.
Fedeli, E., Lanzani, A. and Jacini, G. (1967). *Olii miner.* **44**, 519.
Fedeli, E., Lanzani, A., Capella, P. and Jacini, G. (1966). *J. Am. Oil Chem. Soc.* **43**, 254.
Francis, F. J., Harney, P. M. and Bulstrode, P. C. (1955). *Proc. Am. Soc. hort. Sci.* **65**, 211.
Frey-Wyssling, A. and Kreutzer, E. (1958). *J. Ultrastruct. Res.* **1**, 397.
Fujita, A. and Akatsuka, M. (1949). *J. pharm. Soc. Japan* **69**, 322; *Chem. Abst.* (1950). **44**, 1954.
Fujita, A., Nozoe, N. and Shimoda, T. (1935) *J. pharm. Soc. Japan* **55**, 474.
Galler, M. and Mackinney, G. (1965). *J. Fd Sci.* **30**, 393.
Gallily, B., Shohat, B., Kalish, J., Gitter, S. and Lavie, D. (1962). *Cancer Res.* **22**, 1038.
Gawienowski, A. M. and Gibbs, C. C. (1968). *Steroids* **12**, 545.
Geiger-Vifian, A. and Müller, B. (1945). *Ber. schweiz. bot. Ges.* **55**, 320.
Gill, A. H. (1918). *J. ind. Engng Chem.* **10**, 612.
Gill, A. H. and Greenup, J. (1929). *Oil Fat Ind.* **5**, 288.
Gitter, S., Gallily, R., Shohat, B. and Lavie, D. (1961). *Cancer Res.* **21**, 516.
Goad, L. J. (1967). *In* "Terpenoids in Plants" (J. B. Pridham, ed.) p. 159. Academic Press, London and New York.
Goad, L. J. and Goodwin, T. W. (1969). *Eur. J. Biochem.* **7**, 502.
Goad, L. J., Williams, B. L. and Goodwin, T. W. (1967). *Eur. J. Biochem.* **3**, 232.
Godnew, T. N. and Korschenewsky, S. K. (1930). *Planta* **10**, 811.

Gonzalez, B. R. and Panizo, F. M. (1966). *An. R. Soc. esp. Fís. Quím (Madrid) Ser B.* **62,** 553; *Chem. Abst.* **65,** 18985h.

Gonzalez-Silita, E. (1949). *Bot. inst. nacl. invest. agron.* **9,** 234.

Goodwin, T. W. (1952). "The Comparative Biochemistry of the Carotenoids". Chapman and Hall, London.

Goodwin, T. W. and Jamikorn, M. (1952). *Nature, Lond.* **170,** 104.

Goodwin, T. W. (1956). *Biochem. J.* **62,** 346.

Goodwin, T. W. (1958). *In* "Encyclopaedia of Plant Physiology". (W. Ruhland, ed.) vol. X. Springer, Heidelberg.

Goodwin, T. W. (1966). *In* "Comparative Phytochemistry". (T. Swain, ed.) Academic Press, London and New York.

Goodwin, T. W., Sissins, M. and van Niel, C. B. (1956). *Biochem. J.* **64,** 486.

Goodwin, T. W., Walton, T. J. and Britton, G. (1968). *Pl. Physiol.* Suppl.

Govindachari, T. R., Joshi, B. S. and Sundararajan, V. N. (1964). *Tetrahedron* **20,** 2985.

Graebe, J. (1968). *Phytochem.* **7,** 2003.

Grebensčikov, I. (1954). *Kulturpflanze* **2,** 145.

Grebensčikov, I. (1955). *Kulturpflanze* **3,** 50.

Griebel, C. and Barnes, E. (1916). *Z. Unters. Nahr. u.-Genussmittel* **31,** 282.

Guilliermond, (1941). "The Cytoplasm of the Plant Cell" (trans. L. R. Atkinson). Chronica Botanica Co., Waltham, Mass.

Habaguchi, K., Watanabe, M., Nakadaira, Y., Nakanishi, K., Kiang, A. K. and Lim F. Y. (1968). *Tetrahedron Lett.* p. 3731.

Hall, J., Smith, A. R. H., Goad, L. J. and Goodwin, T. W. (1969). *Biochem. J.* **112,** 129.

Hamilton, B. and Kermack, W. O. (1952). *J. chem. Soc.* p. 5051.

Hassan, A. and Wafa, M. A. (1947). *Nature, Lond.* **159,** 409.

Heftmann, E., Ko, S. T. and Bennett, R. D. (1965). *Naturwissenschaften* **52,** 431.

Heftmann, E., Ko, S. T. and Bennett, R. D. (1966). *Phytochem.* **5,** 1337.

Higby, R. H. (1938). *J. Am. chem. Soc.* **60,** 3013.

Hilbert, G. E. and Jansen, E. F. (1934). *J. biol. Chem.* **106,** 97.

Hill, H. M. and Rogers, L. J. (1969). *Biochem. J.,* **113,** 31P.

Hirose, Y. (1963). *Chem. Pharm. Bull.* **11,** 535.

Holmes, A. D. and Spelman, A. F. (1947). *J. Fd Sci.* **12,** 392.

Holmes, A. D., Spelman, A. F., Kuzmeski, J. W. and Lachman, W. H. (1947). *J. Am. diet. Ass.* **23,** 218.

Holzapfel, C. W. and Enslin, P. R. (1964). *J. S. Afr. chem. Inst.* **17,** 142.

Jacobsohn, G. M., Frey, M. J. and Hochberg, R. B. (1965). *Steroids* **6,** 93.

Jauréguibery, G., Law, J. H., McCloskey, J. and Lederer, E. (1965). *Biochemistry* **4,** 347.

Jenkins, J. A. and Mackinney, G. (1955). *Genetics* **40,** 715.

Joubert, F. J. (1960). *Archs biochem. Biophys.* **91,** 11.

Jungalwala, P. B. and Cama, H. R. (1963). *Indian J. Chem.* **1,** 36.

Jungalwala, F. B. and Porter, J. W. (1968). In press.

Kahn, M. and Mackinney, G. (1953). *Pl. Physiol.* **28,** 550.

Kaminska-Theil, V. and Ludwiczak, R. S. (1967). *Roczn. Chem.* **41,** 409.

Kapil, R. S. (1960). *J. Indian chem. Soc.* **37,** 697.

Kargl, T. E., Quackenbush, F. W. and Tomes, M. L. (1960). *Proc. Am. Soc. hort. Sci.* **75,** 574.

Karrer, P. and Jucker, E. (1947a). *Helv. chim. Acta* **30**, 536.
Karrer, P. and Jucker, E. (1947b). *Helv. chim. Acta* **30**, 266.
Karrer, P. and Jucker, E. (1950). *Carotenoids.* (Translated by E. A. Braude) Elsevier, London.
Karrer, P. and Rutschmann, J. (1945). *Helv. chim. Acta* **28**, 1528.
Karrer, P. and Schlientz, W. (1934). *Helv. chim. Acta* **17**, 55.
Karrer, P. and Solmssen. V. (1935). *Helv. chim. Acta.* **18**, 25.
Karrer, P. and Wehrli, H. (1930). *Helv. chim. Acta* **13**, 1104.
Karrer, P. and Widmer, R. (1928). *Helv. chim. Acta* **11**, 751.
Karrer, P., Morf, R., Krauss, E. von and Zubrys, A. (1932). *Helv. chim. Acta* **15**, 490.
Karrer, P., Rübel, F. and Strong, F. M. (1935). *Helv. chim. Acta* **19**, 28.
Karrer, P., Jucker, E. and Steinlin, K. (1948). *Helv. chim. Acta* **31**, 113.
Kefford, J. F. (1959). *Adv. Fd Res.*, **9**, 285.
Kefford, J. F. and Chandler, B. V. (1961). *Aust. J. agric. Res.* **12**, 56.
Kemmerer, A. R., Fraps, G. S. and Mangelsdorf, P. C. (1942). *Cereal Chem.* **19**, 525.
Kemp, R. J., Hammam, A. S. A., Goad, L. J. and Goodwin, T. W. (1968). *Phytochem.* **7**, 447.
Kiang, A. K., Tan, E. L., Lim, F. Y., Habaguchi, K., Nakanishi, K., Fachan, L. and Ourisson, G. (1967). *Tetrahedron Lett.* p. 3571.
Kincl, F. A., Romo, J., Rosenkranz, G. and Sondheimer, F. (1956). *J. chem. Soc.* p. 4163.
Kirk, J. T. O. and Juniper, B. E. (1966). *In* "Biochemistry of Chloroplasts", Vol. II (T. W. Goodwin, ed.). Academic Press, London and New York.
Kirk, J. T. O. and Tilney-Bassett, R. A. D. (1967). "The Plastids". p. 346. Freeman, London.
Knapp, F. F. and Nicholas, H. J. (1969). *Phytochem.*, **8**, 207.
de Kock, W. T., Enslin, P. R., Norton, K. B., Barton, D. H. R., Sklarz, B. and Bothner-By, A. A. (1963). *J. chem. Soc.* p. 3828.
Konopa, J., Jereczek-Morawska, J., Matuszkiewicz, A. and Nazarewicz, T. (1966). *Neoplasma* **13**, 335.
Konopa, J., Jereczek, E., Matuszkiewicz, A. and Nazarewicz, T. (1967). *Archs Immun. Ther. Exp.* **15**, 129.
Kubota, T. and Tokoroyama, T. (1957). *Chemy. Ind.* p. 1298.
Kubota, T., Matsuura, T., Tokoroyama, T., Kamikawa, T. and Matsumoto, T. (1961). *Tetrahedron Lett.* p. 325.
Kuhn, R. and Lederer, E. (1931). *Ber. dt. chem. Ges.* **64**, 1349.
Kuhn, R. and Brockmann, H. (1933). *Ber. dt. chem. Ges.* **66**, 828.
Kuhn R. and Grundmann, C. (1933). *Ber. dt. chem. Ges.* **66**, 1746
Kuhn, R. and Grundmann, C. (1934). *Ber. dt. chem. Ges.* **67**, 339.
Kuhn, R., Winterstein, A. and Wiegand, W. (1928) *Helv. chim. Acta* **11**, 718.
Kupchan, S. M., Gray, A. H. and Grove, M. D. (1967). *J. med. Chem.* **10**, 337.
Krinsky, N. (1968). *In* "Progress in Photobiology", Vol. 3. (A. C. Giese, ed.).
Kylin, H. (1927). *Hoppe-Seyler's Z. physiol. Chem.* **163**, 229.
Langdon, R. G. and Bloch, K. (1953). *J. biol. Chem.* **200**, 135.
Lanz, E. M. (1943). *Bull. agric. Exp. Stn, New Mexico* No. 306.
Lassen, S., Bacon, K. and Sutherland, J. (1944). *J. Fd Sci.* **9**, 427.
Lavie, D. and Szinai, S. (1958). *J. Am. chem. Soc.* **80**, 707.
Lavie, D. and Benjaminov, B. S. (1964). *Tetrahedron Lett.* **20**, 2665.

Lavie, D. and Benjaminov, B. S. (1965). *J. org. Chem.* **30,** 607.
Lavie, D. and Jain, M. K. (1967). *Chem. Commun.* p. 278.
Lavie, D., Jain, M. K. and Kirson, I. (1966). *Tetrahedron Lett.* p. 2049.
Lavie, D., Jain, M. K. and Kirson, I. (1967a) *J. chem. Soc.* p. 1347.
Lavie, D., Jain, M. K. and Schpan-Gabrielith, S. R. (1967b). *Chem. Commun.* p. 910.
Lavie, D., Shvo, Y. and Gottlieb, O. R. (1962a). *Anais Ass. bras. Quím.* **21,** Numero espee. p. 5.
Lavie, D., Willner, D. and Merenlender, Z. (1964). *Phytochem.* **3,** 51.
Lavie, D., Willner, D., Belkin, M. and Hardy, W. G. (1959). *Acta Un. int. Cancr.* **15,** 177.
Lavie, D., Shvo, Y., Gottlieb, O. R., Desai, R. B. and Khorana, M. L. (1962b). *J. chem. Soc.* p. 3259.
Lavie, D., Shvo, Y., Gottlieb, O. R. and Glotter, E. (1962c). *J. org. Chem.* **27,** 4546.
Lavie, D., Shvo, Y., Gottlieb, O. R. and Glotter, E. (1963). *J. org. Chem.* **28,** 1790.
Lawrie, W., McLean, J. and El-Garby Younes, M. (1967). *J. chem. Soc.* p. 851.
Lederer, E. (1964). *Biochem. J.* **93,** 449.
Lee, K. H. and Yamamoto, H. Y. (1968). *Photochem. Photobiol.* **7,** 101.
Lee, T. C. and Chichester, C. O. (1969). *Phytochem.* **8,** 603.
Lenfant, M., Ellouz, R., Das, B. C., Zissman, E. and Lederer, E, (1969). *Eur. J. Biochem.* **7,** 159.
Le Rosen, A. L., Went, F. W. and Zechmeister, L. (1941). *Proc. natn. Acad. Sci. U.S.A.* **27,** 236.
Le Rosen, A. L. and Zechmeister, L. (1942). *Archs Biochem.* **1,** 22.
Lewis, K. G. (1959). *J. chem. Soc.* p. 73.
Lincoln, R. E. and Porter, J. W. (1950). *Genetics* **35,** 206.
Loesecke, H. von (1929). *J. Am. chem. Soc.* **51,** 2439.
Lubimenko, V. N. (1914). *Rev. gén. Bot.* **25,** 475.
Lubimenko, V. N. (1920). *Mem. Acad. Sci. Petrograd* **33,** No. 8.
Ma, R. M. and Schaffer, P. S. (1953). *Archs biochem. Biophys.* **47,** 419.
MacArthur, J. W. (1934). *J. Genet.* **29,** 123.
McCrindle, R. and Djerassi, C. (1961). *Chemy and Ind.* p. 1311.
Mackinney, G. (1937). *Pl. Physiol.* **12,** 216.
Mackinney, G. (1966) *Qualitas. Pl. Mater. veg.* **13,** 228.
Mackinney, G. and Jenkins, J. A. (1952). *Proc. natn. Acad. Sci. U.S.A.* **38,** 48.
Mackinney, G., Rick, C. M. and Jenkins, J. A. (1954). *Proc. natn. Acad. Sci. U.S.A.* **40,** 695.
Mackinney, G., Rick, C. M. and Jenkins, J. A. (1956). *Proc. natn. Acad. Sci. U.S.A.* **42,** 404.
Magoon, E. F. and Zechmeister, L. (1957). *Archs biochem. Biophys.* **68,** 263.
Maier, V. P. and Dreyer, D. L. (1965). *J. Fd Sci.* **30,** 874.
Maier, V. P. and Beverly, G. D. (1968). *J. Fd Sci.* **33,** 488.
Maier, V. P. and Margileth, D. A. (1969). *Phytochem.* **8,** 243.
Maiti, P. C. and Das, A. K. (1965). *Curr. Sci.* **34,** 179.
Manunta, C. (1939). *Helv. chim. Acta* **22,** 1153.
Marsh, G. L. (1953). *Fd Technol.* **7,** 145.
Matlock, M. B. (1929). *J. Am. pharm. Ass.* **18,** 24.
Matlock, M. B. (1934). *J. Wash. Acad. Sci.* **24,** 385.
Matlock, M. B. (1940). *J. org. Chem.* **5,** 504.
Mazliak, P. and Pommier-Miard, J. (1963). *Fruits* **18,** 177.
Mazur, Y. and Sondheimer, F. (1958). *J. Am. chem. Soc.* **80,** 6296.

Mazur, Y., Weizmann, A. and Sondheimer, F. (1958a). *J. Am. chem. Soc.* **80**, 1007.
Mazur, Y., Weizmann, A. and Sondheimer, F. (1958b). *J. Am. chem. Soc.* **80**, 6293.
Melera, A. and Noller, C. R. (1961). *J. org. Chem.* **26**, 1213.
Miller, E. V., Winston, J. R. and Schomer, H. A. (1940). *J. agric. Res.*, **60**, 259.
Miller, E. V. (1938). *Science, N.Y.* **87**, 394.
Misra, G. and Mitra, C. R. (1968). *Phytochem.* **7**, 2173.
Misra, G. and Mitra, C. R. (1969). *Phytochem.* **8**, 249.
Misra, G., Mitra, C. R. and Kaul, K. N. (1962). *J. scient. ind. Res.* **21B**, 238.
Mitra, C. R. and Misra, G. (1965). *Phytochem.* **4**, 345.
Mogistad, O. C. (1935). *Pl. Physiol.* **10**, 187.
Monteverde, N. A. and Lubimenko, V. N. (1913). *Bull. Acad. Sci. Petrograd* **11**, 1105.
Moss, G. P. (1966). *Planta med.* Suppl. p. 86.
Nath, M. C. (1937) *Hoppe-Seyler's Z. physiol. Chem.* **247**, 9.
Neamtu, G., Illyes, G. and Bodea, C. (1968). *Rev. Roum. Biochim.* **5**, 215.
Nicholas, H. J. (1968) *In* "Biogenesis of Natural Compounds" (P. Bernfeld, ed.), Pergamon.
Nokinov, G. K. (1964). *Med. Prom. S.S.S.R.* **18**, 15; *Chem. Abst.* (1965). **62**, 12157.
Nolte, A. J. and von Loesecke, H. W. (1940). *J. Fd Sci.* **5**, 457.
Ourisson, G., Crabbé, P. and Rodig, O. R. (1964). "Tetracyclic Triterpenes". Holden Day Inc., San Francisco.
Pande, C. S. and Tewari, J. D. (1961). *J. Proc. Oil Technol. Ass. India* **16**, 5; *Chem. Abst.* (1962) **57**, 3576b.
Paquot, C. and Tassel, M. (1966) *Oleagineaux* **21**, 453.
Pathak, G. and Singh, B. (1950). *Indian J. Genet. Pl. Breed* **10**, 28.
Paul, V., Raj, H. and Handa, K. C. (1960). *Proc. natn. Acad. Sci. India* Sect. A. **29**, 218; *Chem. Abst.* (1961) **55**, 19782e.
Ponsinet, G. and Ourisson, G. (1968). *Phytochem.* **7**, 89.
Popják, G. and Cornforth, J. W. (1966). *Biochem. J.* **101**, 553.
Porter, J. W. and Zscheile, F. P. (1946). *Archs Biochem.* **10**, 537, 547.
Porter, J. W. and Lincoln, R. E. (1950). *Archs Biochem.* **27**, 390.
Power, F. B. and Moore, C. W. (1909). *J. chem. Soc.* **95**, 1985.
Purcell, A. E. (1959). *J. Rio Grande Vall. hort. Soc.* **13**, 45.
Quartey, J. A. K. (1961). *Indian J. appl. Chem.* **24**, 57; *Chem. Abst.* **56**, 12015a.
Quinones, Y. L., Guerrant, N. B. and Dutcher, R. A. (1944). *J. Fd Sci.* **9**, 427.
Raab, H. H., De Souza, N. J. and Nes, W. R. (1968). *Biochim. biophys. Acta* **152**, 742.
Rabourn, W. J. and Quackenbush, F. W. (1953). *Archs biochem. Biophys.* **44**, 159.
Rabourn, W. J. and Quackenbush, F. W. (1959). *Archs biochem. Biophys.* **44**, 159.
Ramasarma, G. B., Hakim, D. N. and Rao, S. D. (1943). *Curr. Sci.* **12**, 21.
Ramasarma, G. B. and Banerjee, B. N. (1941). *J. Indian Inst. Sci.* **23A**, 1.
Ramasarma, G. B., Rao, S. D. and Hakim, D. N. (1946). *Biochem. J.* **40**, 657.
Ramirez, D. A. and Tomes, M. L. (1964). *Bot. Gaz.* **125**, 221.
Rao, K. V. and Rao, S. D. T. (1965). *Indian J. appl. Chem.* **28**, 210.
Rao, M. G. and Row, L. R. (1968). *Curr. Sci.* **37**, 361.
Raymundo, L. C., Griffiths, A. E. and Simpson, K. L. (1967). *Phytochem.* **6**, 1527.
Rees, H. H., Goad, L. J. and Goodwin, T. W. (1967). *Biochem. J.* **107**, 417.
Rees, H. H., Goad, L. J. and Goodwin, T. W. (1968). *Tetrahedron Lett.* p. 723.
Rees, H. H., Goad, L. J. and Goodwin, T. W. (1969). *Biochim. biophys. Acta* **176**, 892.
Rehm, S. (1956). *Ber. dt. bot. Ges.* **69**, 26.
Rehm, S. (1960). *Ergebni. Biol.* **22**, 108.
Rehm, S. and Wessels, J. H. (1957). *J. Sci. Fd Agric.* **8**, 687.

366   T. W. GOODWIN AND L. J. GOAD

Rehm, S., Enslin, P. R., Meeuse, A. D. J. and Wessels, J. H. (1957). *J. Sci. Fd Agric.* **8**, 679.
Rosa, J. L. (1952). *Proc. Am. Soc. hort. Sci.* **23**, 233.
Row, L. R., Rao, C. S. and Ramaiah, T. S. (1964). *Curr. Sci.* **33**, 367.
Row, L. R. and Sastry, G. P. (1962). *J. Scient. ind. Res.* **21B**, 343.
Sadana, J. C. and Ahmad, B. (1946). *Indian J. med. Res.* **34**, 69.
Sadana, J. C. and Ahmad, B. (1948). *J. Scient. ind. Res.* **78**, 172.
Sastry, M. S. (1965). *Indian J. Pharm.* **27**, 264; *Chem Abstr.* **63**, 16772g.
Sayre, C. B., Robinson, W. B. and Wishnetzky, T. (1953). *Proc. Am. Soc. hort. Sci.* **61**, 381.
Schabort, J. C., Potgeiter, D. J. J. and Villiers, B. de (1968). *Biochim. biophys. Acta* **151**, 33.
Schabort, J. C. and Teijema, H. L. (1968). *Phytochem.* **7**, 2107.
Schön, K. (1935). *Biochem. J.* **129**, 1782.
Schön, K. (1938). *Biochem. J.* **32**, 1566.
Schöpflin, G., Rumpler, H. and Hänsel, R. (1966). *Planta med.* **14**, 402.
Schpan-Gabrielith, S. R. (1965). "Proceedings XII Congress on Entomology" Section 9a, p. 549. Agricultural Entomology, London.
Schreiber, K., Hammer, V., Ithal, E., Ripperger, H., Rudolph, W. and Weissenborn, A. (1961). *TagBer. dt. Akad. LandwWiss. Berl.* **27**, 47.
Schwartz, H. M., Biedron, S. I., von Holdt, M. M. and Rehms, S. (1964). *Phytochem,* **3**, 189.
Sehgal, S. L., Bhakuni, D. S., Sharma, V. N. and Kaul, K. N. (1961). *J. Scient. ind. Res.* **20B**, 461.
Sharaf, A. and Nigm, S. A. R. (1964). *J. Endocr.* **29**, 91.
Shneour, E. A. (1962). *Biochim. biophys. Acta* **65**, 570.
Singh, A., Srivastava, S. N. and Sharma, V. N. (1964). *Indian J. Chem.* **2**, 82.
Simpson, K. L., Nakayama, T. O. M. and Chichester, C. O. (1964). *J. Bact.* **88**, 1688.
Smith, A. R. H., Goad, L. J., Goodwin, T. W. and Lederer, E. (1967). *Biochem. J.* **104**, 56C.
Smith, L. W. and Smith, O. (1931). *Pl. Physiol.* **6**, 265.
Smith, P. G. (1950). *J. Hered.* **41**, 138.
Snatzke, G., Enslin, P. R., Holzapfel, C. W. and Norton, K. B. (1967). *J. chem. Soc.* (C), p. 972.
Sondheimer, F., Meisels, A. and Kincl, F. A. (1959). *J. org. Chem.* **24**, 870.
Stabursvik, A. (1954). *Acta chem. scand.* **8**, 1305.
Stahl, A. L. and Cain, J. C. (1939). *Fla. Agric. Exp. Sta. Bull.* 111.
Stamberg, O. E. (1947). *J. Fd Sci.* **10**, 392.
Steffen, K. (1964). *Planta* **60**, 506.
Steffen, K. and Walter, F. (1958). *Planta* **50**, 640.
Stone, K. J. and Hemming, F. W. (1967). *Biochem. J.* **104**, 43.
Suarez, A. M. and Cadavieco, R. D. (1956). *Archs Venez. Nut.* **7**, 211.
Subbrarayan, C. and Cama, H. R. (1964). *Indian J. Chem.* **2**, 451.
Subbrarayan, C. and Cama, H. R. (1965). *Indian J. Chem.* **3**, 463.
Sucrow, W. (1966a). *Chem. ber.* **99**, 2765.
Sucrow, W. (1966b). *Chem. ber.* **99**, 3559.
Sucrow, W. (1968). *Tetrahedron Lett.* p. 2443.
Sucrow, W. and Reimerdes, A. (1968). *Z. Naturf.* **23b**, 42.
Swift, L. J. (1952). *J. Am. chem. Soc.* **74**, 1099.

Tokoroyama, T. (1958). *Kashi* **79**, 314.
Thompson, A. E., Tomes, M. L., Wann, E. V., McCollum, J. P. and Stoner, A. K. (1965). *Proc. Am. Soc. hort. Sci.* **86**, 610.
Thompson, W. W. (1965). *Am. J. Bot.* **52**, 622.
Tomes, M. L. (1963). *Bot. Gaz.* **124**, 180.
Tomes, M. L. (1967). *Genetics* **56**, 227.
Tomes, M. L. and Johnson, K. W. (1965). *Proc. Am. Soc. hort. Sci.* **87**, 438.
Tomes, M. L., Quackenbush, F. W. and McQuistan, M. (1954). *Genetics* **39**, 810.
Tomes, M. L., Quackenbush, F. W. and Kargl, T. E. (1956). *Bot. Gaz.* **117**, 248.
Tomes, M. L., Quackenbush, F. W. and Kargl, T. E. (1958). *Bot. Gaz.* **119**, 250.
Tomes, M. L., Johnson, K. W. and Hess, M., (1963). *Proc. Am. Soc. hort. Sci.* **82**, 460.
Vaghani, D. D. and Thakor, V. M. (1958). *Curr. Sci.* **27**, 388.
Valadon, L. R. G. and Mummery, R. S. (1967). *Ann. Bot.* **31**, 497.
Vandercook, C. E. and Yokoyama, H. (1965). *J. Fd Sci.* **30**, 865.
van der Merwe, K. J., Enslin, P. R. and Pachler, K. (1963). *J. chem. Soc.* p. 4275.
van Niel, C. B. (1947). *Lieuwenhock ned. Tijdschr.* **12**, 156.
van Tamelen, E. E., Willett, J. D., Clayton, R. B. and Lord, K. E. (1966). *J. Am. chem. Soc.* **88**, 4752.
Villanueva, V., Barbier, M. and Lederer, E. (1964). *Bull. Soc. chim. Fr.* p. 1423.
Vogele, A. C. (1937). *Pl. Physiol.* **12**, 929.
Walton, T. J., Britton, G. and Goodwin, T. W. (1969). *Biochem. J.* **112**, 383.
Weizmann, A. and Mazur, Y. (1958). *J. org. Chem.* **23**, 832.
Weizmann, A., Meisels, A. and Mazur, Y. (1955). *J. org. Chem.* **20**, 1173.
Went, F. W., Le Rosen, A. L. and Zechmeister, L. (1942). *Pl. Physiol.* **17**, 91.
Wierzchowski, Z. and Bubicz, M. (1961). *Annls Univ. Mariae-Curie-Sklodowska* **14C**, 383.
Williams, B. L. (1966). Ph.D. Thesis, University College of Wales, Aberystwyth.
Williams, B. L., Goad, L. J. and Goodwin, T. W. (1967a). *Phytochem.* **6**, 1137.
Williams, R. J. H., Davies, B. H. and Goodwin, T. W. (1965). *Phytochem.* **4**, 759.
Williams, R. J. H., Britton, G. and Goodwin, T. W. (1967b) *Biochem. J.* **105**, 99.
Willuhn, G. (1966). *Abh. dt. Akad. Wiss. Berl.*, p. 97.
Willstaedt, H. (1935). *Svensk kem. Tidskr.* **47**, 112.
Willstaedt, H. (1936a). *Skand. Arch. Physiol.* **75**, 155.
Willstaedt, H. (1936b). *Svensk kem. Tidskr.* **48**, 212.
Winterstein, A. and Ehrenberg, U. (1932). *Hoppe-Seyler's Z. physiol. Chem.* **207**, 25.
Winterstein, A. (1933) *Hoppe-Seyler's Z. physiol. Chem.* **215**, 51, **219**, 249.
Yamamoto, H. Y. and Tin, S. (1933). *Pap. Inst. Phys. Chem. Res.* **12**, Bull. 354.
Yamamoto, H. Y., Chichester, C. O. and Nakayama, T. O. M. (1962). *Archs Biochem. Biophys.* **96**, 645.
Yamamoto, H. Y. (1964). *Nature, Lond.* **201**, 1049.
Yamamoto, H. Y. and Chichester, C. O. *Biochim. biophys. Acta* **100**, 303.
Yasue, M. and Kato, Y. (1959). *J. pharm. Soc. Japan* **79**, 403; *Chem. Abst.* (1959). **53**, 13286e.
Yokoyama, H. and White, M. J. (1965). *J. org. Chem.* **30**, 2482.
Yokoyama, H. and White, M. J. (1966). *Phytochem.* **5**, 1159.
Yokoyama, H. and White, M. J. (1967). *J. agric. Fd Chem.* **15**, 693.
Yokoyama, H., White, M. J. and Dreyer, D. L. (1969). (In press).
Yokoyama, H. and White, M. J. (1968a). *Phytochem.* **7**, 493.

Yokoyama, H. and White, M. J. (1968b). *Phytochem.* **7**, 1031.
Zechmeister, L. (1950). "Progress in Chromatography (1938–1947)". Chapman and Hall, London.
Zechmeister, L. and Cholnoky, L. v. (1930). *Justus Liebigs Ann. Chem.* **481**, 42.
Zechmeister, L. and Tuyson, P. (1930). *Ber. dt. chem. Ges.* **63**, 2881.
Zechmeister, L. and Cholnoky, L. v. (1931). *Justus Liebigs Ann. Chem.* **489**, 1.
Zechmeister, L. and Cholnoky, L. v. (1934). *Justus Liebigs Ann. Chem.* **509**, 269.
Zechmeister, L. and Tuzson, P. (1934). *Naturwissenschaften* **19**, 307.
Zechmeister, L. and Cholnoky, L. v. (1936). *Ber. dt. chem. Ges.* **69**, 422.
Zechmeister, L. and Tuzson, P. (1936). *Hoppe-Seyler's Z. physiol. Chem.* **240**, 191.
Zechmeister, L. and Polgar, A. (1941). *J. biol. Chem.* **139**, 193.
Zechmeister, L. and Escue, R. B. (1942). *J. biol. Chem.* **144**, 321.
Zechmeister, L. and Schroeder, W. A. (1942). *J. biol. Chem.* **144**, 315.
Zechmeister, L. and Schroeder, W. A. (1943). *J. Am. chem. Soc.* **65**, 1535.
Zechmeister, L. and Pinckard, J. C. (1947). *J. Am. chem. Soc.* **69**, 1930.
Zechmeister, L. and Went, F. W. (1948). *Nature, Lond.* **162**, 847.
Zechmeister, L., Le Rosen, A., Went, F. W. and Pauling, L. (1941). *Proc. natn. Acad. Sci. U.S.A.* **27**, 468.
Zelnik, R. and Rosito, C. M. (1966). *Tetrahedron Lett.* p. 6441.
Zscheile, F. P. and Lesley, J. W. (1967). *J. Hered.* **58**, 194.
Zurzycki, J. (1954). *Acta Soc. Bot. Pol.* **23**, 161.

Chapter 13

Vitamins in Fruits

L. W. MAPSON

A.R.C. Food Research Institute, Norwich, England

I. INTRODUCTION

The main contribution of fruits and their processed products to the nutrition of mankind is undoubtedly their supply of the anti-scorbutic vitamin (L-ascorbic acid—Vitamin C). Fruits, together with vegetables, are the main sources from which all primates derive this vitamin. For this reason we shall concentrate mainly on this vitamin in relation to its occurrence, synthesis and properties in fruits or their products.

Several fruits are also good sources of β-carotene (pro-vitamin A); they include apricots, peaches, melons and cherries. Many fruits contain moderate amounts of pantothenic acid (apricots, gooseberries, blackcurrants, figs and citrus fruits) as well as moderate amounts of biotin. Nicotinic acid and folic acid also occur in small amounts, as do thiamine and riboflavin. However, generally speaking, these latter vitamins are low in concentration compared with other animal or vegetable foods (see Table I), so that in many cases their contribution to the dietary requirement is negligible. Vitamin D, the

TABLE I. Carotene and vitamin B content of apples and pears[a]

Source	Carotene I.U.	Biotin	Nicotinic acid	Vitamin B content Pantothenic acid	Riboflavin	Thiamine
				μg/100 g fresh whole fruit		
Apple	74·3	—	690	—	40	40
Apple	61	—	—	—	—	35
Apple	40–100	0·25	50–100	50–200	5–50	20–60
Apple	—	0·2–0·9	—	—	—	—
(Allington Pippin)	—	0·27	77	49	23	—
(Bramley's Seedling)	—	0·24	50	49	11	—
(Cox's Orange Pippin)	—	0·26	94	43	—	—
(Edward VII)	—	0·24	85	70	—	—
Pear	19·8	—	300	—	70	50
Pear	10–20	0·10	100–400	20–50	10–50	10–70
(Bristol Cross)	—	0·07	183	43	33	—
(Conference)	—	0·07	183	43	33	—
(Williams')	—	0·08	257	50	—	—

[a] From Hulme (1958)

tocopherols and Vitamin B_{12} are either absent from fruits or are present in only minute amounts.

II. L-ASCORBIC ACID

A. Occurrence

The naturally occurring ascorbic acid in fruits is L-ascorbic acid. Other ascorbic analogues have been synthesized but all have less antiscorbutic potency than L-ascorbic acid. There is no evidence that any of these occur in fruits. The concentration of L-ascorbic acid in different fruits varies over a wide range. Apples and pears at one end of the scale contain only 2–30 mg ascorbic acid per 100 g whilst at the upper end of the scale we encounter some of the richest sources of the vitamin in nature. In rose hips the concentration of the vitamin may reach 1% of the fresh weight and the West Indian Cherry has been reported to contain as much as 1·3% of the fresh weight (Olliver, 1967). Between these extremes are the majority of the fruits such as citrus and the berry fruits. A representative list of the concentrations of the vitamin normally found is given in Table II. The figures quoted are average values since variety (cf. Hulme, 1958) and environmental conditions of growth all affect the vitamin content to a greater or lesser extent. The concentration of the vitamin may also vary widely in different tissue of the fruit; in apples

TABLE II. Average ascorbic acid content of fruits (edible portions)

Fruit	Ascorbic acid mg/100 g
Acerola (West Indian cherry)	1300
Apples	2–10
Apricot	7–10
Avocado	15–20
Banana	10–30
Blackberry	15
Cranberry	12
Cherry	5–8
Currant (black)	210
Currant (red)	40
Damson	3
Gooseberry	40
Gourd	8
Granadilla (passion fruit)	25
Grapefruit	40
Greengage	5
Guava	300
Lemon	50
Lime	25
Loganberry	30
Melon	25–35
Orange	50
Tangerine	30
Peach	7
Plum	3
Pear	4
Pineapple	25
Pomegranate	6
Quince	15
Raspberry	25
Squash	10–20
Strawberry	60
Tomato	25

the concentration of the vitamin is two to three times as great in peel as in pulp (Zilva et al., 1935).

B. Genetic Factors

It is not possible to select ascorbic acid-rich plants on the basis of taxonomic relationship. The family Rosaceae includes the common rose whose fruits contain the vitamin in a concentration 200 times greater than that found in the apple which is a member of the same family. A knowledge of the vitamin content of one species of the genus therefore gives no indication of content in another species. White and black currants are two species of the genus

Ribes but there is a wide difference in the ascorbic acid content of their fruits.

Attempts to increase the vitamin content in tomatoes by selective breeding have been reported by Truscott *et al.* (1942). The first generation resulting from crossing a variety poor in ascorbic acid (*Lycopersicum esculentum*) with a variety rich in the vitamin (*Lycopersicum pimpinellifolium*) gave a progeny, the fruits of which tended to be intermediate in vitamin content between those of the parents. However, the commercial variety of tomatoes "Vetmold" containing more ascorbic acid than most others is known to have resulted from a cross involving *L.. pimpinellifolium*. There is at least a strong suggestion that selective breeding could increase the ascorbic acid content of fruits.

Fruits possess an advantage over vegetable foods in that the stability of the vitamin is much greater in the acidic media of fruit juices than in that of the more nearly neutral vegetables. In addition most fruits are eaten raw and all the vitamin is consumed whereas the cooking procedures necessary with most vegetables entails losses due to destruction or leaching into the cooking liquor. Since a daily intake of as little as 5 mg (Medical Research Council Report, 1953) of the vitamin is sufficient to prevent gross symptoms of scurvy in an adult, and an intake of 30–60 mg has been estimated as being required for full health, it is clear that for most fruits a relatively small daily intake is sufficient to supply the daily requirement.

III. BIOGENESIS OF L-ASCORBIC ACID

As in other plant tissues, fruits synthesize L-ascorbic acid from hexose sugar precursors. In the first instance the synthesis depends on an adequate supply of hexose sugars, and thus on photosynthetic activity. As would be expected, a decrease in the photosynthetic activity induced by reducing light intensity is reflected in decreased levels of ascorbic acid. With fruits, therefore, the concentration of ascorbic acid varies with the degree to which the fruit is exposed to sunlight (Kessler, 1939; McCollum, 1944). Conversely a fall in the level of the vitamin may be observed when plants are transferred from light to dark, and also when parts of the plant are shaded (Veselkine, *et al.*, 1934; Brown and Moser, 1941; Woses and Organ, 1943; Hammer *et al.*, 1945).

The connection between the formation of hexose sugars and synthesis of the vitamin has been elucidated during the last decade. For reviews of the literature see Isherwood and Mapson (1961); Mapson (1967). In general two pathways have been proposed for the synthesis in plants and animals, both originating from either D-glucose or D-galactose as follows (Fig. 1).

The evidence for these pathways is based on (i) the feeding of labelled hexose sugars; (ii) the stimulation of synthesis resulting from the administration of derivatives of certain uronic and aldonic acids, and (iii) by the

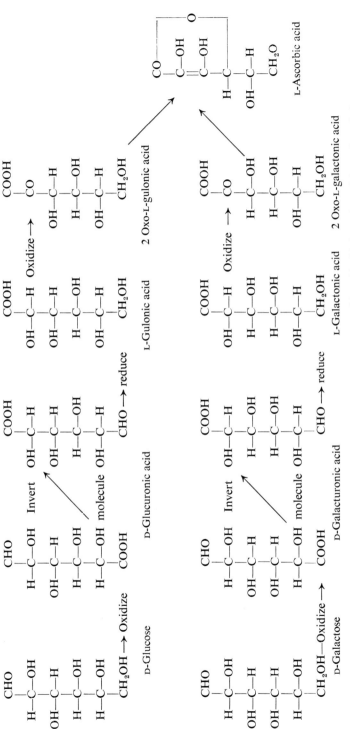

FIG. 1. Steps in the conversion of D-glucose or D-galactose to L-ascorbic acid with inversion of the carbon chain.

extraction and isolation of enzymes and the demonstration of the synthesis *in vitro* by these agents.

In these enzymic studies it was shown that the conversion of the aldonic acid into L-ascorbic acid in both animal and plant required that (i) the hydroxyl on C-2 of the hexose have the L-configuration; (ii) that on C-4 the D-configuration and (iii) that on C-5 the L-configuration. An ascorbic acid could be formed if the configuration on C-5 was D but it was D-arabo-ascorbic not L-ascorbic acid. The configuration on C-3 was also important as far as synthesis in the plant was concerned. The specificity of the plant enzymes required the configuration to be D as in L-galactonic acid and not L as in L-gulonic acid, whereas the specificity of the animal enzymes was such that both acids were equally readily converted to L-ascorbic acid. Thus for the plant the intermediates arising from D-galactose were all much more readily transformed than their analogues from D-glucose, and in some cases the specificity of the plant enzymes for the galactose series was absolute (Mapson and Breslow, 1958). That these enzymic systems are active in fruits is evident from the observations of Jackson *et al.* (1961) who demonstrated the synthesis of L-ascorbic acid when the lactone of L-galactonic acid was supplied to slices of rose hip tissue.

A further point of interest in these studies was the observation that the plant enzymes were incapable of converting either the free uronic acid (D-galacturonic acid) or the free aldonic acid (L-galactonic acid) into ascorbic acid. Only esters or lactones of these acids were converted. It was suggested (Isherwood *et al.*, 1960) that these facts could be explained on the assumption that the enzymes responsible formed ester links with the acids. The reaction with l-galactono-y-lactone could be written as follows:

L-galactono-y-lactone + Enzyme $\longrightarrow$ L-galactonyl-Enzyme $\xrightarrow{O_2}$
2 oxo-L-galactonyl-Enzyme $\longrightarrow$ 2 oxo-L-galactonic acid + Enzyme
$\longrightarrow$ L-ascorbic acid

Both 2 oxo-L-galactonic and 2 oxo-L-gulonic acid are known to pass spontaneously into L-ascorbic acid under physiological conditions.

The plant enzyme catalysing this last step in the synthesis has been isolated and its properties determined (Mapson and Breslow, 1958). It appears to be a flavoprotein and effects the oxidation of L-galactono-y-lactone by catalysing the transfer of electrons to cytochrome C.

Doubt as to whether this route of synthesis represents the main or only pathway in the plant arises from the work of Loewus and his co-workers (1958, 1960), who found that labelling D-glucose on either C-1 or C-6 position gave rise to an ascorbic acid predominantly labelled in identical positions, a result not in accord with the transformation of the hexose sugar via the scheme outlined above in which an inversion of the molecule occurs, that is,

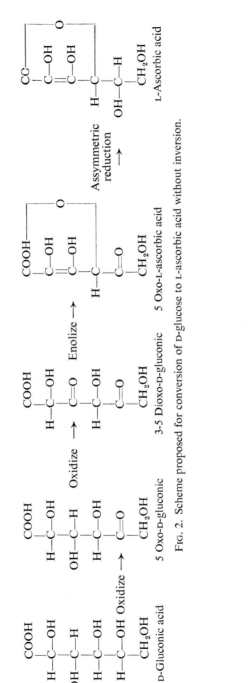

Fig. 2. Scheme proposed for conversion of D-glucose to L-ascorbic acid without inversion.

C-1 labelled glucose should give rise to C-6 labelled ascorbic acid and *vice versa*.

Any scheme whereby L-ascorbic acid is synthesized from a D-sugar, without inversion of the carbon chain, must involve epimerization of the groups in C-5. This might be brought about directly by an enzyme or by oxidation followed by asymmetric reduction. In addition the configuration of the groups on C-2 and C-3 must also be changed. The theoretical scheme suggested by Finkle *et al.* (1960) in which D-glucose is oxidized via gluconic acid to 5 oxo-D-gluconic acid then to 3–5 dioxo-D-gluconic acid followed by enolization of the C-3 oxo group to give 5 oxo-L-ascorbic acid, though attractive, has not received any experimental support (Fig. 2). Changing the configuration of the groups on C-5 of D-gluconic acid yields L-idonic acid— but this is not converted to L-ascorbic acid whether as the free acid or its lactone. Neither does D-tagaturonic acid (5 oxo-L-galactonic acid) or esters yield an ascorbic acid thus negating the possibility that 5 oxo-L-ascorbic acid is an intermediate. The suggestion that oxidation of C-2 or C-3 of D-gluconic acid might occur first to give an oxo derivative followed by enolization to give an ascorbic analogue has been examined. In this case the intermediate product would be D-arabo-ascorbic acid and this would then have to undergo epimerization at C-5 to give L-ascorbic acid. If this were the route then one might expect to find some D-arabo-ascorbic acid in plant tissues—or form L-ascorbic acid by supplying D-arabo-ascorbic acid to them. No evidence of this was found when the synthesis of L-ascorbic acid was studied in cress seedlings (Isherwood *et al.*, 1954). The theoretical scheme whereby derivatives of gluconic acid might be converted to L-ascorbic acid has so far not been substantiated by any experimental evidence, in contrast to the positive results achieved with derivatives postulated in the scheme involving inversion of the molecule as in Fig. 1.

IV. STABILITY OF L-ASCORBIC ACID

A. Enzymic Systems Catalysing the Oxidation of L-Ascorbic Acid

L-Ascorbic acid may be easily oxidized in the presence of oxygen by both enzymic and non-enzymic catalysts. Both copper and iron salts catalyse its oxidation, and the oxidation in many processed products may in fact be due to these metals. Enzymes containing copper and iron in their prosthetic groups are even more efficient catalysts. There are at least four enzymes that occur in fruits which may be responsible for the oxidative destruction of the vitamin; these are ascorbic acid oxidase, phenolase, cytochrome oxidase and peroxidase. Only with ascorbic acid oxidase is there a direct reaction between enzyme and substrate and molecular oxygen, the other three enzymes oxidase the vitamin indirectly. Thus phenolase catalyses the oxidation of mono- and dihydroxy phenols, which latter, as quinones, react directly with ascorbic acid. Cytochrome oxidase oxidizes cytochrome C and the oxidized form of cytochrome reacts directly with L-ascorbic acid. Peroxidase, in combination with phenolic compounds, utilizes hydrogen peroxide to effect the oxidation. Thus any of these enzymes may initiate the oxidative destruction of the vitamin. In the intact fruit these enzymic systems are controlled; only where cellular disorganization occurs, as a result of mechanical damage, rot or senescence do these oxidative activities become effective.

B. Inhibitors of Enzymic and Non-Enzymic Oxidation

There is evidence that many fruits contain substances which inhibit the oxidative activities of these enzymes. Somoygi (1944) first reported the existence of substances which inhibited the oxidation of ascorbic acid by phenolase, peroxidase, ascorbic acid oxidase or by cupric ions. Damodaran and Nair (1936) isolated a tannin from the Indian gooseberry (*Phyllanthus emblica*) which inhibited the oxidation, and Kardo-Sysoerva and Nissenbaum (1938) reported the existence in tomato juice of a thermolabile stabilizer of the vitamin. In blackcurrant juice in which the vitamin is known to be very stable, Hooper and Ayers (1951) isolated an anthocyanin and a flavanone compound which gave protection against oxidation by the phenolase enzyme from apple juices, although the compounds did not inhibit oxidation by ascorbic acid oxidase extracted from cucumbers. Jackson and Wood (1958) showed that phenolic compounds in rose hips were effective in inhibiting the oxidation catalysed by ascorbic acid oxidase, phenolase and peroxidase. Since many of these inhibitors were also effective against the catalytic oxidation by cupric ions, the suggestion that they acted by chelating with metals or metal proteinate enzymes appeared most probable. Clements and Anderson (1966) have now substantiated this work on the antioxidant properties of certain flavanols, rutin and quercetin. They showed that the metal chelating properties which gives them their ability to serve as antioxidants is dependant on the 3-hydroxyl-4 carboxyl group of the γ-pyrone ring and the 3'-4' catechol couplet of the B ring. Pure hesperidin possessing neither of these groupings had no stabilizing effect.

The stability of the vitamin in fruit juices is also no doubt due to the presence, often in high concentration, of polybasic or polyhydroxy acids such as citric and malic, which by virtue of their power to chelate metal ions, reduce the catalytic activity of metals like copper and iron. Inagaki (1944) has claimed that the stability of the vitamin in citrus juices is mainly due to these acids. Sugars, by reason of their concentration in fruit juice, may also contribute to some extent to the stabilizing of the vitamin in view of their tendency to chelate with metal ions.

C. Enzymic Reduction of the Oxidized Forms of L-Ascorbic Acid

Ascorbic acid is lost to the tissues by oxidation. This oxidation, whether occasioned by metal or enzymic catalysis, involves an electron transfer in two stages. The first oxidation product is an unstable semi-quinone-like free radical, mono-dehydro ascorbic acid (MDHA) (Yamazaki *et al.*, 1959). With the transfer of a further electron, dehydro-L-ascorbic acid (DHA) is formed, and this compound is the one which is normally found in conditions where the vitamin is being oxidized. However, DHA is not itself completely stable being converted into 2-3 dioxo-L-gulonic acid by the opening of the lactone ring. The rate at which this change occurs is largely conditioned by pH; at neutral pH it is rapid, in alkaline conditions it is instantaneous, but at pH 3–4 the change is much slower. For these reasons DHA in appreciable amounts may be found in processed fruit or fruit juices.

Dehydro-ascorbic acid is fully as active biologically as ascorbic acid because it is readily reduced *in vivo* to ascorbic acid. Both the oxidized forms of ascorbic acid may be reduced by enzymic systems present in plant tissues. With MDHA the electron donor is $NADH_2$ the reaction being catalysed by flavin enzymes (Kern and Racker, 1954). Ascorbic acid is also regenerated from DHA by an enzyme system involving $NADPH_2$ acting in conjunction with glutathione and the enzymes glutathione reductase and dehydro-ascorbic acid reductase (Mapson, 1961).

The early work of Zilva *et al.* (1938) demonstrated the interplay of both oxidizing and reducing systems in intact fruit. Working with apples they observed that in the immature fruit 50% of the total vitamin C was present as the oxidized form, DHA. As the fruit matured the ratio of oxidized ascorbic acid to the fully reduced form gradually fell until at maturity only 5% was present as DHA. Since that date, other evidence has accumulated indicating that in certain vegetable tissues (peas and potatoes) these enzymic systems are active (Mapson, 1961) and there seems no reason to doubt that they are present and active in fruits.

In so far as the reducing systems operate efficiently, little or no loss of ascorbic acid from the tissue should occur. Both of these enzymic systems are, however, impaired to a greater extent by cellular disorganization than are the enzymes concerned in the oxidation of the vitamin, and thus the balance normally operating *in vivo* is disturbed. Theoretically, inhibition of the oxidative enzymes, or enhancement of the reducing systems will tend to preserve the vitamin in its reduced form. In practice, however, it is usually easier to inhibit the first system rather than enhance the second.

In any evaluation of the antiscorbutic potency of fruit juice, account must be taken of the concentration of DHA as well as of ascorbic acid, bearing in mind that, if the juice is to be stood for any length of time before consumption, the antiscorbutic level may drop owing to the degradative destruction of DHA. *In vivo* there are no means whereby this change to 2-3 dioxo-L-gulonic acid can be reversed, and its formation thus represents a total loss of vitamin potency.

V. ROLE OF ASCORBIC ACID IN PLANT METABOLISM

Very little definite information is available as to the role ascorbic acid plays in plant metabolism. The earlier authors emphasized that the vitamin, a universal component of plant cells, is especially abundant in tissues of high metabolic activity and is rapidly oxidized by at least five enzyme systems extractable from plant tissues. Because of these findings and the ease with which ascorbate may be oxidized and its oxidation products reduced, it appears to fulfil many of the requirements necessary before a substance can be deemed to act as an electron carrier.

There is no real correlation between the level of ascorbic acid and respiration but this does not in itself prove that the vitamin is unconcerned in the respiratory processes. Synthesis of the vitamin proceeds, in so far as we know, independently of its functioning in respiration; its level in the cell may thus simply reflect the excess formed in synthesis over that used in metabolism. Some plant tissues contain so much ascorbic acid that it is difficult to believe that it is all being oxidized and reduced in a cyclic process. It seems possible, although no evidence is available on this point, that much of the ascorbic acid in the cell is in "non-metabolic pools" only a small fraction of which is operating in any possible respiratory system. That ascorbic acid is continually being oxidized *in vivo* is supported by experiments which show: (i) small but significant amounts of DHA are present in plant tissues under aerobic conditions even when methods of extraction are adopted that, as far as can be determined, eliminate any oxidation of ascorbic acid during extraction; and (ii) the fall in the ascorbic acid content of a plant tissue, such as that of potato tubers, stored in air, may be prevented if it is stored in nitrogen. This contrast between loss of ascorbic acid in air, where active synthesis may proceed, and stabilization in nitrogen where synthesis is prevented, underlines the fact that *in vivo* in air a continuous oxidation of ascorbic acid is proceeding; however, it gives no indication of the magnitude of the process.

The greater participation of the ascorbic acid system in the oxygen consumption of extracts compared with its role in the respiration of the intact tissue appears to be related to the greater activity of the oxidizing enzymes in the extracts; the resulting higher concentrations of DHA (and possibly MDHA) lead in turn to a greater rate of electron transport over these compounds. Thus the extent of the traffic over the ascorbic acid system *in vivo* may depend primarily on the rate of oxidation of the vitamin *in vivo*. We have little direct knowledge as to whether this rate of oxidation changes markedly with different metabolic conditions or with different stages of development of the plant, although there is evidence to suggest that changes in the terminal oxidases do occur either during development or as a result of infection by parasites or fungi.

The defective formation of collagen in the vitamin C deficient animal is deemed to be due to an inability to hydroxylate proline when the latter is built into the collagen molecule. The evidence from the animal studies that ascorbate may function as an hydroxylating agent in other reactions is suggestive that this may also be one of its functions in plants. It is well established that hydroxyproline is high in content in plant cell walls, and in some plants a high concentration of ascorbic acid oxidase is also located in this tissue. The possibility that hydroxylation reactions occur when ascorbate is oxidized is a theme which may well repay investigation in the future.

VI. LOSSES OF L-ASCORBIC ACID DURING PROCESSING

As a result of the stability of ascorbic acid in fruit juices, only small losses are usually encountered during actual processing. Thus for example in jam manufacture the chief loss occurs if the harvested fruit is allowed to become over-ripe, or is damaged by mechanical means and is held in this condition for any length of time before processing. During the actual boiling with sugar, the loss is very small (Olliver, 1962). The addition of sulphite is frequently used to protect the vitamin against oxidation during heat treatments involved in pasteurization of fruit juices.

A. Freezing

In the preparation of frozen fruits the actual freezing process, unless unduly slow, appears to have a negligible effect on the ascorbic acid content, but post-freezing storage is important. Freezing of plant cells induces widespread cellular disorganization, and once this has occurred it is necessary to inhibit enzyme action completely. Thus the temperature of storage of the processed product should not be higher than $-20°C$ if satisfactory storage for about one year is desired. At higher temperatures the rate of loss can be quite serious, and increases as the temperature of storage rises (Guardagni et al., 1952).

The contrast between the stability of L-ascorbic acid in fruits in which cellular disorganization has occurred and those in which it has not is well illustrated by experiments on processing rose hips. In these experiments, some of the fruit was frozen and held at different temperatures in storage whilst the unfrozen fruit was held at temperatures above 0°C. Whilst the actual process of freezing did not lead to a loss, in frozen storage at -10°C or above heavy losses of the vitamin were encountered (Table III). On the other hand, little or no losses occurred with the unfrozen fruit held at temperatures of 1–5°C providing that rots due to fungal attack were absent. To prevent deterioration in the frozen sample, temperatures of at least -20°C were essential. It follows that with frozen fruit some loss of the vitamin will occur during thawing especially if it is to be held for any length of time before consumption. In the experiment described above 30% of the

TABLE III. The loss of ascorbic acid from either fresh rose hips held at 0–5°C or of hips frozen and held at temperatures between -20 and 5°C

Length of storage (days)	Initial ascorbic acid value 500 mg/100 g Ascorbic acid, % loss					
	Fresh hips			Frozen hips		
	0°C	1°C	5°C	-10°C	-20°C	5°C
1	—	—	—	—	—	30
3	—	—	—	—	—	66
11	4	0	6	0	0	—
21	0	—	—	2	2	—
28	0	0	0	10	0	—
49	—	—	0	21	0	—
63	—	0	—	33	0	—
70	0	0	—	—	—	—
77	—	—	8	—	0	—
98	8	0	0	—	—	—
120	24	—	—	42	0	—
146	52	0	0	42	0	—
174	—	—	0	60	—	—
188	53	1	—	—	0	—

vitamin was destroyed when the fruit was transferred from -20°C to $+5$°C within 24 hours. The oxidation of ascorbic acid can thus be a major change in the composition of fruit processed by freezing.

Information concerning the retention of other vitamins in fruits is sparse. The stability of the B vitamins are such that they should be unaffected in the frozen state. Retention of carotene has not been extensively studied, but in the absence of enzymes which catalyse its oxidation losses should not be high. Larger losses of carotene may be encountered when any filtration process is employed in the preparation of fruit juices. This is largely because in the cell the carotene will be associated with solid particles and as such these will be retained on the filters.

B. Canning

The vitamins in canned fruit juices appear to be generally stable. The retention of L-ascorbic acid and thiamine in orange juice and tomatoes stored at temperatures of 10–27°C for 12–24 months was of the order of 90% of the original content (Sheft *et al.*, 1949). This stability of ascorbic acid over long periods of storage is undoubtedly due to the fact that in heat treatments prior to canning most of the enzymes are inactivated and that in the can the removal of oxygen prevents oxidative change (Daniel and Rutherford, 1936; Clayton *et al.*, 1944). Tressler and Curran (1937) present data indicating that the oxygen remaining in the head space after canning is an important factor in determining the extent of loss.

There is some evidence that storage temperatures in excess of 27°C can cause a loss of the vitamin, even under anaerobic conditions. Losses of 28%, 40% and 50% of the vitamin in canned apricots, orange and tomato juice occurred at temperatures of 43°C when stored for 18 months (Moschetti *et al.*, 1947; Guerrant *et al.*, 1948). The stability of the vitamin in fruits appears to be less than that of vegetables under these conditions, but the exact cause for this has not been closely defined. Total solids of the canned fruit product rather than the concentration of the vitamin or of copper appears to influence the rate of destruction (Hummel and Okey, 1950). These latter workers suggested that the concentration of citric acid may be an important factor, and Joslyn and Miller (1949) and Huelin (1953) observed that the decomposition of ascorbic acid under anaerobic conditions occurred most rapidly at pH 3–4 and that fructose, or sugars yielding fructose on hydrolysis, was primarily responsible.

C. Dehydration

The loss of ascorbic acid in fruit juices dried by modern freeze drying methods is small. Losses can occur in the dried product during storage unless precautions are taken. The chief of these is to replace the air in the container with an inert gas and to reduce the moisture content to around 2·5%. This latter can be most effectively done by adding a desiccant inside the container. The low moisture content also reduces the incidence of non-enzymic browning which is the cause of deterioration of many dried foods. These conditions will also stabilize carotene.

REFERENCES

Brown, A. P. and Moser, F. (1941). *J. Fd Sci.* **6**, 45–55.
Clayton, M. M., Goos, C., Webb, B. and Murphy, E. F. (1944). Maine Agric. Stat. Progress Rept., July.
Clements, C. A. B. and Anderson, L. (1961). *Ann. N.Y. Acad. Sci.* **136**, 339–76.
Damodaran, M. and Nair, K. (1936). *Biochem. J.* **30**, 1014–20.
Daniel, E. P. and Rutherford, M. B. (1936). *J. Fd Sci.* **1**, 341–7.
Finkle, B. J., Kelly, S. and Loewus, F. A. (1960). *Biochem. Biophys. Acta* **38**, 332–9.
Guadagni, D. G. and Nimmo, C. C. (1953). *Fd Technol.* **1**, 59–61.
Guadagni, D. G., Nimmo, C. C. and Jansen, E. F. (1957). *Fd Tech.* **11**, 33.
Guerrant, N. B., Varvich, M. G. and Dutcher, R. A. (1945). *Ind. engng Chem.* **37**, 1240–2143.
Hammer, K. C., Bernstein, L. and Maynard, L. A. (1945). *J. Nutrit.* **29**, 85–97.
Hooper, F. C. and Ayres, A. D. (1950). *J. Sci. Fd agric.* **1**, 5–8.
Huelin, F. E. (1953). *J. Fd Sci.* **18**, 633–9.
Hulme, A. C. (1958). *Adv. Fd Res.* **8**, 297–413.
Hummell, M. and Okey, R. (1950). *J. Fd Sci.* **15**, 405–14.
Inagaki C. (1944). *J. Agric. Chem. Soc. Japan* **20**, 363–73.
Isherwood, F. A., Chen, Y. T. and Mapson, L. W. (1954). *Biochem J.* **56**, 1–12.
Isherwood, F. A., Mapson, L. W. and Chen, Y. T. (1960). *Biochem. J.* **76**, 157–67.
Isherwood, F. A. and Mapson, L. W. (1962). *A. Rev. Pl. Physiol.* **13**, 329–50.
Jackson, G. A. D. and Wood, R. B. (1959). *Nature, Lond.* **184**, 902–3.
Jackson, G. A. D., Wood, R. B. and Prosser, M. V. (1961). *Nature, Lond.* **191**, 282–3.
Joslyn, M. A. and Miller J. (1949). *J. Fd Sci.* **14**, 325–9.
Kardo-Sysoerva, E. K. and Nisenbaum, R. F. (1938). *Biokhimiya* **3**, 348–54.
Kern, M. and Racker, E. (1954). *Archs Biochem. Biophys.* **48**, 235–9.
Kessler, W. (1939). *Gartenbanwissenschaft* **13**, 619–38.
Loewus, F. A., Jang, R., Mann, W. and Berence, A. (1958). *J. biol. Chem.* **232**, 505–19.
Loewus, F. A., Finkle, B. S. and Jang, R. (1968). *Biochem. Biophys. Acta* **30**, 629–35.
McCollum, J. P. (1944). *Proc. Soc. hort. Sci.* **44**, 398–402.
Mapson, L. W. (1961). *Ann. N.Y. Acad. Sci.* **92**, 21–35.
Mapson, L. W. (1967). "The Vitamins". (Sebrell, W. H., Jr., and Harris, R. S., eds.) Vol. I. pp. 369–85. Academic Press, London and New York.
Mapson, L. W. and Breslow, E. (1958). *Biochem. J.* **68**, 395–404.
Medical Research Council, Spec. Rept. Ser. No. 280. H.M. Stationery Office, 1953.
Moschetti, D. S., Hinman, W. F. and Halliday, E. G. (1947). *Ind. Engng Chem.* **39**, 994–9.
Olliver, M. (1967). "The Vitamins". (Sebrell, W. H., and Harris, R. S., eds.). Vol. I. Academic Press, London and New York.
Sheft, B. B., Griswold, R. M., Tarlowsky, E. and Halliday, E. G. (1949). *Ind. Engng Chem.* (Ind. Edn.) **41**, 144.
Somoygi, J. C. (1944). *Helv. Physiol. pharmac. Acta* **2**, 269–74.
Tresseler, D. K. and Curran, K. (1938). *J. Home Econ.* **30**, 487–8.
Truscott, J. H. L., Johnstone, W. M., Drake, T. G. H., Haarlem, J. R. and Thomson, C. L. (1942). Department of National Health and Welfare, Ottawa, Canada.
Veselkine, N. V., Lubimenko, V. N., Boulgakova, L. P., Tikalsskia, V. V. and Engel, P. S. (1934). *Bul. Inst. Sci. Leshaft* **17**, 389–93.

Wokes, F. and Organ, J. G. (1943). *Biochem. J.* **37**, 259–65.
Yamazaki, I., Mason, H. P. and Pitts, L. (1959). *Biochem. Biophys. Res. Commun.* **1**, 336–40.
Zilva, S., Kidd, F. and West, C. (1935). *New Phyt.* **37**, 345–57.

Part II

Growth and Pre-harvest Factors

Chapter 14

The Physiology and Nutrition of Developing Fruits

Plant Diseases Division, DSIR, Auckland, New Zealand

I. INTRODUCTION

Over the centuries man has selected and cultivated a number of plant species because he found their fruits pleasant to eat. These species are members of various families, both monocotyledons and dicotyledons, and the fruits are borne on a wide variety of types of plant. Table I lists certain basic data concerning those fruits which have been subjected to most scientific investigation. It is clear that, over the years, man has changed the characteristics of many of these fruits by continual selection and, more recently, by breeding. The characters which man has favoured in his selections have affected both the vegetative characters of the fruit-bearing plant and features of the fruit itself. Such features of the fruit as growth rate, size, colour, flavour, sweetness, texture and seediness have influenced selection, and the commercial fruit varieties of today differ from their ancestral wild types in most or all of these characteristics. Today, in seeking to follow and interpret the growth and development of different fruits, one must be aware that the structure and composition of these organs have been substantially determined by such

TABLE I. Systematic position, type of plant and type of fruit of some common horticultural fruits[a]

Family	Fruit	Systematic name	Type of plant	Nature of fruit
Palmaceae	Date	*Phoenix dactylifera* L.	Large, woody evergreen perennial palm	Drupe
Bromeliaceae	Pineapple	*Ananas comosus* Merr.	Evergreen perennial herb	Multiple accessory fruit (sorosis), with individual fruitlets (berries) fused together with associated bracts and floral axis
Musaceae	Banana	*Musa paradisiaca* var. *sapientum* Kuntze	Large evergreen perennial herb	Berry
Moraceae	Fig	*Ficus carica* L.	Deciduous tree	Multiple accessory fruit (syconium), mainly a fleshy hollow receptacle bearing internally numerous small achenes
Lauraceae	Avocado	*Persea americana* Mill.	Evergreen tree	Berry
Saxifragaceae	Blackcurrant	*Ribes nigrum* L.	Deciduous shrub	Berry
Rosaceae	Pear	*Pyrus communis* L.	Deciduous tree	Simple accessory fruit (pome), with drupe-like carpels completely surrounded by fleshy tissue which is variously considered as derived from bases of floral appendages or from receptacle
	Apple	*Malus sylvestris* Mill.	Deciduous tree	
	Raspberry	*Rubus idaeus* L.	Deciduous shrub	Aggregate fruit (etaerio) of numerous small drupes
	Strawberry	*Fragaria vesca* L.	Evergreen perennial herb	Aggregate accessory fruit (etaerio), mainly a large fleshy receptacle bearing externally numerous small achenes
	European plum	*Prunus domestics* L.	Deciduous tree	Drupe
	Japanese plum	*Prunus salicina* Lindl.		
	Apricot	*Prunus armeniaca* L.		
	Peach	*Prunus persica* Batsch		
	Sweet cherry	*Prunus avium* L.		
	Sour cherry	*Prunus cerasus* L.		
Rutaceae	Lemon	*Citrus limon* Burm. f.	Evergreen trees	Modified berry (hesperidium), with considerable development of endocarp
	Grapefruit	*Citrus paradisi* Macf.		
	Orange	*Citrus sinensis* Osbeck		
Anacardiaceae	Mango	*Mangifera indica* L.	Evergreen tree	Drupe
Vitaceae	Grape	*Vitis vinifera* L.	Deciduous shrub	Berry
Ericaceae	Blueberry	*Vaccinium corymbosum* L.	Deciduous shrub	Berry
Oleaceae	Olive	*Olea europaea* L.	Evergreen tree	Drupe
Solanaceae	Tomato	*Lycopersicon esculentum* Mill.	Annual herb	Berry
Cucurbitaceae	Watermelon	*Citrullus vulgaris* Schrad.	Annual herb	Modified berry (pepo), formed from an inferior ovary, with considerable development of carpel walls, and including some receptacular tissue
	Melon	*Cucumis melo* L.		

artificial selection. They have not been exposed to the rigours of natural selection and their predominant characteristics are those of acceptability to man.

This chapter endeavours to describe, in a comparative way, some aspects of the physiology and nutrition of developing fruits. The information available concerning different fruits varies greatly but, even with those which have been more intensively studied, it is still not possible to give more than a cursory outline of their development in physiological terms. The role of plant hormones in fruit development is the subject of a separate chapter and will be referred to only when relevant to the nutrition of developing fruits.

II. THE PHYSIOLOGY OF DEVELOPING FRUITS

A. Diversity of Fruit Structure

The two basic, simple types of fleshy fruit are the berry and the drupe, each of which results from the development of a single ovary. The main distinction between the two types is in the degree of development of the innermost layer of the pericarp—the endocarp—which remains membraneous in the berry but which thickens and hardens in the drupe. There are many differences in detailed structure of the various examples of these two types of fruit, but there is generally little difficulty in following the homologies of the various tissues in comparative growth studies. Results of such studies become more difficult to interpret when compound fruits are considered. These may develop from a number of ovaries of the one flower (aggregate fruits, for example, strawberry, raspberry) or a number of ovaries from different flowers (multiple fruits, for example, pineapple, fig). Further difficulties of growth interpretation arise when it is appreciated that many fruits, both simple and compound, are accessory fruits, that is they include tissues developed from structures other than the gynaecium. Thus a substantial part of the flesh of pome fruits is derived from tissue of either the receptacle or possibly the base of the perianth. Again much of both the fig and strawberry fruits is derived from the receptacle, while the pineapple fruit includes tissues of the entire inflorescence. These accessory tissues however, develop and ripen like the flesh of simple fruits.

B. Growth of Fruits

1. *Measurement of growth*

Growth of fruits has been followed by measuring one or a number of attributes (diameter, volume, fresh weight, dry weight, etc.) of fruits sampled at intervals during the period of growth. In some instances it is possible to measure the diameter of a fruit without detaching it from the parent plant

TABLE II. Growth period, size at maturity and growth rates of representative varieties of some common fruits

Fruit	Variety	Growth period (days from anthesis to maturity)	Size at maturity fr. wt. (g)	dr. wt. (g)	Diam. (mm)	Vol. (cm³)	Growth rate fr. wt. (g/day)	dr. wt. (g/day)	Diam. (mm/day)	Vol. (cm³/day)	Reference
Date	Deglet Noor	208	12	7·5			0·06	0·04			Aldrich and Crawford (1939)
Pineapple	Cayenne	168	2750				16·4				Sideris and Krauss (1938)
Banana	Gros Michel	122	320				2·6				Barnell (1940)
Fig	Mission	90	28	6·8	36		0·31	0·08	0·4		Crane and Brown (1950)
Blackcurrant	Seabrooks' Black	73				0·98				0·013	Wright (1956)
Pear	Bartlett	140	175	28	84		1·25	0·2	0·6		Bain (1961)
Apple	Beauty of Bath	95	63				0·66				Smith (1950)
Apple	King Edward VII	165	138				0·84				
Raspberry	Latham	32	2		16	2	0·06		0·5	0·06	Hill (1958)
Strawberry	Marshall	25			30				1·2		Nitsch (1950)
Plum	Climax	112	29		55	28	0·26		0·5	0·25	Lilleland (1933)
Apricot	Royal	113	36		37		0·32		0·3		Lilleland (1930)
Peach	Greensboro	91			47	54			0·5	0·60	Tukey (1933)
Peach	Chili	114			64	137			0·4	0·95	
Sweet cherry	Napoleon	51			23				0·45		Lilleland and Newsome (1934)
Sour cherry	Early Richmond	41			14	1·6			0·34	0·04	Tukey (1934)
	English Morello	66			17	2·7			0·26	0·04	
Orange	Washington Navel	245	300	47	90		1·22	0·2	0·4		Bouma (1959)
	Valencia	413	150	18	64		0·36	0·04	0·16		Bain (1958)
Mango	Pahei	119			90				0·8		Kennard (1955)
Grape	Concord	100	2·4	0·5		1·5	0·024	0·005		0·03	Nitsch et al. (1960)
Blueberry	Earliblue	49									Shutak et al. (1957)
Olive	Mission	213	3·8	1·9	16	3·8	0·018	0·009	0·08	0·02	Hartmann (1949)
Tomato	Kardine	70	75				1·1				Beadle (1937)
Melon	Cantaloupe	40				1,400				35	McGlasson and Pratt (1963)

and thus to follow the growth of the one fruit through the season. With Bartlett pears Griggs and Iwakiri (1956) showed that there was a close correspondence between the growth curves obtained by measuring the diameters of either the same fruit through the season or samples of fruit picked at intervals.

The fruit attributes which have been most easily and frequently measured are diameter or length, and growth curves based on these measurements often show characteristic forms which have been the subject of much discussion (see below). The effects of treatments which may affect fruit growth have often been studied by following change in diameter only. It should be realized, however, that the growth of an organ cannot be precisely followed by measuring a single linear dimension. Obviously a given increment in diameter with a large fruit implies a much greater increment in fresh or dry weight than does the same increase in diameter when the fruit is small. As a growing spherical object attains 25%, 50% or 75% of its final diameter measurement it has reached only 2%, 13% and 42% respectively of its final volume. For these reasons, in physiological studies, growth of a fruit is preferably followed by volume, fresh weight or dry weight measurements even though these may not follow the same patterns. It should be possible, with many kinds of fruit, to derive formulae for converting diameter or length measurements to equivalent volumes but this does not appear to have been done extensively (Moustafa and Stout, 1967).

2. Growth rates

Different fruits develop at different rates and attain quite different final sizes. Representative data for some of the more common fruits are listed in Table II, but it should be appreciated that marked differences in these growth characteristics may occur between different fruits in a crop, between seasons and between different varieties of the one fruit. For the varieties listed, growth rates range from that of blackcurrants and olives (0·01–0·02 cm^3 per day) to that shown by melons (35 cm^3 per day). Growth rates of fruits of other cucurbits reach very high values—thus field pumpkins have been reported to grow at an overall rate of 356 g fresh weight (equal to 29 g dry weight) per day reaching a maximum rate of about 629 g fresh weight (equal to 41 g dry weight) per day (Crafts and Lorenz, 1944).

3. Growth of pip fruits

The growth of apple fruits has been well documented (Askew, 1935; Harley, 1942; Tukey and Young, 1942; Bain and Robertson, 1951; Pearson and Robertson, 1953; Denne, 1960, 1963; Flood et al., 1960) and there are some data on the growth of pear fruits (Griggs and Iwakiri, 1956; Griggs et al., 1957; Bain, 1961). In all instances the curve for increase of fruit fresh weight shows a smooth sigmoid form (Fig. 1). Denne (1960) has distinguished three phases in the growth rate: an initial slow increase in fruitlet weight (for perhaps 6–12 days from pollination), a rapid exponential increase in fruitlet weight (for about 3 weeks) and a declining rate of growth (until harvest).

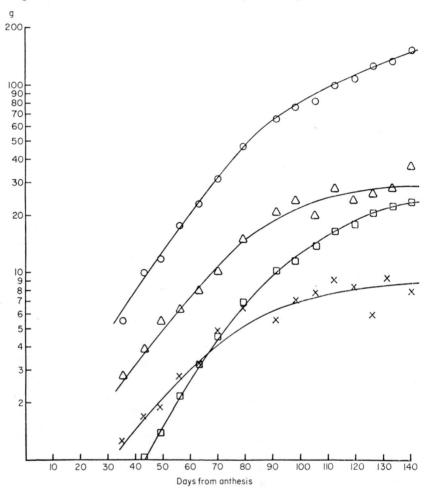

FIG. 1. Increases in fresh weight, dry weight, ash and nitrogen content of growing apple fruits, variety Jonathan. O—O fresh weight (g/fruit); △—△ ash (g/100 fruits); □—□ dry weight (g/fruit); ×—× nitrogen (g/100 fruits). From Askew (1935).

The seeds appear to reach their maximum weight well before the other parts of the fruit (Harley, 1942; Luckwill, 1948).

    There is general agreement that cell division in the flesh (pith and cortex) of developing apple fruits substantially ceases about 3–4 weeks after blossoming (Bain and Robertson, 1951; Denne, 1960; Blanpied and Wilde, 1968) although this period can be prolonged by fruit thinning (Denne, 1960; Sharples, 1964). In the epidermis, cell division continues for considerably longer than in the cortex (Skene, 1966). Flesh cells expand exponentially for some weeks after blossoming and continue to do so at a diminishing rate until the fruit is mature (Pearson and Robertson, 1953; Denne, 1960). Growth is not uniformly distributed through the tissues; for example, longitudinal growth is slower than transverse growth and relative rates in cortex and pith may vary (Skene, 1966).

4. Growth of stone fruits

Over 50 years ago Connors (1919) showed that the growth of peach fruits, as measured by increase in diameter, did not follow a single sigmoid curve (Fig. 2). Since then it has been shown many times that this pattern of fruit growth obtains not only with diameter measurements, but also with volume and fresh weight measurements in most varieties of peach (Blake *et al.*, 1931; Lott, 1932; Lilleland, 1932; Tukey, 1933; Lott and Ashley, 1935; Lee and Tukey, 1942; Lott, 1942; Crane *et al.*, 1961); apricot (Lilleland, 1930, 1935; Crane and Punsri, 1956; Catlin and Maxie, 1959); sweet cherry (Lilleland and Newsome, 1934); sour cherry (Tukey, 1934; Tukey and Young, 1939; Rebeiz and Crane, 1961) and plum (Lilleland, 1933). In each of these fruits there appears to be two phases of active growth separated by a period during which little or no growth occurs (Baker and Davis, 1951).

These observations have led to the concept of cyclic growth in stone fruits. In the three growth phases which are distinguished (and usually designated as periods I, II and III) the various components of the fruit (mesocarp, endocarp and seed) do not develop simultaneously.

Period I: During this initial period of rapid growth the pericarp and seed increase in size and weight. In the pericarp there is usually a period of cell division which is followed by rapid cell enlargement. In this period the endocarp and seed reach almost full size. The nucellus and integuments grow rapidly and cease growth at the same time as the mesocarp. Little development of the embryo occurs during this period.

Period II: In the second period, in which the overall growth rate has slowed down markedly, there is initially rapid hardening of the endocarp. The observed slowing down of fruit growth is essentially a retardation in mesocarp growth. The embryo develops rapidly and may, depending on species, reach maximum size during this period.

Period III: This is a period of "final swell" in which growth in size and weight resumes a rate approaching that of period I. There is usually an increase in both cell size and amount of intercellular space in the flesh. Ripening of the fruit occurs towards the end of this period.

The absolute and relative duration of these three growth periods differ markedly for the different stone fruits and their varieties (Table III). In peaches the difference in fruit growth between early and late varieties appears to be mainly in the relative lengths of period II (Tukey, 1933; Tukey and Lee,

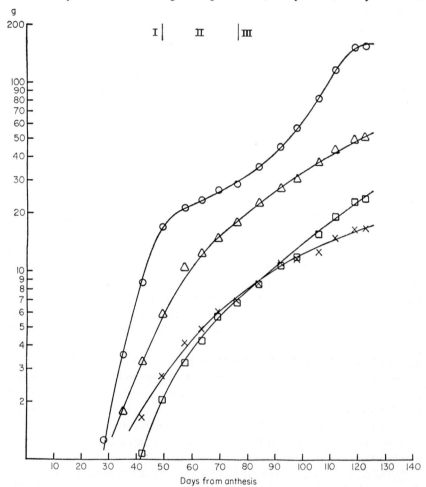

Fig. 2. Increases in fresh weight, dry weight, ash and nitrogen content of growing peach fruits, variety Halehaven. O—O fresh weight (g/fruit); △—△ash (g/100 fruits); □—□ dry weight (g/fruit); ×—× nitrogen (g/100 fruits). From Lott (1942).

1937). Parthenocarpic peaches, set with gibberellic acid, showed normal cyclic growth (Crane *et al.*, 1961).

It is possible in several ways to modify experimentally the rate of growth of stone fruit. For example, with both apricots and cherries, when limbs

TABLE III. Some characteristics of the growth phases in fruits possessing double sigmoidal growth curves

Fruit	Variety		Percentage time in or growth achieved in period			Growth rate					Reference
			I	II	III	Overall	I	II	III		
Fig	Mission	Time	46	14	39						Crane and Brown (1950)
		Diameter	69	2	29	0·40	0·61	0·05	0·29	mm/day	
		Fr. wt.	29	4	68	0·31	0·19	0·07	0·53	g/day	
		Dr. wt.	18	4	79	0·08	0·03	0·02	0·15	g/day	
Blackcurrant	Seabrooks' Black	Time	33	19	48						Wright (1956)
		Volume	36	12	52	13	15	9	15	mm³/day	
Raspberry	Latham	Time	31	28	41						Hill (1958)
		Diameter	50	2	48	0·51	0·82	0·03	0·61	mm/day	
		Volume	12	3	86	60	20	6	130	mm³/day	
		Fr. wt.	12	1	86	0·06	0·03	0·003	0·14	g/day	
Apricot	Royal	Time	37	37	26						Lilleland (1930)
		Diameter	63	7	30	0·32	0·55	0·06	0·37	mm/day	
		Fr. wt.	33	12	55	0·32	0·29	0·10	0·70	g/day	
Peach	Halehaven	Time	40	22	38						Lott (1942)
		Diameter	46	8	46	0·53	0·61	0·19	0·64	mm/day	
		Volume	11	7	82	1·30	0·37	0·39	2·78	cm³/day	
		Fr. wt.	11	8	81	1·26	0·35	0·44	2·69	g/day	
		Dr. wt.	17	25	58	0·13	0·06	0·16	0·20	g/day	
Sweet cherry	Napoleon	Time	29	27	43						Lilleland and Newsome (1934)
		Diameter	48	8	44	0·45	0·73	0·13	0·46	mm/day	
Sour cherry	Early Richmond	Time	54	12	34						Tukey (1934)
		Diameter	69	1	29	0·34	0·44	0·04	0·29	mm/day	
		Volume	30	2	68	39	22	6	78	mm³/day	
Grape	Concord	Time	40	24	36						Nitsch et al. (1960)
		Fr. wt.	58	4	38	0·024	0·035	0·004	0·025	g/day	
		Dr. wt.	32	15	54	4·8	3·8	2·9	7·1	mg/day	
Blueberry	Earliblue	Time	33	24	43						Shutak et al. (1957)
		Volume	32	5	63	31	30	6	45	mm³/day	
Olive	Mission	Time	33	19	48						Hartmann (1949)
		Diameter	80	5	15	0·08	0·19	0·02	0·02	mm/day	
		Volume	51	10	39	0·02	0·03	0·01	0·01	cm³/day	
		Fr. wt.	54	9	37	0·02	0·03	0·01	0·01	g/day	
		Dr. wt.	40	7	52	0·9	11	3	10	mg/day	

bearing developing fruits were artificially heated at night the fruits matured earlier than on control branches, the effect of the heat being mainly to reduce the length of period I, but the characteristic cyclic fruit growth curve was still observed (Lilleland, 1935; Tukey, 1952). When entire peach trees were similarly warmed the fruit growth curve was changed so that its overall cyclic form was almost lost (Batjer and Martin, 1965). It is known that sprays of 2,4,5-T increase the size of apricot fruits at harvest (Crane, 1953). Fruit so treated usually enters period III ahead of untreated fruit and may attain a greater rate of growth, but the cyclic nature of the growth is still apparent (Catlin and Maxie, 1959). Application of nitrogenous fertilizer to apricot trees tended to delay fruit maturation but had little effect on the cyclic nature of the fruit growth curve (Albrigo et al., 1966).

The fruit of almond is similar in many ways to that of peach but with the major exception that the mesocarp is dry and leathery in contrast to the fleshy mesocarp of peach. Again in contrast to peach fruit, growth of the almond fruit clearly follows a single sigmoid curve (Brooks, 1939). It appears that development of the almond fruit closely follows that of the peach through periods I and II, but that, associated with the lack of mesocarp development, is an absence of any renewed fruit growth characteristic of period III in other stone fruit.

5. Growth of other fruits

The growth of a number of other fruits, like that of pip fruit, appears to follow a single sigmoid curve: date (Haas and Bliss, 1935); pineapple (Sideris and Krauss, 1938); banana (Barnell, 1940; Simmonds, 1953); avocado (Schroeder, 1953); strawberry (Crane and Baker, 1953); orange (Bain, 1958; Bouma, 1959); mango (Kennard, 1955); tomato (Beadle, 1937) and melon (Sinnott, 1945; McGlasson and Pratt, 1963).

In contrast, the growth of yet other fruits, like that of stone fruits, follows a double sigmoidal type of curve: fig (Crane, 1948; Crane and Brown, 1950; Crane and Baker, 1953); blackcurrant (Wright, 1956); raspberry (Hill, 1958; Boynton and Wilde, 1959); grape (Tukey, 1958; Weaver and McCune, 1959; Nitsch et al., 1960; Coombe, 1960); blueberry (Young, 1952; Shutak et al., 1957) and olive (Hartmann, 1949). With these fruits, as with stone fruits, the three growth phases are frequently designated as periods I, II and III. When the rates of growth (that is, increase in units of volume or weight per unit time) of these fruit are plotted, characteristic double-humped curves are obtained (Coombe, 1960). Some of the growth cycle characteristics of these fruits are given in Table III. Though the overall patterns of growth shown by these fruits are very similar there are some differences—for example, the proportion of growth achieved in period III varies from over 80% (peach and raspberry) to under 40% (grape and olive). In more detailed aspects of their development these fruits also show similarities to stone fruits. Thus pit hardening in the olive (Hartmann, 1949), and in the drupelets of raspberry (Hill, 1958) occurs during period II.

The fruits showing this cyclic pattern of growth include drupes (stone fruit, olive), berries (blackcurrant, grape, blueberry), and compound fruits (raspberry, fig). With raspberry, both the individual drupelets and the receptacle follow a double sigmoidal curve of development (Boynton and Wilde, 1959). In this fruit there is evidence that growth of the drupelet governs growth of the adjacent areas of the receptacle, as removal of certain drupelets retards growth of the receptacle in that region. On the other hand, in the fig, where most of the fruit tissue is receptacle, growth of both pollinated and parthenocarpic fruit follows the same type of curve (Crane, 1948). With grapes, growth of both seeded and seedless varieties follows a double sigmoidal curve but the cyclic nature of the curve is less marked with seedless varieties (Winkler and Williams, 1935; Nitsch et al., 1960).

The biochemical characteristics of the flesh of fruits may differ between the different growth periods. Thus in developing grapes during period I the flesh has a low pH and accumulates malic and tartaric acids while, during period III, among other changes, it becomes less acid and accumulates reducing sugars (Hale, 1968).

6. Diurnal growth

When changes in diameter of individual growing fruits are followed with continuously recording instruments it can be seen that growth is not uniform throughout a 24 hour period. Thus it has been shown that the rate of volume increase in apple fruits during the night was over 25 times the rate observed during the period from noon to 4 p.m. (Harley and Masure, 1938). Similar phenomena have been observed with avocado (Schroeder and Wieland, 1956); peach (Tukey, 1959); sour cherry (Tukey, 1959; Kozlowski, 1968) and a number of non-horticultural fruits (Chaney and Kozlowski, 1969). These changes in growth rate result in the establishment of daily patterns of growth.

There is general agreement that these changes in fruit growth rate are associated with changes in evaporative capacity of the atmosphere. Reduced rates of fruit growth occur when the atmospheric evaporative capacity and, presumably, transpiration rates are high. It appears that when internal water stresses develop under conditions of high transpiration, water movement to fruits is markedly reduced and even reversed. Shrinkage of fruits during the middle part of the day is regularly observed.

7. Cyclic growth

Reasons for the characteristic cyclic form of the growth curves of stone and other fruits have attracted considerable interest. The question as originally posed by Lilleland and Brown (1936) was: "Why should apricot fruits, which have been growing rapidly for a period of 6 weeks, abruptly slow down and often cease to make any further diameter growth for the ensuing 6 weeks, and then with equal abruptness break into a period of very rapid growth that terminates with maturity?"

Early suggestions were that the slowing down of fruit growth in period II was partly because of competition with growth in other parts of the tree— for example, with vegetative shoot extension (Dorsey and McMunn, 1927) or with fruit bud differentiation (Tukey, 1934). Further field observations, however, suggested that this was unlikely at least in some growing areas (Lilleland, 1932). It has also been possible, in experiments of various types, for example, heating fruit-bearing branches at night (Lilleland, 1935), branch girdling (Lilleland and Brown, 1936) and fruit thinning (Tukey and Lee, 1940), to modify the nutrient supply to developing fruits to such an extent that the rate of development and final size of stone fruit were markedly affected. None the less such treatments had little, if any, effect on the cyclic nature of fruit development. It would thus seem unlikely that the slowing of fruit growth, characteristic of the onset of period II, can be attributed to competitive growth processes in other parts of the tree.

The sequence of development of the various fruit components (mesocarp, endocarp, seed, etc.) are all closely related to phases of overall fruit development. When overall development is altered experimentally so also is the development of these separate fruit components (Lilleland, 1935). Such observations led to the suggestion that competition for nutrients between these components within the developing stone fruit might account for the cyclic nature of its overall development. Most hardening of the endocarp occurs during period II and the requirement for nutrients for this process, for example, might account for retardation of the growth of the fleshy mesocarp during this time. The stony endocarp comprises only 7% of the fresh weight, but about 25% of the dry weight of the fruit (Lott and Ashley, 1935; Lee and Tukey, 1942). It is thus possible that development of this tissue would limit the dry matter available to the mesocarp to such an extent that growth of the latter would be retarded. For example, in developing peach fruits, during period II, the increase in dry matter in the endocarp was twice that of the mesocarp even though the latter had initially twice the dry weight (Lott, 1942). Lott and Ashley (1935) spoke of different components of the developing fruit being dominant at different times. Thus in most peach varieties during period II it was suggested that the endocarp and seed were dominant over the mesocarp.

In contrast to the cyclic nature of the curves for increase in fruit fresh weight the corresponding curves for increase in fruit dry weight show little if any, tendency to follow a similar cyclic pattern in stone fruit (Lott, 1932;

Lee and Tukey, 1942; Lott, 1942), olive (Hartmann, 1949) or raspberry (Boynton and Wilde, 1959). In other words intake of dry matter into the fruits as a whole proceeds at a relatively uniform rate. Increases in ash and nitrogen contents of developing peach fruits follow a similar pattern (Fig. 2). In these fruits the observed differences in rate of increase in volume or fresh weight must result both from movement of nutrients to different tissues at differing periods of development and from differing intakes of water. The curves for increase in dry weight of fig (Crane and Brown, 1950) and grape (Nitsch et al., 1960) tend to follow a cyclic pattern similar to that of the curves for increase in fresh weight, although they are not so accentuated as the latter. In these species it is possible that changes within the developing fruit are themselves affecting the overall supply of nutrients. Coombe (1960) pointed out that the time of commencement of sugar rise in several grape varieties coincides with the commencement of period III and suggested that this more rapid growth is caused by the influx of sugar into the berry. As sugar moved into the cells of the flesh he suggested that water also moved in to adjust diffusion pressure deficits.

Our knowledge of the nutrient interrelations of the various fruit parts is quite limited. Modern techniques have demonstrated the movement of ^{14}C-assimilates into the different tissues of stone fruits at various stages in their development (Kriedemann, 1968a) but many questions remain unanswered. For instance we do not know whether the nutrients arriving in the developing embryo are derived from the endosperm, from the pericarp or from outside the fruit itself. As discussed later in this chapter, it is now believed that developing fruits act as strong physiological sinks, attracting nutrients into their own tissues. It appears likely that differential growth within the fruit, which is observed externally as cyclic growth, could result from variations with time between the capacities of the various tissues of the developing fruit to act as physiological sinks. Further understanding of the competition for nutrients between developing fruit parts and regulation of their movement to different tissues in the developing fruit must await further study.

C. General Characteristics of Fruits

Despite the diversity of fruit structure already discussed and the differences in tissue homologies, in size attained and in time of development, the various fruits have certain features in common. In particular their fleshy tissues, to which they owe their appeal to man, have certain marked physiological and biochemical characteristics and these are discussed in this section.

1. *Cellular development*

In the development of many fruits, cell division is restricted to the first part of the growth period (Table IV). At one extreme, with tomato, there is little cell division after pollination (Davies and Cocking, 1965), but, with

TABLE IV. Duration of cell division and size of cell attained in the flesh of some common fruits

Fruit	Duration of cell division		Cell size in mature fruit		References
	Time	Approximate fraction of growth period	Diameter (μ)	Volume ($mm^3 \times 10^{-4}$)	
Date			120		Long (1943)
Pineapple				19	Singleton (1965)
Fig	6 weeks	0·5			Maxie and Crane (1968)
Avocado	Until harvest		50–60		Schroeder (1953)
Blackcurrant	5 weeks	0·5			Wright (1956)
Pear	6–8 weeks	0·3–0·4		12–30	Bain (1961)
Apple	3–4 weeks	0·15		60–72	Bain and Robertson (1951)
Raspberry	25 days	0·3	110		Denne (1963)
			500		Reeve (1954)
Strawberry	In cortex ceased before anthesis; in pith continued throughout		200–300		Havis (1943)
Plum	4 weeks	0·2	300		Sterling (1953)
Apricot	4 weeks	0·2	240		Crane et al. (1956)
Peach	3 weeks	0·15	180		Ragland (1934)
Sour cherry	10 days	0·2	350–500		Tukey and Young (1939)
Grape	45 days	0·4			Coombe (1960)
Tomato	Mainly before anthesis— none after first week			200–450	Davies and Cocking (1965)
Watermelon			330–700		Sinnott (1939)

most fruits, cell division continues for some weeks after pollination. The avocado fruit appears to be an exception in continuing cell division throughout its development (Schroeder, 1953).

Early cessation of cell division is followed characteristically by considerable cell expansion in the later stages of fruit development. The cells in mature fruits must be among the largest parenchyma cells in the plant kingdom, diameters of 200–700 μ being attained (Table IV). In watermelons, where cell diameters of 700 μ have been reported, the cells have expanded about 350,000 times from their meristematic volume (Sinnott, 1939).

In apricots a considerable proportion of the flesh cells show some degree of polyploidy, some cells containing up to 32n chromosomes (Bradley and Crane, 1955). Treatments, such as spraying young fruit with 2,4,5-T, which increase fruit size, also increase both cell size and degree of cell polyploidy. The possible association of polyploidy with large cell sizes does not appear to have been investigated in other fruit species.

It will be apparent that the production of a large mass of tissue with large cells, such as occurs during fruit development, presents morphogenetic or geometric problems. Both cell shape and relative volume of intercellular space are factors which change during fruit development. Bain and Robertson (1951) have shown, for example, that in small apples the proportion of intercellular space is about 20% but that in large apples this increases to 27%. It has also been shown (Westwood, 1962) that the specific gravity of apple fruits decreases during development, again indicating an increase in intercellular space; in pears and peaches, however, any such change was much less marked. Blanpied and Wilde (1968) used the ratio $\dfrac{\text{circumference}^2}{\text{area}}$ of cells in apple flesh as an indicator of the departure of these cells from circular outline. They found that this ratio increased steadily from mid-season on, indicating an increase in angularity of cells.

In developing apricots, differences in cell shape at various points in the mesocarp tissue became more accentuated as fruits increased in size (Jackson and Coombe, 1966). The cells nearest the endocarp appeared to elongate radially while those nearest the epidermis elongated tangentially. Jackson and Coombe have pointed out that these changes are what might be expected on theoretical grounds, regarding the mesocarp of the fruit as originally simply concentric layers of uniform spherical cells.

Certain problems arise in the expression of analytical data relating to growing fruits. In apples, for example, the dry weight per cell increases relatively more rapidly than cell volume, and Robertson and Turner (1951) have pointed out the advantages of expressing analytical data on a per cell basis. There are, however, relatively few published data on this basis (for example Davies and Cocking, 1965), most data simply being expressed on a fresh or dry weight basis.

2. Moisture content

The moisture contents of the flesh of most fruits at maturity are generally high (Table V), considerably higher than the moisture content of contemporary leaf tissue. For example, the moisture content of apple and peach leaves is about 60% (Lott, 1942; Askew et al., 1959) while these fruits contain about

TABLE V. Moisture and sugar content of the flesh of some common
fruits at time of fruit maturity

Fruit	Moisture content (%)	Reducing sugar (% fr. wt.)		Sucrose (% fr. wt.)	Reference
Date	39		16·7	21·4	Haas and Bliss (1935)
Pineapple			4	9	Singleton and Gortner (1965)
Banana	75	Glucose	2·2	0·4	Barnell (1940)
		Fructose	1·6		
			3·8		
Fig	75		17·2	2·9	Crane and Brown (1950)
Pear	84		8·1	2·9	Bain (1961)
Apple	85	Glucose	1·24	3·80	Askew et al. (1959)
		Fructose	3·88		
			5·12		
Strawberry			3·8	1·5	Knight and Wallace (1932)
Apricot	82		4·1	2·2	Crane et al. (1956)
Peach	85		3·5	4·5	Lott (1942)
Grapefruit			5·3	2·4	Hilgeman and Smith (1939)
Orange	85				Bain (1958)
Grape		Glucose	10·3		Kliewer (1966)
		Fructose	10·4	0·02	
			20·7		
Tomato	95		3·9	Nil	Beadle (1937)

85% moisture. Although the reported moisture content of mature date fruits is low (39%) these fruits have passed through a stage of development when their moisture content was over 80% (Haas and Bliss, 1935).

3. *Sugar content*

The sugar content of the flesh of most fruits at maturity is also characteristically high (Table V). In the few instances where direct comparison is possible these levels are considerably higher than those of leaves (Johnston et al., 1968; Taper and Liu, 1969). In dates, apples, peaches and figs the total sugars present comprise respectively 63, 71, 64 and 81% of the fruit dry weight (Haas and Bliss, 1935; Lott, 1942; Crane and Brown, 1950; Robertson and Turner, 1951). In most species glucose and fructose account for much of the sugar present but, in some, sucrose can also be present at similar levels. In fruit of commercial tomato varieties most of the sugar present is reducing sugar but with other species of Lycopersicon the main sugar in the fruit is sucrose (Davies, 1966). It is interesting that, in grapes, where there is good evidence that sucrose is the sugar which is transported, it is reducing sugars which accumulate in the fruit. In many species there is a period of rapid increase in concentration of some sugars as the fruit approaches maturity; for instance, in pears and apricots reducing sugars, which are quantitatively the more important, increase steadily throughout the period of fruit development, but sucrose, which for much of this period is very low, increases rapidly in the later stages of development (Crane *et al.*, 1956; Bain, 1961). The ability to retain so much carbohydrate in soluble form is characteristic of mature fruit tissues.

4. Acid content

It is frequently stated that fruits have a relatively high acid content. In the few instances, however, where strictly comparable data on the total organic acid content of both leaves and fruit are available it would appear that leaf contents (on a fresh weight basis) are often as high or higher than the contents of mature fruit (Table VI).

TABLE VI. Total acid content of leaves and fruits of some fruit species at time of fruit maturity (Except where indicated all data are m-equiv./100 g fr. wt. tissue)

Fruit	Variety	Leaf	Fruit	Reference
Peach	Several clones	10	18	Ryugo and Davis (1958)
		7	2	
		9	12	
		11	2	
Apple	McIntosh	29·4	13·0	Johnston *et al.* (1968)
	Red Delicious	27·9	7·5	
	Spartan	31·7	11·8	
Orange	Valencia	55–85[a]	33[a]	Rasmussen and Smith (1961) Rasmussen (1964)
Grape	Sultanina	11·3	6·4	Kliewer (1966)
Tomato	Globe	3·8	13·0	Carañgal *et al.* (1954)

[a] m-equiv. 100 g dr. wt. tissue

At maturity, the proportion of acid existing in the free state in the fruit, as opposed to being combined in salt form, varies somewhat. Over a number of peach clones the proportion of free acid varied from 33–87% (Ryugo, 1964), in three apple varieties it ranged from 65–81% (Johnston *et al.*, 1968), while in citrus fruits the proportion was generally higher, 85–97% (Sinclair and Ramsey, 1944; Sinclair and Eny, 1945, 1946).

Most fruits contain several organic acids but often one acid predominates, for example, malic acid in pip fruits, citric acid in citrus fruit and tartaric acid in grapes. During development most fruits show characteristic fluctuations in acid content—usually the initial level is low, it increases steadily with growth reaching a maximum some time in mid-season, and then steadily declines as the fruit matures.

The level of acid contributes markedly to the flavour of fruits. Thus sour lemon (*Citrus limon*) fruit contains 4–9% of organic acids while sweet lemon (*C. limettiodies*) contains less than 1% (Bogin and Wallace, 1966). A "sweet" sport of Jonared apples did not differ from the parent type in sugar content of fruit but contained only 0·12% acid in the juice while the parent strain contained 0·68% (Lott, 1965).

5. Mineral content

The mineral contents of leaves and fruit of some species are given in Table VII. With apples the levels of the major elements in fruits tend to be

TABLE VII. Levels of major nutrient elements present in leaves and flesh of some common fruits at time of fruit maturity[a]

Fruit	Variety	Organ	N	P	K	Ca	Mg	Reference
Date	Deglet Noor	Fruit	0·45	0·08	1·10	0·06	0·08	Haas and Bliss (1935)
Apple	Cox's Orange	Leaf	2·07	0·13	1·20	1·52	0·26	Askew et al. (1959)
	Pippin	Fruit	0·43	0·05	0·70	0·02	0·03	
Peach	Elberta	Leaf	1·40	0·11	2·20	3·60	0·78	Batjer and Westwood
		Fruit	1·00	0·20	2·40	0·09	0·09	(1958)
Orange	Valencia	Leaf	2·82	0·21	2·20	3·42	0·45	Koo and Sites (1956)
		Fruit	0·98	0·13	1·37	0·31	0·09	
Tomato	Hybrid	Leaf	2·60	0·55	4·70	6·08	0·43	Ward (1964)
		Fruit	1·93	0·41	3·77	0·13	0·14	
Melon	Cantaloupe	Leaf	2·56	0·32	1·40	0·56	0·88	Tyler and Lorenz
		Fruit	2·63	0·42	3·30	0·30	0·41	(1964)
Cucumber	Burpee	Leaf	1·90	0·65	2·34	11·49	1·28	Ward (1967)
	hybrid	Fruit	2·74	0·56	3·55	0·49	0·26	

[a] All data are percentages of dry matter.

markedly lower than in leaves. In other species, however, with the exception of calcium, and sometimes magnesium, the levels in fruit and leaves tend to be of the same order. The level of calcium in fruit generally tends to be markedly lower than in leaves and this characteristic is discussed later. An apparent exception to this appears in a number of melon varieties, where the recorded levels of calcium in fruit were, in some instances, higher than the levels in leaves (Tyler and Lorenz, 1964). This is in marked contrast to the situation in another cucurbit fruit—cucumber—where the level of calcium in leaves was 23 times that in the fruit (Ward, 1967).

There has been surprisingly little study of the movement of mineral elements into developing fruit. The literature contains a vast amount of data referring to the percentages of the various elements present in fruit tissue but comparatively few data for fruits other than apple (for example, Hopkins and Gourley, 1933; Rogers and Batjer, 1954) on the total amounts of element present in fruits at different stages of development. Figures 1 and 2 show the increase in ash and nitrogen in developing apple and peach fruits. It is apparent that these increases follow closely the increase in dry weight of each fruit.

D. INTERRELATIONS OF FRUIT AND VEGETATIVE GROWTH

1. Relationships of fruits to vegetative parts

Fruits are borne on a wide range of plant types (Table I) and there will be corresponding differences in both the spatial and temporal relationships of developing fruits to the various vegetative organs from which they draw their nutrients. Such differences may present some difficulties in the physiological interpretation of comparative fruit growth studies.

(a) In annual plants, such as tomato and melon, growth of the developing fruits must be closely related to the current acquisition of nutrients from the environment; in perennial shrubs and trees, on the other hand, developing fruits may draw to varying extents on nutrients which have been earlier stored in perennial organs. Again the pattern of nutrient acquisition and storage in deciduous perennials will differ from that in evergreen perennials, with possible consequential effects on pattern of fruit development in these two types of plant.

(b) In some perennial species floral buds are morphologically defined in the season preceding that in which fruits develop; even limited development of ovular tissue in one season may affect development of fruits in the following season. In some citrus species, for example Valencia oranges, fruit development takes about 15 months and competition is likely to occur between successive annual crops.

(c) In many fruit species blossoming and fertilization occur over a relatively short period and subsequent development of all fruits tends to occur more or less simultaneously. In some species production of blossoms continues over an extended period; for example, in tomato, blossoms may still be produced as the first fruit approaches maturity. Fruits developing at such different times may well be affected by differing endogenous and environmental factors.

(d) Some differences in fruit development may also be implicit in the fruit-bearing habits of the different species, because of the effects of developing fruits on each other. The distribution of nutrients to (and hence pattern of growth in) fruits borne singly among the vegetative parts (for example, pineapple) will be different from that to fruits which are borne in multiple clusters or bunches (for example, bananas, grapes).

2. Leaf to fruit ratios

In the integration of plant growth there is considerable interaction between vegetative growth and fruit development. The onset of senescence in annual plants, for instance, can be considerably delayed by removal of flowers and developing fruits (Leopold et al., 1959; Lockhart and Gottschall, 1961).

It has long been observed that plants bearing a substantial crop of fruit make relatively weak vegetative growth (Murneek, 1924; Haller, 1930). Removal of some fruit from such plants allows an increase in vegetative growth.

The size attained by individual fruits is clearly affected by the ratio of leaves to fruit present. In pineapples, for example, a highly significant correlation has been demonstrated between the number of leaves present and the final fruit weight (van Overbeek, 1946). In other species, as different in growth habit as tomatoes and apples, removal of some of the developing fruits leads to an increase in the size attained by the remaining fruits (Haller and Magness, 1925; Gustafson and Stoldt, 1936; Gustafson and Houghtaling, 1939). Studies of the effect of removing blossoms and young fruitlets on the subsequent cellular development of remaining apple fruitlets led Quinlan and Preston (1968) to conclude that competition for nutrients was most severe at the time of blossoming but that it decreased somewhat thereafter. Attempts have been made with apples to calculate the minimum number of leaves needed to support the growth of a single fruit (Hansen, 1969). Not unexpectedly, perhaps, there were considerable differences between varieties and time of season.

Most attempts to explain the interrelations of fruiting and vegetative growth have been on the basis of competition between the two for available nutrients, although clear distinctions were not always made between nutrients needed in quantity, such as carbohydrates, and growth factors needed in small amounts only (Murneek, 1924; Ryugo and Davis, 1959; Maggs, 1963). However, a series of experiments with tomatoes, in which leaves and fruits were removed producing a range of leaf area to fruit volume ratios, showed that a check to vegetative growth was not necessarily related to the amount of fruit developing on the plant. For instance plants from which all flower buds were removed underwent a check in vegetative growth at the same time as plants developing normally (Cooper, 1961, 1964). This observation suggests the existence of some overall regulatory mechanism which maintains a balance between fruit and leaf growth.

3. Effects of fruits on leaf efficiency

Some observations suggest that the presence of developing fruits has a direct effect on the photosynthetic capacity of leaves. Apple trees bearing fruit produced more dry matter per unit area of leaf than trees bearing no fruit (Maggs, 1963). In other experiments the rate of photosynthesis in leaves close to fruits was higher than in other leaves (Kazaryan et al., 1965). Such effects have been attributed to an increased rate of translocation of photosynthetic products from leaves on trees or branches bearing developing fruits (Maggs, 1963; Hansen, 1967a, 1969).

III. THE NUTRITION OF DEVELOPING FRUITS

Fuller understanding of the growth and nutrition of fruits (as of any other organ or organism) requires some knowledge of both their basic nutrient requirements and how these requirements are actually supplied during the various phases of normal growth. With developing fruit there has been comparatively little work on determining their basic nutrient requirements—the results of some experiments using the techniques of organ and tissue culture are described below. Study of the actual supply of nutrients from the parent plant has, in contrast, been undertaken from several points of view—the mobilization of stored nutrient reserves, the movement of assimilates from leaves, the recirculation of mineral elements, etc.

A. Organ and Tissue Culture

The techniques of tissue culture are widely used today in studies on the growth and metabolism of plant tissues. Tissues from the fleshy portions of a number of fruits have been successfully grown in culture: avocado (Schroeder, 1955, 1960, 1961); citron (Schroeder and Spector, 1957; Schroeder, 1960, 1961); lemon (Kordan, 1959, 1963; Schroeder, 1961; Nitsch, 1965a; Murashige et al., 1967); banana (Schroeder, 1961); olive (Schroeder, 1961); mango (Schroeder, 1961); peach (Nitsch, 1965b; Sommer et al., 1962); apple (Letham, 1958; Nitsch, 1959); pear (Letham, 1960); quince (Letham, 1960); orange (Nitsch, 1965a) and strawberry (Bajaj and Collins, 1968). With some of these species, tissues have been cultured from young fruits only, but with others tissues from ripening fruits have also been grown successfully. In most instances the tissue growth appears to consist of small dividing cells characteristic of the very young stages of fruit development. With one species—lemon—tissue will grow in a medium containing only mineral salts and sucrose, but most species require a number of vitamins and plant hormones for growth. None of these studies has yet been developed to the stage where we can begin to understand the normal development of fruits in terms of the *in vitro* behaviour of their tissues.

It is also possible to grow entire developing fruits in sterile culture commencing with flowers taken either before or after pollination. This has been achieved with tomatoes (Nitsch, 1949, 1951, 1963) and strawberries (Bajaj and Collins, 1968). If pollinated flowers were used, growth was obtained on a medium containing only mineral salts and sucrose. The pattern of growth obtained with each species was very similar to normal but the size of fruits was somewhat smaller. If unpollinated flowers were used, additions of various plant hormones to the culture medium were necessary for any development to proceed. This interesting and promising technique does not appear yet to have been applied to other fruit species.

B. Sources and Transport of Nutrients

As with other plant organs, we can expect that developing fruits will receive part of their nutrients from the xylem stream and part through the phloem tissues. Nutrients being supplied to the developing fruit may be directly derived from the environment—either mineral nutrients in the xylem stream from the roots or soluble carbohydrates via the phloem from the leaves. Other nutrients may reach the developing fruit indirectly. Thus, some mineral nutrients, which have earlier been supplied to the leaves in the xylem stream, may be re-circulated to developing fruits through the phloem tissue.

Many perennial species build up substantial amounts of carbohydrate and nitrogenous reserves which are known to be available for growth in the current or following season. The course of starch deposition in and disappearance from both bark and wood tissues suggests that this material is an important reserve which can be readily used as occasion demands (Ryugo and Davis, 1959; Hansen, 1967b). In apple trees it has been shown that both soluble and insoluble forms of nitrogen can act as reserves (Oland, 1959). The soluble forms, consisting substantially of arginine and amides, are quantitatively more important. In peach trees storage nitrogen also consists mainly of soluble nitrogen and principally of arginine (Taylor, 1967; Taylor and May, 1967). Little is known of the storage of mineral elements in perennial parts.

It was suggested some time ago that the vascular system of the tomato fruit imposes a limitation on the entry of nutrients as the fruit grows larger (Gustafson, 1927; Gustafson and Houghtaling, 1939). In the ovary or young fruit the vascular strands appear to be relatively numerous and well-developed. As the fruit enlarges, however, there is no corresponding increase in vascular structure and as it approaches maturity it would appear to be relatively poorly supplied with such structures. This interesting idea does not appear to have been considered in relation to other fruits. Most modern cultivated fruit varieties are considerably larger than the corresponding wild types, and a relatively inadequate fruit vascular system may be a general characteristic of such varieties. This possibility would appear to be worthy of investigation with modern techniques.

Our knowledge of the overall supply of nutrients to fruits is fragmentary. We know little, for example, of the relative importance of the different sources of nutrients or transport pathways at different stages of fruit development. Some aspects of the nutrition of developing fruit where some information is available are discussed in the following sections.

C. Supply of Carbohydrates

1. *Photosynthesis in fruits*

Many developing fruits contain chlorophyll and it is usually assumed that they can assimilate CO_2 in the light. This phenomenon has been demonstrated with apple (Kidd and West, 1947), citrus fruit (Bean and Todd, 1960; Todd *et al.*, 1961), avocado (Todd *et al.*, 1961), stone fruit (Kriedemann, 1968a) and grape (Kriedemann, 1968c). By applying $^{14}CO_2$ to portions of the surface of developing apricot fruits it has been shown that the resulting fixed carbon is uniformly distributed through the fruit tissue (Kriedemann, 1968a). The rate of such photosynthesis is relatively low, however, and its contribution to fruit dry weight is small. In apple the rate per unit area of fruit surface is generally less than one-tenth the rate per unit area of leaf surface (Kidd and West, 1947). In citrus fruit the ratio of photosynthesis rate to respiration rate approached unity—that is the contribution of photosynthesis was no more than to supply enough energy to replace that used in respiration. As fruit coloured and ripened, rates of fruit photosynthesis fell still lower (Bean *et al.*, 1963; Kriedemann, 1968c).

2. *Leaves as donor organs*

It has been shown with a herbaceous plant, soybean, that each leaf in course of its development passes from a stage during which it imports photosynthates, through a phase of simultaneous export and import, to a stage where export of photosynthates is predominant (Thrower, 1962). Though the stage of leaf development at which such export commences may vary, similar phenomena have now been observed with grape, peach, apricot and orange leaves (Hale and Weaver, 1962; Kriedemann, 1968a, 1969).

There is evidence that carbohydrates can move freely within the structure of a tree or vine. Fruit thinning and defoliation experiments have shown that growth of fruit can be sustained by leaves situated a considerable distance away. With apples and grapes growth of fruits was maintained when no leaves were closer than 4–10 feet and 3 feet respectively (Haller and Magness, 1925; Haller, 1930; Winkler, 1932). ^{14}C-assimilates were translocated from leaves on one half of a double-stemmed grape vine to fruits developing on the opposite half, a distance of over 12 feet (Meynhardt and Malan, 1963). With both apples and grapes ^{14}C-assimilates moved into developing fruits from leaves situated either above or below them on the stem (Hale and Weaver, 1962; Hansen, 1969). Despite this apparent freedom of movement of nutrients, however, there is a marked tendency for leaves close to a given developing fruit to supply that fruit (Hansen, 1969). In young tomato plants, all leaves were capable of supplying fruit on all trusses, but as the number of trusses increased particular groups of leaves came to be the principal suppliers of particular trusses (Khan and Sagar, 1966).

In a particular species the restrictions imposed by the phyllotaxy on the vascular anatomy basically determine the vertical path of movement of nutrients from particular leaves (McCollum and Skok, 1960; Hale and Weaver, 1962; Jankiewicz et al., 1967). The presence of both internal and external phloem in some species, for example, tomato, may allow for greater flexibility of nutrient transport (Bonnemain, 1965). It is clear, however, that the vascular connections are not the only factors determining the pattern of distribution of nutrients. Quinlan (1966) showed that, by removing leaves from an apple shoot, the direction in which assimilate is transported from a particular leaf could be reversed. It is also known that the presence of developing fruits can change the basic pattern of nutrient distribution (Hale and Weaver, 1962).

3. Carbohydrates of transport

Several soluble carbon compounds—reducing sugars, sucrose, several organic acids, sugar alcohols, etc.—appear in developing fruits in varying quantities, depending on species and stage of development. The question arises as to which of these compounds are synthesized in the leaves or other organs and then translocated to the fruit and which are synthesized in the fruit tissues. Translocation of carbohydrates from leaves to fruits is generally regarded as occurring in the phloem (Othlinghaus et al., 1968), but our knowledge about which carbon compounds are translocated in this tissue is far from complete. There is a general belief that in many plants sucrose is the most important translocating carbohydrate and this would appear to be so for some fruit species. Thus, in analyses of labelled sugars in the bark following the application of $^{14}CO_2$ to a grape leaf, Swanson and El-Shishiny (1958) found that sucrose contained over 90% of the radioactivity present. The label present in other compounds probably resulted from metabolism of sucrose.

The sugar alcohol, sorbitol (D-glucitol), is known to be a major constituent of the leaves and fruit of a number of Rosaceous species such as apple and plum; for example, the content of sorbitol in apple leaves and fruits is approximately 2·2% and 0·6% of the fresh weight respectively (Anderson et al., 1961; Whetter and Taper, 1963; Taper and Liu, 1969). Following application of $^{14}CO_2$ to leaves on an apple shoot Webb and Burley (1962) found three times as much radioactivity in sorbitol extracted from the bark, at distances of up to 60 cm, as in sucrose. This finding, together with the observation that sorbitol and sucrose were major constituents of the sieve-tube exudate of apples, led these workers to suggest that sorbitol was also an important translocating compound in this species. In support of this view Williams et al. (1967) showed that when ^{14}C-sorbitol was applied to apple leaves radioactivity moved much faster than when ^{14}C-sucrose was applied.

In contrast, however, stems of young apple seedlings contained a high level of sucrose and only traces of sorbitol, even though this compound was present in the cotyledons (Whetter and Taper, 1966).

It has now been confirmed (Bieleski, 1969) that, in the phloem tissue of apple shoots bearing leaves which had been exposed to $^{14}CO_2$, sorbitol contained about four times as much radioactivity as sucrose. It was also shown that excised phloem tissue could accumulate sorbitol and that, once there, it did not appear to be metabolized, thus being a suitable compound for translocation. Bieleski has suggested that the apparently contradictory results of Whetter and Taper could be explained by the fact that they were studying translocation from germinating seeds in which the relative concentrations of the different sugars could result in sucrose being preferentially accumulated in the phloem. It thus appears that, in apple at least, sorbitol plays a major role in the translocation of carbohydrates to the developing fruit. It may well be that this compound plays a similar role in other Rosaceous plants, and the possibility that sorbitol or similar compounds are involved in translocation in other species should not be overlooked.

Some earlier work suggested that certain of the organic acids found in fruits were synthesized in leaves and translocated to fruit. However, studies in which ^{14}C-labelled CO_2 and sucrose were fed to grape berries, and enzymic studies with lemon fruits suggest that these fruits, at least are capable of considerable synthesis of acid in their own tissues (Hale, 1962; Bogin and Wallace, 1966; Hardy, 1967). Tissue from vesicles of lemon fruit growing in sterile culture with sucrose as sole source of carbon, accumulated citric acid much as do the tissues of the intact fruit (Kordan, 1965).

D. Movement of Nutrients in the Xylem Stream

1. *Attempts to examine xylem nutrients*

The nature of nutrients moving in the xylem stream has been studied by analysing either sap extracted from woody shoots, for example apple (Bollard, 1953), or sap exuding naturally from cut stems, for example tomato (van Die, 1958). Most of this work has been aimed at studying the form and levels of the nitrogenous compounds being translocated. It has been found, for example, that, with some Rosaceous plants, the nitrogen present in extracted xylem sap occurred as a range of amino acids and amides with aspartic acid and asparagine predominating (Bollard, 1957a, b). The level of nitrogen in sap varied through the season, and with nitrogen status of trees, but there was comparatively little change in the relative proportions of nitrogenous compounds present (Hill-Cottingham and Bollard, 1965; Tromp and Ovaa, 1967, 1969). In exuded sap of tomatoes a rather similar picture has been recorded with glutamine as the predominant compound (van Die, 1958;

B FP—P

Pate *et al.*, 1964). Through this work there has been the assumption that the compounds detected in sap, extracted either way, are those being translocated and which would be supplied to developing fruits by the xylem stream.

It has long been evident, however, that transport of nutrients in the xylem may not be as simple and direct a process as was once considered and some consideration must be given to the validity of examining xylem sap samples. Anderssen (1929) showed that sap extracted from the outer regions of the xylem of a woody stem of pear had a higher concentration of mineral nutrients than that obtained from inner regions. The former also contained a significant level of reducing substances while none was detected in the latter. These differences imply that some physiological barrier exists between the sap of these two xylem regions. Morrison (1965) fed ^{32}P-phosphate to roots of willow cuttings and examined the radioactivity in both sap exuding from the stump of a decapitated plant and sap extracted from the shoot of the same plant. The former contained several times the radioactivity of the latter. The exudate contained both inorganic and organic phosphorus while the extracted sap contained only inorganic phosphate. In contrast to these findings, Jones and Rowe (1968) found no differences in concentrations of several elements (including phosphorus) between exuded sap and extracted sap of apples. These results are difficult to reconcile unless species react differently to removal of tops. Changes in the roots following top removal might affect the composition of exuded sap in some species.

Changes may apparently occur in composition of the transpiration stream as it passes througn the xylem. In experiments with detached apple stem pieces Hill-Cottingham and Lloyd-Jones (1968) showed that there was adsorption of amino acids, more particularly of basic and neutral compounds within xylem vessels. They observed competition for adsorption between arginine and inorganic cations, and their results further suggested that there was a second phase of adsorption in which amino acids became irreversibly bound. A similar adsorption of amino acids in the xylem has been observed with tomato stems (van Die and Vonk, 1967). It had earlier been shown in tomato that there was movement of amino acids from xylem vessels to adjacent tissues (van Die, 1963).

2. *Translocation of carbohydrates*

The question of carbohydrate movement in the xylem stream also raises difficulties. In xylem sap extracted from some species, for example apple, little if any sugar can be detected (Bollard, 1953) but in sap from others considerable amounts may be present. On the one hand, in sap extracted from grape shoots, Hardy and Possingham (1969) found 0·50, 0·73 and 0·26 mg/litre of sucrose, glucose and fructose respectively. Exuding or bleeding sap, on the other hand, contained none, 0·75 and 0·38 mg/litre respectively.

In a series of ringing experiments with grapevines these authors also found that, although radioactive sugars were important components of sap extracted from wood close to a leaf which had been exposed to $^{14}CO_2$, only minor amounts of labelled sugar were found in sap from the wood above a ring. It has long been known (Bollard, 1960) that lateral interchange of some nutrients can occur between xylem and phloem. The results of Hardy and Possingham with grapes have shown that there is ready lateral movement of ^{14}C-assimilates into the xylem from the phloem but that these compounds apparently do not then move in the xylem stream. They suggest that there is some barrier within the wood which prevents diffusion of sugar into the transpiration stream and that, because extracted sap contains substantial amounts of sugar, it cannot be regarded as necessarily representative of the ascending sap.

3. *Effect of high rates of transpiration*

Further evidence conflicting with accepted views on the supply of nutrients to developing fruits through the xylem stream comes from the work of Wiersum (1966a, b). Wiersum supplied solutions containing both the dye, light green, and ^{45}Ca to roots of tomato plants and to excised branches of apples and then followed their movement into developing fruits. Both dye and isotope appeared to behave alike. His observations suggested that, during periods when conditions led to high rates of transpiration, movement of water to developing fruits through the xylem was considerably reduced. He concluded that under these conditions there must be continued movement of water into developing fruits through the phloem.

It is clear that there is still much to learn about the role of the xylem in supplying nutrients to developing fruits. The conventional view that the xylem transports nutrients from the roots to the various growing organs is obviously over-simplified. Substantial nutrient reserves can be located in xylem tissues, but little is known of the route and control of their deposition and mobilization. There may well be major differences between species in both the nature of nutrients transported in the xylem and the efficiency of the xylem in developing fruit species during periods of high rates of transpiration.

E. Recirculation of Mineral Elements in the Phloem

1. *Movement of elements out of leaves*

It is usually assumed that, in addition to the mineral elements supplied in the xylem stream, further amounts of most elements reach developing fruits through the phloem tissues. This belief is partly based on our knowledge of the movement of elements out of leaves. Oland (1963) has, for example, measured the net movement of several elements from the foliage of apple trees during the latter part of the season. During the period under observation 52, 27 and 36% of the leaf content of nitrogen, phosphorus and potassium respectively were shown to leave the foliage. There have also been many reports of the movement of various ions in plants following their external application to leaves. Thus, with both tomatoes and strawberries, radioactive phosphate was readily absorbed by leaves and then translocated to all parts of the plant (McCollum and Skok, 1960; Norton and Wittwer, 1963). However, beyond the fact that such movement of mineral elements from leaves may occur, we have little information on the relative quantitative importance of the xylem and phloem in the supply of mineral nutrients to developing fruits.

2. The supply of calcium to developing fruits

It has been known for some time that the pattern of movement of calcium within plants is markedly different from that of most other mineral nutrients. Thus Oland (1963) showed that this element continued to rise in senescing apple leaves over a period when a loss of most other elements was occurring. Again, when ^{45}Ca was applied to the leaves of a strawberry plant there was negligible movement of this element away from the treated leaves, in contrast to the behaviour of phosphate as discussed above (Norton and Wittwer, 1963). Such observations have led to the belief that calcium is immobile in phloem tissues and that, once delivered to an organ in the transpiration stream, this element tends to remain there (Bollard and Butler, 1966).

This phenomenon is of particular importance to developing fruit. These organs will receive calcium only from the ascending transpiration stream whereas they will also receive supplies of other elements through the phloem. This situation will result in a steadily decreasing proportion of calcium relative to other elements in growing fruits. Furthermore, Wiersum's observation that under conditions of high transpiration no water enters the fruits directly from the xylem suggests that under these conditions no calcium will be supplied to the fruits.

The immobility of calcium in the phloem may also assist in the interpretation of other effects in developing fruit. Early thinning of apple fruits, for example, resulted in significantly higher levels of phosphorus, potassium and magnesium in mature fruits, but the calcium level was not affected (Sharples, 1964). Fruit thinning, by altering the leaf/fruit ratio, may well increase the amount of nutrients, other than calcium, available to fruit from the leaves, without affecting to any extent the nutrients available through the xylem.

It has already been noted that calcium is present in mature fruits at a level which is frequently much lower than the level of this element in leaves. Table VIII contains data relating to the potassium and calcium contents of apple leaves and fruit during the growing season. The difference in behaviour of the two elements in leaves and fruit is clearly seen by contrasting the ratio of K to Ca in leaves and fruit as the season progresses. In leaves, this ratio changes from 1·5 to 0·6, but in fruit the change is from 8·1 to 34·8. Again the leaf to fruit ratio for potassium changes from 0·8 to 1·6 while the same ratio for calcium changes from 4·1 to 90·4. All these figures are indicative of a limitation in calcium supply to the growing fruit relative to the supply of both this element to leaves and other elements to the fruit.

There appear to be relatively few other data in the literature which illustrate the progressive relative deficiency of calcium in developing fruit so

TABLE VIII. Levels of potassium and calcium in apple leaves and fruits and ratios between them at different stages of growth[a]

Days from start of sampling[b]	Leaves			Fruit			Leaf/Fruit	
	K content (% dr. wt.)	Ca content (% dr. wt.)	K/Ca	K content (% dr. wt.)	Ca content (% dr. wt.)	K/Ca	K	Ca
0	1·72	1·16	1·5	2·27	0·28	8·1	0·8	4·1
12	1·58	1·25	1·3	1·92	0·25	7·7	0·8	5·0
21	1·25	1·28	1·0	1·72	0·21	8·2	0·7	6·1
29	1·52	1·46	1·0	1·65	0·17	9·7	0·9	8·6
40	1·50	1·58	1·0	1·55	0·15	10·3	1·0	10·5
54	1·60	1·76	0·9	1·10	0·10	11·0	1·5	17·6
69	1·22	1·70	0·7	1·13	0·053	21·3	1·1	32·1
86	1·34	1·85	0·7	0·98	0·042	23·3	1·4	44·0
97	1·37	1·91	0·7	0·81	0·032	25·3	1·7	59·7
110	1·29	2·08	0·6	0·80	0·023	34·8	1·6	90·4

[a] From Askew et al. (1959).
[b] Sampling began approximately one month from time of blossoming.

clearly. However, with several kinds of fruit, for example, peach, tomato, cucumber (see Table VII), the ratios of K to Ca, for mature fruit, are considerably higher than those for leaves, suggesting that these fruits are also relatively calcium deficient.

3. Bitter pit of apples and blossom-end rot of tomatoes

It is now known that the incidence of some characteristic physiological disorders of fruits can be markedly reduced or eliminated by application of solutions of calcium salts, for example bitter pit of apples (Garman and Mathis, 1956; Askew et al., 1960; Drake et al., 1966) and blossom-end rot of tomatoes (Evans and Troxler, 1953; Geraldson, 1957; Fisher, 1967). It now appears likely that symptoms of these disorders result from localized deficiencies of calcium in developing fruits, even though such fruits are borne on plants with supplies of calcium adequate by such criteria as leaf analysis. When crops are sprayed with solutions of calcium salts to reduce the incidence of these disorders it is presumably only that portion of the spray falling on the fruit surface itself which is effective. Moreover Chittenden et al., (1969) have shown that when calcium nitrate solution was applied to only one side of an apple fruit, bitter pit symptoms still developed on the other half of the fruit. Different varieties of tomatoes and apples show marked differences in susceptibility to these two physiological disorders but little is known of the basis for such differences. Greenleaf and Adams (1969) have shown that varying incidence of blossom-end rot in two tomato varieties can be accounted for by differing efficiency in absorbing and accumulating calcium in the fruit.

F. Developing Fruits as Physiological Sinks

1. Preferential movement of nutrients to fruits

It has long been recognized that fruits exhibit a relative stability in chemical composition under changing conditions of nutrition (Murneek, 1924; Arnon and Hoagland, 1943). This implies that available nutrients move preferentially to developing fruits at the expense of other plant organs. In a series of ringing and defoliation experiments with apples Haller (1930) showed that the movement of nutrients was towards the developing fruits regardless of whether this movement was upwards or downwards or from one branch to another. Arnon and Hoagland (1943) regarded developing tomato fruits as sinks attracting nutrients at the expense of vegetative tissue.

Most subsequent descriptions of the relationships between developing fruits and leaves have been in terms of their competition for available nutrients and of the relative capacity of these organs as physiological or metabolic sinks. A sink is a region of tissue or organ into which nutrients, either inorganic ions or organic metabolites, appear to move preferentially. The region or organ appears to possess the ability to attract nutrients from other parts of the plant. Active regions of growth such as shoot apices are known to act as strong sinks. A young developing leaf while importing photosynthate is acting as a sink. There is much current interest in the concept of physiological sinks in attempts to explain many aspects of plant growth (Watson, 1968).

Many studies of the movement of ^{14}C-assimilates, from leaves treated with $^{14}CO_2$ to developing fruits, have illustrated the capacity of these latter to act as sinks: apple (Hansen, 1967a, 1969); peach and apricot (Kriedemann, 1968a); orange (Kriedemann, 1969); grape (Hale and Weaver, 1962) and tomato (Khan and Sagar, 1966, 1967). There is now abundant evidence confirming that nutrients move preferentially into developing fruits, even if this means an alteration or reversal of translocation patterns that existed before fruit set.

It is clear that active competition exists between developing fruits and developing leaves and shoots and that the situation is constantly changing. Thus, when a bourse shoot develops in apples it initially competes with the developing fruit for incoming nutrients but later it will export assimilates (Abbott, 1960). Developing peach and apricot fruits at an early stage apparently compete successfully for available nutrients with newly expanding foliage (Kriedemann, 1968a), but developing oranges are not relatively so successful at a corresponding stage (Kriedemann, 1968b, 1969). With oranges, a developing fruit close by was necessary for a leaf to export assimilate. Coombe (1962) found that removal of immature leaves and shoot tips from ringed branches increased fruit set in grapes. He attributed these results to the superior ability of immature leaves and shoot apices to procure nutrients at the expense of the developing fruit. If branches were not girdled, leaf removal had no effect on fruit set; presumably, under these conditions, nutrients moved into the defoliated shoot from elsewhere (Coombe, 1965).

Competition between individual fruits developing at the same time also occurs. Within a truss on a tomato plant there is a reduction in fruit size on passing down the truss from the main axis (Beadle, 1937). The first-set fruit commences growth and, although the other fruits may be fertilized in quick succession, it appears that the first fruit monopolizes the available nutrients to the extent that the remaining fruits grow less quickly.

An investigation of the mechanism of the directional transport of nutrients into developing fruits has been attempted by following the movement of ^{32}P-phosphate and ^{42}K into developing strawberry fruits (Antoszewski and Lis, 1967, 1968; Antoszewski et al., 1968). Injection of these nutrients into the peduncle allowed movement into the developing fruits but not back to the mother plant. The excised peduncle showed no such polarity of movement. Further experiments showed that movement of isotope into fruits was determined by the presence of the fruits, not by the mother plant. When radioactive material was applied to the surface of, or injected into, the developing receptacle, activity spread throughout the receptacle but did not move out of this organ, except for a day or so after pollination. Prevention of fruit transpiration did not inhibit movement of nutrients into the fruits. These results appear to show that the strawberry fruit develops the ability to bring about movement of nutrients from the mother plant, that this attraction is independent of transpiration, and that the developing receptacle offers some kind of physiological trap to these nutrients once they arrive there. It would be most interesting to see similar experiments performed on the movement of carbohydrates.

Whereas nutrients appear to move preferentially into developing fruits, moisture can apparently be drawn from fruits to leaves. The occurrence of diurnal changes in fruit growth rate and of daily fruit shrinkage have already been discussed. To some extent fruits appear to act as reservoirs of moisture from which leaves can draw. Thus it has been observed that leaves on detached lemon shoots bearing fruits do not wilt as rapidly as those on similar shoots bearing no fruits (Bartholomew, 1926). Leaves could apparently not withdraw water from young orange fruits, but once these attained 35 mm diameter they behaved similarly to lemons (Rokach, 1953). This situation is in marked contrast to the ability of fruits to act as stronger sinks for nutrients than leaves.

2. *Role of hormones in directional transport*

The idea that the ability of developing fruits to attract nutrients was under some sort of hormonal control appears to have been first stated by Murneek (1926), before the nature of any plant hormones was known: "It is conceivable that plants may have a controlling glandular organization or a system of secretions similar to that existing in animals. If such an organization of secretions or hormones were to come into play at certain stages of development of particular organs, one would more or less be able to account for the control by and diversion to the fruit of certain food constituents." Arnon and Hoagland (1943) also suggested that the mechanism for movement of nutrients into developing tomato fruits might be "incited by some hormone-like substance."

More recent work clearly suggests that translocation is under some sort of hormonal control. In excised leaves, for example, kinetin will bring about movement of amino acids and phosphate to localized areas of application (Mothes et al., 1959; Engelbrecht, 1961). In intact plants there have been demonstrations that applications of either auxin (Davies and Wareing, 1965), gibberellin (Denisova and Lupinovich, 1961) or cytokinin (Muller and Leopold, 1966) can increase the movement of phosphate and other inorganic ions. In a soybean plant from which the apical meristem was removed, application of either indole acetic acid or gibberellic acid increased the movement of labelled assimilate from a primary leaf and affected its distribution throughout the plant (Hew et al., 1967). When either cytokinins or gibberellic acid were applied to grape shoots or portions of shoots the normal pattern of translocation of labelled assimilate was altered in that there was augmented movement into the treated regions (Shindy and Weaver, 1967). These effects are all most easily explained on the hypothesis that application of various plant growth substances increases the capacity of some tissues to accumulate photosynthetic products—that is, increases their capacity as physiological sinks.

There is an increasing belief that hormone-directed transport is important in the normal redistribution of nutrients from various parts of the plant to growing organs, even though details of the process still remain obscure. Coombe (1965), from experiments on the effects of leaves on fruit set in grapes, suggested that once set has occurred the developing berries become strong sinks. He suggested that this might be due to either the occurrence of intensive cell division in the young fruit or an increase in content of growth substances, although these two factors might well be causally interrelated. Crane (1965) and Crane and Van Overbeek (1965) considered the effect of growth substances in inducing parthenocarpic fruits in figs as, basically, a triggering by these substances of movement of metabolites, produced in other parts of the tree, into the developing fruits. They suggested that, following normal pollination, the fertilized ovule or seed synthesized hormones which initiate a similar metabolic gradient.

Direct proof of the similarity between effects of normally developing fruits and application of growth substances on nutrient transport has been provided by Seth and Wareing (1967) in experiments with French bean plants. They showed that ^{32}P-activity from adjacent leaves normally moved into the fruit peduncle but that this movement was greatly reduced if the developing fruit had been removed. However, if indoleacetic acid in lanolin paste was applied to the peduncle when the fruit was removed, substantial movement of ^{32}P again occurred. Transport of ^{14}C-labelled assimilates from leaves to the fruit peduncle was stimulated in the same way. In this experimental system neither gibberellic acid nor kinetin had any effect when applied individually but there was a synergistic interaction when the three hormones were applied together. The time within which these effects could be observed made it unlikely that the nutrient movement was a direct result of growth. Seth and Wareing suggested that, at the point of application of the hormones, there was a stimulation of nucleic acid and protein synthesis thereby establishing a metabolic sink.

Application of growth substances to normally developing fruits often increases their rate of development and their final size. For instance, certain auxins increase the size of apricots (Crane et al., 1956) and gibberellic acid the size of grapes, apricots and peaches (Weaver and McCune, 1959; Jackson, 1968a). Such effects can probably be explained by an effect of the growth substance on nutrient transport into developing fruits. It has been shown for example, that applications of kinetin to developing oranges, or of gibberellic acid to developing grapes, increase the movement of ^{14}C-labelled assimilates into fruits from leaves exposed to ^{14}CO$_2$ (Kriedemann, 1968b; Weaver et al., 1969).

In much recent work it is presumed that other effects of growth substances can be explained in terms of effects on nutrient movement into developing fruits, although there is usually no demonstration of such enhanced nutrient movement. Thus the effects of ethylene in modifying the growth curve of fig fruits, and of gibberellic acid in inducing parthenocarpy in plums, are each discussed in terms of the ability of the particular growth substance to bring about movement of nutrients into developing fruits (Maxie and Crane, 1968; Jackson, 1968b).

While it has been established that growth substances, either naturally produced in the fruit tissues or artificially applied, can affect the movement of nutrients into developing fruits the mechanism of such effects is not at all understood. It may be that growth substances stimulate some aspect of metabolism, and that it is this increased metabolic activity which establishes or enhances the physiological sink. Our knowledge of the properties of such sinks is meagre. It would be interesting to know, for example, something of the specificity of such sinks—is a sink for carbohydrates also a sink for inorganic ions? The suggestion of Coombe (1960) that the second phase of growth in grapes is a movement of water following a large influx of sugar into the developing berry, does not eliminate the possibility of hormone action, as the movement of sugar has itself to be explained.

At present we have little knowledge of the basic mode of action of the several kinds of plant hormone and little understanding of the complex interactions which occur between them. It is clear that we can make a first approach to an understanding of their role in fruit development on the basis of their ability to mobilize nutrients, but this would appear to be a relatively crude process to explain the nicely integrated phases of growth observed in developing fruits. Any theory of the action of growth substances in fruit development has to explain a number of phenomena: the role of seeds, the development of normally parthenocarpic fruits, the development of parthenocarpic fruits following application of a growth substance, the effects of added growth substances on development of fertilized fruits and the two-phase growth cycle in stone and other fruits. In addition to these effects on organ development, the cellular requirements for growth substances shown by fruit tissues growing in culture has also to be explained. It is likely that further understanding of the role of growth substances in fruit development must await advances in our understanding of their molecular action.

REFERENCES

Abbott, D. L. (1960). *Ann. appl. Biol.* **48**, 434.
Albrigo, L. G., Claypool, L. L. and Uriu, K. (1966). *Proc. Am. Soc. hort. Sci.* **89**, 53.
Aldrich, W. W. and Crawford, C. L. (1939). *Proc. Am. Soc. hort. Sci.* **37**, 187.
Anderson, J. D., Andrews, P. and Hough, L. (1961). *Biochem. J.* **81**, 149.
Anderssen, F. G. (1929). *Pl. Physiol., Lancaster* **4**, 459.
Antoszewski, R., Dzięciol, U. and Lis, E. K. (1968). *Acta Soc. Bot. Pol.* **37**, 433.
Antoszewski, R. and Lis, E. K. (1967). *Acta Soc. Bot. Pol.* **36**, 411.
Antoszewski, R. and Lis, E. (1968). *Bull. Acad. pol. Sci. Sér. Sci. biol.* **16**, 443.
Arnon, D. I. and Hoagland, D. R. (1943). *Bot. Gaz.* **104**, 576.

Askew, H. O. (1935). *J. Pomol.* **13**, 232.
Askew, H. O., Chittenden, E. T., Monk, R. J. and Watson, J. (1959). *N.Z. Jl agric. Res.* **2**, 1167.
Askew, H. O., Chittenden, E. T., Monk, R. J. and Watson, J. (1960). *N.Z. Jl agric. Res.* **3**, 141.
Bailey, L. H. (1949). "Manual of Cultivated Plants", 2nd edition, 1116 pp. Macmillan, New York.
Bain, J. M. (1958). *Aust. J. Bot.* **6**, 1.
Bain, J. M. (1961). *Aust. J. Bot.* **9**, 99.
Bain, J. M. and Robertson, R. N. (1951). *Aust. J. scient. Res. B* **4**, 75.
Bajaj, Y. P. S. and Collins, W. B. (1968). *Proc. Am. Soc. hort. Sci.* **93**, 326.
Baker, G. A. and Davis, L. D. (1951). *Proc. Am. Soc. hort. Sci.* **57**, 104.
Barnell, H. R. (1940). *Ann. Bot.* **4**, 39.
Bartholomew, E. T. (1926). *Am. J. Bot.* **13**, 102.
Batjer, L. P. and Martin, G. C. (1965). *Proc. Am. Soc. hort. Sci.* **87**, 139.
Batjer, L. P. and Westwood, M. N. (1958). *Proc. Am. Soc. hort. Sci.* **71**, 116.
Beadle, N. C. W. (1937). *Aust. J. exp. Biol. med. Sci.* **15**, 173.
Bean, R. C., Porter, G. G. and Barr, B. K. (1963). *Pl. Physiol., Lancaster* **38**, 285.
Bean, R. C. and Todd, G. W. (1960). *Pl. Physiol., Lancaster* **35**, 425.
Bieleski, R. L. (1969). *Aust. J. biol. Sci.* **22**, 611.
Blake, M. A., Davidson, O. W., Addoms, R. M. and Nightingale, G. T. (1931). *Bull. New Jers. agric. Exp. Stn* **525**, 35 pp.
Blanpied, G. D. and Wilde, M. H. (1968). *Bot. Gaz.* **129**, 173.
Bogin, E. and Wallace, A. (1966). *Proc. Am. Soc. hort. Sci.* **89**, 182.
Bollard, E. G. (1953). *J. exp. Bot.* **4**, 363.
Bollard, E. G. (1957a). *Aust. J. biol. Sci.* **10**, 279.
Bollard, E. G. (1957b). *Aust. J. biol. Sci.* **10**, 288.
Bollard, E. G. (1960). *A. Rev. Pl. Physiol.* **11**, 141.
Bollard, E. G. and Butler, G. W. (1966). *A. Rev. Pl. Physiol.* **17**, 77.
Bonnemain, J.-L. (1965). *C. r. hebd. Séanc. Acad. Sci., Paris* **260**, 2054.
Bouma, D. (1959). *Aust. J. agric. Res.* **10**, 804.
Boynton, D. and Wilde, M. H. (1959). *Proc. Am. Soc. hort. Sci.* **73**, 158.
Bradley, M. V. and Crane, J. C. (1955). *Am. J. Bot.* **42**, 273.
Brooks, R. M. (1939). *Proc. Am. Soc. hort. Sci.* **37**, 193.
Carañgal, A. R., Alban, E. K., Varner, J. E. and Burrell, R. C. (1954). *Pl. Physiol., Lancaster* **29**, 355.
Catlin, P. B. and Maxie, E. C. (1959). *Proc. Am. Soc. hort. Sci.* **74**, 159.
Chaney, W. R. and Kozlowski, T. T. (1969). *Can. J. Bot.* **47**, 1033.
Chittenden, E. T., Stanton, D. J. and Watson, J. (1969). *N.Z. Jl agric. Res.* **12**, 240.
Connors, C. H. (1919). *Rep. New Jers. St. agric. Exp. Stn* **40**, 82.
Coombe, B. G. (1960). *Pl. Physiol., Lancaster* **35**, 241.
Coombe, B. G. (1962). *J. hort. Sci.* **37**, 1.
Coombe, B. G. (1965). *J. hort. Sci.* **40**, 307.
Cooper, A. J. (1961). *J. hort. Sci.* **36**, 55.
Cooper, A. J. (1964). *J. hort. Sci.* **39**, 173.
Crafts, A. S. and Lorenz, O. A. (1944). *Pl. Physiol., Lancaster* **19**, 131.
Crane, J. C. (1948). *Proc. Am. Soc. hort. Sci.* **52**, 237.
Crane, J. C. (1953). *Proc. Am. Soc. hort. Sci.* **61**, 163.
Crane, J. C. (1965). *Pl. Physiol., Lancaster* **40**, 606.
Crane, J. C. and Baker, R. E. (1953). *Proc. Am. Soc. hort. Sci.* **62**, 257.

Crane, J. C. and Brown, J. G. (1950). *Proc. Am. Soc. hort. Sci.* **56**, 93.
Crane, J. C., De Kazos, E. D. and Brown, J. G. (1956). *Proc. Am. Soc. hort. Sci.* **68**, 105.
Crane, J. C. and Punsri, P. (1956). *Proc. Am. Soc. hort. Sci.* **68**, 96.
Crane, J. C., Rebeiz, C. A. and Campbell, R. C. (1961). *Proc. Am. Soc. hort. Sci.* **78**, 111.
Crane, J. C. and Van Overbeek, J. (1965). *Science, N.Y.* **147**, 1468.
Davies, J. N. (1966). *Nature, Lond.* **209**, 640.
Davies, C. R. and Wareing, P. F. (1965). *Planta* **65**, 139.
Davies, J. W. and Cocking, E. C. (1965). *Planta* **67**, 242.
Denisova, A. Z. and Lupinovich, I. S. (1961). *Pl. Physiol., Wash.* **8**, 360.
Denne, M. P. (1960). *Ann. Bot.* **24**, 397.
Denne, M. P. (1963). *N.Z. Jl Bot.* **1**, 265.
Dorsey, M. J. and McMunn, R. L. (1927). *Proc. Am. Soc. hort. Sci.* **24**, 221.
Drake, M., Weeks, W. D., Baker, J. H., Field, D. L. and Olanyk, G. W. (1966). *Proc. Am. Soc. hort. Sci.* **89**, 23.
Engelbrecht, L. (1961). *Flora, Jena* **150**, 73.
Evans, H. J. and Troxler, R. V. (1953). *Proc. Am. Soc. hort. Sci.* **61**, 346.
Fisher, K. J. (1967). *J. hort. Sci.* **42**, 243.
Flood, A. E., Hulme, A. C. and Wooltorton, L. S. C. (1960). *J. exp. Bot.* **11**, 316.
Garman, P. and Mathis, W. T. (1956). *Bull. Conn. agric. Exp. Stn* **601**, 19 pp.
Geraldson, C. M. (1957). *Proc. Am. Soc. hort. Sci.* **69**, 309.
Greenleaf, W. H. and Adams, F. (1969). *J. Am. Soc. hort. Sci.* **94**, 248.
Griggs, W. H, and Iwakiri, B. T. (1956). *Proc. Am. Soc. hort. Sci.* **67**, 91.
Griggs, W. H., Iwakiri, B. T. and Claypool, L. L. (1957). *Proc. Am. Soc. hort. Sci.* **70**, 74.
Gustafson, F. G. (1927). *Pl. Physiol., Lancaster* **2**, 153.
Gustafson, F. G. and Houghtaling, H. B. (1939). *Pl. Physiol., Lancaster* **14**, 321.
Gustafson, F. G. and Stoldt, E. (1936). *Pl. Physiol., Lancaster* **11**, 445.
Haas, A. R. C. and Bliss, D. E. (1935). *Hilgardia* **9**, 295.
Hale, C. R. (1962). *Nature, Lond.* **195**, 917.
Hale, C. R. (1968). *Aust. J. agric. Res.* **19**, 939.
Hale, C. R. and Weaver, R. J. (1962). *Hilgardia* **33**, 89.
Haller, M. H. (1930). *Proc. Am. Soc. hort. Sci.* **27**, 63.
Haller, M. H. and Magness, J. R. (1925). *Proc. Am. Soc. hort. Sci.* **22**, 189.
Hansen, P. (1967a). *Physiologia Pl.* **20**, 382.
Hansen, P. (1967b). *Physiologia Pl.* **20**, 1103.
Hansen, P. (1969). *Physiologia Pl.* **22**, 186.
Hardy, P. J. (1967). *Aust. J. biol. Sci.* **20**, 465.
Hardy, P. J. and Possingham, J. V. (1969). *J. exp. Bot.* **20**, 325.
Harley, C. P. (1942). *Proc. Am. Soc. hort. Sci.* **40**, 165.
Harley, C. P. and Masure, M. P. (1938). *J. agric. Res.* **57**, 109.
Hartmann, H. T. (1949). *Proc. Am. Soc. hort. Sci.* **54**, 86.
Havis, A. L. (1943). *Am. J. Bot.* **30**, 311.
Hew, C. S., Nelson, C. D. and Krotkov, G. (1967). *Am. J. Bot.* **54**, 252.
Hilgeman, R. H. and Smith, J. G. (1939). *Proc. Am. Soc. hort. Sci.* **37**, 535.
Hill, R. G. (1958). *Res. Bull. Ohio agric. Exp. Stn.* **803**, 35 pp.
Hill-Cottingham, D. G. and Bollard, E. G. (1965). *N.Z. Jl agric. Res.* **8**, 778.
Hill-Cottingham, D. G. and Lloyd-Jones, C. P. (1968). *Nature, Lond.* **220**, 389.
Hopkins, E. F. and Gourley, J. H. (1933). *Bull. Ohio agric. Exp. Stn* **519**, 30 pp.

Jackson, D. I. (1968a). *Aust. J. biol. Sci.* **21**, 209.
Jackson, D. I. (1968b). *Aust. J. biol. Sci.* **21**, 1103.
Jackson, D. I. and Coombe, B. G. (1966). *Aust. J. agric. Res.* **17**, 465.
Jankiewicz, L. S., Antoszewski, R. and Klimowicz, E. (1967). *Biologia Pl.* **9**, 116.
Johnston, F. B., Spangelo, L. P., Watkins, R. and Hammill, M. M. (1968). *Can. J. Pl. Sci.* **48**, 473.
Jones, O. P. and Rowe, R. W. (1968). *Nature, Lond.* **219**, 403.
Kazaryan, V. O., Balagezyan, N. V. and Karapetyan, K. A. (1965). *Pl. Physiol., Wash.* **12**, 265.
Kennard, W. C. (1955). *Bot. Gaz.* **117**, 28.
Khan, A. A. and Sagar, G. R. (1966). *Ann. Bot.* **30**, 727.
Khan, A. A. and Sagar, G. R. (1967). *Hort. Res.* **7**, 61.
Kidd, F. and West, C. (1947). *New Phytol.* **46**, 274.
Kliewer, W. M. (1966). *Pl. Physiol., Lancaster* **41**, 923.
Knight, L. D. M. and Wallace, T. (1932). *J. Pomol.* **10**, 147.
Koo, R. C. J. and Sites, J. W. (1956). *Proc. Am. Soc. hort. Sci.* **68**, 245.
Kordan, H. A. (1959). *Science, N.Y.* **129**, 779.
Kordan, H. A. (1963). *Nature, Lond.* **198**, 867.
Kordan, H. A. (1965). *Bull. Torrey bot. Club* **92**, 209.
Kozlowski, T. T. (1968). *J. hort. Sci.* **43**, 1.
Kriedemann, P. E. (1968a). *Aust. J. agric. Res.* **19**, 775.
Kriedemann, P. E. (1968b). *Aust. J. biol. Sci.* **21**, 569.
Kriedemann, P. C. (1968c). *Aust. J. biol. Sci.* **21**, 907.
Kriedemann, P. E. (1969). *Aust. J. agric. Res.* **20**, 291.
Lee, F. A. and Tukey, H. B. (1942). *Bot. Gaz.* **104**, 348.
Leopold, A. C., Niedergang-Kamien, E. and Janick, J. (1959). *Pl. Physiol., Lancaster* **34**, 570.
Letham, D. S. (1958). *Nature, Lond.* **182**, 473.
Letham, D. S. (1960). *Nature, Lond.* **188**, 425.
Lilleland, O. (1930). *Proc. Am. Soc. hort. Sci.* **27**, 237.
Lilleland, O. (1932). *Proc. Am. Soc. hort. Sci.* **29**, 8.
Lilleland, O. (1933). *Proc. Am. Soc. hort. Sci.* **30**, 203.
Lilleland, O. (1935). *Proc. Am. Soc. hort. Sci.* **33**, 269.
Lilleland, O. and Brown, J. G. (1936). *Proc. Am. Soc. hort. Sci.* **34**, 264.
Lilleland, O. and Newsome, L. (1934). *Proc. Am. Soc. hort. Sci.* **32**, 291.
Lockhart, J. A. and Gottschall, V. (1961). *Pl. Physiol., Lancaster* **36**, 389.
Long, E. M. (1943). *Bot. Gaz.* **104**, 426.
Lott, R. V. (1932). *Proc. Am. Soc. hort. Sci.* **29**, 1.
Lott, R. V. (1942). *Bull. Ill. agric. Exp. Stn* **493**, 323.
Lott, R. V. (1965). *Proc. Am. Soc. hort. Sci.* **87**, 47.
Lott, R. V. and Ashley, T. E. (1935). *Proc. Am. Soc. hort. Sci.* **33**, 258.
Luckwill, L. C. (1948). *J. hort. Sci.* **24**, 32.
McCollum, J. P. and Skok, J. (1960). *Proc. Am. Soc. hort. Sci.* **75**, 611.
McGlasson, W. B. and Pratt, H. K. (1963). *Proc. Am. Soc. hort. Sci.* **83**, 495.
Maggs, D. H. (1963). *J. hort. Sci.* **38**, 119.
Maxie, E. C. and Crane, J. C. (1968). *Proc. Am. Soc. hort. Sci.* **92**, 255.
Meynhardt, J. T. and Malan, A. H. (1963). *S. Afr. J. agric. Sci.* **6**, 337.
Morrison, T. M. (1965). *Nature, Lond.* **205**, 1027.
Mothes, K., Engelbrecht, L. and Kulajewa, O. (1959). *Flora, Jena* **147**, 445.
Moustafa, S. and Stout, B. A. (1967). *Q. Bull. Mich. St. Univ. agric. Exp. Stn* **49**, 450.

424   E. G. BOLLARD

Müller, K. and Leopold, A. C. (1966). *Planta* **68**, 167.
Murashige, T., Nakano, R. and Tucker, D. P. H. (1967). *Phytomorphology* **17**, 469.
Murneek, A. E. (1924). *Proc. Am. Soc. hort. Sci.* **21**, 274.
Murneek, A. E. (1926). *Pl. Physiol., Lancaster* **1**, 3.
Nitsch, J. P. (1949). *Science, N. Y.* **110**, 499.
Nitsch, J. P. (1950). *Am. J. Bot.* **37**, 211.
Nitsch, J. P. (1951). *Am. J. Bot.* **38**, 566.
Nitsch, J. P. (1959). *Bull. Soc. bot. Fr.* **106**, 420.
Nitsch, J. P. (1963). *In* "Plant Tissue and Organ Culture—a Symposium" (P. Maheshwari and N. S. Ranga Swamy, eds) pp. 198–214. International Society of Plant Morphologists, Delhi.
Nitsch, J. P. (1965a). *Bull. Soc. bot. Fr.* **112**, 19.
Nitsch, J. P. (1965b). *Bull. Soc. bot. Fr.* **112**, 22.
Nitsch, J. P., Pratt, C., Nitsch, C. and Shaulis, N. J. (1960). *Am. J. Bot.* **47**, 566.
Norton, R. A. and Wittwer, S. H. (1963). *Proc. Am. Soc. hort. Sci.* **82**, 277.
Oland, K. (1959). *Physiologia Pl.* **12**, 594.
Oland, K. (1963). *Physiologia Pl.* **16**, 682.
Othlinghaus, D., Schmitz, K. and Willenbrink, J. (1968). *Planta* **80**, 89.
Pate, J. S., Wallace, W. and van Die, J. (1964). *Nature, Lond.* **204**, 1073.
Pearson, J. A. and Robertson, R. N. (1953). *Aust. J. biol. Sci.* **6**, 1.
Quinlan, J. D. (1966). *Rep. E. Malling Res. Stn 1965*, 128.
Quinlan, J. D. and Preston, A. P. (1968). *J. hort. Sci.* **43**, 373.
Ragland, C. H. (1934). *Proc. Am. Soc. hort. Sci.* **31**, 1.
Rasmussen, G. K. (1964). *Proc. Am. Soc. hort. Sci.* **84**, 181.
Rasmussen, G. K. and Smith, P. F. (1961). *Pl. Physiol., Lancaster* **36**, 99.
Rebeiz, C. A. and Crane, J. C. (1961). *Proc. Am. Soc. hort. Sci.* **78**, 69.
Reeve, R. M. (1954). *Am. J. Bot.* **41**, 152.
Robertson, R. N. and Turner, J. F. (1951). *Aust. J. scient. Res. B* **4**, 92.
Rogers, B. L. and Batjer, L. P. (1954). *Proc. Am. Soc. hort. Sci.* **63**, 67.
Rokach, A. (1953). *Palest. J. Bot. Rehovot Ser.* **8**, 146.
Ryugo, K. (1964). *Proc. Am. Soc. hort. Sci.* **85**, 154.
Ryugo, K. and Davis, L. D. (1958). *Proc. Am. Soc. hort. Sci.* **72**, 106.
Ryugo, K. and Davis, L. D. (1959). *Proc. Am. Soc. hort. Sci.* **74**, 130.
Schroeder, C. A. (1953). *Proc. Am. Soc. hort. Sci.* **61**, 103.
Schroeder, C. A. (1955). *Science, N.Y.* **122**, 601.
Schroeder, C. A. (1960). *Proc. Am. Soc. hort. Sci.* **76**, 248.
Schroeder, C. A. (1961). *Bot. Gaz.* **122**, 198.
Schroeder, C. A. and Spector, C. (1957). *Science, N.Y.* **126**, 701.
Schroeder, C. A. and Wieland, P. A. (1956). *Proc. Am. Soc. hort. Sci.* **68**, 253.
Seth, A. K. and Wareing, P. F. (1967). *J. exp. Bot.* **18**, 65.
Sharples, R. O. (1964). *J. hort. Sci.* **39**, 224.
Shindy, W. and Weaver, R. J. (1967). *Nature, Lond.* **214**, 1024.
Shutak, V. G., Hindle, R. and Christopher, E. P. (1957). *Bull. Rhode Isl. agric. Exp. Stn 339*, 18 pp.
Sideris, C. P. and Krauss, B. H. (1938). *Growth* **2**, 181.
Simmonds, N. W. (1953). *J. exp. Bot.* **4**, 87.
Sinclair, W. B. and Eny, D. M. (1945). *Bot. Gaz.* **107**, 231.
Sinclair, W. B. and Eny, D. M. (1946). *Pl. Physiol., Lancaster* **21**, 140.
Sinclair, W. B. and Ramsey, R. C. (1944). *Bot. Gaz.* **106**, 140.
Singleton, V. L. (1965). *J. Fd Sci.* **30**, 98.

Singleton, V. L. and Gortner, W. A. (1965). *J. Fd Sci.* **30**, 19.
Sinnott, E. W. (1939). *Am. J. Bot.* **26**, 179.
Sinnott, E. W. (1945). *Am. J. Bot.* **32**, 439.
Skene, D. S. (1966). *Ann. Bot.* **30**, 493.
Smith, W. H. (1950). *Ann. Bot.* **14**, 23.
Sommer, N. F., Bradley, M. V. and Cresay, M. T. (1962). *Science, N.Y.* **136**, 264.
Sterling, C. (1953). *Bull. Torrey bot. Club* **80**, 457.
Swanson, C. A. and El-Shishiny, E. D. H. (1958). *Pl. Physiol., Lancaster* **33**, 33.
Taper, C. D. and Liu, P. S. (1969). *Can. J. Pl. Sci.* **49**, 97.
Taylor, B. K. (1967). *Aust. J. biol. Sci.* **20**, 379.
Taylor, B. K. and May, L. H. (1967). *Aust. J. biol. Sci.* **20**, 389.
Thrower, S. L. (1962). *Aust. J. biol. Sci.* **15**, 629.
Todd, G. W., Bean, R. C. and Propst, B. (1961). *Pl. Physiol., Lancaster* **36**, 69.
Tromp, J. and Ovaa, J. C. (1967). *Z. PflPhysiol.* **57**, 11.
Tromp, J. and Ovaa, J. C. (1969). *Z. PflPhysiol.* **60**, 232.
Tukey, H. B. (1933). *Proc. Am. Soc. hort. Sci.* **30**, 209.
Tukey, H. B. (1934). *Proc. Am. Soc. hort. Sci.* **31**, 125.
Tukey, H. B. and Lee, F. A. (1937). *Bot. Gaz.* **98**, 586.
Tukey, H. B. and Lee, F. A. (1940). *Bot. Gaz.* **101**, 818.
Tukey, H. B. and Young, J. O. (1939). *Bot. Gaz.* **100**, 723.
Tukey, H. B. and Young, J. O. (1942). *Bot. Gaz.* **104**, 3.
Tukey, L. D. (1952). *Bot. Gaz.* **114**, 155.
Tukey, L. D. (1958). *Proc. Am. Soc. hort. Sci.* **71**, 157.
Tukey, L. D. (1959). *Bull. Pa agric. Exp. Stn* **661**, 21 pp.
Tyler, K. B. and Lorenz, O. A. (1964). *Proc. Am. Soc. hort. Sci.* **84**, 364.
van Die, J. (1958). *Proc. K. ned. Akad. Wet.* **C61**, 572.
van Die, J. (1963). *Acta bot. neerl.* **12**, 269.
van Die, J. and Vonk, C. R. (1967). *Acta bot. neerl.* **16**, 147.
Van Overbeek, J. (1946). *Bot. Gaz.* **108**, 64.
Ward, G. M. (1964). *Pl. Soil* **21**, 125.
Ward, G. M. (1967). *Pl. Soil* **26**, 324.
Watson, D. J. (1968). *Ann. appl. Biol.* **62**, 1.
Weaver, R. J. and McCune, S. B. (1959). *Hilgardia* **29**, 247.
Weaver, R. J., Shindy, W. and Kliewer, W. M. (1969). *Pl. Physiol., Lancaster* **44**, 183.
Webb, K. L. and Burley, J. W. A. (1962). *Science, N.Y.* **137**, 766.
Westwood, M. N. (1962). *Proc. Am. Soc. hort. Sci.* **80**, 90.
Whetter, J. M. and Taper, C. D. (1963). *Can. J. Bot.* **41**, 175.
Whetter, J. M. and Taper, C. D. (1966). *Can. J. Bot.* **44**, 51.
Wiersum, L. K. (1966a). *Acta horticulturae* **4**, 33.
Wiersum, L. K. (1966b). *Acta bot. neerl.* **15**, 406.
Williams, M. W., Martin, G. C. and Stahly, E. A. (1967). *Proc. Am. Soc. hort. Sci.* **90**, 20.
Winkler, A. J. (1932). *Proc. Am. Soc. hort. Sci.* **29**, 335.
Winkler, A. J. and Williams, W. O. (1935). *Proc. Am. Soc. hort. Sci.* **33**, 430.
Wright, S. T. C. (1956). *J. hort. Sci.* **31**, 196.
Young, R. S. (1952). *Proc. Am. Soc. hort. Sci.* **59**, 167.

Chapter 15

Hormonal Factors in Growth and Development

J. P. NITSCH

Laboratoire de Physiologie Pluricellulaire, CNRS,
91, Gif-sur-Yvette, France

In the previous chapter, emphasis has been laid upon the diversity of the fruit types from which man derives his food. When looked at from the physiological point of view of growth regulation, however, this diversity can be unified by defining fruits as entities which surround the ovules of a plant and whose development is linked to that of the ovules (see Nitsch, 1952). The physiological relationships between ovules and fruit tissues are to a great

427

extent hormonal in nature. In fact, hormones play a great role in the life of fruits, a role which will be the subject of the present chapter.

I. EXAMPLES OF HORMONAL EFFECTS IN THE LIFE OF FRUITS

Several phases can be distinguished in the life of fruits, namely:
   (i) the formation of the primordia;
   (ii) development before anthesis;
   (iii) the phase of anthesis, pollination and fertilization;
   (iv) growth after fruit "set";
   (v) ripening;
   (vi) senescence.
Hormonal effects may be detected at each of these stages.

A. Formation of Fruit Primordia Before Flower Opening

The tissues of the ovary are initiated last during the process of flower formation. In certain dioecious species, such as *Lychnis dioica*, the development of an ovary depends upon the presence of a particular sex chromosome (Westergaad, 1958). In other species, the sex character is not strongly impressed and can be modified by environmental factors.

In monoecious species, for example those belonging to the cucurbitaceae, the development of ovarian tissues can be profoundly influenced by environmental factors such as amount of daylight and temperature. In general, long days and high temperatures repress, whereas short days and low temperatures favour the development of flowers with ovaries (female flower), as shown by Nitsch *et al.* (1952) for *Cucurbita pepo* and *Cucumis sativus*. In the case of the cucumber, these studies have been extended by Galun (1956), Saito (1961), Fukushima *et al.* (1968), Matsuo (1968), Matsuo *et al.* (1968), etc. The papaya (*Carica payaya*) seems to behave similarly (Lange, 1961a).

Hormonal influences in these systems were first brought to light when Minina and Tylkina (1947) showed that carbon monoxide or ethylene stimulated the development of female flowers in cucumbers. These results were extended by Minina (1952). When a more convenient way of applying ethylene was found in the form of 2-chloroethanephosphonic acid ("Ethrel") which can be sprayed onto plants and disperses ethylene inside the tissues, the effect of ethylene in stimulating the formation of ovary-bearing flowers in Cucurbits was confirmed (Sims and Gledhill, 1969; Rudich *et al.*, 1969).

Auxins at relatively high concentrations were shown to stimulate also the formation of female flowers in cucumbers (Laibach and Kribben, 1949, 1950; Galun, 1956; Ito and Saito, 1956), *Cucurbita pepo* (Nitsch *et al.*, 1952) and *Luffa acutangula* (Satyanarayana and Rangaswamy, 1959). Since the concentrations used are those which cause the endogenous formation of ethylene (Burg and Burg, 1966), it is likely that auxins stimulate the development of pistillate flowers indirectly, by triggering off the production of ethylene. Recently, cytokinins have also been found to be involved in sex expression. Thus Negi and Olmo (1966) found that applying a cytokinin to flowers of a male grapevine three weeks before anthesis converted the flower sex from male to hermaphrodite; Durand (1967, 1969) reported that cytokinins can cause feminization in male individuals of *Mercurialis annua*, and Bose and Nitsch (1970) showed that soaking seeds of *Luffa acutangula* in a solution of N_6-benzyladenine stimulates the precocious formation of female flowers. It should be noted in this connection that cytokinins have also been reported to cause ethylene formation in plant tissues (Fuchs and Lieberman, 1968). In the case of the papaya, applications of 2,3-dichloroisobutyrate were found to stimulate the formation of flowers bearing ovaries instead of flowers bearing stamens only (Lange, 1961b). The exact mode of action of this chemical—which has been used to induce male sterility—remains to be elucidated in the case of the papaya. On the other hand, gibberellins prevent the formation of female flowers in Cucurbits. In fact, they are even able to induce the formation of male flowers on gynoecious lines of cucumbers which normally produce only pistillate flowers (Peterson and Anhder, 1960; Mitchell and Wittwer, 1962). On the contrary, allyl-trimethylammonium bromide enhances the production of female flowers in cucumber (Mitchell and Wittwer, 1962) and *N*-dimethyl-aminosuccinamic acid ("B-9") has a similar effect on cucumber, melon, watermelon, *Momordica charantia* and *Luffa acutangula* (Bose and Ghosh, 1968). These compounds may well act by lowering the level of endogenous gibberellins.

These few facts show that, even before anthesis, auxins, gibberellins, cytokinins and ethylene play a role in the development of the tissues which will give rise to fruits.

B. Anthesis, Pollination and Fertilization

1. *Anthesis*

Anthesis, that is the opening of the flower and the shedding of pollen, constitutes a critical phase in fruit development. The tissues of the fruit which have been growing regularly with the whole flower bud will cease to do so unless special events occur, namely, pollination and the fertilization of the ovules.

The precise cause of the cessation of growth resulting from the failure of these phenomena is not yet fully elucidated. Apparently the level of endogenous growth-promoting substances drops to a low level at this time. The results obtained by Ito *et al.* (1969) for the grape berry clearly show this fact in the case of auxins and gibberellins (Fig. 1).

(a) *Abscission.* In some cases, if unpollinated, the flower is cut off from the line of nutrient by the phenomenon of abscission. An abscission layer is clearly present in the apple (Pfeffer, 1904; MacDaniels, 1937), the tomato (Kendall, 1918), the grape etc. It is known that abscission is retarded by auxin, but only if applied to the blade end of a petiole (Addicott and Lynch, 1951) or the fruit end of the pedicel (Barlow, 1950). However, spraying synthetic auxins such as 1-naphthylacetic acid on the whole plant may promote

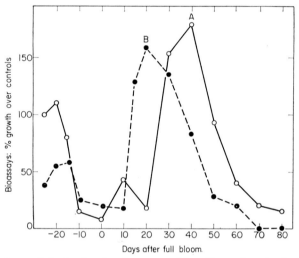

FIG. 1. Variations of the levels of endogenous gibberellins and auxins in the Delaware grape. A: gibberellins as measured in the rice seedling test. B: auxins as measured in the oat coleoptile straight growth test. Each point corresponds to an extract of 20 berries. Redrawn from Ito *et al.* (1969).

abscission, either because they are carried with the photosynthates in the fruit in an acropetal direction or because they actually kill the young ovules which are very sensitive to auxins (Luckwill, 1953; Murneek and Teubner, 1953; Teubner and Murneek, 1955). Thus, synthetic auxins have become effective thinning agents in apples (Gardner, 1951; Murneek, 1951), pears (Nitsch, 1954), peaches (Hibbart and Murneek, 1951), olives (Hartmann, 1952), dates (Nixon and Gardner, 1939), pecans, *Carya illinoensis* (Harris and Smith, 1957), and grapes (Weaver, 1954).

On the other hand, an increase in abscisic acid has also been detected at anthesis, for example in cotton (Addicott and Lyon, 1969) (Fig. 2).

(b) *Lack of growth without fertilization.* Obviously, the fruit tissues that abscise cannot continue to increase in size, severed as they are from the supply of nutrients. Conversely, the mere fact that ovaries remain attached to the plant is not sufficient to keep them growing. For example, unpollinated flowers of strawberries do not abscise; yet they stop growing and shrivel. This inability to use nutrients has been clearly demonstrated by excising pollinated and unpollinated ovaries and growing them *in vitro*. Thus ovaries of *Cucumis anguria* are able to grow on a relatively simple medium consisting of mineral salts and sugar when planted two days after pollination; similar ovaries, excised before pollination two days earlier are unable to grow on the same medium, although they may remain green and apparently healthy for some time (Nitsch, 1951).

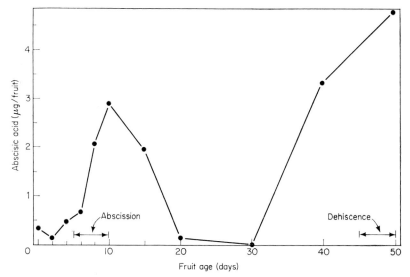

FIG. 2. Variations of the levels of abscisic acid in the developing cotton fruit. From Addicott and Lyon (1969).

It can be concluded that, aside from abscission, some positive growth stimulus is lacking once the flower has opened.

2. Pollination

This positive growth stimulus is usually generated by the pollen during its germination, during the growth of the pollen tube and, finally, with the fusion of one of the male nuclei with the egg cell (syngamy) and of the other with the two polar nuclei (triple fusion). These various events cannot always be easily separated from each other.

As early as 1901, Millardet reported that pollination of grape flowers (*Vitis vinifera*) with pollen of *Ampelopsis hederacea* caused the formation of seedless grape berries. Massart (1902) performed several experiments with melons and pumpkins, showing that the application of ground pollen, even of a different species, was able to cause at least the first symptoms of fruit set. The experiments of Fitting (1909) who could reproduce the effects of pollination by applying dead pollen or pollen extracts demonstrated further that pollen was contributing chemical substances which prevented abscission and caused the growth of the fruits. These substances are not species-specific since extracts of pollen of *Hibiscus* were active on the ovaries of orchids. The injection into eggplants (*Solanum melongena*) of *Petunia* pollen ground in cold water caused very active cell division in the eggplant (Yasuda, 1934). Ether extracts of pollen were also able to cause fruit development (Gustafson, 1937).

The types of growth substances by which pollen stimulates fruit development include auxins and gibberellins. Auxins have been found in orchid pollinia (Laibach, 1932; Thimann, 1934; Nitsch, 1965a), in the pollen of hazelnut (Yakushkina, 1947), tobacco (Lund, 1956a), maize (Fukui *et al.* 1958), etc. Giberellins have been detected in the pollen of maize (Mitchell and Whitehead, 1941) and *Brassica napus* (Nitsch, 1965a).

The quantities of extractable auxins may be too small in pollen to account for the effects observed. Thus, in tobacco, appreciable quantities of auxin start to diffuse out of the base of the style after 14 hours, out of the base of the ovary after 35 hours and out of the pedicel 60 hours after pollination (Muir, 1942). This wave of auxin may be due to actual synthesis under the influence of enzymes or co-factors contributed by the pollen. Thus the conversion of tryptophan into auxin was found to proceed more vigorously in tobacco styles after pollination (Lund, 1956a, b). Applications of gibberellic acid to unpollinated tomato (Sastry and Muir, 1963) or grape (Ito *et al.*, 1969) flowers causes an increase in auxin. Gibberellins contributed by the pollen may thus also play a role in increasing the auxin production which is observed after pollination.

C. Fruit Set and Growth

Abscission of fruit tissues is not restricted to the unpollinated flower. It may also happen to fruitlets after pollination, either because syngamy (leading to embryo formation) or triple fusion (leading to the formation of the endosperm) or both have not taken place, or because of the degeneration of the endosperm and embryo.

In fact, after pollination, the leading role in controlling fruit development is taken up by the developing seeds. Numerous observations and experiments contributed by various workers over 70 years have demonstrated this point. The evidence runs generally along the following lines:

(i) If some of the young seeds do not develop, lop-sided fruits result, the developed parts occurring near the viable seeds, the retarded portions where seed development has not occurred, for example, in the apple (Heinicke, 1917; Roberts, 1946; Luckwill, 1949) or the strawberry (Nitsch, 1950). Various fruit shapes can be obtained with the strawberry by removing some of the achenes at selected sites (Nitsch, 1950). With this fruit, as with that of the cashew (Bose, 1964), it can be clearly demonstrated that developing seeds stimulate the development of fruit tissues around them (Fig. 3).

FIG. 3. Stimulation of growth in the strawberry receptacle by three developing achenes. From Nitsch (1950).

(ii) The final weight of a fruit is often proportional to the number of developed seeds, as shown in the case of the grape berry (Müller-Thorgau, 1898) or of the strawberry (Fig. 4).

(iii) The developing seeds contain much more growth substances than the surrounding fruit tissues, whether in squashes and tomatoes (Gustafson, 1939a, b), strawberries (Nitsch, 1950), green beans (Nitsch and Nitsch, 1955), peas (Gandar, 1964), etc. Fruit set can be achieved with extracts of immature seeds. Thus Wittwer (1943) and Redemann et al. (1951) caused fruit development in pepper (*Capsicum*) and tomato with extracts of immature maize kernels, and Luckwill (1948b) in tomato with extracts of immature apple seeds. As with pollen extracts, here again there is no species specificity.

All these facts show that seeds exert a profound influence upon the development of the surrounding tissues of the fruit and regulate their growth by hormonal means, that is, by means of substances which they possess and which are limiting for the fruit tissues. The case of seedless fruits will be discussed later (see Section V).

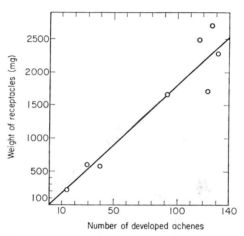

FIG. 4. Relationship between the number of developed achenes and the weight of the strawberry receptacle. From Nitsch (1950).

D. Ripening

Ripening is also controlled by hormones. On the one hand, it is triggered by an increase in the endogenous level of ethylene, for example in the Honeydew melon (*Cucumis melo*), as shown by Goeschl and Pratt (Fig. 5). On the other hand, it is delayed by gibberellins and cytokinins, as shown by Eilati *et al.* (1969) in the case of the peel of the orange.

II. THE HORMONES OF FRUITS

The examples which have been cited above clearly show that hormones of several kinds play an important role in the various phases of fruit growth. In this section their chemical nature and metabolism will be presented.

There are five main categories of plant hormones known today to take part in the regulation of fruit growth, namely: (a) the auxins; (b) the gibberellins; (c) the cytokinins; (d) abscisic acid and (e) ethylene. We will review briefly, in each case, the chemical nature of the substances involved, the site

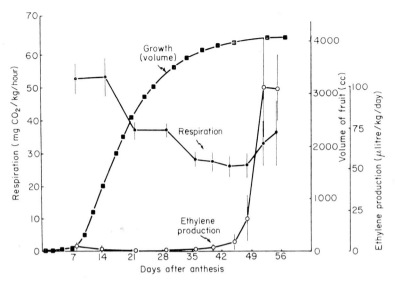

FIG. 5. Production of ethylene in the developing fruit of the Honeydew melon, picked at the indicated ages. From J. D. Goeschl and H. K. Pratt (unpublished).

of production of the hormones, the variations of their level during development and their metabolism.

A. Auxins in Fruits

1. Chemical identity

The auxins which have been isolated and chemically identified in fruits all belong to the indole family (Table I), although non-indolic auxins have been reported in citrus and other fruits (Lewis et al., 1965; Khalifah et al., 1965, Khalifah, 1966). In the latter case, however, only the scopoletin moiety of the compound has been identified; the moiety with auxin properties is still unknown (Lewis, personal communication, 1969). The presence of indolyl-3-acetic acid (IAA) and of its ester in the apple has been a subject of controversy. Thus Teubner (1953) reported that one of the auxins present in the apple endosperm was the ethyl ester of IAA, whereas Luckwill and Powell (1956) denied that this ester or even IAA was present in apple seeds. Von Raussendorff-Bargen (1962), however, also reported the presence of the ethyl ester of IAA in immature apple seeds and that of IAA in ripe apples. The ethyl ester of IAA extracted by Redemann et al. (1951) from immature maize kernels could also be an artefact, according to Fukui et al. (1957). Along similar lines, one could also think that the methyl ester of 4-chloro-indolyl-3-acetic acid isolated by Gandar and C. Nitsch (1967) and

Marumo *et al.* (1968) from immature pea seeds could be due to an esterification which might have occurred during the extraction with methanol. However, since the ratios between the acid and the ester vary with the age of the pea seed, this seems rather unlikely, unless the changes could be accounted

TABLE I. Chemical nature of the auxins and related substances isolated from pollen, fruits and immature seeds

Compound	Source	Reference
Indolyl-3-acetic acid (IAA)	*Cattleya labiata*, pollen and ovaries	Nitsch (1965a)
	Citrus sinensis cv. Washington Navel, young ovaries	C. Beyers (1958) (see Nitsch 1965a)
	Fragaria, immature achenes	Nitsch (1955)
	Malus sylvestris	von Raussendorff-Bargen (1962)
	Musa sapientum	Khalifah (1966)
	Prunus persica	Powell and Pratt (1966)
	Ribes nigrum	Neumann (1955)
	Zea mays, immature kernels	Haagen-Smit *et al.* (1946)
4-Chloro-indolyl-3-acetic acid	*Pisum sativum*, immature seeds	Marumo *et al.* (1968b)
Methyl 4-chloroindolyl-3-acetate	*Pisum sativum*, immature seeds	Gandar and C. Nitsch (1967); Marumo *et al.* (1968a)
IAA-arabinoside	*Zea mays*, immature kernels	Shantz and Steward (1957)
IAA-*myo*-inositol	*Zea mays*, immature kernels	Nicholls (1967)
IAA-*myo*-inositol-arabinoside	*Zea mays*, immature kernels	Labarca *et al.* (1965)
Ethyl indolyl-3-acetate	*Zea mays*, immature kernels	Redemann *et al.* (1951)
	Malus sylvestris, immature fruits	Teubner (1953); von Raussendorff-Bargen (1962)
2-Hydroxy-indolyl-3-acetic acid	*Malus sylvestris*, ripe fruits	von Raussendorff-Bargen (1962)
Malonyl-tryptophan[a]	*Malus sylvestris*, ripe fruits	von Raussendorff-Bargen (1962)
Indolyl-3-aldehyde[a]	*Malus sylvestris*, ripe fruits	von Raussendorff-Bargen (1962)
Indolyl-3-carboxylic acid[a]	*Malus sylvestris*, ripe fruits	von Raussendorff-Bargen (1962)

[a] Not biologically active as an auxin.

for by a variation in the activity of enzymes capable of esterifying the acid under the conditions used for extraction.

Aside from the auxins which have been chemically identified in fruits, several active substances remain to be isolated. A list of some unknown substances producing peaks of biological activity in various tests can be found in Nitsch (1965a).

2. Site of production

In young fruits, the site of production of the auxins in fruits is the seed. Later on, some auxin production may take place in the flesh itself. Thus, when tested with the Avena curvature test (which is specific for auxins) ether extracts of strawberry achenes yielded positive responses at all stages, whereas extracts from the flesh did not (Nitsch, 1950). In the case of the apple, Luckwill (1948a) found that endosperm tissues had the greatest concentration of auxin. A detailed investigation of the concentrations of various active substances in the integuments, endosperm and embryo of *Pisum sativum* was performed by Gandar (1964). Among the five substances studied, a mixture of a gibberellin and 4-chloro-indolyl-3-acetic acid (substance "B") was mostly concentrated in the endosperm, whereas its methylester (substance "F") reached the highest concentration in the embryo (Gandar and Nitsch, 1964).

3. Variations during development

The level of endogenous auxins in seeds does not remain constant but fluctuates widely. In the strawberry achene, the concentration of the total auxin readily extractable with ether increases about twenty-fold between the 3rd and the 12th day after pollination (Fig. 6). The peak in auxin concentration corresponds with the moment at which the endosperm has just become cellular (Nitsch, 1952). Such a correlation had been pointed out first by Luckwill (1948b) for the apple where a double peak occurs. The first maximum can be seen at the time the endosperm changes from a coenocytic condition to a cellular one. This change is rapid (1–2 days) which may explain the steepness of the curve in Fig. 6. At the same time, the embryo starts growing actively and digests the central region of the endosperm tissue. However, active cell divisions at the outer surface of the endosperm replenish the tissue. As the volume of the new endosperm thus formed reaches a maximum, a second peak of auxin activity can be detected.

In the case of the blackcurrant (*Ribes nigrum*), three different auxins have been separated by paper chromatography by Wright (1956). Two of them— IAA and another one resembling indoleacetonitrile—give a two peaked curve (Fig. 7); the level of the third substance (A_2) goes through one maximum only. Another example of the auxin changes during development can be found in data concerning the grape berry (Fig. 1 and Nitsch *et al.*, 1960).

4. Metabolism of auxins in fruits

One of the main auxins in fruits being IAA, tryptophan has been suspected as a possible precursor. Production of auxin from tryptophan has been obtained by incubating pollen with it for four hours (Nitsch, 1952) in the case of *Lilium regale* or by Lund (1956b) in the case of tobacco. Ovary tissues, before and after pollination, were also able to convert tryptophan into auxin in the case of lily (Nitsch, 1952), tobacco (Lund, 1956b) and watermelon (Dannenburg and Liverman, 1957). Since zinc has been shown to be essential for the synthesis of tryptophan (Tsui, 1948) it is perhaps not surprising to note that zinc has been found to be necessary for the normal development of the ovules in *Pisum* and that it accumulates preferentially in ovules (Reed, 1944). An intermediate between tryptophan and IAA may be

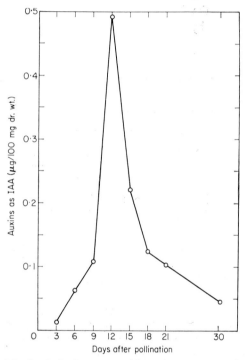

FIG. 6. Variation of the level of ether-extractable auxins in the strawberry achene, variety Marshall, during development. From Nitsch (1955).

indolepyruvic acid which has been detected in extracts of immature maize kernels (Stowe and Thimann, 1953). The application of gibberellic acid (GA) has been found to increase the internal level of endogenous auxins, for example, in bean seedlings (Nitsch, 1961a). Similarly, dipping clusters of Delaware grapes into a GA solution 10 days before full bloom increases the auxin level at bloom three-fold (Ito *et al.*, 1969). It seems likely, therefore, that gibberellins are capable of enhancing auxin production in fruits.

Very little is known about the catabolism of auxins in fruits. Preliminary investigations by Teubner and Murneek (1955) have indicated that IAA oxidase is present in apple embryos. The relative inefficiency of applied IAA in comparison with artificial auxins (see below) might be due to its rapid inactivation by fruit tissues. Fruit tissues are very rich in phenolic compounds which may either enhance or inhibit the activity of IAA oxidase. A study of

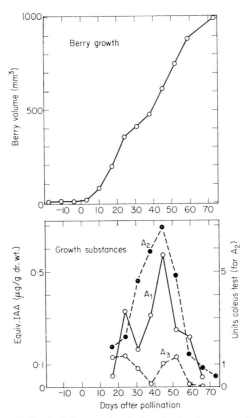

FIG. 7. Variations in the level of three auxins during the development of the berry of black-currant. $A_1 =$ IAA (presumably). $A_2 =$ substance active on the *Coleus* rooting test and moving to Rf 0·42. $A_3 =$ substance causing elongation in the wheat coleoptile section test and moving to Rf 0·87 in descending paper chromatography in butanol-ammonia-water (100 : 100 : 8, upper layer). Data from Wright (1956); reproduced by courtesy of Dr S. T. C. Wright.

various compounds from simple phenols to flavonoids has shown that, in general, substances of this type having only one —OH group (for example p-coumaric acid) strongly enhance IAA destruction (Nitsch and Nitsch, 1962). In fact, p-coumaroyl-quinic acid is present in apples (Williams, 1958). On the other hand, compounds having two or more—OH groups in the *ortho* position protect the IAA from inactivation, as shown by Rabin and Klein

(1957). Such compounds are also abundant in fruits: caffeoyl-quinic acid (= chlorogenic acid) is present in apples (Hulme, 1953) and in many other fruits; leucoanthocyanins have been isolated from the immature endosperms of *Cocos nucifera* and *Aesculus worlitzensis* (Steward and Shantz, 1955) and are present in the apple, Cox's Orange Pippin, or the pear, Conference (Hulme, 1958). Quercetin and its glycosides—which are also good protectors of IAA (Nitsch and Nitsch, 1962)—are abundant in fruits, for example in the grape berry (Williams and Wender, 1952), the blackcurrant (Williams *et al.*, 1952), the apricot (Williams and Wender, 1953a), the plum (Williams and Wender, 1953b) etc. All these substances may play a role in regulating the level of endogenous IAA.

Von Raussendorff-Bergen (1962) has found several indole derivatives in ripe apples, amongst them indolylealdehyde and indolyl-3-carboxylic acid, which are most probably degradation products of IAA.

The significance of IAA esters with arabinose (Shantz and Steward, 1957) and inositols (Labarca *et al.*, 1965; Nicholls, 1967) which have been found in immature seeds is not clear; perhaps they represent storage forms of auxin which would be released during seed germination, as seems to be the case for gibberellin-conjugates (see below). Zenk (1964) has proposed that the unused IAA in ripening fruits might be converted into conjugation products with aspartic and glutamic acids. In fact, hydrolysates of ripe apples yield IAA-aspartate (von Raussendorff-Bergen, 1962). According to Zenk's hypothesis, the metabolic chain which yields IAA during growth from the indolic precursor would be altered during ripening and yield D-tryptophan, which would be conjugated into malonyl-D-tryptophan, a compound which is also present in ripe apples.

B. Gibberellins in Fruits

1. *Chemical nature*

The chemical nature of the gibberellins in fruits is summarized in Table II. Of course, not all substances with gibberellin activity which have been reported in seeds or fruits have yet been identified. A list of some of the unknown compounds can be found in Nitsch (1965a).

2. *Site of production*

A factor B, found by Gandar (1964) to have gibberellin activity was found to be concentrated in the endosperm, rather than in the integuments or embryo of the young pea seed. It is likely that gibberellins are mostly synthesized in the nucellus in seedless fruits, in the nucellus and endosperm in seeded ones.

TABLE II. Gibberellins present in immature seeds

Gibberellin A	Source	Reference
1	*Phaseolus multiflorus*	MacMillan and Suter (1958)
	Phaseolus vulgaris	West and Phinney (1959)
4	*Malus sylvestris*	Dennis and Nitsch (1966)
		Luckwill *et al* (1968)
	Phaseolus multiflorus	Cavell *et al.* (1967)
5	*Phaseolus multiflorus*	MacMillan *et al.* (1959)
	Phaseolus vulgaris	West and Phinney (1959)
6	*Phaseolus multiflorus*	MacMillan *et al.* (1961)
7	*Malus sylvestris*	Dennis and Nitsch (1966)
		Luckwill *et al.* (1968)
8	*Phaseolus multiflorus*	MacMillan *et al.* (1961)
13	*Phaseolus multiflorus*	Cavell *et al.* (1967)
17	*Phaseolus multiflorus*	MacMillan *et al.* (1967)
18	*Lupinus luteus*	Koshimizu *et al.* (1966a)
20	*Pharbitis nil*	Takahashi *et al.* (1967)
	Pisum sativum (pods)	Komoda *et al.* (1968)
21	*Canavalia gladiata*	Tamura *et al.* (1967a)
22	*Canavalia gladiata*	Tamura *et al.* (1967a)
23	*Lupinus luteus*	Koshimizu *et al.* (1968b)
26	*Pharbitis nil*	Yokota *et al.* (1969)
27	*Pharbitis nil*	Yokota *et al.* (1969)
2-O-β-glucosyl-A_3	*Pharbitis nil*	Tamura *et al.* (1968)
3-O-β-glucosyl-A_8	*Phaseolus coccineus* (pods and ripe seeds)	Sembdner *et al.* (1968)
	Pharbitis nil	Yokota *et al.* (1969)
2-O-β-glucosyl-A_{26}	*Pharbitis nil*	Yokota *et al.* (1969)
2-O-β-glucosyl-A_{27}	*Pharbitis nil*	Yokota *et al.* (1969)

3. Variations during development

As with auxins, the levels of gibberellins also fluctuate widely during development, as has been shown by Ogawa (1965) for the peach. Figure 1A shows such a variation in the case of the grape berry. If one compares the curves A and B of Fig. 1, one can notice that the peak in gibberellin activity occurs before that of auxin. Data contributed by other authors also indicate that, in general, the wave of endogenous gibberellins precedes that of endogenous auxins.

4. Metabolism of gibberellins in fruits

Much more is known about the biosynthesis of gibberellins in immature seeds than about that of auxins. Incubation of enzyme fractions separated from the endosperm of immature seeds of *Echinocystis macrocarpa* have led West and co-workers to propose the scheme represented in Fig. 8. The coenocytic endosperm of *Echinocystis* is capable of carrying out all the steps from mevalonate to kaurene and 7-OH-kaurenoic acid (West *et al.*, 1968).

With immature endosperms of pumpkin (*Cucurbita pepo*), Graebe (1969) was able to obtain kaurene from ^{14}C-labelled mevalonic acid. These endosperms are also able to transform kaurene into GA_3, GA_8 and GA_9 (J. E. Graebe, private communication, 1969).

In *Pisum sativum*, flower primordia are able to synthesize kaurene from mevalonate, but this property disappears at anthesis. Growing pea ovules produce much kaurene, the maximum production occurring at the time when

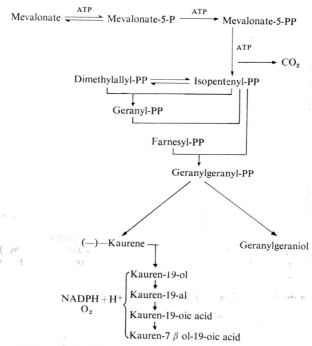

FIG. 8. Biosynthesis of gibberellin precursors from mevalonate in coenocytic endosperm of *Echinocystis macrocarpa*. From West *et al.*, 1968.

the seed is fully grown. It seems that kaurene formation may regulate gibberellin synthesis. On the other hand, the synthesis of geranylgeranyl-pyrophosphate continues undisturbed when gibberellin synthesis ceases (J. E. Graebe, private communication, 1969).

As far as the fate of gibberellins in the fruit is concerned, studies in which radioactive gibberellic acid has been injected into developing bean pods have shown that this substance is very quickly bound in the form of glucosides: one obtains in labelled form the glucosides of both GA_3 and GA_8 (Sembdner *et al.*, 1968). The GA_8 glucoside may be a storage form of gibberellin which might be re-used during seed germination. The production of labelled GA_8

from radioactive GA_3 also indicates that one gibberellin may be converted into another.

In fact, it is now known that, in higher plants, GA_1 can be converted to either GA_3 or GA_5 and that these, in turn, can be transformed into GA_8, according to the scheme indicated in Fig. 9.

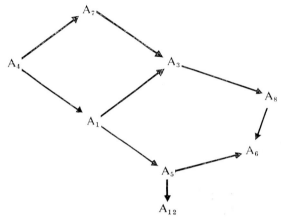

FIG. 9. Transformations of several gibberellins *in vivo*.

FIG. 9. Transformations of several gibberellins *in vivo*.

C. Cytokinins in Fruits

1. *Chemical nature*

Table III summarizes the main cytokinins which have been identified to

TABLE III. Chemical nature of the cytokinins isolated from immature seeds and fruits

Compounds	Source	Reference
Diphenylurea	*Cocos nucifera*, liquid endosperm	Shantz and Steward (1955)
Zeatin	*Cucurbita pepo*, immature seeds	Gupta and Maheshwari (1970)
	Malus sylvestris, immature fruitlets	Letham and Williams (1969)
	Prunus, immature fruitlets	Letham (1964)
	Zea mays, immature kernels	Letham (1963)
Zeatin riboside	*Cocos nucifera*, liquid endosperm	Letham (1968)
	Zea mays, immature kernels	Miller (1967)
		Letham (1966b)
Zeatin ribotide	*Zea mays*, immature kernels	Letham (1966b)
Dihydrozeatin	*Lupinus luteus*, immature seeds	Koshimizu et al. (1967)

date in immature seeds and fruits. Aside from the actual chemical isolations, cytokinins have been detected and purified to some extent from several other fruits and seeds as tabulated by Nitsch (1965a). To these data could be added other reports of cytokinins in immature seeds, for example in *Pisum sativum*

(Rogozinska *et al.*, 1965) or *Helianthus annuus* (Miller and Witham, 1964), in plum fruitlets (Letham, 1964) and juice of *Citrullus vulgaris* (Maheshwari and Prakash, 1966). A cytokinin which has been extracted from the immature endosperm of *Aesculus woerlitzensis* is thought not to be an adenine derivative (Shantz and Steward, 1968).

2. *Site of production*

Here again, as shown by Steward and Caplin (1952) for the coconut or by Powell and Pratt (1964) for the peach, although a certain amount of cytokinins also exist in the immature embryo, the greatest concentrations have been found in the endosperm. Here these growth factors can either accumulate from the sap (which contains cytokinins, as shown by various authors), be synthesized from precursors, or be liberated from certain t-RNA's during the breakdown of the endosperm. At the present time, our knowledge is too meagre to allow a clear decision to be made between these possibilities.

3. *Variations during development*

In the case of maize, Steward and Caplin (1952) found that the peak of cytokinin content occurred around the week after pollination. This timing was confirmed by Miller (1967) who observed the greatest amount of cytokinin activity on the 11th day after pollination. On the following collection, made on the 21st day, the activity had declined notably.

4. *Metabolism of cytokinins*

Practically nothing is known about the biochemical pathways which lead to the production of cytokinins in immature fruits. The presence of the nucleotide and the nucleoside in immature maize kernels suggests the possibility of an interconversion between these two compounds (Miller, 1967).

D. Abscisic Acid in Fruits

Since its isolation from young cotton fruits (Okhuma *et al.*, 1963; Addicott *et al.*, 1964), abscisic acid has been found in numerous fruits and seeds (Table IV) where it occurs free or as the β-D-glucopyranoside, as determined by Koshimizu *et al.* (1968a) for *Lupinus luteus*. In the rose hip of *Rosa arvensis*, it occurs in very large quantities (Milborrow, 1967). The level of abscisic acid varies during fruit development, as shown for cotton in Fig. 2.

E. Ethylene in Fruits

Ethylene is produced by many fruits even when young (Burg and Burg, 1965). It was thought to be mainly responsible for abscission and ripening

TABLE IV. Presence of abscisic acid and derivatives in seeds and fruits

Compound	Source	Concentration mg/kg fr. wt.	Reference
Abscisic acid	*Ceratonia siliquastrum*, fruits		Most *et al.* (1970)
(ABA)	*Citrus medica*, rind	0·097	Milborrow (1967)
	fruit pulp	0·086	Milborrow (1967)
	Cocos nucifera, liquid endosperm		Milborrow (1967)
	Fragaria, fruits		Rudnicki *et al.* (1968)
	Gossypium hirsutum, young fruits		Okhuma *et al.* (1963)
	Lupinus luteus, young fruits		Cornforth *et al.* (1966) Koshimizu *et al.* (1966)
	Lycopersicon esculentum, ripe fruits		Dörffling and Böttger (1968)
	Malus sylvestris, fruit		Milborrow (1967)
	Persea gratissima, fruit pulp	0·76	Milborrow (1967)
	seed	0·034	Milborrow (1967)
	Pisum sativum, immature seeds		Isogai *et al.* (1967)
	Olea europaea, half-size fruit	0·53	Milborrow (1967)
	mature (green) fruit	0·39	Milborrow (1967)
	mature (black) fruit	0·36	Milborrow (1967)
	Rosa arvensis, achenes	0·016	Milborrow (1967)
	pseudocarp	4·1	Milborrow (1967)
	Rosa canina, achenes	0·53	Milborrow (1967)
	Zea mays, kernel	0·083	Milborrow (1967)
ABA-glucoside	*Ceratonia seliquastrum*, fruits		Most *et al.* (1970)
	Lupinus luteus, young fruits	0·617	Koshimizu *et al.* (1968a)

until Maxie and Crane (1968) reported that it could actually cause fruit growth in the fig (Fig. 10) by triggering off period III (see Chapter 14). Ethylene must therefore be regarded, not only as a ripening, but also as a growth hormone. Ripening is prevented from occurring on the tree in the case of avocados by a factor coming from the leaves (Burg, 1964). When the fruit is cut off, ripening starts (see Vol 2, Chapter 1). In general, the level of ethylene increases just before the climacteric rise in respiration which marks the beginning of the ripening period. Such a pattern has been clearly shown in the Honeydew melon (Pratt and Goeschl, 1968). The relation of ethylene to fruit ripening has been discussed in detail in Chapter 16.

Ethylene production can be triggered off by auxins at relatively high concentrations (Hall and Morgan, 1964; Abeles and Rubinstein, 1964; Burg and Burg, 1966). The ripening effect of 2,4,5-trichlorophenoxyacetic acid in figs can be accounted for by a stimulation of ethylene production (Maxie and Crane, 1967). A very ancient practice consists of stimulating the growth and ripening of figs by placing a drop of vegetable oil in the ostiole. Hirai *et al.* (1967) have shown that such a treatment enhances ethylene production.

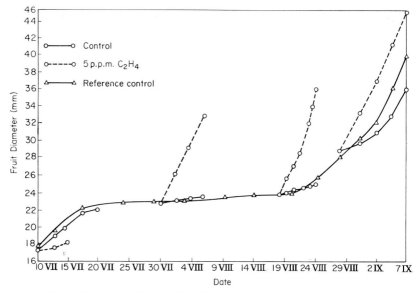

FIG. 10. Effect of ethylene (5 p.p.m.) applied at various stages of development on the growth of fig fruits. *Triangles:* mean growth curve of 30 undisturbed fruits. *Circles and solid lines:* bagged control fruits. *Circles and dotted lines:* bagged fruits treated with ethylene. From Maxie and Crane (1968).

III. EFFECTS OF APPLIED GROWTH SUBSTANCES

Proof that hormones play a crucial role in the development of fruits is contributed by experiments in which normal pollination and seed development are prevented. In most cases, fruits fail to develop under such conditions. However, when certain substances are then applied, fruit growth may occur. In this way Gustafson (1936) performed his classical experiments with tomatoes and other plants, showing that fruit set and growth could be obtained by the application of synthetic auxins. Similarly, Nitsch (1950) demonstrated that the effect of developing achenes in stimulating the growth of the fleshy strawberry receptable could be duplicated by the application of a lanolin paste containing a synthetic auxin (Fig. 11).

Synthetic growth regulators can be either sprayed on the whole plant or applied selectively to the flowers and young fruits by dipping the clusters individually (for example grapes), by painting the compound on the flower or fruit with a paint brush, or by applying a lanolin paste into which the active compound has been dissolved. The first technique is used commercially because it involves much less labour than the others which remain experimental techniques used on a small scale.

In applying growth regulators, penetration into the tissues must be ensured. Thus a wetting agent is usually incorporated into spray mixtures. Certain types of compounds have a greater power of penetration, the esters of auxins for example. Accordingly, the ethyl ester of IAA is about 100 times more efficient than the acid itself in stimulating fruit set in tomatoes (Redeman *et al.*, 1951).

Another factor which may modify the effectiveness of applied substances is their resistance to destruction. For example, IAA is usually a poor fruit-setting agent, probably because it is inactivated too rapidly. Indolyl-3-butyric

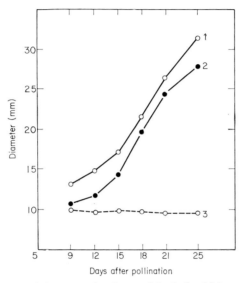

FIG. 11. Growth curves of three strawberries, cv. Marshall, which were pollinated on the same day. 1: control; 2: fruit which had all its achenes removed on the ninth day and replaced with a lanolin paste containing 100 p.p.m. of 2-naphthoxyacetic acid; 3: as 2, but without NOA in the lanolin paste. From Nitsch (1950).

acid, which is destroyed less readily by IAA oxidase (Wagenknecht and Burris, 1950), gives much better results.

A. Applied Auxins

Not all species can be made to produce fruits without pollination by the application of auxins. Among the species which respond well are those which have numerous seeds, such as tomatoes, cucurbits, strawberries, blackberries, grapes, figs, etc.

In general, substances which are active as auxins in other tests are also active in setting fruits. There is a definite relationship between the molecular configuration of a compound and its biological activity. For example, the relative effectiveness of phenoxy- (Osborne *et al.*, 1952), indole- (Sell *et al.*, 1953) and naphthoxy- (Luckwill and Woodcock, 1956) derivatives, of thiocarbamate derivatives having auxin activity and of substituted benzoic acids

TABLE V. Examples of relationships between chemical structure and fruit-setting properties

1. Indole derivatives on tomato[a]

| | Activity (applied in lanolin paste) | | |
	10 p.p.m.	100 p.p.m.	1000 p.p.m.
Indolyl-3-acetic acid (IAA)	0	+	+++
4-Chloro-IAA	0	+++	+++
5-Chloro-IAA	0	+++	+++
6-Chloro-IAA	0	+++	+++
7-Chloro-IAA	0	+++	+++
5, 7-Dichloro-IAA	0	+	+++
2-Methyl-IAA	0	0	0
IAA-methyl ester	++	+++	+++
IAA-ethyl ester	++	+++	+++
Indolyl-3-ethanol	0	0	0
Indolyl-3-butyric acid	0	++	+++
Indolyl-3-propionic acid	0	0	0
Indolyl-3-carboxylic acid	0	0	0
Indole	0	0	0

2. Naphthoxy derivatives on tomato[b]

	Relative molar activity at ED 50
Naphthyl-2-oxy-acetic acid (NOA)	1000
Naththyl-2-oxy-propionic acid	0
Naphthyl-2-oxy-butyric acid	1000
Naphthyl-2-oxy-valeric acid	0
Naphthyl-2-oxy-caproic acid	1000
Naphthyl-2-oxy-heptanoic acid	0
Naphthyl-2-oxy-octanoic acid	180
Naphthyl-2-oxy-nonanoic acid	0
1-Chloro-naphthyl-2-oxy-acetic acid	1
3-Chloro-naphthyl-2-oxy-acetic acid	1000
4-Chloro-naphthyl-2-oxy-acetic acid	2
5-Chloro-naphthyl-2-oxy-acetic acid	0
6-Chloro-naphthyl-2-oxy-acetic acid	72
7-Chloro-naphthyl-2-oxy-acetic acid	19
8-Chloro-naphthyl-2-oxy-acetic acid	280
1, 3-Dichloro-naphthyl-2-oxy-acetic acid	0
3-Chloro-naphthyl-2-oxy-propionic acid	0
3-Chloro-naphthyl-2-oxy-butyric acid	0

3. *Synthetic auxins on the calimyrna fig[c]*

	Concentration giving best results (p.p.m.)	% set	Dr. wt. g/fruit
Caprified controls	—	45	16·9
Indolyl-3-butyric acid	1500	79	13·4
Naphthyl-1-acetic acid	250	85	16·4
4-Chlorophenoxyacetic acid	60	76	17·2
2,4,5-Trichlorophenoxyacetic acid (2,4,5-T)	75	72	—
Isopropyl ester of 2,4,5-T	50	83	—

4. *Activity of various compounds on Black Corinth grapes[d]*

	Concentrations tested (p.p.m.)	Activity
Indolyl-3-acetic acid	2–200	0
Indolyl-3-propionic acid	20, 200	0
Indolyl-3-butyric acid	20–1000	0
Naphthoxy-2-acetic acid	2–200	0
Naphthoxy-2-propionic acid	2–200	+
Naphthyl-1-acetic acid	2–200	0
N-1-naphthylphthalamic acid	2–200	+
N-2-chlorophenylphthalamic acid	50, 500	+
N-phenylphthalimide	100–1000	+
2,3,5-Triiodobenzoic acid	20, 200	+
2,4-Dichlorophenoxyacetic acid	0·2–200	+
2,4,5-Trichlorophenoxyacetic acid	0·5–50	0
4-Chlorophenoxyacetic acid	0·5–50	+ +
Benzothiazol-2-oxyacetic acid	2·5–100	+ +[e]

[a] From Sell *et al.* (1953).
[b] From Luckwill and Woodcock (1956).
[c] From Blondeau and Crane (1950).
[d] From Weaver (1956).
[e] Small berries.

(Nitsch, 1960) in setting fruit of the tomato has been examined. Another compound having strong auxin activity, 4-amino-3,5,6-trichloropicolinic acid, was found also to be effective in stimulating fruit development in figs (Crane, 1965). Examples of the relationships between chemical structure and fruit-setting ability are given in Table V for the tomato, the fig and the grape.

B. Applied Gibberellins

Although generally less effective than auxins on tomatoes (Nitsch, 1960) or strawberries (Thompson, 1969), gibberellins are much more effective on stone and pome fruits, as well as on blueberries (Barker and Collins, 1965) and cranberries (Devlin and Demoranville, 1967).

Among stone fruits, parthenocarpic (that is, produced without pollination) almonds, apricots and peaches have been produced with GA_3 sprays (Crane et al., 1960). With cherries, GA_3 alone was unable to ensure a crop of fruits, although it caused an initial set of small cherries which shrivelled after a month. The incorporation of 2,4-dichlorophenoxyacetylmethionine in the GA_3 spray resulted in the production of nearly normal cherries, although this compound had no fruit-setting properties by itself. Presumably, this substance is slowly converted by the tissues into a strong auxin, 2,4-dichloro-phenoxy-acetic acid, which prevents the abscission of the fruitlets (Rebeiz and Crane, 1961).

The pome fruits which have been set with gibberellins include several varieties of apples and pears (Luckwill, 1960; Davison, 1960; Griggs and Iwakiri, 1961; Dennis and Edgerton, 1962). The varieties which respond best seem to be those which have a natural tendency to develop partheno-carpically, such as the apples "Laxton's Superb" (Modlibowska, 1961) and "Wealthy" (Wittwer and Bukovac, 1962), or the pears "Durondeau" and "Williams" as opposed to "Comice" (Modlibowska, 1961). The latter pear variety, however, could be set well with GA_3, but better still by a mixture of GA_4 and GA_7, as were the apples "Cox's Orange Pippin" and "Golden Delicious" (Varga, 1969). In the case of the apple "Wealthy", GA_4 is about 5 times more active than GA_3 (Wittwer and Bukovac, 1962). In this connec-tion it should be noted that GA_4 and GA_7 have been found to occur naturally in the young apple fruitlets (Dennis and Nitsch, 1966; Luckwill et al., 1968).

Applied gibberellins are effective in increasing fruit size in seedless grape varieties, such as "Thompson Seedless" (that is "Sultanna"), "Black Cor-inth" and "Black Monukka" (Weaver and McCune, 1959b), whereas they do not generally have this effect on seeded varieties of Vitis vinifera (Weaver and McCune, 1959a). In the seeded "Delaware" grape, however, dipping the flower clusters about 10 days before bloom into a solution of GA_3 or GA_7 at 100 mg/litre caused seedless berries of nearly normal size to develop (Ito et al., 1969).

Gibberellins have also been found to be effective in setting fruits of the guava (Psidium guajava) (Teaotia et al., 1961), Prunus spp. (Crane and Grossi, 1960), etc.

C. Applied Cytokinins

Applied cytokinins have also resulted in the stimulation of fruit growth, at least in the grape (Weaver et al., 1965, 1966), and the "Carlimyrna" fig (Crane and Van Overbeek, 1965). The effect of growth-retarding chemicals such as (2-chloroethyl)-trimethylammonium chloride (CCC) or tributyl-2,4-dichlorobenzylphosphonium chloride (Phosfon-D) in increasing fruit set in *Vitis vinifera* (Coombe, 1965) can probably be ascribed to the twenty-fold increase in endogenous cytokinins which has been observed in the sap of CCC treated grapes (Skene, 1968).

D. Applied Abscisic Acid

Abscisic acid is especially abundant in rose hips (Milborrow, 1967), and as was shown by Jackson and Blundell (1966) this compound can also act as a fruit-setting agent in this genus.

E. Applied Ethylene

Most of the growth-promoting and ripening effects of 2,4,5-T sprayed on figs at the end of period II (Crane and Blondeau, 1949) can be accounted for by the fact that such a treatment causes a clear-cut increase in the production of ethylene by the tissues (Maxie and Crane, 1967). Such an interpretation has been confirmed by Maxie and Crane (1968) who actually caused fruit growth in the fig by exogenous applications of ethylene (Fig. 10).

IV. MODE OF ACTION OF HORMONES IN FRUITS

Even though the ultimate mode of action of the plant hormones is still unknown, one may bring together the results which have been obtained so far in this direction. In general, growth substances play a role in directing the movement and the utilization of nutrients and in stimulating metabolism, cell division, cell enlargement and cell maturation.

A. The Attraction of Nutrients—Competition Phenomena

A growing fruit constitutes a very active metabolic centre towards which flow large amounts of nutrients. Thus in *Pisum sativum* up to 90% of the labelled photosynthates (mostly sucrose) can be recovered in the pod and ovules of the fruits located in the axil of a leaf treated with $^{14}CO_2$ (Linck and Sudia, 1962). If the same leaf is treated with ^{32}P instead, most of the phosphorus also moves to the nearest carpel. This mobilization out of the leaf is practically nil at anthesis but becomes very strong after fertilization (Linck and Swanson, 1960). A few facets of this phenomenon may now be presented.

1. *Vascular development*

Soon after fruit set, there starts in the peduncle an increase in vascular development; existing vascular strands enlarge and new ones are differentiated. This change is in sharp contrast to the reduced vascular system of the flower which, in certain cases, ends blindly without connecting with the vascular system of the stem. The increase in the vascularization of the peduncle is spectacular in Cucurbits (Nitsch, 1952). In fact, the fruit pedicel may become thicker than the stem itself (Fig. 12).

Fig. 12. Development of the fruit stalk in *Cucurbita maxima*. The fruit stalk has increased in diameter more than the stem, possibly because the latter had its structure fixed long before the fruit started developing. From Nitsch (1952).

Experiments performed on *Coleus* stems (Jacobs, 1952; Jacobs and Morrow, 1957; La Motte and Jacobs, 1963) or woody plants (Digby and Wareing, 1966) have clearly shown that the development of both xylem and phloem elements is regulated by auxins and gibberellins. Applications of synthetic auxins such as 2,4-D and naphthyl-1-acetic acid greatly increase the vascularization of fruits and pedicels of the cherry (Tukey and Hammer, 1949). Thus it seems likely that one way by which endogenous hormones help in enabling fruits to develop is by promoting the development of a good vascular system connecting them to the circulatory system of the plant.

2. *Metabolic stimulation*

As early as 1907, J. White showed that pollination and fertilization strongly increase the respiratory rate of ovary tissues. Hsiang (1951b) observed a 3·5-fold increase in respiration some 48 hours after the application of pollen to the stigma of tropical orchids. In petunia, the oxygen uptake was found to increase in the styles as early as one hour after pollination (Linskens, 1953). Water uptake also increases after the pollination of tropical orchids, an effect which can be duplicated by a treatment with synthetic auxins (Hsiang, 1951a).

After an auxin treatment, the activity of malic dehydrogenase increases three times and that of fumaric dehydrogenase twice in tomato ovaries, while that of succinic and glutamic dehydrogenases is slightly depressed (Teubner and Murneek, 1952). Starch synthesis accompanies the phases of rapid development of the fruit and seed. The centre which directs the translocation of carbohydrates and the accumulation of starch is the fertilized ovule (Marré, 1948a, b). Auxins have been shown to mimic the effect of developing seeds in processes such as starch fixation (Marré, 1949), maintenance of a high concentration of sucrose and reducing sugars (Marré, 1951), the pattern of carbohydrate metabolism (Marré and Murneek, 1953a, b) and dehydrogenase activity (Marré, 1954).

3. Competition between fruits and vegetative growth

A definite relationship exists between the extent of the development of shoots and leaves on the one hand and of fruits on the other. When a plant produces fruits, growth of the vegetative parts is curtailed. The magnitude of the effect depends on the extent of fruit set and the "vigour" of the plant at flowering time. Such a relationship holds true for herbaceous species as well as for woody ones. A study of such a relationship and its bearing on endogenous growth substances made with the okra (*Hibiscus esculentus*) showed that less growth substances are diffused out from a flower at anthesis than from the vegetative tip (Fig. 13). However, one day after pollination, the young fruit diffuses out more growth substances than does the vegetative tip. On the fourth day after pollination, the growth rate of the young fruit exceeds 1·5 cm per day, while the growth rate of the stem drops below 50% of that of the defruited controls. At this time also, diffusion of growth substances from the fruits reaches a maximum, while that from the vegetative tips drops, the minimum being reached two days later. Once the fruit has reached its final size and ripening begins, the amount of growth substances decreases in the diffusate from the fruit and increases in that from the vegetative tip. Growth resumes in the latter a few days later (Nitsch, 1961b). This example shows that changes in the level of endogenous substances of the auxin and gibberellin type (which were measured by the oat first-internode test used in the okra experiment) precede changes in the growth rate of the vegetative parts which are inhibited during active fruit development.

If heavy fruit set is capable of reducing vegetative growth, for example

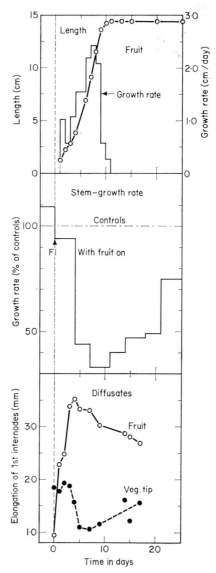

FIG. 13. Correlation between fruit growth and vegetative growth in the okra. *Top:* cumulative growth curve and growth rate of the fruit. *Middle:* growth rate of the stem bearing one fruit, as compared with defruited control stems. *Bottom:* growth-promoting activities of diffusates from one fruit and from the vegetative tip of the same plant. From Nitsch (1961b).

in the tomato (Murneek, 1926) as well as in the apple (Roberts, 1948), conversely, exuberant vegetative growth may compete with fruit development and reduce fruit set. For example, when vigorous varieties of pear such as "Doyenné du Comice" are pruned back severely, many sucker shoots develop and many young fruits drop off. Reducing the pulling power of vegetative shoots by interfering with the polar transport of auxin by sprays of 2,3,5-triiodobenzoic acid (5 mg/litre) doubled fruit set, but the size of the individual fruits was reduced (Nitsch, 1954). Removing the competition by cutting off the tips of vigorous shoots also favours fruit set in grapes (Olmo, 1937), or in the Adriatic fig (Crosby and Crane, 1952).

4. Competition between fruits

Waves of fruitlessness occur in species such as the melon (Rosa, 1924) or the okra (Perkins et al., 1952); the flowers which open while young fruits develop actively do not set, but fruit set resumes in other flowers which open when the first fruits are ripening. This intermittent sterility has been thoroughly studied in Cleome spinosa (Murneek, 1927).

Even when two neighbouring fruits are set at approximately the same time one may inhibit the growth of the other if it develops ahead of the latter, as is the case in cucumbers (Golinska, 1952) or apples (Howlett, 1931). Experiments performed by Marré (1954) on Convolvulus indicate that auxin is involved in this phenomenon. Young fruits of this species gave an intense reaction to triphenyltetrazolium chloride (TTC) whereas unpollinated ovaries did not. Removal of the seeds after pollination caused a sharp decrease in the intensity of the colouration 1–2 days later. This decrease, however, was not observed when the fruit operated on was alone in a cluster, but only when there was at least one normal fruit present or a de-seeded fruit treated with auxin.

B. Regulation of Cell Division

In general, the production of new cells accounts for most of the growth of fruits before anthesis. During anthesis, cell division may stop altogether, for example, in the apple (Smith, 1950) (Fig. 14). In this fruit, there is a new surge of cell division after pollination which lasts about three weeks (Bain and Robertson, 1951). Cell division continues for about 30 days after pollination in stone fruits such as the peach (Addoms et al., 1930) and the plum (Sterling, 1953), but only for five days in Cucurbita moschata cv. "Kogitu" (Kano et al., 1957). In the avocado, however, cell division proceeds regularly until fruit maturation (Schroeder, 1953). Occasionally, one finds in the literature discrepancies about the exact time at which cell division ceases. This is due to differences in varieties and in the particular tissue under consideration (Sinnott, 1939, 1945; Kano *et al.*, 1957). In the case of *Cucurbita*, for example, cell division stops first in the placental tissue, then in the inner, middle and outer tissues of the ovary, in that order.

Cytokinins which are present in immature seeds and fruitlets are, together with auxins, responsible for cell division in fruits. This result has been mainly attained through the use of tissue culture. Thus, apple mesocarp proliferated *in vitro* when both a strong auxin such as 2,4-D or 2,3-dichlorophenylacetic acid were added to the medium together with a source of cytokinins such as coconut milk (Letham, 1958) or an extract of immature maize kernels (Nitsch, 1959). These natural cytokinins can now be replaced by synthetic cytokinins such as kinetin (Letham, 1960) or N_6-benzyladenine (Nitsch *et al.*, 1970). In this way, tissues of various apple and pear varieties as well as of

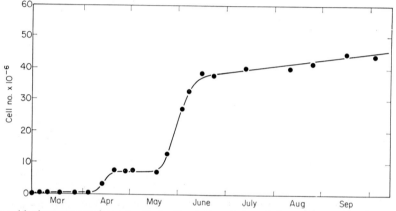

FIG. 14. Average number of cells in developing fruits of the apple, variety Bramley's Seedling. Reproduced by courtesy of Dr W. W. Smith; see also Smith (1950).

orange (Nitsch, 1965b) have been subcultured successfully for many years (Fig. 15). A combination of an auxin and a cytokinin has also been found to be necessary for cell division in tissues excised from the strawberry receptacle (Lis and Antoszewski, 1968) and, in certain cases, in tissues from banana pulp (Mohan Ram and Steward, 1964). Kinetin alone (Sommer *et al.* 1961), N_6-benzyladenine (Fig. 16) or its 9-tetrahydropyran derivative (SD-8339), have been found to stimulate cell division in immature peach tissues, but this effect occurs mostly in the cells of the endocarp (Nitsch, 1965c). In some cases, however, proliferation has been obtained on media devoid of added cytokinins, for example in the case of the pericarp of the avocado (Schroeder, 1955), the citron (Schroeder and Spector, 1957), or the juice vesicles of lemon (Kordan, 1958; Nitsch, 1965b), etc. However, it is most likely that here, the tissues themselves have the ability to synthesize the cytokinins they need. In fact, lemon juice is known to contain cell division factors (Kovoor, 1954). A further indication that cytokinins are involved is provided by the fact that cell division usually begins around vascular elements in the case of mesocarp tissues of the apple (Letham, 1958), the banana (Mohan Ram and Steward, 1964), the strawberry (Lis and Antoszewski, 1968). Vascular tissue has been shown to produce cytokinin-like effects in the tobacco-pith system (Jablonski and Skoog, 1954), and poplar cambium has been found to be a rich source of natural cytokinins (Nitsch and Nitsch, 1965). Applications of zeatin or of SD-8339 to apple flowers and fruitlets on

Fig. 15. Aspect of tissues of pear mesocarp, variety Epine du Mas, which has been sub-cultured *in vitro* for 2 years. (Original).

the tree did not increase fruit weight but altered fruit shape (wider and flatter apples were produced) and caused a greater number of smaller cells to be formed (Letham, 1969), a condition which may lead to better storage quality (Martin *et al.*, 1954).

The exact role of cytokinins in cell division is unknown. Cytokinins have been shown to help in the division of polyploid tissues (Torrey, 1961). In fact, cells of the mesocarp of apricot have been found to be highly polyploid, especially after an application of 2,4,5-T, which increases fruit size (Bradley and Crane, 1955). One possible explanation of the role of cytokinins in such cases might involve an action on the contraction of chromosomes (Mann *et al.*, 1967).

Gibberellins which have been reported to favour cell division in the citron mesocarp (Schroeder and Spector, 1957) and the placental tissue of *Opuntia dillenii* (Sachar and Iyer, 1959), were found to be rather detrimental in the case of the strawberry receptacle (Antoszewski and Lis, 1968) and of the mesocarp of the peach, apple and pear (Nitsch *et al.*, 1970).

FIG. 16. Proliferation of an explant of nectarine fruit, variety Gold Mine, under the influence of benzyladenine (1 mg/litre). From Nitsch *et al.* (1970).

C. Regulation of Cell Enlargement

After the period of cell division, fruit growth is mostly due to an increase in cell volume. This enlargement can be enormous and yield cells that are visible to the naked eye, in watermelons for example.

The hormones which are mostly responsible for such an increase in size are the auxins. They are responsible for the increase in extensibility of cell walls (Heyn, 1931, 1940). Auxin-treated tissues show a greater activity of the pectin methyl esterase than the controls (Osborne, 1958; Yoda, 1958) and cause an increased synthesis of pectic substances (Albersheim and Bonner, 1959).

Auxins are also responsible for an increased water uptake both in slices of potato (Hackett and Thimann, 1952) and in orchid ovaries (Hsiang, 1951a). This effect involves respiratory activity. As early as 1917, Heinicke had shown that seeds in the apple are important in its water metabolism. By letting young apples dry in the laboratory, he observed that shrivelling occurred in the regions where no seeds had developed. Synthetic auxins are also known to promote water retention in detached bean fruits (Mitchell and Marth, 1950).

One striking feature of fruits is that they often assume shapes that are much rounder than those of stems. In other words, fruit cells tend to become more isodiametrical than stem cells, in which growth takes place mostly along one axis. One substance, ethylene, has been known to cause isodiametrical growth in stem cells (Burg and Burg, 1968). Recent findings have shown that relatively high concentrations of auxins cause ethylene formation in plant tissues (Burg and Burg, 1966). Thus applications of 2,4,5-T to fig fruits or leaves has been shown to promote the production of ethylene (Maxie and Crane, 1967). The ethylene produced by the fruit may cause a loss of polarity in the fruit cells and be responsible for the shape of these cells at maturity.

D. Regulation of Cell Ripening

Several features characterize cell ripening: (i) a loss of chlorophyll if the cell contained chloroplasts; (ii) leakage of the cell membrane and (iii) the hydrolysis of macromolecules.

Plant hormones affect all these processes. For example gibberellins and cytokinins delay the loss of chlorophyll in the peel of oranges (Eilati et al., 1969), whereas ethylene enhances this loss. The role of cytokinins in delaying senescence has been clearly demonstrated in leaves (Richmond and Lang, 1957; Mothes et al., 1959). Apparently cytokinins maintain a high level of proteins in cells. Auxins, in the case of bean endocarp, prevent the leakage of cell membranes and retard the loss of nucleic acids and proteins by maintaining a high level of RNA synthesis (Sacher, 1967).

By far the most dramatic effect on cell ripening is caused by ethylene which is produced in minute amounts throughout the life of the fruit. Its level, however, increases before the onset of ripening—10 days in the case of the Honeydew melon (Pratt and Goeschl, 1968)—and reaches the threshold concentration which triggers an increase in RNA synthesis. Thus an increase in RNA per cell has been reported in the tomato (Davies and Cocking, 1965). This RNA is in turn responsible for the new synthesis of proteins which had been observed by Hulme (1948) to occur in the apple before maturation. Further details of the mechanism of ripening and the action of ethylene can be found elsewhere in this book (Chapter 16).

V. A COMPREHENSIVE PICTURE OF THE ROLE OF HORMONES IN FRUIT DEVELOPMENT

A. Parthenocarpy

Noll (1902) introduced the word "parthenocarpy" to designate fruit formation without pollination or other stimulation, whereas, for Winkler (1908), a parthenocarpic fruit was a fruit without seeds or with empty seeds. To-day, parthenocarpy is generally considered as "the development of a fruit without fertilization of the ovules" (Nitsch, 1952), a definition which parallels that of parthenogenesis, which is the formation of an embryo without fertilization.

1. Characteristics of parthenocarpy

The important point in deciding if a particular fruit has been set parthenocarpically is to know if fertilization has occurred or not. In the latter case, Winkler (1908) has distinguished between "stimulative" (that is, caused by the stimulus of pollination) and "vegetative" parthenocarpy (without any pollination). The absence of seeds in the mature fruit is not sufficient to decide whether or not a fruit is parthenocarpic. They may have degenerated after an initial period of growth. Furthermore, fruits which are naturally parthenocarpic, such as those of mangosteens (*Garcinia mangostana*; Horn, 1940), certain strains of cucumbers (Nitsch, 1952) or figs (Crane *et al.*, 1959), may also be seeded. Persimmons (*Diospyros kaki*) may contain apogamous seeds (that is, with embryos produced without the formation of a zygote) and a sort of "endosperm" (Woodburn, 1911). All these seeds are really pseudo-seeds.

2. Causes of parthenocarpy

Parthenocarpy can be of genetical origin, as in oranges (cv. "Valencia" and "Hamlin" cited by Wong, 1939), cucumbers (Wellington and Hawthorn, 1929), figs, pears, grapes, etc. In the case of the banana, a single gene accounts for the parthenocarpic behaviour of certain strains; in addition, a number of modifiers influence the extent of parthenocarpic development (Dodds and Simmonds, 1948).

Environmental factors, especially temperature, may also cause the development of parthenocarpic fruits. Parthenocarpic pears have been observed to develop after a frost (Höstermann, 1913; Lewis, 1942), and low temperatures have also been shown to cause the formation of parthenocarpic eggplants (Yasuda, 1939), squashes and cucumbers (Nitsch *et al.*, 1952), tomatoes (Osborne and Went, 1953), etc.

Gustafson's experiments (1936) which established that parthenocarpic tomatoes could be produced at will by applying synthetic auxins to emasculated blossoms have been followed by many others in which parthenocarpy has been obtained by applying various chemical substances belonging to the classes of auxins, gibberellins and cytokinins.

3. Role of growth substances in parthenocarpy

Comparison of the endogenous levels of native growth regulators in seeded and seedless strains have been made by several workers, for example, by Gustafson (1939a) in oranges, lemons and grapes, Crane *et al.* (1959) in

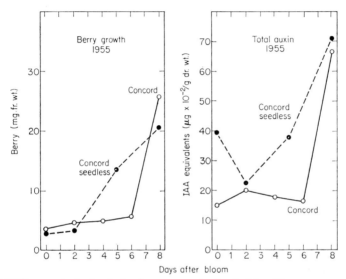

FIG. 17. Differences in the level of endogenous auxins (and gibberellins, as measured by the oat first internode test) in very young berries of *Vitis labrusca* varieties Concord and Concord Seedless. From Nitsch *et al.* (1960).

figs, Nitsch *et al.* (1960) in *Vitis labrusca*, Coombe (1960) in *Vitis vinifera*. In all these cases, it was found that the seedless variety, while having generally a lower level of auxins and gibberellins in the developing fruits, had a "head start" over the seeded strains (Fig. 17). Thus, what seems to be important is the ability to create a certain threshold concentration at the critical time of anthesis.

As observed by numerous authors, treatments capable of causing parthenocarpy also stimulate the early development of seeds. Thus auxin applications have led to the production of empty seeds in *Citrus* (Stewart and Klotz, 1947; Stewart and Parker, 1947), grapes (Weaver, 1952, 1953; Weaver and Williams, 1951), figs (Crane, 1952), watermelons (Wong, 1941) and even pineapples (W. S. Stewart, personal communications). Gibberellic acid has

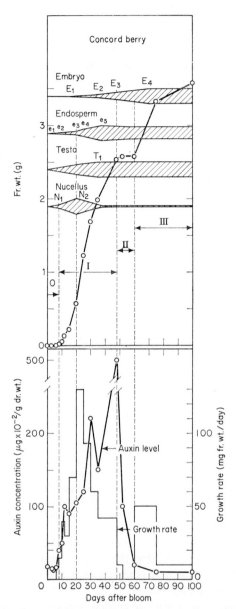

FIG. 18. Development of the grape berry (*Vitis labrusca*), variety Concord, as related to the level of extractable growth substances active on the oat first internode bioassay (auxins and gibberellins). *Above:* solid line = growth curve (fresh weight) of an average berry plotted against time (days after anthesis); *nucellus:* N_1 = rapid development, N_2 = maximum volume; *testa:* T_1 = full size and beginning of hardening of the seed coats; *endosperm:* e_1 = beginning of free-nuclear state, e_2 = beginning of cellular state, e_3 = beginning of rapid development, e_4 = 100% cellular state, e_5 = maximum development; *embryo:* E_1 = first division of zygote, E_2 = 50 cells, E_3 = cotyledons differentiated, E_4 = full length. *Below:* heavy line = auxin level expressed in IAA equivalents ($\mu g \times 10^{-2}$ per g dry weight); thin line = growth rate of the berry (mg fresh weight per day). From Nitsch *et al.* (1960).

stimulated the development of seeds in the seedless orange, "Washington Navel" (Hield *et al.*, 1958). A detailed study of the stimulatory effect on ovule development caused by growth substances applied to the tomato (Asahira *et al.*, 1967) showed that both a synthetic auxin (2-hydroxymethyl-4-chloro-phenoxyacetic acid) and GA caused the endothelial cells to fill more or less completely the cavity of the embryo-sac. All these results fit with the suggestion made earlier (Nitsch, 1952) that, far from being absent, the ovules are in fact crucial for the development of parthenocarpic fruits. These ovules may degenerate later on and practically disappear, but their effect is exerted very clearly at the time of flowering. Thus the parthenocarpic grape "White Corinth" has an overgrown nucellus which is larger, at full bloom, than that of a seeded variety (Pearson, 1932). In the banana, the ovules of parthenocarpic varieties are 10–25% larger at anthesis than those of seeded ones. Moreover, these ovules have a greater vigour and increase in size by 50% in one week compared with 15% for those of seeded varieties (Simmonds, 1953).

If the young ovules are indeed the operative factor in the development of parthenocarpic fruits, then one can understand why a single application of a growth substance made at full bloom can suffice to obtain full-sized fruits. In addition to direct effects, the applied chemical may also stimulate the activity of the nucellus and the seed coats of the ovules which, in turn, may produce substances activating fruit growth.

B. The Phases of Fruit Development

The analyses which have been made of the levels of endogenous growth factors during fruit development have yielded certain puzzling results. Thus, no clear relationships have emerged from comparisons between the growth rate of fruits and the variations in endogenous substances (see, for example, Luckwill, 1948b; Crane *et al.*, 1959; Nitsch *et al.*, 1960; Collins *et al.*, 1966; Powell and Pratt, 1966). In the grape berry, the peak in extractable auxins actually follows the peak in growth rate (Fig. 18).

As indicated by Nitsch (1965a), several possibilities have to be borne in mind in trying to understand this situation:

(i) The data given in the literature generally concern the growth substances which have been extracted with organic solvents. It is not known if this fraction represents the metabolically active one or merely what is left over during the growth process. In fact a better correlation with growth rate occurs when diffusible substances are measured (See Fig. 13).

(ii) The tests used for the determination of fruit growth substances, with the exception of Luckwill's test (1948a), have no direct relationship to actual fruit growth. The possibility exists that present techniques do not measure all the growth regulators that are crucial for fruit growth, as suggested by Luckwill (1957).

However, the real situation is probably that fruit development is a complex phenomenon for a least two different reasons:

(i) The fruit itself is a composite organ in which the development of the seeds (which are themselves complex) and that of the various fruit tissues have to occur harmoniously. These various components grow in a certain sequence, in which different factors become limiting at different stages. For example, the supply of gibberellins may become critical very early, before or immediately after anthesis, whereas that of auxins may have a particular importance a little later, together with cytokinins. On the contrary, ethylene may trigger off the last step in fruit development, especially in fruits which have three distinct periods (stone fruits), by initiating starch hydrolysis and the formation of soluble sugars which enable the cells of the ripening fruit to accumulate more water. As will be seen in chapter 8 and Vol. 2, chapter 10, ethylene induces a sequence of enzyme changes during the ripening of fruits.

(ii) While fruits develop, other processes go on in the plant, for example the development of vegetative buds. These processes vary in intensity, and so does, consequently, the demand they exert on the nutrients available. At certain times, acute conflicts may arise between vegetative development and fruit growth. If these conflicts occur at periods which are critical for fruit growth, such as anthesis or the beginning of embryo development, they may be fatal to fruit development. In this situation, any stimulus which can give an advantage to fruits over shoots may be decisive for fruit growth. This may explain why so many different types of substances, as stressed by Crane (1969), may be efficient at various times and in different situations; all they do is to bring fruit development over a particular hurdle.

Whatever the limitations of our present knowledge, it remains certain that all categories of plant hormones, auxins, gibberellins, cytokinins, inhibitors and ethylene generally play an important role in fruit development.

REFERENCES

Abeles, F. B. and Rubinstein, B. (1964). *Pl. Physiol., Lancaster* **39**, 963.

Addicott, F. T. and Lynch, R. S. (1951). *Science, N.Y.* **114**, 688.

Addicott, F. T. and Lyon, J. L. (1969). *Ann. Rev. Pl. Physiol.* **20**, 139.

Addicott, F. T., Carns, H. R., Lyon, J. L., Smith, O. E. and McMeans, J. L. (1964). *In* "Régulateurs Naturels de la Croissance Végétale", Colloque Int. CNRS No. 123, 687–703.

Addoms, R. M., Nightingale, G. T. and Blake, M. A. (1930). *New Jersey Agric. exp. Sta. Bull.* **507**, 19 pp.

Albersheim, P. and Bonner, J. (1959). *J. biol. Chem.* **234**, 3105.

Antoszewski, R. and Lis, E. (1968). *Wiss. Zeit. Univ. Rostock, Math. Nat. Reihe* **16**, 541.

Asahira, T., Takeda, Y., Nishio, T., Hirabayashi, M. and Tsukamoto, Y. (1967). *Mem. Res. Inst. Fd Sci., Kyoto Univ.* **28**, 47.
Bain, J. M. and Robertson, R. N. (1951). *Aust. J. Scient. Res.* **B4**, 75.
Barker, W. G. and Collins, W. B. (1965). *Proc. Am. Soc. hort. Sci.* **87**, 229.
Barlow, H. W. B. (1950). *J. exp. Bot.* **1**, 264.
Blondeau, R. and Crane, J. C. (1950). *Pl. Physiol., Lancaster* **25**, 158.
Bose, T. K. (1964). *Curr. Sci. (Calcutta)* **33**, 120.
Bose, T. K. and Ghosh, M. S. (1968). *Sci. and Culture (Calcutta)* **34**, 216.
Bose, T. K. and Nitsch, J. P. (1970). *Physiol. Pl.* **23** (in press).
Bradley, M. V. and Crane, J. C. (1955). *Am. J. Bot.* **42**, 273.
Burg, S. P. (1964). *In* "Régulateurs Naturels de la Croissance Végétale", Coll. Int. CNRS No. 123, Paris, 719-25.
Burg, S. P. and Burg, E. A. (1965). *Science, N.Y.* **148**, 1190.
Burg, S. P. and Burg, E. A. (1966). *Proc. natn Acad. Sci. U.S.A.* **55**, 262.
Burg, S. P. and Burg, E. A. (1968). *In* "Biochemistry and Physiology of Plant Growth Substances" (F. Wightman and G. Setterfield, eds) pp. 1275-94. Runge Press, Ottawa.
Cavell, B. D., MacMillan, J., Pryce, R. J. and Sheppard, A. C. (1967). *Phytochem.* **6**, 867.
Collins, W. B., Irving, K. H. and Barker, W. G. (1966). *Proc. Am. Soc. hort. Sci.* **89**, 243.
Coombe, B. G. (1960). *Pl. Physiol., Lancaster* **32**, 241.
Coombe, B. G. (1965). *Nature, Lond.* **205**, 305.
Cornforth, J. W., Milborrow, B. V., Ryback, G., Rothwell, K. and Wain, R. L. (1966). *Nature, Lond.* **211**, 742.
Crane, J. C. (1952). *Bot. Gaz.* **114**, 102.
Crane, J. C. (1965). *Pl. Physiol. Lancaster* **40**, 606.
Crane, J. C. (1969). *Hortscience* **4**, 108.
Crane, J. C. and Blondeau, R. (1949). *Proc. Am. Soc. hort. Sci.* **54**, 102.
Crane, J. C., Bradley, M. V. and Luckwill, L. C. (1959). *J. hort. Sci.* **34**, 142.
Crane, J. C. and Grossi, N. (1960). *Proc. Am. Soc. hort. Sci.* **76**, 139.
Crane, J. C., Primer, P. E. and Campbell, R. C. (1960). *Proc. Am. Soc. hort. Sci.* **75**, 129.
Crane, J. C. and Van Overbeek, J. (1965). *Science, N.Y.* **147**, 1468.
Crosby, E. A. and Crane, J. C. (1952). *Proc. Am. Soc. hort. Soc.* **59**, 196.
Dannenburg, W. N. and Liverman, J. L. (1957). *Pl. Physiol., Lancaster* **32**, 263.
Davies, J. W. and Cocking, E. C. (1965). *Planta* **67**, 242.
Davison, R. M. (1960). *Nature, Lond.* **188**, 681.
Dennis, F. G. and Edgerton, L. J. (1962). *Proc. Am. Soc. hort. Sci.* **80**, 58.
Dennis, F. G., and Nitsch, J. P. (1966). *Nature, Lond.* **211**, 781.
Devlin, R. M. and Demoranville, I. E. (1967). *Physiologia Pl.* **20**, 587.
Digby, J. and Wareing, P. F. (1966). *Ann. Bot.* **30**, 539.
Dodds, K. S. and Simmonds, N. W. (1948). *Heredity* **2**, 101.
Dörffling, K. and Böttger, M. (1968). *Planta* **80**, 299.
Durand, B. (1967). *Bull. Soc. Franç. Physiol. Vég.* **13**, 195.
Durand, B. (1969). *C.r. hebd. Séanc. Acad. Sci., Paris* **268(D)**, 2049.
Eilati, S. K., Goldschmidt, E. E. and Monselise, S. P. (1969). *Experientia* **25**, 209.
Fitting, H. (1909). *Z. Bot.* **1**, 1.
Fuchs, Y. and Lieberman, M. (1968). *Pl. Physiol., Lancaster* **43**, 2029.

Fukui, H. N., De Vries, J. E., Wittwer, S. H. and Sell, H. M. (1957). *Nature, Lond.* **180,** 1205.

Fukui, H. N., Teubner, F. G., Wittwer, S. H. and Sell, H. M. (1958). *Pl. Physiol., Lancaster,* **33,** 144.

Fukushima, F., Matsuo, E. and Fujieda, K. (1968). *J. Fac. Agric. Kyushu Univ.* **14,** 349.

Galun, E. (1956). *Experientia* **12,** 218.

Gandar, J. C. (1964). Thèse, University of Paris.

Gandar, J. C. and Nitsch, J. P. (1964). *In* "Régulateurs naturels de la croissance végétale", Coll. Int. CNRS No. 123, Paris, 169–78.

Gandar, J. C. and Nitsch, C. (1967). *C.r. hebd. Séanc. Acad. Sci., Paris* **265(D),** 1795.

Gardner, F. E. (1951). *In* "Plant Growth Substances" (F. Skoog, ed.) pp. 207–23. University of Wisconsin Press, Madison, Wisconsin, U.S.A.

Golinska, J. (1925). *Acta soc. bot. Pol.* **3,** 97.

Graebe, J. E. (1969). *Planta* **85,** 171.

Griggs, W. H. and Iwakiri, B. T. (1961). *Proc. Am. Soc. hort. Sci.* **77,** 73.

Gupta, G. R. P. and Maheshwari, S. C. (1970). *Pl. Physiol.* **45,** 14.

Gustafson, F. G. (1936). *Proc. natn. Acad. Sci., U.S.A.* **22,** 628.

Gustafson, F. G. (1937). *Am. J. Bot.* **24,** 102.

Gustafson, F. G. (1939a). *Am. J. Bot.* **26,** 135.

Gustafson, F. G. (1939b). *Am. J. Bot.* **26,** 189.

Haagen-Smit, A. J., Dandliker, W. B., Wittwer, S. H. and Murneek, A. E. (1946). *Am. J. Bot.* **33,** 118.

Hackett, D. P. and Thimann, K. V. (1952). *Am. J. Bot.* **39,** 553.

Hall, W. C. and Morgan, P. W. (1964). *In* "Régulateurs Naturels de la Croissance Végétale", Coll. Int. CNRS No. 123, Paris, 727.

Harris, O. W. and Smith, C. L. (1957). *Proc. Am. Soc. hort. Sci.* **70,** 204.

Hartmann, H. T. (1952). *Proc. Am. Soc. hort. Sci.* **59,** 187.

Heinicke, A. J. (1917). *Cornell Univ. agric. Exp. Sta. Bull.* **393,** 43–114.

Heyn, A. N. J. (1931). *Recl Trav. bot. Néerl.* **28,** 113.

Heyn, A. N. J. (1940). *Bot. Rev.* **6,** 515.

Hibbard, A. D. and Murneek, A. E. (1951). *Proc. Am. Soc. hort. Sci.* **56,** 65.

Hield, H. Z., Coggins, C. W., Jr. and Garber, M. J. (1958). *Calif. Agric.* **12,** 9.

Hirai, J., Hirata, N. and Horiuchi, S. (1967). *J. Japan Soc. hort. Sci.* **36,** 36.

Horn, C. L. (1940). *Science, N.Y.* **92,** 237.

Höstermann, G. (1913). *Ber. K. Gärt. Lehreanst. Dahlem,* 54.

Howlett, F. S. (1931). *Ohio agric. Exp. Sta. Bull.* No. 483.

Hsiang, T. H. T. (1951a). *Pl. Physiol., Lancaster* **26,** 441.

Hsiang, T. H. T. (1951b). *Pl. Physiol., Lancaster* **26,** 708.

Hulme, A. C. (1948). *Biochem. J.* **43,** 343.

Hulme, A. C. (1953). *Biochem. J.* **53,** 337.

Hulme, A. C. (1958). *Bull. Soc. fr. Physiol. vég.* **4,** 43.

Isogai, Y., Okamoto, T. and Komoda, Y. (1967). *Chem. pharm. Bull., Tokyo* **15,** 1256.

Ito, H. and Saito, T. (1956). *J. hort. Ass. Japan* **25,** 101.

Ito, H., Motomura Y., Konno, Y. and Hatayama, T. (1969). *Tohoku J. agric. Res.* **20,** 1.

Jablonski, J. R. and Skoog, F. (1954). *Physiologia Pl.* **7,** 16.

Jackson, G. A. D. and Blundell, J. B. (1966). *Nature, Lond.* **212,** 1470.

Jacobs, W. P. (1952). *Am. J. Bot.* **39,** 301.

Jacobs, W. P. and Morrow, I. B. (1957). *Am. J. Bot.* **44,** 823.
Kano, K., Fujimura, T., Hirose, T. and Tsukamoto, Y. (1957). *Mem. Res. Inst. Fd Sci., Kyoto Univ.* **12,** 45.
Kendall, J. N. (1918). *Univ. Calif. Pub. Bot.* **5,** 347.
Khalifah, R. A. (1966). *Nature, Lond.* **212,** 1471.
Khalifah, R. A., Lewis, L. N., Coggins, C. W., Jr. and Radlick, P. C. (1965). *J. exp. Bot.* **16,** 511.
Komoda, Y., Isogai, Y. and Okamoto, T. (1968). *Sci. Papers College Gen. Educ. Univ., Tokyo* **18,** 221.
Kordan, H. A. (1958). *Science, N.Y.* **129,** 779.
Koshimizu, K., Fukui, H., Kusaki, T., Mitsui, T. and Ogawa, Y. (1966a). *Tetrahedron Lett.* p. 2459.
Koshimizu, K., Fukui, H., Kusaki, T., Mitsui, T. and Ogawa, Y. (1966b). *Agric. Biol. Chem. (Tokyo)* **30,** 941.
Koshimizu, K., Matsubara, S., Kusaki, T. and Mitsui, T. (1967). *Agric. Biol. Chem. (Tokyo)* **31,** 795.
Koshimizu, K., Inui, M., Fukui, H. and Mitsui, T. (1968a). *Agric. Biol. Chem. (Tokyo)* **32,** 789.
Koshimizu, K., Fukui, H., Inui, M., Ogawa, Y. and Mitsui, T. (1968b). *Tetrahedron Lett.* p. 1143.
Kovoor, A. (1954). *Année biol.* **30,** 417.
Labarca, C. C., Nicholls, P. B. and Bandurski, R. S. (1965). *Biochem. biophys. Res. Commun.* **20,** 641.
Laibach, F. (1932). *Ber. dt bot. Ges.* **50,** 383.'
Laibach, F. and Kribben, F. J. (1949). *Ber. dt bot. Ges.* **62,** 53.
Laibach, F. and Kribben, F. J. (1950). *Beitr. Biol. Pfl.* **28,** 131.
LaMotte, C. E. and Jacobs, W. P. (1963). *Devl Biol.* **8,** 80.
Lange, A. H. (1961a). *Proc. Am. Soc. hort. Sci.* **77,** 252.
Lange, A. H. (1961b). *Proc. Am. Soc. hort. Sci.* **78,** 218.
Letham, D. S. (1958). *Nature, Lond.* **182,** 473.
Letham, D. S. (1960). *Nature, Lond.* **188,** 425.
Letham, D. S. (1963). *Life Sci.* **2,** 569.
Letham, D. S. (1964). *In* "Régulateurs Naturels de la Croissance Végétale", Coll. Int. CNRS No. 123, Paris p. 109.
Letham, D. S. (1966a). *Life Sci.* **5,** 551.
Letham, D. S. (1966b). *Life Sci.* **5,** 1999.
Letham, D. S. (1968). *In* "Biochemistry and physiology of plant growth substances" (F. Wightman and G. Setterfield, eds) pp. 19–31. Runge Press, Ottawa.
Letham, D. S. (1969). *N.Z. Jl agric. Res.* **12,** 1.
Letham, D. S. and Williams, M. W. (1969). *Physiologia Pl.* **22,** 925.
Lewis, D. (1942). *J. Pomol.* **20,** 40.
Lewis, L. N., Khalifah, R. A. and Coggins, C. W., Jr. (1965). *Phytochem.* **4,** 203.
Linck, A. J. and Sudia, T. W. (1962). *Experientia* **18,** 69.
Linck, A. J. and Swanson, C. A. (1960). *Pl. Soil* **12,** 57.
Linskens, H. F. (1953). *Naturwissenschaften* **40,** 28.
Lis, E. K. and Antoszewski, R. (1968). *Acta Soc. Bot. Pol.* **37,** 217.
Luckwill, L. C. (1948a). *J. hort. Sci.* **24,** 19.
Luckwill, L. C. (1948b). *J. hort. Sci.* **24,** 32.
Luckwill, L. C. (1949). *Endeavour* **8,** 188.
Luckwill, L. C. (1953). *J. hort. Sci.* **28,** 14.

Luckwill, L. C. (1957). *Symp. Soc. exp. Biol.* **11**, 63.

Luckwill, L. C. (1960). *Rep. Long Ashton Res. Sta.* for 1959: 59.

Luckwill, L. C., MacMillan, J. and Weaver, P. (1968). *J. hort. Sci.* **44**, 413.

Luckwill, L. C. and Powell, L. E., Jr. (1956). *Science, N.Y.* **123**, 225.

Luckwill, L. C. and Woodcock, D. (1956). *In* "The chemistry and mode of action of plant growth substances" (R. L. Wain and F. W. Wightman, eds), pp. 195–204. Academic Press, London and New York.

Lund, H. A. (1956a). *Am. J. Bot.* **43**, 562.

Lund, H. A. (1956b). *Pl. Physiol., Lancaster* **31**, 334.

MacDaniels, L. H. (1937). *Proc. Am. Soc. hort. Sci.* **34**, 122.

MacMillan, J. and Suter, P. J. (1958). *Naturwissenschaften* **45**, 46.

MacMillan, J., Pryce, R. J., Eglington G. and McCormick, A. (1967). *Tetrahedron Lett.* p. 2241.

MacMillan, J., Seaton, J. C. and Suter, P. J. (1959). *Proc. chem. Soc.* 325.

MacMillan, J., Seaton, J. C. and Suter, P. J. (1961). *Adv. Chem.* **28**, 18.

Maheshwari, S. C. and Prakash, R. (1966). *Naturwissenschaften* **53**, 558.

Mann, J. D., Yung, K. H., Storey, W. B., Pu, M. and Conley, J. (1967). *Pl. Cell Physiol., Tokyo* **8**, 613.

Marrè, E. (1948a). *Boll. Soc. ital. Biol. sper.* **24**, 599.

Marrè, E. (1948b). *Boll. Soc. ital. Biol. sper.* **24**, 602.

Marrè, E. (1949). *Boll. Soc. ital. Biol. sper.* **25**, 331.

Marrè, E. (1951). *Atti Accad. ligure* **8**, 1.

Marrè, E. (1954). *Ist Lombardo di Scienze e Lettere, Rendiconti, Cl. Sc.* **87**, 37.

Marrè, E. and Murneek, A. E. (1953a). *Science, N.Y.* **117**, 661.

Marrè, E. and Murneek, A. E. (1953b). *Pl. Physiol. Lancaster* **28**, 255.

Martin, D., Lewis, T. L. and Cerny, J. (1954). *Aust. J. biol. Sci.* **7**, 211.

Marumo, S., Abe, H., Hattori, H. and Munakata, K. (1968a). *Agric. biol. Chem.* **32**, 117.

Marumo, S., Hattori, H., Abe, H. and Munakata, K. (1968b). *Nature, Lond.* **219**, 959.

Massart, J. (1902). *Bull. Jard. bot. État Brux.* **1**, 89.

Matsuo, E. (1968). *J. Fac. Agric. Kyushu Univ.* **14**, 483.

Matsuo, E., Minohara, Y. and Takanashi, S. (1968). *J. Jap. Soc. hort. Sci.* **37**, 32.

Maxie, E. C. and Crane, J. C. (1967). *Science, N.Y.* **155**, 1548.

Maxie, E. C. and Crane, J. C. (1968). *Proc. Am. Soc. hort. Sci.* **92**, 255.

Milborrow, B. V. (1967). *Planta* **76**, 93.

Millardet, A. (1901). *Rev. de Viticulture* **16**, 677.

Miller, C. O. (1967). *Ann. N.Y. Acad. Sci.* **144**, 251.

Miller, C. O. and Witham, F. H. (1964). *In* "Régulateurs Naturels de la Croissance Végétale, Coll. Int. CNRS, Paris No. 123, pp. I–VI.

Minina, E. G. (1952). *Izdatel'stvo Akad. Nauk. SSSR, Moscow,* 198 pp.

Minina, E. G. and Tylkina, L. G. (1947). *Dokl. Acad. Nauk. SSSR* **55**, 165.

Mitchell, J. W. and Marth, P. C. (1950). *Bot. Gaz.* **112**, 70.

Mitchell, J. W. and Whitehead, M. R. (1941). *Bot. Gaz.* **102**, 770.

Mitchell, W. D. and Wittwer, S. H. (1962). *Science, N.Y.* **136**, 880.

Modlibowska, I. (1961). *Rep. East Malling Res. Stat.* (1960) 46.

Mohan Ram, H. Y. and Steward, F. C. (1964). *Can. J. Bot.* **42**, 1559.

Most, B. H., Gaskin, P. and MacMillan, J. (1970). *Planta* **92**, 41.

Mothes, K., Engelbrecht, L. and Kulajewa, O. (1959). *Flora* **147**, 445.

Muir, R. M. (1942). *Am. J. Bot.* **29**, 716.

Müller-Thürgau, H. (1898). *Landw. Jb Schweiz* **12**, 135.

Murneek, A. E. (1926). *Pl. Physiol., Lancaster* **1**, 3.

Murneek, A. E. (1927). *Missouri agric. exp. Sta. Res. Bull.* **106,** 1.
Murneek, A. E. (1951). *In* "Plant growth substances", (F. Skoog, ed.) pp. 329. University of Wisconsin Press, Madison, U.S.A.
Murneek, A. E. and Teubner, F. G. (1953). *Proc. Am. Soc. hort. Sci.* **61,** 149.
Negi, S. S. and Olmo, H. P. (1966). *Science, N.Y.* **152,** 1624.
Neumann, U. (1955). *Archs Gartenb.* **3,** 274.
Nicholls, P. B. (1967). *Planta* **72,** 258.
Nitsch, J. P. (1950). *Am. J. Bot.* **37,** 211.
Nitsch, J. P. (1951). *Am. J. Bot.* **38,** 566.
Nitsch, J. P. (1952). *Q. Rev. Biol.* **27,** 33.
Nitsch, J. P. (1954). *Fruits* **9,** 157.
Nitsch, J. P. (1955). *Pl. Physiol., Lancaster* **30,** 33.
Nitsch, J. P. (1959). *Bull. Soc. bot. Fr.* **106,** 420.
Nitsch, J. P. (1960). *Bull. Soc. bot. Fr.* **107,** 251.
Nitsch, J. P. (1961a). *In* "Advances in Horticultural Science and their Applications", **1,** 55–65. Pergamon Press, Oxford.
Nitsch, J. P. (1961b). *In* "Recent Advances in Botany" (from lectures and symposia presented to the IXth Int. Bot. Congress, Montreal 1959), Toronto University Press **2,** 1089.
Nitsch, J. P. (1965a). *Encycl. Pl. Physiol.* (W. Ruhland, ed.), **15,** (1): 1537. Springer, Berlin.
Nitsch, J. P. (1965b). *Bull. Soc. bot. Fr.* **112,** 19.
Nitsch, J. P. (1965c). *Bull. Soc. bot. Fr.* **112,** 22.
Nitsch, J. P. and Nitsch, C. (1955). *Bull. Soc. bot. Fr.* **102,** 528.
Nitsch, J. P. and Nitsch, C. (1962). *Ann. Physiol. Vég.* **4,** 211.
Nitsch, J. P. and Nitsch, C. (1965). *Bull. Soc. bot. Fr.* **112,** 1.
Nitsch, J. P., Kurtz, E., Jr., Liverman, J. and Went, F. W. (1952). *Am. J. Bot.* **39,** 32.
Nitsch, J. P., Pratt, C., Nitsch, C. and Shaulis, N. J. (1960). *Am. J. Bot.* **47,** 566.
Nitsch, J. P., Asahira, T., Rossini, L. and Nitsch, C. (1970). *Bull. Soc. bot. Fr.* (in press).
Nixon, R. W. and Gardner, F. E. (1939). *Bot. Gaz.* **100,** 868.
Noll, F. (1902). *Sitzber. niederrhein. Ges. nat. Heilk., Bonn* 149.
Ogawa, Y. (1965). *Bot. Mag.* **78,** 412.
Okhuma, K., Lyon, J. L., Addicott, F. T. and Smith, O. E. (1963). *Science, N.Y.* **142,** 1592.
Olmo, H. P. (1937). *Proc. Am. Soc. hort. Sci.* **34,** 402.
Osborne, D. J. (1958). *J. exp. Bot.* **9,** 446.
Osborne, D. J., Wain, R. L. and Walker, R. D. (1952). *J. hort. Sci.* **27,** 44.
Osborne, D. J. and Went, F. W. (1953). *Bot. Gaz.* **114,** 312.
Pearson, H. M. (1932). *Proc. Am. Soc. hort. Sci.* **29,** 169.
Perkins, D. Y., Miller, J. C. and Dallyn, S. L. (1952). *Proc. Am. Soc. hort. Sci.* **60,** 311.
Peterson, C. E. and Anhder, L. D. (1960). *Science, N.Y.* **131,** 1673.
Pfeffer, W. (1904). *Pflanzenphysiologie* **2,** 276.
Powell, L. E. and Pratt, C. (1964). *Nature, Lond.* **204,** 602.
Powell, L. E. and Pratt, C. (1966). *J. hort. Sci.* **41,** 331.
Pratt, H. K. and Goeschl, J. D. (1968). *In* "Biochemistry and Physiology of Plant Substances" (F. Wightman and G. Setterfield, eds.), pp. 1295–1302. Runge Press, Ottawa.
Rabin, R. S. and Klein, R. M. (1957). *Archs Biochem. Biophys.* **10,** 11.

Raussendorff-Bargen, G. von (1962). *Planta* **58,** 471.

Redemann, C. T., Wittwer, S. H. and Sell, H. M. (1951). *Archs Biochem. Biophys.* **32,** 80.

Reed, H. S. (1944). *Am. J. Bot.* **31,** 193.

Rebeiz, C. A. and Crane, J. C. (1961). *Proc. Am. Soc. hort. Sci.* **78,** 69.

Richmond, A. E. and Lang, A. (1957). *Science, N.Y.* **125,** 650.

Roberts, R. H. (1946). *Proc. Am. Soc. hort. Sci.* **48,** 59.

Roberts, R. H. (1948). *Proc. Am. Soc. hort. Sci.* **51,** 51.

Rogozinska, J. H., Helgeson, J. P., Skoog, F., Lipton, S. H. and Strong, F. M. (1965). *Pl. Physiol., Lancaster* **40,** 469.

Rosa, J. T. (1924). *Proc. Am. Soc. hort. Sci.* **21,** 51.

Rudich, J., Halevy, A. H. and Kedar, N. (1969). *Planta* **86,** 69.

Rudnicki, R., Pieniazek, J. and Pieniazek, N. (1968). *Bull. Acad. pol. Sci. Cl. II Sér. Sci. biol.* **16,** 127.

Sachar, R. C. and Iyer, R. D. (1959). *Phytomorphology* **9,** 1.

Sacher, J. A. (1967). *Symp. Soc. exp. Biol.* **21,** 269.

Saito, T. (1961). *Jap. Soc. hort. Sci.* **30,** 1.

Sastry, K. K. S. and Muir, R. M. (1963). *Science, N.Y.* **140,** 494.

Satyanarayana, G. and Rangaswamy, G. (1959). *Curr. Sci. (Calcutta)* **28,** 376.

Schroeder, C. A. (1953). *Proc. Am. Soc. hort. Sci.* **61,** 103.

Schroeder, C. A. (1955). *Science, N.Y.* **122,** 601.

Schroeder, C. A. and Spector, C. (1957). *Science, N.Y.* **126,** 701.

Sell, H. M., Wittwer, S. H., Rebstock, T. L. and Redemann, C. T. (1953). *Pl. Phys., Lancaster* **28,** 481.

Sembdner, G., Weiland, J., Aurich, O. and Schreiber, K. (1968). *In* "Plant Growth Regulators" p. 70. Soc. Chem. Ind. Monograph No. 31, London.

Shantz, E. M. and Steward, F. C. (1955). *J. Am. chem. Soc.* **77,** 6351.

Shantz, E. M. and Steward, F. C. (1957). *Pl. Physiol., Lancaster* **32** (Suppl.): VIII.

Shantz, E. M. and Steward, F. C. (1968). *In* "Biochemistry and Physiology of Plant Growth Substances" (F. Wightman and G. Setterfield, eds.) pp. 893–909. Runge Press, Ottawa.

Simmonds, N. W. (1953). *J. exp. Bot.* **4,** 87.

Sims, W. L. and Gledhill, B. L. (1969). *Calif. Agric.* **23 (2),** 4.

Sinnott, Ed. W. (1939). *Am. J. Bot.* **26,** 179.

Sinnott, Ed. W. (1945). *Am. J. Bot.* **32,** 439.

Skene, K. G. M. (1968). *Science, N.Y.* **159,** 1477.

Smith, W. H. (1950). *Ann. Bot.,* **14,** 23.

Sommer, N. F., Bradley, M. V. and Creasy, M. T. (1962). *Science, N.Y.* **136,** 264.

Sterling, C. (1953). *Bull. Torrey bot. Club* **80,** 457.

Steward, F. C. and Caplin, S. M. (1952). *Ann. Bot.* **16,** 491.

Steward, F. C. and Shantz, E. M. (1955). *In* "The Chemistry and Mode of Action of Plant Growth Substances" (R. L. Wain and F. Wightman, eds), pp. 165–86. Academic Press, New York and London.

Stewart, W. S., Ching, F. T. and Halsey, D. D. (1957). *Lasca Leaves* **7,** 80.

Stewart, W. S. and Klotz, L. J. (1947). *Bot. Gaz.* **109,** 150.

Stewart, W. S. and Parker, E. R. (1947). *Proc. Am. Soc. hort. Sci.* **50,** 187.

Stowe, B. B. and Thimann, K. V. (1953). *Nature, Lond.* **172,** 764.

Takahashi, N., Murofushi, N., Yokota, T. and Tamura, S. (1967). *Tetrahedron Lett.* p. 1065.

Tamura, S., Takahashi, N., Murofushi, N., Yokota, T., Kato, J. and Shiotani, Y. (1967). *Planta* **75**, 279.

Tamura, S., Takahashi, N., Yokota, T., Murofushi, N. and Ogawa, Y. (1968). *Planta* **78**, 208.

Teaotia, S. S., Pandey, I. C. and Mathur, R. S. (1961). *Curr. Sci. (Calcutta)* **30**, 312.

Teubner, F. G. (1953). *Science, N.Y.* **118**, 418.

Teubner, F. G. and Murneek, A. E. (1952). *Science, N.Y.* **116**, 39.

Teubner, F. G. and Murneek, A. E. (1955). *Missouri Agric. exp. Sta. Res. Bull.* **590**, 1.

Thimann, K. V. (1934). *J. gen. Physiol.* **18**, 23.

Thompson, P. A. (1969). *J. exp. Bot.* **20**, 629.

Torrey, J. G. (1961). *Expl Cell. Res.* **23**, 281.

Tukey, H. B. and Hammer, C. L. (1949). *Proc. Am. Soc. hort. Sci.* **54**, 95.

Tsui, C. (1948). *Am. J. Bot.* **35**, 172.

Varga, A. (1969). *Neth. J. agric. Sci.* **17**, 229.

Wagenknecht, A. C. and Burris, R. H. (1950). *Archs Biochem.* **25**, 30.

Weaver, R. J. (1952). *Bot. Gaz.* **114**, 107.

Weaver, R. J. (1953). *Proc. Am. Soc. hort. Sci.* **61**, 135.

Weaver, R. J. (1954). *Proc. Am. Soc. hort. Sci.* **63**, 194.

Weaver, R. J. (1956). *Calif. agric. exp. Sta. Bull.* No. 752, 1–26.

Weaver, R. J. and McCune, S. B. (1959a). *Hilgardia* **28**, 297.

Weaver, R. J. and McCune, S. B. (1959b). *Hilgardia* **29**, 247.

Weaver, R. J. and Van Overbeek, J. and Pool, R. M. (1965). *Nature, Lond.* **206**, 952.

Weaver, R. J., Van Overbeek, J. and Pool, R. M. (1966). *Hilgardia* **37**, 181.

Weaver, R. J. and Williams, W. O. (1951). *Bot. Gaz.* **113**, 75.

Wellington, R. and Hawthorn, L. R. (1929). *Proc. Am. Soc. hort. Sci.* **25**, 97.

West, C. A., Oster, M., Robinson, D., Lew, F. and Murphy, P. (1968). *In* "Biochemistry and Physiology of Plant Growth Substances" (F. Wightman and G. Setterfield, eds) pp. 313–32. Runge Press, Ottawa.

West, C. A. and Phinney, B. O. (1959). *J. Am. chem. Soc.* **81**, 2424.

Westergaard, M. (1958). *Adv. Genet.* **9**, 217.

White, J. (1907). *Ann. Bot.* **21**, 487.

Williams, A. H. (1958). *Chemy Ind.* 1958, 1200.

Williams, B. L., Ice, C. H. and Wender, S. H. (1952). *J. Am. chem. Soc.* **74**, 4566.

Williams, B. L. and Wender, S. H. (1952). *J. Am. chem. Soc.* **74**, 4372.

Williams, B. L. and Wender, S. H. (1953a). *Archs Biochem. Biophys.* **43**, 319.

Williams, B. L. and Wender, S. H. (1953b). *J. Am. chem. Soc.* **75**, 4363.

Winkler, H. (1908). *Prog. Rei Bot.* **2**, 293.

Wittwer, S. H. (1943). *Missouri agric. exp. Sta. Res. Bull.* No. 371.

Wittwer, S. H. and Bukovac, M. J. (1962). Proc. Plant Sci. Symp. (Camden, N. J.: Campbell Soup Comp.), pp. 65–83.

Wong, C. Y. (1939). *Proc. Am. Soc. hort. Sci.* **37**, 158.

Wong, C. Y. (1941). *Bot. Gaz.* **103**, 64.

Woodburn, W. L. (1911). *Bull. Torrey bot. Club* **38**, 379.

Wright, S. T. C. (1956). *J. hort. Sci.* **31**, 196.

Yakushkina, N. I. (1947). *Doklady Akad. Nauk. SSSR* **56**, 549.

Yasuda, S. (1934). *Jap. J. Genet.* **9**, 118.

Yasuda, S. (1939). *Mem. Fac. Sci. Agric., Taihoku imp. Univ., Formosa* **27**, 1.

Yoda, S. (1958). *Bot. Mag.*, *Tokyo* **71**, 1.
Yokata, T., Takahashi, N., Murofushi, N. and Tamura, S. (1969). *Planta* **87**, 180.
Zenk, M. H. (1964). *In* "Régulateurs Naturels de la Croissance Végétale", Coll. Int. CNRS Paris, No. 123, 241–9.

Part IIIa

Biochemistry of Maturation and Ripening

Chapter 16

The Ethylene Factor

W. B. McGLASSON

C.S.I.R.O., Division of Food Preservation, New South Wales, Australia

I. INTRODUCTION

Recognition that ethylene can cause physiological responses in plant tissues dates back at least to 1901. In that year, Neljubow reported ethylene to be most potent in causing changes in the growth patterns of dark-grown plant seedlings (see Pratt and Goeschl, 1969). An early report that ethylene could exert physiological effects on fruits can be traced to Cousins (1910) who found that gases from oranges caused premature ripening of bananas. Soon afterwards Sievers and True (1912) demonstrated that incomplete combustion products from kerosene stoves hastened the changes from green to yellow (de-greening) in citrus fruits. Twelve years later, Denny (1924) showed that the active gas could be absorbed in bromine and that small amounts of pure ethylene were effective. Then followed a number of reports of the effects of emanations from ripening fruits on (i) the onset of ripening in unripe fruits and (ii) various vegetative tissues including the inhibition of germination of bean seedlings and sprouting of potato tubers, and epinasty of leaves (see Biale, 1950). Chemical proof that ethylene is produced by ripening fruits was eventually provided by Gane (1934).

By 1940, most of the important qualitative principles of ethylene physiology had been established (Porritt, 1951; Burg, 1962) including (i) the activity of ethylene at low concentrations and (ii) the greatly superior activity of ethylene compared with other volatile compounds evolved by fruits. During this period several chemical procedures were developed for ethylene assay (Pratt, 1961). In the most specific and sensitive chemical method eventually developed, ethylene is absorbed in a mercuric perchlorate solution at 0°C, quantitatively released with chloride ion, and measured manometrically (Young et al., 1952). The smallest volume of ethylene that can be accurately measured by this method is 0·2 ml.

Crocker et al. (1935) stated that "there is much evidence that it (ethylene) acts as a fruit-ripening hormone in plants, and a possibility that it acts as a growth-rate and organization hormone in vegetative organs of plants". From their long experience, especially with pome fruits, Hansen (1943) and Kidd and West (1945) concluded that endogenous ethylene is the factor responsible for the induction of the climacteric and the associated ripening changes.

Biale et al. (1954) put forward the opposing view that native ethylene is a product of the ripening process, rather than a causal agent. Their conclusions were drawn from studies of the concurrent rates of ethylene and carbon dioxide production by 14 varieties of tropical, sub-tropical and temperate fruits. Ethylene measurements were made by the manometric procedure of Young et al. (1952). Fruit studied included oranges and lemons, which undergo no marked ripening phase, and mango, which does undergo a respiratory climacteric and associated ripening changes. These three fruits evolved no ethylene measurable by the method used. However, Biale et al. (1954) recognized the lack of knowledge on the relationship between external and internal ethylene concentrations in the fruit and of the possibility "that small quantities sufficient to induce ripening are produced prior to the rise of respiration, but measurable amounts are detected only after the onset of the climacteric".

Little progress was made towards resolution of these opposing viewpoints on the role of ethylene in fruit ripening until the advent of gas chromatography. Burg and Stolwijk (1959) were the first to describe the design and construction of a gas chromatograph for the measurement of traces of ethylene and other gases of biological importance, and Burg and Thimann (1959) were the first to apply the technique to studies on ethylene physiology in fruit. This instrument permitted the analysis of gas samples of less than 1 ml withdrawn from an apple with a syringe. Further development soon followed and instruments employing a flame ionization detector were constructed (Meigh, 1960). With the most sensitive instruments it is possible to measure accurately 0·001 p.p.m. in a 5-ml air sample (Goeschl et al., 1967). Using gas chromatography, Lyons et al. (1962) and Burg and Burg (1962a) established that several varieties of fruit accumulate intercellular concentrations of ethylene high enough to stimulate ripening at or several hours before the beginning of the climacteric rise in respiration.

Since 1959 there has been a resurgence of interest in ethylene, not only in terms of its role in fruit ripening, but also in growth regulation. Ethylene may now be regarded as a universal product or constituent of higher plants (Burg, 1962) and probably of fungi (Ilag and Curtis, 1968). Some bacteria also evolve ethylene (Freebairn and Buddenhagen, 1964). It may even be evolved by human subjects (Chandra and Spencer, 1963a).

Despite the large expansion of knowledge, the three most important questions posed in a review by Pratt (1961) have not all been satisfactorily answered. These questions were:

(i) What is the mechanism of ethylene production?

(ii) What is the mechanism of the effect of applied ethylene?

(iii) Does the naturally produced ethylene have a positive role in fruit ripening?

The state of knowledge relating to these questions and the possibilities for the application of this knowledge are discussed in the following sections of this chapter. A complete review of the literature has not been attempted since this topic has been the subject of a number of recent reviews (Biale, 1964; Burg, 1962, 1968; Jansen, 1965; Spencer, 1965; Hansen, 1966; Yang, 1968; Mapson, 1969; Pratt and Goeschl, 1969).

II. BIOGENESIS OF ETHYLENE

Continued progress with this problem has been made possible by the development of highly sensitive gas chromatographic and radiotracer techniques. Even with these techniques, studies on ethylene biogenesis are difficult because ethylene is a gas at normal temperatures and pressures and because the actual amounts produced by plant tissues and micro-organisms are small. For example, it may be calculated from the data of Biale et al. (1954) that at 20°C, ripe McIntosh apples release over 200 times more carbon as carbon dioxide than as ethylene.

In radiotracer studies, activity in ethylene may be measured by means of a gas counting device attached directly to a thermal conductivity gas chromatograph or by trapping the $^{14}CO_2$ or ^3H_2O released at the burner of a flame ionization gas chromatograph. Another method involves complexing ethylene with mercuric perchlorate (Thompson and Spencer, 1966) or mercuric acetate (Gibson and Crane, 1963) and counting in a scintillation spectrometer.

In studies on biogenesis, care has to be taken that the gas evolved by a system under test is ethylene. Standard methods for identifying ethylene have been listed by Burg (1962). Other gases evolved by fruit include acetylene, propylene, ethane and propane by apples (Meigh, 1959) and ethane and propane by bananas (Burg and Burg, 1965a). Nothing is known of the significance of the presence of these other gases in fruit.

There are three aspects to the problem of ethylene biogenesis: (i) What is the intracellular site of synthesis? (ii) What are the biochemical pathways concerned? (iii) How is biogenesis regulated in living cells?

A. Intracellular Origin

This aspect has been approached indirectly through studies with sections or pieces of tissue, and directly by studies with subcellular fractions. It has been shown that ethylene production by sections of apple (Burg and Thimann, 1960) and pear (Burg, 1962) may be suppressed by immersing the tissue in water or hypotonic solutions, but this effect could be largely prevented by transferring the tissue to a solution of high tonicity. The choice of osmoticum was not specific, provided that the substances were not toxic to the tissue respiration (Burg, 1962). Glycerol at 0·3M and KCl at 0·15M were equally effective (Burg and Thimann, 1960). An interesting finding was that solutions of 0–1M had no effect on respiration. Burg and Thimann concluded that the source of ethylene production could be an organelle other than the mitochrondrion. In a later interpretation of this work, and in the light of studies by others on ethylene production by subcellular particles, Burg (1962) suggested that solution tonicity affects both permeability and the site of ethylene production. These findings together with the work by Ku and Pratt (1968) indicate that the site of ethylene biogenesis is located in the cytoplasm rather than in the mitochondria.

Spencer (1959) was probably the first to report data suggesting ethylene production by mitochondria isolated from tomato fruits. Maximum ethylene production was associated with mitochondria isolated from fruit at the half to three-quarter coloured stage which are known to produce ethylene maximally. No ethylene production was detected in mitochondria from mature green fruit. However, this apparent association between the stage of ripeness in whole fruit and the ability of mitochondria isolated therefrom to produce ethylene was probably fortuitous since the content of phenolic substances in fruit declines during ripening. Some of these phenolic substances, particularly the orthodihydric phenols, are known to inhibit particulate and enzymic activities (Jones and Hulme, 1961; Loomis and Battaille,

1966; Anderson, 1968). Spencer did not include in the initial tomato fruit homogenates any of the phenol absorbents now considered necessary for the preparation of active mitochondria.

Chandra and Spencer (1962) went on to show that a number of subcellular fractions, prepared from tomato fruit as previously described, produced ethylene. Ethylene production was again ascribed mainly to the mitochondria. However, sonication of all fractions prepared at centrifugal forces up to 105,000 $\times$ **g** greatly stimulated ethylene production. Chandra and Spencer (1963b) extended these studies to preparations of subcellular particles from rat liver, rat intestinal mucosa and *Penicillium digitatum*. Again disintegration of the particles stimulated ethylene production.

Following these reports from Spencer's laboratory, Meigh (1962) re-examined the effects of sonication on ethylene production by particulate suspensions prepared and incubated essentially as described by Chandra and Spencer (1962). Meigh found by direct assay of gas samples drawn from the reaction vessels that ethylene plus acetylene and ethane were generated and, futhermore, that small amounts of these gases could be produced simply by sonicating the reaction medium. He visualized that free radicals generated in the sonication process were responsible for the production of the hydrocarbons. Further studies with sonicated mitochondrial suspensions were made by Meheriuk and Spencer (1967a, b, c). They examined the effect on ethylene production of the addition of several potential substrates, co-factors, cations and inhibitors. The results were consolidated into a general scheme suggesting possible pathways for ethylene biogenesis.

Lieberman and Craft (1961) claimed that cytoplasmic particles which were prepared from acidic homogenates of apple and tomato fruits evolved ethylene in the presence of thiomalic and thioglycolic acids. The production of the gas by these particles, which were unable to oxidize Krebs cycle substrates, was inhibited by the chelating agents diethyldithiocarbamate (DIECA) and ethyldiaminetetraacetic acid (EDTA). The addition of cupric ions partially restored activity. Burg and Burg (1961) repeated this work and found that the gas evolved was not ethylene. Lieberman and Mapson (1962a) later identified the "ethylene-like" gas reported by Lieberman and Craft as ethane. Meigh (1962) provided further light on the nature of this system. Cellular particles were not necessary for ethane production from a reaction medium containing thio acids and linolenic acid as the cellular particles could be substituted by cytochrome C or ATP, or ferric or ferrous salts. Substitution of other C_{18} acids showed that the efficiency as a substrate for ethane production is linolenic $\gg$ linoleic $>$ oleic and stearic acids.

Shimokawa and Kasai (1967) reported that ^{14}C-ethylene was produced optimally at pH 6·0 from ^{14}C-pyruvate by a particulate preparation (13,000 $\times$ **g**) from climacteric apples in the presence of phosphate buffer, $MgSO_4$, thamine pyrophosphate (TPP) and flavin mononucleotide (FMN). The addition of Co-enzyme A (CoA) did not enhance ethylene production. Since label appeared rapidly in acetaldehyde, these authors suggested that this compound is an intermediate between pyruvate and ethylene. Shimokawa and Kasai did not overlook the possibility that ethylene production in their system was non-enzymic.

At this stage of our knowledge it must be concluded that none of the studies at the cellular and subcellular levels provide strong evidence favouring the idea that an organelle is the site of ethylene biogenesis. However, the studies with subcellular particles emphasize the ever present risk of artefacts. This risk is exemplified by the findings of Meigh (1962). Although it is likely that ethylene production associated with subcellular particles, especially after disruption, is not representative of an *in vivo* system, none the less these studies have provided useful experimental leads on the nature of the pathways of biogenesis. An example of such a lead is the report by Lieberman and Hochstein (1966) of a possible mechanism for ethylene formation in rat liver microsomes by way of lipid peroxidation in the presence of cuprous ions. As discussed in the next section, a peroxidase system has been strongly implicated in ethylene biogenesis.

B. Pathways of Biogenesis

Studies on ethylene biogenesis have included (i) measurements of the yield of labelled ethylene following application of labelled substrates to sections of fruit tissue and to mycelial mats of *Penicillium digitatum*; (ii) application of labelled ethylene of high specific activity to tissue in the hope of "backing-up" the pathway, and (iii) preparation of enzyme fractions capable of producing high yields of ethylene from specific substrates. Additionally, possible mechanisms of ethylene synthesis have been investigated with non-enzymic model systems. Although one tends to think solely in terms of enzyme mediated reactions in living tissue, there is the possibility that the final reactions resulting in ethylene production are non-enzymic.

1. *Studies with* ^{14}*C-labelled respiratory intermediates and related compounds*

Burg and Thimann (1959) examined the effects of anaerobiosis on ethylene production by whole apples and sections of apple tissue. They confirmed earlier reports that ethylene production ceases or declines to a very low level in the absence of oxygen (half maximum values for oxygen consumption and ethylene production were reached at $1 \cdot 5$–$2 \cdot 0\%$ oxygen) and also showed that a substance accumulated under anaerobiosis which was rapidly converted to ethylene when the tissue was returned to air. It thus seemed possible that ethylene production is associated with the major respiratory pathways. This possibility has been studied with *Penicillium digitatum* (Phan, 1960, 1962; Wang *et al.*, 1962; Sprayberry *et al.*, 1965; Gibson and Young, 1966; Ketring *et al.*, 1968) and apple tissue (Burg and Thimann, 1961; Burg and Burg, 1964; Shimokawa and Kasai, 1966). The fungus was used because it produces ethylene prolifically.

Phan concluded that in *P. digitatum* ethylene is derived from carbons 2 or 3 of glucose and is readily formed from glycerol, alanine and ethanol. It was suggested that ethanol is the closest precursor of ethylene. Wang *et al.* administered specifically labelled glucose, alanine, glycine, aspartate and glutamate to cultures of the fungus and measured the average specific activities of ethylene collected over a six day test period. These authors deduced that carbons 1, 2, 5 and 6 of glucose were converted to ethylene more efficiently than carbons 3 and 4. This deduction was supported by measurements which showed carbons 2 and 3 of alanine were converted more efficiently to ethylene than carbon 1, the latter carbon being equivalent to carbons 3 and 4 of glucose. From this, Wang *et al.* concluded that pyruvate from glucose is decarboxylated to acetyl co-enzyme A before conversion to ethylene. Tests with ^{14}C-glycine, aspartate and glutamate indicated that ethylene production was associated with the Krebs cycle rather than the glyoxylate pathway and that the middle carbons of fumarate give rise to ethylene.

Using improved techniques, Gibson and Young (1966) further examined the efficiency of conversion of specifically labelled organic acids to ethylene by *P. digitatum*. The specific activity of ethylene and carbon dioxide was measured at hourly intervals for the first six hours after adding the substrates to the culture. They found that carbon 2 of acetate and carbon 3 of pyruvate were converted more efficiently to ethylene than to carbon dioxide. Carbon 3 of malate was also converted efficiently to ethylene but initially at a slower rate than to carbon dioxide. Gibson and Young concluded that the biogenesis of ethylene proceeds not through steps of the Krebs cycle, but, rather, that intermediates in the cycle go to pyruvate or glycolate and acetate carbons 2 or 3 of which combine with another molecule, which in turn leads to ethylene synthesis. The findings of Sprayberry *et al.* (1965) agreed with those of Gibson and Young although these authors got a higher conversion of radioactivity to ethylene from 3-^{14}C serine. Ketring *et al.* (1968) continued studies along the same lines as those described by Gibson and Young. Measurements over the first 30 minutes after adding substrates of high specific activity showed that only carbon 2 of acetate and the methylene carbons of citrate were converted to ethylene. Addition of monofluoroacetate to the cultures blocked conversion of 1-^{14}C-acetate to $^{14}CO_2$ and of the 2-^{14}C-acetate to labelled ethylene and led to accumulation of citrate. Adding isocitrate to the poisoned cultures restored ethylene production but was less effective in restoring carbon dioxide production. It was concluded that the pathway of ethylene production is acetate → citrate → isocitrate → → ethylene. No ethylene was evolved over a period of one hour following the administration of U-[14]C- methionine, however there was a substantial production of $^{14}CO_2$.

Jacobsen and Wang (1968) also obtained no evidence of direct conversion of methionine to ethylene. A significant new finding was the demonstration that *cis*-3-chloroacrylic acid inhibited production of labelled ethylene but not $^{14}CO_2$ from 1-^{14}C-acetate. It was suggested that acrylic acid could be related to the precursor of ethylene.

Burg and Thimann (1961) found that following treatment of sections of McIntoch apples with U-^{14}C-glucose there was a rapid production of $^{14}CO_2$, followed after a slight lag by significant incorporation of activity into ethylene. With specifically labelled glucose, carbon 6 was converted more efficiently to ethylene than carbon 1, while the converse was true for carbon dioxide. 2-^{14}C-glucose was converted to ethylene about as effectively as 1-^{14}C-glucose. Neither ^{14}C-shikimic acid nor ^{14}C-D-xylose yielded measurable amounts of labelled ethylene. From these and previous studies Burg and Thimann concluded that ethylene production was not directly associated with glycolysis, the Krebs acid cycle, carbon dioxide fixation, aromatic metabolism, the pentose phosphate cycle or the glucuronate-xylulose pathway.

Burg and Burg (1964) continued these studies. They measured the specific activity of carbon dioxide and ethylene over the periods 0–80 and 80–200 minutes following the addition of specifically labelled substrates. In contrast to the findings of Wang *et al.* (1962) and Gibson and Young (1966) with *P. digitatum*, they found that the short-term yields of ethylene were similar from carbons 1 and 2 of acetate and carbons 2 and 3 of pyruvate although the lower-numbered carbons in each compound yielded higher proportions of radio carbon dioxide as expected. Burg and Burg (1964) also found that carbons 1,4 and 2,3 of fumarate yielded ethylene about equally whereas according to Wang *et al.* in *P. digitatum*, the middle carbons should be differentially converted to ethylene. Burg and Burg considered that in general their results for apple tissue could be equated with those of Wang *et al.* and Gibson and Young. The considerably greater recycling of ^{14}C which would have occurred during the long-term measurements made by Wang *et al.* was suggested as an explanation for at least some of the disparities. Thus Burg and Burg, in contrast with the earlier conclusion by Burg and Thimann (1960), agreed that ethylene production in apple tissue is related to the metabolism of Krebs cycle acids but, because of the low per cent conversion of label to ethylene "it is presumptious to conclude that the relationship is a direct one". However, the one major difference between the metabolism of *P. digitatum* and apple tissue, namely the disparate yields of ethylene from carbons 1 and 2 of acetate and carbons 2 and 3 of pyruvate in the fungus, and the approximately equal yields from these respective pairs of carbons in apple tissue, has not been satisfactorily explained. A possible explanation is provided by the report that cells of *P. digitatum* retain carbon 2 of acetate to about twice the extent of carbon 1 (Noble *et al.*, 1958). Thus carbon 2 could possibly be retained in a compartment closely associated with the site of ethylene biogenesis.

Shimokawa and Kasai (1966) reported further data—for slices of tissue from Golden Delicious apples—which are largely compatible with previous work. However, in contrast with the findings of Burg and Burg they showed that carbon 2 of acetate was converted to ethylene more efficiently than carbon 1 as in *P. digitatum*, but in agreement with Burg and Burg carbons 2 and 3 of pyruvate were converted equally.

A new contribution by Shimokawa and Kasai (1968) was the finding that in the absence of oxygen the conversion of 2-^{14}C-acetate was depressed while that of ^{14}C-pyruvate was not affected. This result was extended by the observation that 1,2-^{14}C-acetaldehyde was efficiently converted to ethylene without conversion to ethanol. Thus both pyruvate and acetaldehyde may serve as precursors of ethylene. Since acetaldehyde may be expected to accumulate under anaerobiosis these findings may explain those of Burg and Thimann (1959) who showed that ethylene production by apple tissue stopped or declined to a low level under anaerobiosis but proceeded at an accelerated rate for a short time after the tissue was returned to air. Shimokawa and Kasai also examined the effects of iodoacetate, EDTA, fluoride, 2,4-dinitrophenol, malonate, cyanide and arsenite on endogenous ethylene production and conversion of labelled substrates to ethylene. All except cyanide and arsenite markedly inhibited ethylene production. However, interpretation of such data is difficult since inhibitors may produce a variety of non-specific effects in plant tissue.

2. Studies with ^{14}C- and ^{3}H-ethylene

An approach allied to the studies discussed in the previous section is to apply concentrations of labelled ethylene of high specific activity to fruit tissue in the hope that ethylene may be incorporated into fruit constituents by way of exchange reactions related to the pathway of biogenesis. Buhler *et al.* (1957) reported an experiment in which ^{14}C-labelled ethylene was applied to ripe avocado and green pear fruits. The fruit were exposed in large desiccators to 0·2 mCi portions of 1,2-^{14}C-ethylene (sp. act. 1·4 × 10^8 c.p.m./mole) in concentrations of 1000 p.p.m. over several days. Respired carbon dioxide was absorbed in potassium hydroxide, and oxygen was replenished periodically. About 0·05% of the applied ^{14}C was incorporated and most of this appeared in the organic acid fractions. No radioactivity appeared in respired carbon dioxide. Other experiments with ripe oranges, limes, papayas, green apples, tomatoes and grapes failed to show any incorporation of ^{14}C into these fruits.

Fumaric and succinic acids were isolated from the organic acid extracts of avocado and pear fruit. These acids were degraded to establish the specific activities of the component carbons. Approximately three times more ^{14}C was located in the carbonyl carbons than in the middle carbon atoms. This work suggested to Buhler *et al.* that an unsymmetric intermediate close to organic acid metabolism is involved in ethylene biogenesis, despite the low incorporation of ^{14}C-labelled ethylene.

Hall *et al.* (1961) exposed growing plants of cotton and *Coleus blumei* to atmospheres containing up to 1000 p.p.m. of ^{14}C-labelled ethylene (1 mCi/mmole) for periods up to 15 hours in the dark and in the light. Two-thirds or more of the absorbed radioactivity was readily removed by oven-drying or other techniques. The fixed ethylene apparently did not enter readily into normal metabolic pathways. Incorporated radioactivity was readily translocated. At least 18 radioactive metabolites were formed in leaves. Two water soluble acidic compounds giving a positive phosphate reaction contained most of the water soluble radioactivity. Radioactivity was also associated with compounds in the ether soluble fraction, particularly carotene, and also with alcohol soluble compounds. However, after extraction the bulk of the radioactivity was found associated with the cell wall constituents.

A puzzling feature of this work was the report that ethylene which had been recovered from the mercuric perchlorate complex after a period of storage ("aged" ethylene) was metabolized to a much larger extent than "fresh" ethylene. Jansen (1965) confirmed this finding in studies with avocado fruit. No satisfactory explanation of these observations has been provided and there must be some doubt as to whether the incorporated radioactivity originated from ethylene or some other volatile compound. However it was reported that aged ethylene induced essentially the same physiological responses as fresh ethylene. Hall (1962) later reported that at least three labelled gases were present in aged ethylene. One of the active ingredients could be acetylene as suggested by the work of Jansen and Wallace (1965). However, if acetylene was generated during storage of the labelled ethylene-mercuric perchlorate complex, acetaldehyde rather than acetylene would have been released upon the addition of chloride ion (Whitmore, 1921). Acetaldehyde would be more readily metabolized than acetylene.

Jansen (1963, 1964) continued studies of the metabolic fate of ethylene applied to ripening avocado fruit. Fruit were treated for four hours with U-^3H-ethylene (40 mCi/mmole). At ethylene concentrations of 250 and 2000 p.p.m., 0·015 and 0·042% respectively of the labelled ethylene was taken up. Approximately three-quarters of the incorporated activity was recovered in volatile compounds. Of this activity, 12·5% was recovered in toluene and the remainder in other hydrocarbons. Approximately 95% of the radioactivity of toluene was located in its methyl group. To further test these findings avocado fruit were treated with U-^{14}C-ethylene (20 mCi/mmole) under the same conditions. At ethylene concentrations of 250 and 2000 p.p.m., 0·018 and 0·043% respectively of the radio-ethylene was taken up. About one-quarter of the activity was incorporated into volatile compounds; there was also some conversion to carbon dioxide. Of the total incorporated ^{14}C, 3·8% was recovered in benzene and 0·2% in toluene. Further examination of the incorporation data for ^{3}H-ethylene showed that 1% of the ^{3}H-ethylene was incorporated in benzene. On the basis of these results, Jansen (1964) suggested that in the metabolism of ethylene a considerable portion of the hydrogen is removed by some dehydrogenation process, and this hydrogen proceeds along a pathway different from that followed by the carbon, as illustrated by the labelling of toluene. However, part of the hydrogen and carbon is metabolized along the same route as illustrated by the labelling of benzene.

In view of these suggestions Jansen and Wallace (1965) postulated that acetylene may be metabolized more directly to some of the same metabolites as ethylene. Studies with ^{14}C-acetylene showed that acetylene was metabolized much more readily than ethylene. A much higher proportion of the label appeared in carbon dioxide and benzene but not in toluene. No plausible explanation of the significance of these results in relation to ethylene bio-genesis has been offered. It is possible that ethylene and acetylene merely act in avocado and some other fruits as oxidizing agents in a way similar to that shown in the reduction of acetylene by cell-free extracts of Soyabean root nodules (Klucas and Evans, 1968). The findings obtained from treating fruit with radioactive ethylene strongly suggest that applied ethylene does not normally operate by reacting chemically with key cell constituents.

3. Studies with enzyme systems

(a) *Formation from lipids.* In Section IIA data obtained from studies with subcellular fractions were discussed. Lieberman and Mapson (1962a) and Meigh (1962) showed that in the presence of appropriate reactants ethane rather than ethylene could be generated. Lieberman and Mapson (1962a, b) suggested that a relationship may exist between this system and that which produces ethylene in cells. Lieberman and Mapson (1964) then described a model non-enzymic system which produced mainly ethylene. This system required cuprous ion as a catalyst and ascorbic acid as a reducing agent. Activation of linolenic acid was found to be a critical prerequisite for operation of the model system. Activation which involved conjugation of the three double bonds followed by some degree of oxidation could be brought about by exposure to air and light at room temperatures, exposure to ultra-violet light or by incubation in phosphate buffer at pH 7·0 with lipoxidase.

Lieberman and Mapson (1964) considered that the model system could be related to the natural pathway of biogenesis on the basis of observations with plugs of apple tissue and subcellular particles and the fact that all the components of the system are found in fruit.

They proposed the following scheme for the biogenesis of ethylene:

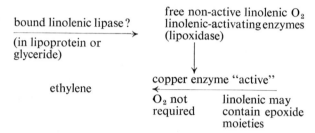

In an extension of this work Lieberman and Mapson also found that methionine, but no other amino acid, would yield significant amounts of ethylene in the copper-ascorbate model system and that unlike the linolenate system it did not yield ethane nor did it form ethylene in nitrogen.

This work led to considerable activity in several laboratories. Lieberman and Hochstein (1966) showed that the model system could operate in a microsomal preparation from rat liver. The addition of vitamin E, a free radical terminator, inhibited ethylene formation. Abeles (1966) studied the relationship between levels of linolenate and ethylene production in a number of plant tissues, including sections of apple pulp. He concluded that in apples the yield of ethylene from linolenate was too small to account for normal production and the need for peroxidation of the linolenate raised the question whether fatty acid peroxides occur in normal tissues. Other fatty acids including stearic, oleic, linoleic and arachidonic were inactive. Active compounds contain the terminal group CH_3—CH_2—CH=. However Wooltorton et al. (1965) and Meigh et al. (1967) showed that lipoxidase activity in apples rose just before ethylene production increased during the climacteric rise in respiration. The rise in respiratory activity was accompanied by rapid accumulation of free and esterified fatty acids on and in the skin (Meigh et al., 1967). Following these results and those of a series of experiments with discs of apple peel cut from both pre-climacteric fruit and fruit in the climacteric phase (Galliard et al., 1968a, b; Hulme et al., 1968; Rhodes et al., 1968a, b). Hulme et al. (1968) suggested that the climacteric in apples is initiated by a turnover of lipids leading to an increased production of ethylene.

Hulme and his co-workers showed that a sequential development of a series of enzyme systems occurs both in the peel of the apple as the climacteric develops in the whole fruit and in peel discs cut from preclimacteric apples and allowed to age for 24 hours at 25°C in a medium containing 0·05M potassium phosphate (pH 4·5) and chloramphenicol (50 μg/ml). These systems included acetate incorporation into lipid, production of ethylene, incorporation of amino acid into protein and the decarboxylation of added malate.

Rhodes et al. (1968b) showed an increase in ethylene production by apple peel discs to a peak about six hours after cutting. A similar pattern was observed in slices of banana fruit cut several days before the onset of ripening, but not in potato discs (McGlasson, 1969). Galliard et al. (1968b) found that the presence of cycloheximide (1 μg/ml) during ageing inhibited ethylene production by discs of apple peel but cycloheximide applied after normal ageing had no effect. It was concluded that the development of the ethylene producing system is dependent upon protein synthesis. Similar effects of cycloheximide on the incorporation of 1-^{14}C-acetate into lipids were also observed (Galliard et al., 1968a). In the absence of cycloheximide about 60% of the ^{14}C incorporated in fresh discs was recovered in phospholipids, about 30% in neutral lipids and the remainder in free fatty acids. In discs aged for 24 hours in the absence of cycloheximide there was increased incorporation of ^{14}C in most fractions but there was a particularly large increase in the free acid fraction. Preliminary examination of the distribution of ^{14}C among fatty acid methyl esters prepared from total lipid extracts showed no incorporation into linolenic acid with either fresh or aged discs. Further study of lipid metabolism appears necessary to establish conclusively whether there is a direct relationship between increased lipid turnover and ethylene biogenesis.

Direct evidence that in apple peel at least ethylene production may be associated with lipid metabolism was provided by the observation that the addition of linolenate plus lipoxidase stimulated ethylene production by discs of apple peel (Galliard et al., 1968b). Galliard et al. (1968c) have also prepared an enzyme extract from apple peel which produced large amounts of ethylene and ethane from linolenate in the presence of oxygen and ascorbate. The activity of the extracts increased as the apples from which they were prepared developed their respiration climacteric (Rhodes et al., 1970). Methionine was inactive while methional and propanal gave less ethylene and ethane than linolenate. Lieberman and Kunishi (1967) reported that propanal, a product of the decomposition of peroxidized linolenate, is a very effective precursor of ethylene in the copper-catalysed model system. Baur and Yang (1969) confirmed this result but found that propanal was not incorporated into ethylene in mature apple tissue.

Practical evidence that linolenic acid may be a precursor of ethylene is provided by the report that application of linolenic acid to the bracts of fig fruit induced ripening within five days and caused respiration to rise rapidly the day after treatment. The climacteric was reached within two days (Hirai et al., 1967). Ethylene levels increased rapidly in the fruit, but it was not reported whether the increase was detected before or after the respiration changes.

(b) *Formation from methionine, β-alanine and related compounds.* A number of workers have prepared enzyme fractions capable of evolving ethylene from both vegetative tissues and fruits. In these studies as in those with subcellular fractions, it must be ensured that the ethylene generating system is genuinely enzymic. The risk of confusion is illustrated by the report by Abeles and Rubinstein (1964) of the preparation of a cell-free fraction which evolved ethylene in both an enzymic and a non-enzymic manner. A protein fraction was prepared from a water extract by ammonium sulphate precipitation and a substrate by acetone precipitation. Optimum enzymic release of ethylene from the substrate was obtained in acetate buffer at pH 4·5–4·7 in the presence of manganese. A number of SH compounds inhibited ethylene production and stimulated the production of equivalent amounts of ethane. These compounds also initiated ethane production in the absence of protein. In addition, ferric ions and FMN caused ethylene evolution from the substrate alone at a greater rate than that obtained with a saturating amount of the protein fraction. The active component in the substrate has since been identified as methionine (Yang *et al.*, 1966).

Hall (1957) was one of the earliest workers to claim production of ethylene by acetone powders derived from plants such as oats and peas. Thompson and Spencer (1966) using more sensitive and specific assay procedures have also prepared enzyme powders capable of producing ethylene from oat and wax bean seedlings and from wax bean cotyledons. Crude powders produced by ammonium sulphate precipitation evolved ethylene in the presence of ATP and β-alanine. Ethylene production was augmented by the addition of the co-factors pyridoxal phosphate and ferric ion for transamination, and thiamine pyrophosphate and magnesium ion for decarboxylation. Apparently CoA could be substituted for pyridoxal phosphate and ferric ion. Further purification of the enzyme powder by removal of lipids by butanol extraction and intensive ammonium sulphate precipitation yielded a preparation which was essentially inactive in the absence of the above compounds. Addition of α-oxoglutarate to the mixture augmented ethylene production. An even greater augmentation was obtained by the addition of malonic acid. Lipoic acid decreased production by 73% suggesting that decarboxylation was probably non-oxidative. The enzyme preparations were active only within the range pH 6·7–7·2.

About 0·001% of added 2-^{14}C-β-alanine was converted to ^{14}C-ethylene, a figure comparable to the molar conversion of β-alanine to ethylene. Thompson and Spencer (1966) proposed the following scheme for the conversion of β-alanine to ethylene.

Evidence supporting this scheme was obtained from quantitative deter-

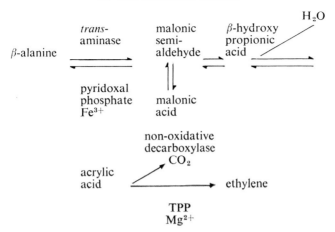

minations of the incorporation of ^{14}C in the postulated intermediates (Thompson and Spencer, 1967). Jacobsen and Wang (1968) reported the production of labelled ethylene from $2\text{-}^{14}C\text{-}\beta$-alanine and $2(3)\text{-}^{14}C$-acrylate by *P. digitatum*. Further data from Spencer's laboratory obtained with a subcellular fraction from tomato fruit have been interpreted in general to agree with the proposed scheme (Meheriuk and Spencer, 1967a, b, c).

Lieberman *et al.* (1965) continued studies on the finding that the copper-ascorbate model system would also yield ethylene from methionine (Lieberman and Mapson, 1964). They showed that in a phosphate buffer of pH 6·8 at 30°C in air, ethylene was derived from carbons 3 and 4 of D- or L-methionine. Hydrogen peroxide was shown to be an intermediate in the reaction which could support ethylene production in anaerobic atmospheres. Cuprous ion was the active form of copper, the reduction of cupric ion apparently being mediated by ascorbate. Ferrous ion was also effective as a catalyst but only in the presence of hydrogen peroxide. Cobalt, magnesium, lead, zinc and manganese were completely ineffective. Methional was the most active producer of ethylene in the model system and appeared to be an intermediate in the reaction. DL-Ethionine was more active than L-methionine. These results, taken with the low or zero yields of ethylene from a series of related sulphur containing compounds and amino acids, indicated that the molecular structure required for ethylene production in this system is a $-CH_2.CH_2$-grouping in the centre of the molecule with one end attached to a sulphur atom linked to a methyl or similar group, and the other end attached to an aldehyde or acetyl group linked to an amino or hydroxy moiety.

Mapson and Wardale (1967) proposed the existence of a natural enzyme system that generated ethylene from methionine or methional. They prepared cell-free extracts from cauliflower florets and found that both particulate and non-particulate fractions were necessary for the formation of ethylene from methionine, but only a non-particulate fraction was necessary for its formation from methional. In addition, the conversion of methional into ethylene was found to require the presence of two enzyme systems, one generating peroxide and the second catalysing the conversion of methional into ethylene in the presence of peroxide. A heat-stable factor in the cauliflower extracts was required for full enzyme activity. Mapson and Mead (1968) and Mapson *et al.* (1969) have since shown that the heat-stable factor consists of two essential components, an ester of p-coumaric acid and methane sulphinic acid. An interesting feature of this work was the demonstration of a lag in ethylene production from methionine in both excised florets aged on a sucrose medium, and by cell-free extracts prepared from the florets. This lag was shown to be due mainly to a lag in the generation of hydrogen peroxide in the system. The peroxide generating enzyme was located in an extract of the non-particulate fraction prepared by precipitation with 30–60% saturated ammonium sulphate. The active component may have been glucose-oxidase since D-glucose was the only substance found to act as substrate. Methional has not been isolated from extracts of cauliflower florets.

Mapson and Wardale (1968) have recently reported data confirming these results and have also shown that dihydroxy phenols including caffeic, ferulic, chlorogenic and sinapic acids, catechol and resorcinol inhibit ethylene production by the methional cleaving enzyme system isolated from cauliflower florets. Sinapic acid was identified in the extract. Thus the lag in ethylene production was apparently due to the consumption of peroxide by the enzymic oxidation of the phenols. A possible connection between the earlier peroxidized linolenate system was established by the demonstration that hydroperoxides of linolenic acid could substitute for hydrogen peroxide in the production of ethylene from methional. Hydroperoxides of linoleic and arachidonic acids were much less effective.

Mapson and Wardale (1968) in a comparison of the properties of their methional cleaving enzyme with those of the systems described by Abeles and Rubinstein (1964) and Yang *et al.* (1966) could find no evidence of the involvement of flavins either in their active extracts or as a prosthetic group of the enzyme. It was suggested from inhibitor studies that the prosthetic group contains copper although iron was not excluded. Thiol reagents were ineffective. Mapson and Wardale also considered the possibility that their methional cleaving enzyme could be a peroxidase. This was suggested by the report by Yang (1967) of a model system in which horseradish peroxidase in the presence of hydrogen peroxide and other co-factors produced ethylene from methional. However, the horseradish system differs in a number of respects. There was a specific requirement for manganic ion, sulphite ion, resorcinol and oxygen. Hydrogen peroxide could substitute for manganic ion, and cupric ion inhibited the enzyme reaction. In agreement with the properties of the cauliflower enzyme, ethylene production by horseradish peroxidase appeared to involve hydrogen peroxide production and to be inhibited by o-dihydric phenols and diethyldithiocarbamate. With regard to this chelating agent it was noted that horseradish peroxidase is an iron-containing enzyme whereas it was proposed that the cauliflower enzyme contains copper. On the basis of the stimulatory effect of monophenols and the inhibitory effect of certain o-diphenols Yang (1967) suggested that the levels of these compounds might regulate ethylene production *in vivo*.

Takeo and Lieberman (1969) reported the isolation from apple tissue of a 3-methylthiopropionaldehyde peroxidase which forms ethylene from methional. The properties of the enzyme are similar to the methional cleaving enzyme from cauliflower florets (Mapson and Wardale, 1967, 1968; Mapson and Mead, 1968) and horseradish peroxidase (Yang, 1967). The enzyme from apple tissue was shown also to produce ethylene from L-methionine in a two-step reaction. Some of the requirements for this activity suggested that *in vivo* the two steps are separated within the cell. The successful isolation of an ethylene-producing enzyme which involved an initial separation from phenols and polyphenols by dialysis and gel-filtration on Sephadex G-25 provides an explanation for previous observations that although apple slices produce large quantities of ethylene, apple homogenates evolve practically none.

Yang *et al.* (1966) further examined the non-enzymic system described by Abeles and Rubinstein (1964). The substrate in active extracts from etiolated pea seedlings was identified as methionine. Yang *et al.* showed that no ethylene was produced by the system in the dark or in the absence of FMN and that production dropped in the absence of glucose-oxidase. Flushing with nitrogen was found to substitute for glucose plus glucose-oxidase, but the addition of hydrogen peroxide could not. Thus this system does not bear a close resemblance to the enzymic system from cauliflower florets but appears similar to a Strecker degradation reaction described by Lieberman *et al.* (1965). This conclusion is further supported by the observations that ethylene could be generated non-enzymically from substrates found inactive with enzyme preparations from cauliflower florets.

Ku *et al.* (1967) prepared an enzyme extract from pea seedlings which appeared to have some similarities to the methional cleaving enzyme from cauliflower florets. However, there were two major differences—it possessed catalase activity and cupric ions inhibited the enzyme. Ku *et al.* suggested that the reaction catalysed by their enzyme did not proceed through a hydrogen peroxide-mediated non-enzymic evolution of ethylene, but they admitted that a definite conclusion depended on the preparation of an enzyme free of catalase activity.

(c) *Addition of methionine, β-alanine and related compounds to tissue.* The results of studies involving treatment of plant tissues with methionine and

492   W. B. McGLASSON

other potential precursors of ethylene have been contradictory. Lieberman *et al.* (1966) found that methionine stimulated ethylene production in senescent apple tissue but not in pre-climacteric tissue; methional was ineffective and ethionine and chelating agents that tend to bind copper were inhibitory. Methionine was ineffective in pre-climacteric tomato slices, avocado slices (Lieberman *et al.*) and in discs of both fresh and aged discs of apple peel (Galliard *et al.*, 1968b). Synthesis of ethylene from methionine or its hydroxy analogue but not from methional was observed in intact cauliflower florets (Mapson and Wardale, 1967).

Burg and Clagett (1967) reported that methionine was actively metabolized in the dark in sections of pea stem, sections of ripe McIntosh apple tissue and in slices of green banana. Carbon 1 was released as carbon dioxide, carbons 3 and 4 as ethylene, and the methyl carbon, carbon 2 and sulphur were retained in the tissue. In apples, concentrations of methionine lower than 10^{-5}M did not stimulate ethylene production but permitted the greatest overall conversion of metabolized methionine to ethylene. In banana tissue, ethylene formation was stimulated almost equally by L-methionine, DL-homocysteine, DL-homoserine and methionine hydroxy analogue. The second and third of these compounds were not converted efficiently in the model system of Lieberman *et al.* (1965). However, competition studies by Burg and Clagett suggested that methionine is closer to the immediate precursor of ethylene than either of these compounds. Methional at the same concentration as methionine was slightly inhibitory. β-Alanine did not stimulate ethylene production by either banana or apple tissue as expected from the work of Thompson and Spencer (1967). However, the latter workers reported only 0·001% conversion in a 21 hour incubation. Thus β-alanine cannot be an immediate precursor of ethylene.

The data in this and previous sections highlight the rather confusing array of information a reviewer is faced with on reading the literature on the biogenesis of ethylene. On the one hand there are the sometimes conflicting reports that a particular compound or even a particular carbon atom of a compound is converted to ethylene in one tissue but not in another. Then there are the reports of differing requirements for substrates and co-factors etc. in model systems which have been derived either from components "off the shelf" or from extracts of plant tissue.

However, some order seems to be emerging. The recent reports of the efficient conversion of carbons 3 and 4 of methionine by some plant tissues as well as by model systems indicates that this amino acid is closer to the immediate precursor of ethylene than any of the potential precursors previously tested. The isolation of enzyme systems capable of utilizing methionine and methional is also encouraging. Armed with this information it is now worth while to construct charts similar to the one prepared by Meheriuk and

Spencer (1967c) which inter-relate the various compounds which have been found to contribute carbons to ethylene. Such charts can be expected to aid in studies on regulation of ethylene biogenesis.

Some investigators have stated that the biogenesis of ethylene in *P. digitatum* may be different from that in higher plants. However, there are enough similarities to encourage further studies with the fungus which will ultimately contribute to knowledge on pathways of ethylene biogenesis and their regulation.

4. *Non-enzymic systems*

The most recent studies by Yang (1967), Mapson and Wardale (1968) and Takeo and Lieberman (1969) suggest that in higher plant tissues ethylene may be generated enzymically from methionine via methional in reactions which involve the generation of hydrogen peroxide or fatty acid hydroperoxides and possibly also from the breakdown products of linolenic acid (Galliard *et al.*, 1968c). However, the evidence from studies with non-enzymic systems beginning with the work of Lieberman and Mapson (1964) and continuing with those of Abeles and Rubinstein (1964) and Yang *et al.* (1966) equally strongly suggests that at least part of the *in vivo* production of ethylene could arise non-enzymically. Indeed, as suggested by Lieberman *et al.* (1966), there is no reason to believe that all of the ethylene produced by a living tissue need be produced by a single system. For example, although the precursors undoubtedly arise enzymically, it is possible that a non-enzymic system(s) is responsible for the low background production of ethylene by higher plants and that an enzymic system dominates once ageing or ripening starts. Some support for this idea is provided by the observations that ethane and propane are produced by at least some fruit, for example, apples (Meigh, 1959) and bananas (Burg and Burg, 1965a). Ethane and some other hydrocarbons have been evolved by some of the enzymic and non-enzymic systems previously discussed. Unpublished observations in the author's laboratory indicate that the production of ethane and propane by bananas changes very little during ripening whereas there is a many-fold increase in ethylene production.

Evidence of a mechanism for the non-enzymic production of ethylene has been presented by Kumamoto *et al.* (1969). Ethylene was produced from potassium ethyl sulphate in an atmosphere of nitrogen by reaction with tert-butylhydroperoxide in the presence of ferrous sulphate. A "Taube Bridge" mechanism was proposed for the process. According to this mechanism there is a concerted process whereby a free radical abstracts a hydrogen atom from the substrate while the ferrous iron is oxidized. Sufficient energy becomes available from this redox process to permit the formation of ethylene as follows:

$$R. \text{---} H\text{---}CH_2\text{---}CH_2\text{---}O\text{---}SO_2\text{---}O^- \text{---} Fe^{+2} \rightarrow RH + CH_2{=}CH + SO_4^{=} + Fe^+$$

The proposed mechanism suggested that a large variety of organic ligands can be expected to produce ethylene when they are exposed to a one-electron reducing agent such as ferrous or cuprous ion and coupled with a one-electron oxidizing agent such as a free radical or oxygen. In preliminary experiments Kumamoto et al. found that some ethylene could be produced from methionine, monoethyl phosphate, diethyl phosphate, butyric acid, ethyliodide, ethanol and methional. This work thus provides a common basis for comparison of the several model systems which have been previously described.

C. Regulation of Biogenesis

Present knowledge suggests that ethylene may be generated either entirely by an enzymic system or partly enzymically, with the final reactions being mediated non-enzymically. Obviously regulation of production can be achieved at a number of points including availability of substrates and the various co-factors and by the redox state of some metal ions. Possible examples of regulation through co-factors are the observations of Yang (1967), Mapson and Wardle (1968) and Takeo and Lieberman (1969) on the effects of phenols on the enzymic production of ethylene. This type of regulation is consistent with the observations that wounding or γ and X irradiation of unripe fruit cause an immediate large increase in ethylene production (Burg, 1962; Lee et al., 1968; McGlasson, 1969). When fruit tissue is damaged in these ways "browning" reactions involving phenolic compounds usually occur. However the increase in ethylene production associated with mechanical stress in elongating etiolated pea epicotyls (Goeschl et al., 1966) does not fit this model. The existence of specific regulators or inhibitors of ethylene biogenesis are also suggested by the observation of Meigh et al. (1967) that ethylene production is partially inhibited in apples attached to the tree. Burg and Burg (1965b) have also presented evidence for the occurrence of a natural inhibitor in mango trees. A similar situation probably exists in avocado fruit in which the climacteric and ripening do not occur while the fruit remains attached to the tree (Biale, 1950).

Plant hormones such as the auxins, gibberellins and phytokinins are currently prominent candidates for a regulatory role in the biogenesis of ethylene, especially since the appearance of numerous reports that both natural and synthetic auxins may stimulate ethylene production by a wide range of plant tissues (Burg, 1968). The stimulatory effects of applied auxins on ethylene production are apparently not due to a direct participation in biogenesis since indoleacetic acid had little effect on ethylene production in the horseradish model system (Yang, 1967) and no label was transferred to ethylene from ^{14}C-2,4-dichlorophenoxyacetic acid when cotton plants were treated with the latter compound (Morgan and Hall, 1962).

Light may regulate ethylene production during seed germination and growth of seedlings (Abeles *et al.*, 1967; Kang *et al.*, 1967; Goeschl *et al.*, 1967). Goeschl *et al.* (1967) showed that red light can cause a decrease in ethylene production by the plumular portion of etiolated pea seedlings and that far-red irradiation following exposure to red light decreased the red effect. These results suggested that the phytochrome system is implicated in ethylene production. No reports have been seen of specific light effects on ethylene production in fruit tissues. Aspects of regulation are also discussed in connection with the role of ethylene in fruit ripening.

III. ROLE IN FRUIT RIPENING

A. Concept of Ripening

The relationship of ethylene to fruit ripening is perhaps best considered in terms of current hypotheses explaining the initiation of the ripening process. The many hypotheses which have been proposed can be consolidated and discussed in terms of two main concepts.

According to the first, ripening may be regarded as a manifestation of senescence in which intracellular organization begins to break down (Bain and Mercer, 1964; Sacher, 1967). This disorganization leads to the random mixing of enzymes and their substrates which could account for the apparent activity of various hydrolases (destruction of chlorophyll, starch and pectin degradation and inactivation of "tannins") as well as those enzymes which are responsible for the synthesis of compounds such as ethylene, pigments, flavour constituents, high energy phosphorylated compounds and perhaps polypeptides. According to the second concept ripening (senescence) represents a final stage of differentiation and is thus a directed process requiring the synthesis of specific enzymes (Varner, 1965; Frenkel *et al.*, 1968; Hulme *et al.*, 1968).

In reality, probably both of these concepts apply. There is considerable evidence that ethylene is an essential factor (ripening hormone) in the sequence of events which constitute ripening; there is also no doubt that in many fruits amounts of ethylene considerably in excess of hormone levels are evolved during ripening. These higher levels of ethylene production generally coincide with the period when the various changes listed under the first concept become readily apparent.

Fruits have been divided into climacteric and non-climacteric classes on the basis of respiration patterns during maturation and ripening (Biale, 1960a, b, 1964). Most species of fruits which belong to the first class undergo a distinct ripening phase, for example, apples, bananas, pears, melons and avocados, while typical members of the second class, for example, citrus, grape, strawberry and pineapple do not. The two classes of fruits are further distinguished by their responses to treatment with ethylene. In immature fruits of the climacteric type, ethylene treatment hastens the onset of the climacteric and the associated ripening changes, generally without appreciably altering the pattern or the magnitude of the respiratory changes. In non-climacteric types of fruit the magnitude of the respiratory response increases as a function of ethylene concentration at least up to 100 p.p.m. (Fig. 1). These respiratory increases in citrus are accompanied by loss of chlorophyll, pectic changes in the peel and abscission of the calyxes. Despite these differ-

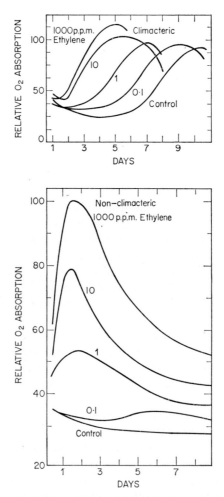

Fig. 1. Oxygen uptake by fruits which show the climacteric phenomenon and by fruits which do not, in relation to concentration of external ethylene (Biale, 1964) (Copyright Science 1964 by the American Association for the Advancement of Science).

ences, the pattern of senescence in non-climacteric types of fruit does not necessarily conflict with the concept of senescence as a directed process.

B. Ripening Hormone or By-Product of Ripening

Crocker *et al.* (1935) considered that ethylene acts as a fruit ripening hormone. Biale *et al.* (1954) concluded from studies with 14 varieties of fruit that ethylene is a by-product of the fruit ripening process. With the advent of gas chromatography it was shown that in a number of varieties of fruit, higher than ambient concentrations of ethylene, were present in developing fruit and that ethylene production rose at or before the beginning of the respiratory climacteric (Table I).

TABLE I. Internal ethylene concentrations

Fruit	Variety	Concentration (p.p.m.) At beginning of climacteric rise	Climacteric peak	Reference
Avocado	Choquette	>0·5–1·0	300–700	Burg and Burg (1962b)
Banana	Gros Michel	1·5	40	Burg and Burg (1962a)
Banana	Apple	1	25	Burg and Burg (1965a)
Mango	Kent and Haden	0·04–0·08	3	Burg and Burg (1962a)
Melon	Cantaloupe PMR 45	>0·3	30–70	Lyons *et al.* (1962)
Melon	Honeydew	3·0	25	Pratt and Goeschl (1968)
Tomato	VC–243–20	0·8	27	Lyons and Pratt (1964a)

The minimum ethylene concentration necessary to initiate the climacteric in the various fruits is not apparent from Table I. However, examination of the changes in ethylene concentrations during development and maturation show that in bananas the internal concentrations remain at about 0·1–0·2 p.p.m. until a few hours before the increase in respiration rate (Burg and Burg, 1962a, 1965a). A similar situation was apparent in the avocado (Burg and Burg, 1962b), the tomato (Lyons and Pratt, 1964a) and the cantaloupe (Lyons *et al.*, 1962) in which the pre-climacteric levels were about 0·04 p.p.m. Mangos (Burg and Burg, 1962a) and Honeydew melons (Pratt and Goeschl, 1968) seem to be special cases.

In the latter two fruits (or at least until a certain physiological stage of development is reached in the Honeydew) the ability to produce ethylene seems to be much less than in the others listed. Results of studies with a range of concentrations of applied ethylene indicated that the 0·04–0·08 p.p.m. present in mangos immediately after harvest was enough to start the fruit towards the climacteric. Unlike other climacteric fruits, the rise in ethylene production which accompanied the onset of the climacteric was slow, so that even during the early stages of the climacteric ripening could be hastened by the addition of ethylene. Honeydew melons are not self-ripening until a certain stage of development on the plant has been reached. Ripening in such young fruit can be induced after harvest by applied ethylene concentrations above a threshold of 3 p.p.m. In older self-ripening fruits, ethylene production was shown to begin to rise at least eight days before the climacteric minimum. An internal concentration of about 3 p.p.m. was reached at the pre-climacteric respiratory minimum. Also self-ripening fruits apparently became less sensitive to applied ethylene. However, these differences in apparent sensitivity in fruits of different physiological ages were due to the changes in endogenous ethylene production. This was confirmed by the demonstration that application of 10 p.p.m. ethylene stimulated endogenous ethylene production in fruit picked at a self-ripening age, but not in younger fruit.

In addition to the measurements which showed that physiologically active amounts of ethylene are produced by mangoes, Burg and Burg (1962a) found that contrary to the report by Biale *et al.* (1954), citrus fruits and pineapples produce small amounts of the gas. However, Vines *et al.* (1968) reported endogenous production only by citrus fruit subjected to stress. It has been suggested that their instrumentation was insufficiently sensitive to detect the levels present under non-stressed conditions (Pratt and Goeschl, 1969).

As discussed in Section IIIA, one of the characteristics of a non-climacteric fruit, as typified by citrus, was the increase in the magnitude of the maximum respiratory responses with increasing concentrations of applied ethylene at least up to 100 p.p.m. Burg and Burg (1962a) suggested that it is unlikely that applied ethylene stimulates endogenous ethylene production in non-climacteric fruit and possibly the differences in the responses of climacteric and non-climacteric fruit to applied ethylene reflect only their relative abilities to produce the gas. This is apparently the case with Honeydews picked at a non-self-ripening age although when treated with ethylene such fruits undergo the full range of ripening changes found in fruit picked at a self-ripening age. Further study of the responses of citrus fruit, picked over a wide range of physiological ages, to applied ethylene seems necessary in view of the recent report by Aharoni (1968) that immature oranges and grapefruits show climacteric patterns of respiration and ethylene production.

Burg and Burg (1962a, 1965b) found that Fick's Law for diffusion applies to the movement of ethylene, carbon dioxide and oxygen through the flesh and skin of fruit. They deduced that, as an approximation, the 2 p.p.m. per μ litre/kg/hour of ethylene produced gives a means of conservatively estimating the internal concentration of ethylene in fruit from measurements of the external rates of production. Actual values of this ratio for several varieties of fruit range from 1·7–9·0 with most values lying below 5·0.

The diffusivity of ethylene and other gases can be increased by placing fruit in a partial vacuum (Burg and Burg, 1965b, 1966). An approximately four-fold increase in storage life was achieved in several varieties of fruit by holding the fruit at a pressure of 150 mm Hg. Part of this effect is due to the reduction in oxygen concentration in the fruit. It was clear, however, that part of the effect was also due to reduced ethylene content in the tissue when it was shown that the extension in storage life was not as great when the fruit was stored in pure oxygen at a partial pressure of 0·21 as in air at one atmosphere. Applied ethylene was not as effective in air at low pressure as at normal atmospheric pressures but it was equally effective in pure oxygen at a partial pressure of 0·21.

These findings are supported by the work of Mapson and Robinson (1966) and Scott et al. (1970). Mapson and Robinson showed that synthesis of ethylene is retarded in green bananas ventilated with atmospheres containing 1–7·5% oxygen at 18°C. Such fruit ripened normally on return to air. Scott et al. found that the storage life of green bananas could be extended for at least two weeks by enclosing the fruit in sealed polyethylene bags with an ethylene absorbent.

There is also much evidence that ethylene plays a wider role as a plant growth regulator. The earliest observations on the effects of ethylene on plant tissue were those made with growing plants (see reviews by Burg, 1962; Pratt and Goeschl, 1969).

C. Interactions with Other Growth Regulators

It was proposed by Zimmerman and Wilcoxon (1935) that certain effects of auxins on plant growth were due to their stimulation of ethylene production. Later it was shown that ripening in freshly harvested apples, pears and green bananas could be hastened by treating the fruit with 2,4-dichlorophenoxyacetic acid (2,4-D) (Mitchell and Marth, 1944; Hansen, 1946; Blake and Stevenson, 1959). Hansen found that 2,4-D increased the maximum rates of respiration and ethylene production by pears. Morgan and Hall (1962, 1964) also found that 2,4-D and indoleacetic acid (IAA) induced increased ethylene production by cotton plants. Since then there have been numerous reports relating various auxin effects (IAA as well as synthetic) to increased ethylene production. These have included induction of flowering in pineapple (Burg, 1962), abscission (Burg, 1968) and accelerated growth in fig fruit (Maxie and Crane, 1968). The stimulatory effects of auxins on ripening contrast with their effects on detached leaves (Osborne, 1967) and segments of bean pericarp tissue (Sacher, 1967) in which senescence is delayed.

These apparently contradictory results may be explained by uneven penetration of the applied auxins into intact fruit. This contention is supported by recent experiments with slices of green banana fruit. Vendrell (1969) employed vacuum infiltration to treat thick slices with solutions of 2,4-D. This technique ensures even distribution of test substances throughout the slices (Palmer and McGlasson, 1969). Although 2,4-D caused an initial stimulation of respiration and ethylene production, ripening was delayed. The delay in ripening was a function of the concentration of 2,4-D in the range 10^{-5} to 10^{-3}M. The delay was even more marked when 2,4-D-treated slices were gassed with 10 p.p.m. ethylene for 24 hours, one to three days after infiltration. A complete climacteric pattern in untreated slices was induced by ethylene, but in slices treated with 10^{-4} and 10^{-3}M 2,4-D, after an initial burst of respiration, the respiratory rates returned to normal preclimacteric levels. 2,4-D Treated slices which "recovered" from the ethylene treatment subsequently ripened normally without additional ethylene. These slices could also be induced to ripen by further exposure to 10 p.p.m. ethylene. Vendrell suggested that in banana slices 2,4-D causes a reversion of the tissue to a more juvenile state which is less sensitive to applied ethylene.

Unlike 2,4-D, which appears to have a generalized effect on metabolism of banana slices, gibberellic acid (GA_3) generally only delays the disappearance of chlorophyll and it does not stimulate respiration and ethylene production (M. Vendrell, personal communication). Kinetin produces a similar delay in the loss of chlorophyll, but with slices cut from relatively immature fruit ripening of the pulp may also be delayed (N. L. Wade, personal communication). Kinetin also causes an initial stimulation of respiration and ethylene production. Russo et al. (1968) found that 10^{-4}M GA_3 had no effect on whole banana fruit, but Dostal and Leopold (1967) reported that GA_3 delayed lycopene production in intact tomato fruit, or in pieces in tissue culture, without affecting the respiratory climacteric. Abdel-Gawad and Romani (1967) reported a reversal in the pattern of chlorophyll loss during maturation in apricots following a pre-harvest treatment with GA_3. GA_3 also delays the loss of chlorophyll in citrus fruit (Coggins and Lewis, 1962).

Abscisic acid is a natural growth regulator involved in leaf abscission and seed and bud dormancy (Addicott, 1968). Abscisic acid may promote senescence in mature leaves and may inhibit growth responses in other tissues. Although it has been isolated from apple, pear and strawberry fruit (Pienazek and Rudnicki, 1967; Rudnicki et al., 1968), little is known of its role in fruit. Applied abscisic acid has been found to stimulate ripening in banana slices (M. Vendrell, personal communication).

Natural compounds apparently exist in plants which inhibit or antagonize the action of endogenous ethylene. So far none of these compounds has been isolated or identified. Among synthetic compounds, ethylene oxide (0.75% for 16 to 22 hours) has been found to block ethylene production and ripening of green tomato fruit (Lieberman and Mapson, 1962b). Respiration was not altered in treated fruit except in a few experiments in which it was increased.

There was no retardation of ethylene production or of ripening after the climacteric rise had started. In contrast, in apples producing high levels of ethylene and presumably on the climacteric rise, 0.75% ethylene oxide depressed ethylene production but did not retard ripening. Ripening was accelerated and the skin injured in preclimacteric apples by 0.1% ethylene oxide (Meigh, 1963). From a study of the molecular structure required for ethylene action, Burg and Burg (1965c) concluded that ethylene oxide is not a competitive inhibitor of ethylene action.

Ripening of McIntosh apples has been delayed by tree sprays of succinic acid 2,2-dimethyl hydrazide (B9, Alar*) applied before bloom (Looney, 1968). It was suggested that Alar suppresses ethylene biogenesis or action within the fruit and that this suppression is not related to fruit maturity. The effect could be overcome by ethylene treatment.

The recently developed 2-chloroethanephosphonic acid (Ethrel, CEPHA†) which decomposes and releases ethylene at pH 4·1 or higher shows promise for studies on the growth regulatory properties of ethylene (Cooke and Randall, 1968; Russo et al., 1968). Solutions of this compound may be applied where it is inconvenient to employ the free gas.

D. Specificity of Applied Ethylene

It is generally accepted that ripening induced by ethylene treatment is biochemically the same as ripening which occurs naturally. This effect, together with the observed increases in endogenous ethylene production which precede natural ripening, is taken as evidence that ethylene is a natural ripening factor. An important criterion that this assumption is valid is the observed specificity of applied ethylene in comparison with other hydrocarbons.

Comparative measurements of the effectiveness of ethylene and other hydrocarbon gases have been made mainly with vegetative tissues. Crocker et al. (1932) found that of 38 gases tested only ethylene, propylene, acetylene, butylene and carbon monoxide produced characteristic leaf epinasty in tomato plants, and that of these gases, ethylene was 500 to 500,000 times more effective than the other four. Burg and Burg (1965c, 1967) made an intensive kinetic study of the inhibitory effects of ethylene and other hydrocarbon gases on straight growth of etiolated pea stem sections. They found that only unsaturated gases inhibited growth and that ethylene was by far the most effective (Table II). The same gases were tested for their effectiveness in stimulating ripening in green bananas. From these results and those reported

* Trade name. United States Rubber Company Chemical Division, Naugatuck, Connecticut, U.S.A.
† Trade names. Amchem Products Inc., Ambler, Pennsylvania, U.S.A.

Table II. Biological activity of ethylene and other unsaturated compounds as determined by the pea straight growth test[a]

Compound	K_A relative to ethylene[b]	P.p.m. in gas phase for half-maximum activity
Ethylene	1	0·1
Propylene	130	10
Carbon monoxide	2370	270
Acetylene	2900	280
Allene	7100	2900
Methyl acetylene	12,500	800

[a] Burg and Burg (1967).
[b] K_A is the Michaelis–Menten constant for ethylene at 24°C. The value was 0·62 nM in the presence of an infinite concentration of oxygen.

by Crocker et al., Burg and Burg concluded that each of these compounds has about the same efficacy in promoting fruit ripening, inhibiting the elongation of pea tissue, and causing epinasty. Following the work of Abeles and Gahagan (1968) with some of these gases, abscission can also be added to this list.

One of the interesting aspects of ethylene physiology is the requirement that to induce a complete climacteric ripening pattern in pre-climacteric fruit it is necessary to treat the fruit with an optimal or higher concentration of ethylene for a certain minimum period of time (Fig. 2). Figure 2 shows that in 10 day cantaloupe melons (about one-quarter grown) 24 to 48 hours of treatment with 100 p.p.m. ethylene is required to induce a complete clim-acteric pattern but in 30 day fruit the period was 12 to 24 hours. This apparent decrease in sensitivity to applied ethylene as fruit approach the onset of the natural climacteric has also been shown for green bananas (Burg and Burg, 1965a), Honeydew melons (Pratt and Goeschl, 1968) and pears (Hansen and Blanpied, 1968). An extreme example of changing sensitivity to applied ethylene is provided by developing tomato fruit (Lyons and Pratt, 1964a). The time taken to develop red colour in 64% grown fruit was reduced from 17 days to 7 days by treatment with 1000 p.p.m. ethylene while in 93% grown fruit the time was reduced from 3·5 days to 2 days. There is no ready explanation of these observations. Reference was made in Section IIC to the possible involvement of translocated substances to and from the parent plant, but it is also likely that changing sensitivity to ethylene is an intrinsic part of the regulatory systems built into determinate structures such as fruit. Kidd and West (1924) for the apple and Clendenning (1942) for the tomato demon-strated the occurrence of the climacteric in attached fruit. There seems to be no information on ethylene production by attached developing fruit.

Eaks (1967) demonstrated that if persimmons were treated with ethylene,

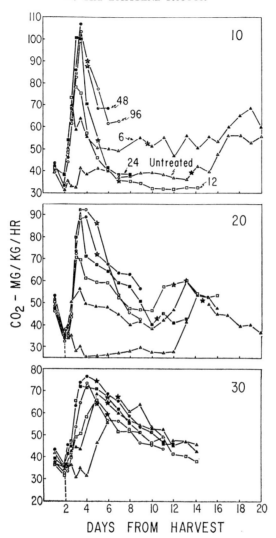

Fig. 2. Carbon dioxide production by cantaloupe fruits of three ages (10, 20 and 30 days after anthesis) under treatment with 100 p.p.m. ethylene for varying lengths of time (0, 6, 12, 24, 48, 96 hours), beginning 48 hours after harvest (broken vertical line). Stars indicate the beginning of external yellowing, and the legends shown for 10 day fruits apply to the corresponding symbols for all ages (McGlasson and Pratt, 1964a).

ripening was hastened and the final product was soft and free of astringency; but if the fruit were treated with carbon dioxide, astringency disappeared and the fruit remained firm even under ethylene treatment. This response has interesting commercial possibilities.

E. Influence of Temperature on the Production and Action of Ethylene

The influence of temperature on ethylene stimulation of respiration has been reviewed by Biale (1960a) and Burg (1962). The response to ethylene decreases with lowered temperature. Green fruit such as apples may be stored in high concentrations of ethylene at 3°C without measurable effects on respiration or ripening (Fidler, 1960). However, data which precisely relate the effects of ethylene treatments to temperature are meagre. At temperatures in the range 10–25°C the respiration data for avocado (Biale, 1960a) indicate that the rate of response to ethylene is reduced with lowered temperatures in proportion to the reduction in respiration rate. If this result is extrapolated to lower temperatures with other fruits, then it is conceivable that fruit would have to be exposed to ethylene for very long periods before a response would be observed. This view gains added weight with the report by Fidler and North (1967) that the long term respiration rates of Cox's Orange Pippin apples are linearly related to temperature, at least in the range 3·3–12·2°C. The graph of respiration rate *v*. temperature was inflected below 3·3°C. The latter observation draws attention to the difficulties which may be interposed by the onset of physiological disorders in studies on the effects of temperature on the responses to applied ethylene. Cox's Orange Pippin are subject to low temperature breakdown below 3·3°C while most warm season fruits such as bananas and tomatoes suffer chilling injury at temperatures below 10°C.

A similar situation probably applies to the effect of lowered temperatures on ethylene production. Burg and Thimann (1959) found that between 10 and 25°C the Q_{10} for ethylene production in McIntosh apples was similar to that for carbon dioxide production and oxygen uptake.

At temperatures above about 35°C many fruits fail to produce ethylene and ripen normally (Burg, 1962). Surprisingly the optimum temperature for ethylene production in some fruits (for example, tomatoes and apples) is about 32°C but in others it is much lower (for example, some varieties of plums and bananas). The ability to produce ethylene and to resume normal ripening may be regained in some fruits after the temperature is lowered from inhibitory levels. Whether abnormal ripening at high temperatures is due to lack of ethylene production, inability to respond to ethylene or to other effects on the ripening process has not been resolved.

F. Influence of Stress on the Production and Action of Ethylene

Ethylene production by plant tissues is generally stimulated by mechanical injury and infection (Williamson, 1950; Burg, 1962; Imaseki *et al.*, 1968b; Vines *et al.*, 1968; McGlasson, 1969). In fruit picked at advanced stages of development, mechanical injury may hasten ripening (Ben-Yehoshua *et al.*,

1963; McGlasson and Pratt, 1964b; Maxie et al., 1968). Mechanical injury stimulates respiration at least temporarily and in slices of fruits may also lead to the development of induced respiration similar to that described for slices of underground storage organs and other plant tissues (Ap Rees, 1966; Laties, 1967; Lee, 1968; Palmer and McGlasson, 1969).

The increased emanation of ethylene immediately following injury is due not merely to improved ventilation of the tissue (Burg, 1962) but to an actual increase in production. This was borne out in studies with tissue pieces from immature fruit of cantaloupe (McGlasson and Pratt, 1964b), tomato (Lee, 1968) and banana (McGlasson, 1969; Vendrell, 1969). In each of these tissues ethylene production an hour or more after cutting was at least ten times the rate for intact fruit.

In slices of green banana (McGlasson, 1969) and in discs of tomato fruit wall (Lee, 1968) "induced" patterns of ethylene production have been observed. These patterns were most distinct in slices of banana in which the proportion of cut surface to volume was relatively large. From one to three hours after cutting ethylene production by banana slices remains steady and then increases abruptly to a peak three to five hours later. Ethylene production then declines to very low levels until the slices ripen. The induced rise in respiration begins at about the same time as that for ethylene but peak respiration rates are not reached until about 18 hours after cutting (Palmer and McGlasson, 1969).

Slices of unripe fruit tissue may provide a useful system for studying the regulation of ethylene biogenesis since it is apparent that the ability to produce ethylene in such tissue is well developed (Galliard et al., 1968b).

Although ethylene production is also stimulated in potato (Solanum) and sweet potato (Ipomoea) tissue by cutting, there is no further rise in production during the development of induced respiration (Imaseki et al., 1968a; McGlasson, 1969). Thus considering the responses of slices of fruit and underground storage tissues there is no simple relationship between ethylene production and respiration rates following injury and, in this respect, responses to injury do not differ from normal ripening.

It has been speculated that the induced rise in ethylene production in banana slices plays a role in recovery from injury, perhaps by temporarily stimulating the mobilization of reserves to provide the energy needed for repair processes (McGlasson, 1969).

Increased ethylene production in underground storage tissues has been implicated in disease resistance (Stahmann et al., 1966). Some of the increased ethylene production may be due to the production in diseased tissue of compounds which serve as specific factors in the enzymic synthesis of ethylene (Imaseki et al., 1968b).

Increased rates of ethylene production and respiration are widely recognized responses of fruit and other plant tissues to ionizing radiations (Shah and Maxie, 1965; Maxie and Abdel-Kader, 1966; Romani, 1966a, b). Radiation-induced ethylene production has been observed in the following pre-climacteric fruit: peaches and nectarines (Maxie and Sommer, 1963), tomatoes (Abdel-Kader et al., 1964, 1965; Lee et al., 1968), pears (Maxie et al., 1966) and avocados (Young, 1965). Rates reaching almost half of those observed during the ripening of normal untreated fruit have been recorded for immature tomatoes (Lee et al., 1968). A peak in ethylene production is reached a few hours after irradiation. In most fruits this radiation stimulated ethylene production largely diminishes within two days to pre-climacteric levels. No simple relationship has been found between radiation dose and ethylene production as responses vary among varieties.

It has been suggested that some of the ethylene evolved immediately following irradiation arises non-enzymically from free-radical reactions (Shah and Maxie, 1965; Maxie et al., 1966). However, most appears to arise from stimulated metabolic reactions. When autoclaved lemon fruit were irradiated, ethylene production ceased 30 minutes after completion of irradiation (Shah and Maxie, 1965). Young (1965) made a similar deduction following studies of the effects of doses of 5–100 krad γ-radiation on ethylene production by avocadoes.

As in the case of responses to cutting, ethylene production is stimulated by ionizing radiations to about the same extent in both immature and mature fruit (Lee, 1968). However, the effects of ionizing radiations cannot be simply regarded as a wounding response because irradiation may also reduce the sensitivity of the fruit to ethylene. Internal ethylene concentrations in imature tomato fruit treated with 400 krad have been found to remain above 1 p.p.m. for two days after irradiation (Lee et al., 1968). Fruit picked at the 72% stage of growth and treated with 1 p.p.m. ethylene for two days, ripened three days earlier than untreated fruit. In contrast, ripening is delayed in fruit picked older than the 83% stage and dosed with 200 and 400 krad, whereas no delay is found in fruit irradiated at a younger stage.

Additional evidence that irradiation may reduce the sensitivity of pre-climacteric fruit to ethylene was obtained with pears (Maxie et al., 1966) and bananas (Maxie et al., 1968). However, treatment of pre-climacteric peaches and nectarines with 600 krad of γ-radiation stimulated ethylene production, the onset of the respiratory climacteric and ripening. Mature green lemon fruit showed a stimulation of ethylene production and respiration rate following treatment with 50–100 krad. De-greening was also stimulated. De-greening in lemons is not normally associated with increased respiration and ethylene production (Maxie et al., 1965).

In addition to the immediate effects, irradiation also has some delayed effects on ethylene production which become apparent during the respiratory climacteric. Tomato fruit picked at the 48% stage were able to recover from or repair the damage caused by doses up to 400 krad and pass through a normal climacteric rise in respiration. However, ethylene production during the climacteric was greater in treated fruit than in the controls (Lee *et al.*, 1968). Enhanced ethylene production during the climacteric has also been reported for mature green pears which seemed to have partly recovered from the effects of radiation doses below 300 krad (Maxie *et al.*, 1966). At radiation doses which inhibit or seriously retard ripening namely, 600–700 krad for tomatoes (Abdel-Kader *et al.*, 1968; Lee *et al.*, 1968), 35 krad for pre-climacteric bananas (Maxie *et al.*, 1968) and 300 krad for pre-climacteric pears (Maxie *et al.*, 1966), the amount of ethylene produced during this period is reduced. Avocado fruit appear to be exceptional, ripening is delayed but otherwise normal in fruit treated with 5 and 10 krad although the fruit evolve only a small fraction of the ethylene produced by control fruit. However, treatment with 100 krad inhibits ripening and damages the fruit, but ethylene production is similar to that of untreated fruit undergoing ripening (Young, 1965).

Lee (1968) compared the patterns of respiration and ethylene production of discs cut from the fruit wall of both irradiated and untreated immature tomato fruit. Soon after cutting, discs of fruit treated with 200 krad showed increases in respiration rate greater than the corresponding increases in discs cut from untreated fruit. The rates of ethylene production soon after cutting were similar for discs from both irradiated and untreated fruit, namely about twenty-fold higher than those of intact untreated fruit. Ethylene production rose for a time after cutting. In discs from untreated fruit it reached a maximum 100-fold higher than the rates of intact fruit about five hours after cutting, and then diminished. Peak rates of ethylene production were not reached in discs from irradiated fruit until 10–15 hours after cutting. These rates were double those for intact irradiated fruit or about 150-fold higher than those of intact untreated fruit. The maximum rates of ethylene production of discs cut two or more days after irradiation were similar to those of discs cut on the day of irradiation although the intact fruit rates had declined to low levels. Discs from irradiated fruit ripened at the same time or just after intact fruit.

These findings further support previous observations that irradiation may reduce the sensitivity of fruit tissue to ethylene but they throw no additional light on the role of increased ethylene production in the responses of fruit tissues to stress.

IV. MECHANISM OF ACTION

Any hypothesis on the mechanism of action of ethylene has to account for (i) its specificity in fruit ripening and other regulatory responses in plants;

(ii) the small amounts which are physiologically active ($<$ 1 p.p.m.); (iii) the duration of exposure required to induce complete ripening, and (iv) the evidence that the sensitivity of plant tissues to low concentrations of ethylene may vary with physiological age. Of the three aspects of ethylene physiology, namely, biogenesis, role and mechanism of action, the latter has proved to be the most elusive. On present knowledge it is not certain that the action of ethylene is the same in all of the physiological situations in which it is involved, but it seems improbable that such a simple compound could act in more than one way. Several hypotheses have been proposed which variously explain the action of ethylene in terms of effects on enzyme activities, interactions with nucleic acids, effects on lipoprotein membranes and the formation of complexes with metallo-enzymes.

A. On Enzyme Activities

The early studies on the compositional changes induced in plant tissues by ethylene date back at least to 1915. These naturally led to examination of the effects of ethylene on enzyme activities. By 1940 a number of reports of such effects were presented but these effects have been shown to be largely secondary. There is at present no evidence that, in fruit, ethylene *directly* stimulates the activity of any specific enzyme system nor is there any evidence that it acts as a co-enzyme, co-factor or uncoupling agent (Burg, 1962; Lyons, 1962; Pratt and Goeschl, 1969).

Recent studies with labelled ethylene support these views since there is strong evidence that applied ethylene normally does not react chemically with key cell constituents. However, it is possible that ethylene may form rather delicate associations with particular cell constituents which are readily disrupted by the usual extraction procedures. Thus, it can be visualized that ethylene acts as an effector compound as has been proposed for other growth regulators. The recent report by Shimokawa and Kasai (1968) of the possible incorporation of ^{14}C-ethylene into RNA in Japanese Morning Glory seedlings lends credence to such a suggestion. Confirmation of this result with ^{14}C-ethylene of established high purity is necessary since these authors used ^{14}C-ethylene which had been regenerated after complexing with mercuric-perchlorate (see Section IIB 2).

There have been several indications that ethylene may induce the synthesis of RNA and certain enzymes in fruit and other tissues. Holm and Abeles (1967) reported that ethylene increased incorporation of ^{32}P into RNA in the abscission zone of bean explants and in banana peel tissue. Rhodes *et al.* (1968b) showed that the activity of a malate decarboxylating system increases more rapidly in discs of apple peel treated with ethylene. Furthermore these authors showed that the highest rate of incorporation of ^{14}C-valine into protein occurred soon after the peak of endogenous ethylene production. Both of these events preceded the attainment of maximum malate decarboxylating activity. Cycloheximide (0·1 μg/ml) prevented each of these changes. Frenkel *et al.* (1968) studied the interactions of ethylene and cycloheximide in whole pears. They found that cycloheximide prevented ethylene production and ripening in pre-climacteric fruit but was less effective at later stages. Treatment with 1000 p.p.m. ethylene for 12 hours did not overcome the cycloheximide inhibition of ripening. However, more work is required to establish whether ethylene induces RNA and protein synthesis in fruit tissues. One of the main difficulties is to clearly demonstrate that the event being studied is a primary effect of ethylene. Care is necessary in interpreting data from inhibitor studies. MacDonald and Ellis (1969) have recently warned of some of the side effects which occur when higher plant tissues are treated with supposedly specific inhibitors such as cycloheximide.

There is some evidence in non-fruit tissues that ethylene treatment may induce biochemical changes quantitatively greater than those which normally occur. Imaseki *et al.* (1968a) claimed that treatment of slices of sweet potato root with low concentrations of ethylene increased the actual amounts of phenylalanine ammonia lyase, peroxidase and chlorogenic acid in the tissue above those which are normally induced by cutting. Stahman *et al.* (1966) have shown that ethylene treatment may induce resistance to infection by the fungus, *Ceratocystis fimbriata*, in a normally susceptible variety of sweet potato. Ethylene treatment also has been shown to stimulate the production of isocoumarin in stored carrots (Carlton *et al.*, 1961; Chalutz *et al.*, 1969).

B. On Membranes and Other Physical Systems

In lieu of evidence of a more specific action, the suggestion has frequently been made that ethylene affects membrane permeability but little direct evidence has been offered to support this view until recently. (For a review of earlier work see Lyons, 1962; Pratt and Goeschl, 1969.)

One of the pieces of evidence which points to lipoprotein membranes as a possible site of action is the relatively greater solubility of ethylene in oils than in water. A figure of 14 times has been measured for olive or cotton seed oil (Cullen and Gross, 1951). However, there seems to be no information available on the actual solubility of ethylene in lipoprotein membranes in plants. Since the solubility of ethylene in blood is only about one tenth of that in oil (Eger and Larson, 1964) its solubility in plant lipoprotein should also be much less than in oil.

One of the earliest conceptions of the action of ethylene was presented by Blackman and Parija (1928). The effect of ethylene was to lower the "organization resistance" of the protoplasm. Organization resistance was pictured as "a resistance or hindrance to reactions as achieved either by spatial separation of the reactants by impermeable protoplasmic membranes, or by absorption or combination of reactants by stabilized components of the protoplasm; changes in the grade of organization resistance could occur either spontaneously (for example, during senescence) or by experimental treatment, viz. ethylene".

Since ethylene production in several varieties of fruit increases before the onset of the climacteric (Burg and Burg, 1965a; Pratt and Goeschl, 1969) it seems logical to attempt to correlate permeability changes with increased ethylene production. Increases in cell permeability become very apparent as ripening progresses but it has been difficult to establish whether in the early stages these changes are a cause or a consequence of ripening. Care is necessary in interpreting results based on increased leakage of solutes since in some fruits large increases in sugar content occur during ripening (Burg et al., 1964).

Sacher (1967) has been one of the recent proponents of the idea that increases in cell permeability precede the onset of senescence in plant tissues. Sacher (1966) reported that in 1 mm discs of banana fruit tissue permeability changes preceded the beginning of the climacteric by up to 44 hours and that at the climacteric the slices exhibited 100% free space.

The validity of extrapolating findings from such thin discs of material to whole fruit has been questioned because of the changes induced by cutting (Palmer and McGlasson, 1969; Brady et al., 1970). Brady et al. found that leakage did not increase until much later in the climacteric rise in banana tissue induced to ripen with ethylene than in tissue allowed to ripen naturally. They concluded that permeability changes are not necessarily a prerequisite to ripening. Hulme et al. (1968) drew similar conclusions but did not rule out the possibility that small, selective changes in permeability mediated by enzyme carriers could occur. Von Abrams and Pratt (1967) found that one to three hour treatments with 100 p.p.m. ethylene increased water flux in 2 mm discs cut from approximately 40% grown cantaloupe fruit but not from 75% grown fruit. A three hour treatment did not accelerate the climacteric or otherwise alter the respiration patterns in fruit of either age. The lack of an ethylene effect on flux in 75% grown fruit tissue could have been due to an existing effect of endogenous ethylene, or to a lack of precision of the measuring system. Both cell size and sugar contents are larger in fruit tissue of this age and therefore a higher proportion of the cells in a disc would have been injured by cutting and also the cells would be subject to more osmotic stress when placed in de-ionized water for measurement of water flux.

Lyons and Pratt (1964b) measured the effects of ethylene and other compounds on the osmotic or spontaneous swelling properties of cauliflower and rat liver mitochondria in solutions of KCl and sucrose. Significant effects on swelling were produced only in KCl solutions equilibrated with 1000 p.p.m. of ethylene in air or with pure ethylene, i.e. at a concentration well above "physiologically active" levels.

These studies have been extended by Olson and Spencer (1968a, b) and Olson et al. (1968). Olson and Spencer prepared mitochondria with respiratory control from bean cotyledons, yeast and rat liver. In near isotonic solutions of mannitol, sucrose or KCl the addition of ADP caused the mitochondria from bean cotyledons and yeast to swell, while the addition of ATP had the reverse effect. These changes were more rapid when the solutions were equilibrated with ethylene at concentrations as low as 20 p.p.m., but the spontaneous changes in mitochondrial volume were not affected. A similar effect of ethylene on rat liver mitochondria was found only when the particles were suspended in KCl.

No direct measurements of the effects of ethylene on mitochondrial respiration were made because ethylene interfered with the polarographic measurement of oxygen uptake. However, inhibitors of oxidative phosphorylation or electron transport (arsenate, azide and DNP) inhibited the effects of ethylene on the ADP- or ATP-induced volume changes in bean cotyledon mitochondria. Since ouabain also inhibited these responses but not general mitochondrial volume changes it was suggested that ethylene may effect a mitochondrial ATPase system. This suggestion was supported by measurements which showed that in the presence of ATP, ethylene increased the liberation of inorganic phosphate from mitochondria from bean cotyledons, yeast and rat liver. Ouabain inhibited this effect in bean cotyledon mitochondria only. DNP which uncouples oxidative phosphorylation and increases mitochondrial ATPase activity had little effect on ethylene stimulated liberation of inorganic phosphate in bean cotyledon mitochondria but increased it in yeast and rat liver mitochondria. Olson and Spencer considered that ethylene could bring about an increase in ATPase activity which would result in an increase in the turnover of phosphate acceptors and make possible an increase in cellular respiration. Olson et al. (1968) carried out an interesting computer simulation of the effects of ethylene on mitochondrial respiration which supported this suggestion.

On the assumption that a possible site of ethylene action is the mitochondrial ATPase system, Olson and Spencer (1968b) examined the effects of ethylene on partially purified ATPase from bean cotyledon and rat liver mitochondria. Neither of the enzymic preparations responded. This negative result could be explained either by a modification in the enzymes during their preparation or that the enzymes are only active in situ. If ethylene only increases ATPase activity in situ this could indicate the existence of a specific conformational relationship between the mitochondrial membrane and the enzyme that is affected by ethylene, or that ethylene affects the movement of components of the ATPase system through the membranes.

Mehard (1969) obtained data which show that *in vivo* ethylene does not act by causing overt changes in membranes. He found that saturated aqueous solutions of propylene, butene, ethane and propane caused mitochondria from green tomato fruit to swell to the same extent or greater than saturated solutions of ethylene. Further tests with model membranes of fatty acids, phospholipids, protein and phospholipid plus protein showed that these gases reduced surface tension. This effect was correlated with molecular size. Mehard's findings emphasize the need to include in *in vitro* studies tests with other gases to establish the specificity of effects attributed to ethylene.

Pauling (1961) determined that narcotic concentrations of some anaesthetic gases form hydrate crystals of the clathrate type. Such an action would not apply to the action of ethylene in plants for two reasons; the high concentrations which are required to form hydrate crystals, and the fact that ethylene forms hydrate crystals at about the same concentrations as ethane, which is physiologically inactive in plants.

There is some evidence that ethylene may affect movements of substances other than water through membranes. Van Fleet (1963) found that treatment of vegetative plant tissues with high concentrations of ethylene or etherized water caused a redistribution of lipids and lipid enzymes and a change in tissue differentiation. Jones (1968) reported that low concentrations of ethylene enhanced the secretion of α-amylase by barley aleurone cells. Burg (1968) has concluded that ethylene causes abscission *in vivo* by inhibiting auxin synthesis and transport or enhancing auxin destruction. He also suggested that ethylene may influence abscission through an action on cell walls although conclusive data on this effect are lacking.

C. Formation of a Complex with a Metallo-Enzyme

Burg and Burg (1965c, 1967) investigated the molecular requirements for the biological action of ethylene using the pea straight growth test. It was proposed that biological activity (i) requires an unsaturated bond adjacent to a terminal carbon atom; (ii) is inversely related to molecular size, and (iii) is decreased by substitutions which lower the electron density in the unsaturated position. Evidence based on the ability of unsaturated aliphatic compounds to form complexes with silver was presented in support of a proposal that, *in vivo*, ethylene binds to a metal-containing receptor site. It was suggested that the metal may be zinc.

Burg and Burg further proposed that the well known delay in ripening obtained by storing fruit in atmospheres containing increased concentrations of carbon dioxide and reduced concentrations of oxygen may be due in part to interference with the binding of ethylene to the receptor site. This proposal was based on an analysis (Michaelis–Menten kinetics and Lineweaver–Burk plots) of the interactions of ethylene with carbon dioxide and oxygen in the pea straight growth test. According to the kinetic models thus derived, carbon dioxide competitively inhibits the binding of ethylene to the receptor site while it was envisaged that ethylene only attaches to the receptor site after the metal of the receptor has been directly or indirectly oxidized by molecular oxygen. The affinity of ethylene for the receptor site was found to be one million-fold greater than that of carbon dioxide.

In view of the similarity of the competition between carbon dioxide and ethylene in other physiological situations including flower fading, abscission and epinasty, and the similar relative effectiveness of ethylene and its analogues in the promotion of fruit ripening, the inhibition of elongation in pea tissue and causing epinasty (Table II), Burg and Burg (1967) suggested "that triggering a single primary mechanism with ethylene gives rise to a wide variety of responses, just as light and the phytochrome system control a multiplicity of events". However, there are at least two exceptions to these generalizations. Young et al. (1962) found that in lemons, treatment with a gas mixture containing 10 p.p.m. ethylene and 5% carbon dioxide stimulated respiration more than either gas did separately. Also, Imaseki et al. (1968b) showed that increased concentrations of carbon dioxide increased ethylene production by infected sweet potato tissue.

V. CONCLUSIONS

The growing weight of evidence indicates that ethylene acts in vivo as a ripening hormone and that at least in the early stages of ripening, ethylene biogenesis is a regulated process since the capacity to produce ethylene exists in fruit at an early stage of development. The nature of this regulation must remain a subject for speculation until the pathway for the biogenesis of ethylene has been established.

Of the three major aspects of ethylene physiology, the problem of biogenesis appears closest to solution. There is strong evidence that, at least in higher plants, L-methionine is closer to the immediate precursor of ethylene than any other naturally occurring metabolite so far tested. The breakdown products of linolenic acid may also be implicated.

The mechanism of action of ethylene is still an open question despite the recent stimulating findings on the molecular specifications of the biological activity of ethylene. Present indications are that the action of ethylene is a subtle one perhaps involving small changes in the conformation of enzymes embedded in membranes or elsewhere, or the movement of enzymes or specific components of enzyme reactions across membranes. Action through overt changes in membrane permeability appears unlikely since the actual solubility of ethylene in membranes is probably not as great as hitherto assumed. The actual amounts of ethylene dissolved in membranes would be very low at the low ethylene in air concentrations known to be biologically active ($<$ 1 p.p.m.).

Currently one of the most promising areas for research is that concerned with the existence of natural compounds affecting the sensitivity of fruit tissues to ethylene or even inhibiting the action of ethylene. Further studies to identify these compounds and to establish the nature of the delays in ripening achieved by infiltrating auxins, as in the case of banana tissue, seem justified. Indeed, the initial events leading to senescence (ripening) in fruits may be reversible.

ACKNOWLEDGEMENT

Helpful criticism by Dr James M. Lyons during the preparation of the chapter is gratefully acknowledged.

REFERENCES

Abdel-Gawad, H. A. and Romani, R. J. (1967). *Pl. Physiol. Lancaster*, **42**, S43.

Abdel-Kader, A. S., Morris, L. L. and Maxie, E. C. (1964). *In* "Radiation technology in conjunction with post-harvest procedures as a means of extending the shelf-life of fruits and vegetables". A. Rep. At. Energy Comm. Contract AT. (11–1)-34 Project 80 (OTS, Dept. of Comm.), pp. 7–47.

Abdel-Kader, A. S., Morris, L. L. and Maxie, E. C. (1965). *In* "Radiation technology in conjunction with post-harvest procedures as a means of extending the shelf-life of fruits and vegetables". A. Rep. At. Energy Comm. Contract AT. (11–1)-34 Project 80 (OTS, Dept. of Comm.), pp. 99–175.

Abdel-Kader, A. S., Morris, L. L. and Maxie, E. C. (1968). *Proc. Am. Soc. hort. Sci.* **92**, 553–67.

Abeles, F. B. (1966). *Nature, Lond.* **210**, 23–5.

Abeles, F. B. and Rubinstein, B. (1964). *Biochim. Biophys. Acta.* **93**, 675–7.

Abeles, F. B. and Gahagan, H. E. (1968). *Pl. Physiol., Lancaster* **43**, 1255.

Abeles, F. B., Holm, R. E. and Gahagan, H. E. (1967). *Pl. Physiol., Lancaster* **42**, S9.

Addicott, F. D. (1968). *Pl. Physiol., Lancaster* **43**, 1471–9.

Aharoni, Y. (1968). *Pl. Physiol., Lancaster* **43**, 99–102.

Anderson, J. W. (1968). *Phytochem.* **7**, 1973–8.

Ap Rees, T. (1966). *Aust. J. biol. Sci.* **19**, 981–90.

Bain, J. M. and Mercer, F. V. (1964). *Aust. J. biol. Sci.* **17**, 78–85.

Baur, A. and Yang, S. F. (1969). *Pl. Physiol.* **44**, 189–92.

Ben-Yehoshua, S., Robertson, R. N. and Biale, J. B. (1963). *Pl. Physiol., Lancaster* **38**, 194–201.

Biale, J. B. (1950). *A. Rev. Pl. Physiol.* **1**, 183–206.

Biale, J. B. (1960a). *In* "Handbuch der Pflanzenphysiologie" (W. Ruhland, ed.) **12** (2), 536–92. Springer Verlag, Berlin.

Biale, J. B. (1960b). *Adv. Fd Res.* **10**, 293–354.

Biale, J. B. (1964). *Science, N.Y.* **146**, 880–8.
Biale, J. B., Young, R. E. and Olmstead, A. (1954). *Pl Physiol., Lancaster* **29**, 168–74.
Blackman, F. P. and Parija, P. (1928). *Proc. R. Soc. (Lond.)* **103**, 422–45.
Blake, J. R. and Stevenson, C. D. (1959). *Qd J. agric. Sci.* **16**, 87–90.
Brady, C. J., O'Connell, P. B. H., Smydzuk, J. and Wade, N. L. (1970). *Aust. J. biol. Sci.* **22**, (in press).
Buhler, D. R., Hansen, E., and Wang, C. H. (1957). *Nature, Lond.* **179**, 48–9.
Burg, S. P. (1962). *A. Rev. Pl. Physiol.* **13**, 265–302.
Burg, S. P. (1968). *Pl. Physiol, Lancaster* **43**, 1503–11.
Burg, S. P. and Stolwijk, J. A. A. (1959). *J. biochem. microbiol. Technol. Engng* **1**, 245–59.
Burg, S. P. and Thimann, K. V. (1959). *Proc. natn. Acad. Sci. U.S.A.* **45**, 335–44.
Burg, S. P. and Thimann, K. V. (1960). *Pl. Physiol., Lancaster* **35**, 24–35.
Burg, S. P. and Burg, E. A. (1961). *Nature, Lond.* **191**, 967–9.
Burg, S. P. and Thimann, K. V. (1961). *Archs Biochem. Biophys.* **95**, 450–7.
Burg, S. P. and Burg, E. A. (1962a). *Pl. Physiol., Lancaster* **37**, 179–89.
Burg, S. P. and Burg, E. A. (1962b). *Nature, Lond.* **194**, 398–9.
Burg, S. P. and Burg, E. A. (1964). *Nature, Lond.* **203**, 869–70.
Burg, S. P. and Burg, E. A. (1965a). *Bot. Gaz.* **126**, 200–4.
Burg, S. P. and Burg, E. A. (1965b). *Physiologia Pl.* **18**, 870–84.
Burg, S. P. and Burg, E. A. (1965c). *Science, N.Y.* **148**, 1190–6.
Burg, S. P. and Burg, E. A. (1966). *Science, N.Y.* **153**, 314–15.
Burg, S. P. and Burg, E. A. (1967). *Pl. Physiol., Lancaster* **42**, 144–52.
Burg, S. P. and Clagett, C. O. (1967). *Biochem. biophys. Res. Commun.* **27**, 125–30.
Burg, S. P., Burg, E. A. and Marks, R. (1964). *Pl. Physiol., Lancaster* **39**, 185–95.
Carlton, B. C., Peterson, C. E. and Tolbert, N. E. (1961). *Pl. Physiol., Lancaster* **36**, 550–2.
Chalutz, E., DeVay, J. E. and Maxie, E. C. (1969). *Pl. Physiol., Lancaster* **44**, 235–41.
Chandra, G. R. and Spencer, M. (1962). *Nature, Lond.* **194**, 361–4.
Chandra, G. R. and Spencer, M. (1963a). *Biochim. Biophys. Acta* **63**, 423–5.
Chandra, G. R. and Spencer, M. (1963b). *Nature, Lond.* **197**, 366–7.
Clendenning, K. A. (1942). *Can. J. Res.* **20C**, 197–203.
Coggins, C. W., Jr. and Lewis, L. N. (1962). *Pl. Physiol., Lancaster* **37**, 625–7.
Cooke, A. R. and Randall, D. I. (1968). *Nature, Lond.* **218**, 974–5.
Cousins, H. H. (1910). *Jamaica Dept. Agr. Ann. Rept*, 1910, **7**, 15.
Crocker, W., Zimmerman, P. W. and Hitchcock, A. E. (1932). *Contr. Boyce Thompson Inst. Pl. Res.* **4**, 177–218.
Crocker, W., Hitchcock, A. E. and Zimmerman, P. W. (1935). *Contr. Boyce Thompson Inst. Pl. Res.* **7**, 231–48.
Cullen, S. C. and Gross, E. G. (1951). *Science, N.Y.* **113**, 580–2.
Denny, F. E. (1924). *J. Agric. Res.* **27**, 757–71.
Dostal, H. C. and Leopold, A. C. (1967). *Science, N.Y.* **158**, 1579–80.
Eaks, I. L. (1967). *Proc. Am. Soc. hort. Sci.* **91**, 868–75.
Eger, E. I. and Larson, C. P., Jr. (1964). *Br. J. Anaesth.* **36**, 140–9.
Fidler, J. C. (1960). *In* "Handbuch der Pflanzenphysiologie" (W. Ruhland, ed.) **12** (2), 347–59. Springer Verlag, Berlin.
Fidler, J. C. and North, C. J. (1967). *J. hort. Sci.* **42**, 189–206.
Freebairn, H. T. and Buddenhagen, I. W. (1964). *Nature, Lond.* **202**, 313–14.

Frenkel, C., Klein, I. and Dilley, D. R. (1968). *Pl. Physiol., Lancaster* **43**, 1146–53.
Galliard, T., Rhodes, M. J. C., Wooltorton, L. S. C. and Hulme, A. C. (1968a). *Phytochem.* **7**, 1453–63.
Galliard, T., Rhodes, M. J. C., Wooltorton, L. S. C. and Hulme, A. C. (1968b). *Phytochem.* **7**, 1465–70.
Galliard, T., Hulme, A. C., Rhodes, M. J. C. and Wooltorton, L. S. C. (1968c). *Febs Letters* **1**, 283–6.
Gane, R. (1934). *Nature, Lond.* **134**, 1008.
Gibson, M. S. and Crane, F. L. (1963). *Pl. Physiol., Lancaster* **38**, 729–30.
Gibson, M. S. and Young, R. E. (1966). *Nature, Lond.* **210**, 529–30.
Goeschl, J. D., Rappaport, L. and Pratt, H. K. (1966). *Pl. Physiol., Lancaster* **41**, 877–84.
Goeschl, J. D., Pratt, H. K. and Bonner, B. A. (1967). *Pl. Physiol., Lancaster* **42**, 1077–80.
Hall, W. C. (1957). *Pl. Physiol. Proc.* **32**, VII–VIII.
Hall, W. C. (1962). "Radiochemical studies with ethylene in plant metabolism". U.S. At. Energy Comm. TID-17421, p. 17.
Hall, W. C., Miller, C. S. and Herrero, F. A. (1961). 4th Intern. Conf. Plant Growth Regulation pp. 751–78. Iowa State University Press, Ames, Iowa.
Hansen, E. (1943). *Proc. Am. Soc. hort. Sci.* **43**, 69–72.
Hansen, E. (1946). *Pl. Physiol., Lancaster* **21**, 588–92.
Hansen, E. (1966). *A. Rev. Pl. Physiol.* **17**, 459–80.
Hansen, E. and Blanpied, G. D. (1968). *Proc. Am. Soc. hort. Sci.* **93**, 807–12.
Hirai, J., Hirata, N. and Horiuchi, S. (1967). *J. hort. Ass. Japan* **36**, 268–74.
Holm, R. E. and Abeles, F. B. (1967). *Pl. Physiol., Lancaster* **42**, 1094–1102.
Hulme, A. C., Rhodes, M. J. C., Galliard, T. and Wooltorton, L. S. C. (1968). *Pl. Physiol., Lancaster* **43**, 1154–61.
Ilag, L. and Curtis, R. W. (1968). *Science, N.Y.* **159**, 1357–8.
Imaseki, H., Uchiyama, M. and Uritani, I. (1968a). *Agr. Biol. Chem.* **32**, 387–9.
Imaseki, H., Teranishi, T. and Uritani, I. (1968b). *Pl. Cell Physiol., Tokyo* **9**, 769–81.
Jacobsen, D. W. and Wang, C. H. (1968). *Pl. Physiol., Lancaster* **43**, 1959–66.
Jansen, E. F. (1963). *J. biol. Chem.* **238**, 1552–5.
Jansen, E. F. (1964). *J. biol. Chem.* **239**, 1664–7.
Jansen, E. F. (1965). *In* "Plant Biochemistry" (J. Bonner and J. E. Varner, eds), pp. 641–64. Academic Press, New York and London.
Jansen, E. F. and Wallace, J. M. (1965). *J. biol. Chem.* **240**, 1042–4.
Jones, J. D. and Hulme, A. C. (1961). *Nature, Lond.* **191**, 370.
Jones, R. L. (1968). *Pl. Physiol., Lancaster* **43**, 442–4.
Kang, B. G., Yocum, C. S., Burg, S. P. and Ray, P. M. *Science, N.Y.* **156**, 958–9.
Ketring, D. L., Young, R. E., Biale, J. B. (1968). *Pl. Cell Physiol., Tokyo* **9**, 617–31.
Kidd, F. and West, C. (1924). *Rept Food Invest Board, London 1924,* pp. 27–30.
Kidd, F. and West, C. (1945). *Pl. Physiol., Lancaster* **20**, 467–504.
Klucas, R. V. and Evans, H. J. (1968). *Pl. Physiol., Lancaster* **43**, 1458–60.
Ku, H. S. and Pratt, H. K. (1968). *Pl. Physiol., Lancaster* **43**, 999–1001.
Ku, H. S., Yang, S. F. and Pratt, H. K. (1967). *Archs Biochem. Biophys.* **118**, 756–8.
Kumamoto, J., Dollwet, H. H. A. and Lyons, J. M. (1969). *J. Am. chem. Soc.* **91**, 1207.
Laties, G. G. (1967). *Aust. J. Sci.* **30**, 193–203.
Lee, T. H. (1968). Ph.D. Thesis, University of New South Wales, Kensington.
Lee, T. H., McGlasson, W. B. and Edwards, R. A. (1968). *Radiat. Bot.* **8**, 259–67.

Lieberman, M. and Craft, C. C. (1961). *Nature, Lond.* **189**, 243.

Lieberman, M. and Mapson, L. W. (1962a). *Nature, Lond.* **195**, 1016–17.

Lieberman, M. and Mapson, L. W. (1962b). *Nature, Lond.* **196**, 660–1.

Lieberman, M. and Mapson, L. W. (1964). *Nature, Lond.* **204**, 343–5.

Lieberman, M. and Hochstein, P. (1966). *Science, N.Y.* **152**, 213–14.

Lieberman, M. and Kunishi, A. T. (1967). *Science, N.Y.* **158**, 938.

Lieberman, M., Kunishi, A., Mapson, L. W. and Wardale, D. A. (1965). *Biochem. J.* **97**, 449–59.

Lieberman, M., Kunishi, A., Mapson, L. W. and Wardale, D. A. (1966). *Pl. Physiol., Lancaster* **41**, 376–82.

Loomis, W. D. and Battaille, J. (1966). *Phytochem.* **5**, 423–38.

Looney, N. E. (1968). *Pl Physiol., Lancaster* **43**, 1133–7.

Lyons, J. M. (1962). Ph.D. Thesis, University of California, Davis.

Lyons, J. M. and Pratt, H. K. (1964a). *Proc. Am. Soc. hort. Sci.* **84**, 491 500.

Lyons, J. M. and Pratt, H. K. (1964b). *Archs Biochem. Biophys.* **104**, 318–24.

Lyons, J. M., McGlasson, W. B. and Pratt, H. K. (1962). *Pl. Physiol., Lancaster* **37**, 31–6.

MacDonald, I. R. and Ellis, R. J. (1969). *Nature, Lond.* **222**, 791–2.

McGlasson, W. B. (1969). *Aust. J. biol. Sci.* **22**, 489–91.

McGlasson, W. B. and Pratt, H. K. (1964a). *Pl. Physiol., Lancaster* **39**, 120–7.

McGlasson, W. B. and Pratt, H. K. (1964b). *Pl. Physiol., Lancaster* **39**, 128–32.

Mapson, L. W. (1969). *Biol. Rev.* **44**, 155–87.

Mapson, L. W. and Mead, A. (1968). *Biochem. J.* **108**, 875–81.

Mapson, L. W. and Robinson, J. E. (1966). *J. Fd Technol* **1**, 215–25.

Mapson, L. W. and Wardale, D. A. (1967). *Biochem. J.* **102**, 574–85.

Mapson, L. W. and Wardale, D. A. (1968). *Biochem. J.* **107**, 433–42.

Mapson, L. W., Self, R. and Wardale, D. A. (1969). *Biochem. J.* **111**, 413–18.

Maxie, E. C. and Abdel-Kader, A. (1966). *Adv. Fd Res.* **15**, 105–45.

Maxie, E. C. and Crane, J. C. (1968). *Proc. Am. Soc. hort. Sci.* **92**, 255–67.

Maxie, E. C. and Sommer, H. P. (1963). In "Radiation technology in conjunction with post-harvest procedures as a means of extending the shelf life of fruits and vegetables". Ann. Rept. At. Energy Comm. Contract AT(11–1)-34 Project 80 (OTS, Dept of Comm.).

Maxie, E. C., Sommer, N. F., Muller, C. J. and Rae, H. L. (1966). *Pl. Physiol., Lancaster* **41**, 437–42.

Maxie, E. C., Amezquita, R., Hassan, B. M. and Johnson, C. F. (1968). *Proc. Am. Soc. hort. Sci.* **92**, 235–54.

Maxie, E. C., Eaks, I. I., Sommer, N. F., Rae, H. L. and El-Batal, S. (1965). *Pl. Physiol., Lancaster* **40**, 407–9.

Mehard, C. (1969). Ph.D. Thesis. University of California, Riverside.

Meheriuk, M. and Spencer, M. (1967a). *Phytochem.* **6**, 535–43.

Meheriuk, M. and Spencer, M. (1967b). *Phytochem.* **6**, 545–9.

Meheriuk, M. and Spencer, M. (1967c). *Phytochem.* **6**, 551–8.

Meigh, D. F. (1959). *Nature, Lond.* **184**, 1072–3.

Meigh, D. F. (1960). *J. Sci. Fd Agric.* **11**, 381–5.

Meigh, D. F. (1962). *Nature, Lond.* **196**, 345–7.

Meigh, D. F. (1963). *G. Brit. Agr. Res. Council Ditton Covent. Labs* Ann. Rept 1962–3, pp. 23–4.

Meigh, D. F., Jones, J. D. and Hulme, A. C. (1967). *Phytochem.* **6**, 1507–15.

Mitchell, J. W. and Marth, P. C. (1944). *Bot. Gaz.* **106**, 199–207.

518   W. B. McGlasson

Morgan, P. W. and Hall, W. C. (1962). *Physiologia Pl.* **15,** 420–7.
Morgan, P. W. and Hall, W. C. (1964). *Nature, Lond.* **201,** 99.
Neljubow, D. (1901). *Beih. bot. Central Bl.* **10,** 128–38.
Noble, E. P., Reed, D. R. and Wang, C. H. (1958). *Can. J. Microbiol.* **4,** 469–76.
Olson, A. O. and Spencer, M. (1968a). *Can. J. Biochem.* **46,** 277–82.
Olson, A. O. and Spencer, M. (1968b). *Can. J. Biochem.* **46,** 283–8.
Olson, A. O., Spencer, M. and Svrcek, W. V. (1968). *Can. J. Biochem.* **46,** 513–20.
Osborne, D. J. (1967). *Symp. Soc. exp. Biol.* **21,** 305–21.
Palmer, J. K. and McGlasson, W. B. (1969). *Aust. J. biol. Sci.* **22,** 87–99.
Pauling, L. (1961). *Science, N.Y.* **134,** 15–21.
Phan, C. T. (1960). *C. r. hébd. Seanc. Acad. Sci., Paris* **251,** 122–4.
Phan, C. T. (1962). *Rev. gén. Bot.* **69,** 505–43.
Pienazek, J. and Rudnicki, R. (1967). *Bull. Acad. pol. Sci. Sér. Sci. kch.* **15,** 251–4.
Porritt, S. W. (1951). *Scient. Agric.* **31,** 99–112.
Pratt, H. K. (1961). *Recent Adv. Botany,* 1160–5. (University of Toronto Press).
Pratt, H. K. and Goeschl, J. D. (1968). *In* "Biochemistry and physiology of plant growth substances" (Wightman, F., Setterfield, G., eds). p. 1285. The Runge Press, Ottawa.
Pratt, H. K. and Goeschl, J. D. (1969). *A. Rev. Pl. Physiol.* **20,** 541–84.
Rhodes, M. J. C., Wooltorton, L. S. C., Galliard, T. and Hulme, A. C. (1968a). *Phytochem.* **7,** 405–8.
Rhodes, M. J. C., Wooltorton, L. S. C., Galliard, T. and Hulme, A. C. (1968b). *Phytochem.* **7,** 1439–51.
Rhodes, M. J. C., Wooltorton, L. S. C., Galliard, T. and Hulme, A. C. (1970). *J. exp. Bot.* **21,** 40.
Romani, R. J. (1966a). *Radiat. Bot.* **6,** 87–104.
Romani, R. J. (1966b). *Adv. Fd Res.* **15,** 57–103.
Rudnicki, R., Pienazek, J. and Pienazek, N. (1968). *Bull. Acad. pol. Sci.* **16,** 127–30.
Russo, L. Jr., Dostal, H. C. and Leopold, A. C. (1968). *Bioscience* **18,** 109.
Sacher, J. A. (1966). *Pl. Physiol., Lancaster* **41,** 701–8.
Sacher, J. A. (1967). *Symp. Soc. exp. Biol.* **21,** 269–304.
Scott, K. J., McGlasson, W. B. and Roberts, E. A. (1970). *Aust. J. exp. Agr. Animal Husbandry* **10,** 237.
Shah, J. and Maxie, E. C. (1965). *Physiologia Pl.* **16,** 1115–20.
Shimokawa, K. and Kasai, Z. (1966). *Pl. Cell Physiol., Tokyo* **7,** 1–9.
Shimokawa, K. and Kasai, Z. (1967). *Pl. Cell Physiol., Tokyo* **8,** 227–30.
Shimokawa, K. and Kasai, Z. (1968). *Agr. Biol. Chem.* **32,** 680–2.
Sievers, A. F. and True, R. H. (1912). *U.S. Dept Agr. Bur. Plant Ind. Bul.* **232,** 1–38.
Spencer, M. S. (1959). *Nature, Lond.* **184,** 1231–2.
Spencer, M. (1965). *In* "Plant Biochemistry" (J. Bonner and J. E. Varner, eds), pp. 793–825. Academic Press, New York and London.
Sprayberry, B. A., Hall, W. C. and Miller, C. S. (1965). *Nature, Lond.* **208,** 1322–3.
Stahmann, M. A., Clare, B. G. and Woodbury, W. (1966). *Pl. Physiol., Lancaster* **41,** 1505–12.
Takeo, T. and Lieberman, M. (1969). *Biochim. Biophys. Acta* **178,** 235–47.
Thompson, J. E. and Spencer, M. (1966). *Nature, Lond.* **210,** 595–7.
Thompson, J. E. and Spencer, M. (1967). *Can. J. Biochem.* **45,** 563–71.
Van Fleet, D. S. (1963). *Nature, Lond.* **200,** 889.
Varner, J. E. (1965). *In* "Plant Biochemistry" (J. Bonner and J. E. Varner, eds), pp. 867–72. Academic Press, New York and London.

Vendrell, M. (1969). *Aust. J. biol. Sci.* **22**, 601–10.

Vines, H. M., Grierson, W. and Edwards, G. J. (1968). *Proc. Am. Soc. hort. Sci.* **92**, 227–34.

Von Abrams, G. J. and Pratt, H. K. (1967). *Pl. Physiol., Lancaster* **42**, 299–301.

Wang, C. H., Persyn, A. and Krackov, J. (1962). *Nature, Lond.* **195**, 1306–8.

Whitmore, F. C. (1921). "Organic Compounds of Mercury". The Chemical Catalogue Co., New York.

Williamson, C. E. (1950). *Phytopathology* **40**, 205–8.

Wooltorton, L. S. C., Jones, J. D. and Hulme, A. C. (1965). *Nature, Lond.* **207**, 999–1000.

Yang, S. F. (1967). *Archs Biochem. Biophys.* **122**, 481–7.

Yang, S. F. (1968). *In* "Biochemistry and Physiology of Plant Growth Substances" (Wightman, F. and Setterfield, G., eds), p. 1217. The Runge Press, Ottawa.

Yang, S. F., Ku, H. S. and Pratt, H. K. (1966). *Biochem. biophys. Res. Commun.* **24**, 739–43.

Young, R. E. (1965). *Nature, Lond.* **205**, 1113–14.

Young, R. E., Romani, R. J. and Biale, J. B. (1962). *Pl. Physiol., Lancaster* **37**, 416–22.

Young, R. E., Pratt, H. K. and Biale, J. B. (1952). *Analyt. Chem.* **24**, 551–5.

Zimmerman, P. W. and Wilcoxon, F. (1935). *Contr. Boyce Thompson Inst. Pl. Res.* **7**, 209–29.

Chapter 17

The Climacteric and Ripening of Fruits

M. J. C. RHODES

A.R.C. Food Research Institute, Norwich, England

I. INTRODUCTION

The ripening of fruits may be defined as the sequence of changes in colour, flavour and texture which lead to the state at which the fruit is acceptable to eat. This does not necessarily mean that this is a fixed physiological state— it can and does vary from one type of fruit to another and in some cases the changes may even run in opposite directions. For instance, in pome fruits, there is a loss of malic acid as the fruit ripens (Kidd *et al.*, 1951), while in the banana the reverse occurs and malate accumulates (Wyman and Palmer, 1964). The readily apparent phenomena associated with the ripening of the majority of fruits include changes in colour, which involve loss of chlorophyll leading to the unmasking of underlying pigments, and the synthesis of new pigments; alteration in flavour, which includes changes in acidity, astringency and sweetness themselves dependent on the organic acids, phenolics, sugars and volatiles present in the tissue and changes in texture. Other visible changes include the abscission of the fruit from the vine or tree and, in some fruits, increased wax development on the skin. Underlying these changes, observed by the sense of colour, taste and texture (sensory changes) are a series of basic changes in the composition and metabolism of the fruit. In this chapter, we are concerned with these underlying changes and their relationship to the sensory changes in the fruit.

The modern study of the ripening processes stems from the investigation

521

of the physiology of the apple fruit undertaken by Kidd and West in the early 1920's. They studied the changes in respiratory activity of Bramley Seedling apples picked at various stages in the growth of the fruit and subsequently stored at various temperatures. They found that, after picking, the CO_2 production of the fruit fell to a minimum value and then rose more or less rapidly, depending on the temperature (Kidd and West, 1922, 1923, 1924). Subsequently the respiration declined. Visible changes in ripening occurred shortly after the peak in rate of respiration. This pattern of respiratory changes had previously been demonstrated in the very early experiments of Gerber (1897), but its significance in the physiology of the fruit had not been realized at the time. Kidd and West (1924) considered that the relatively sudden alteration in the level of respiration marked the transition from the growth to the senescence phase in the life of the fruit. They recognized that the increase in respiration was a critical phase in the life of the fruit and hence termed it "the climacteric".

In subsequent work, Kidd and West (1945) showed that a similar rise in respiration occurred during the maturation of apples still attached to the tree. This "on tree" climacteric is characterized by a slower rise in respiration which eventually reaches values 50% higher than at the climacteric peak in detached fruit (Hulme et al., 1963). Kidd and West showed that once the fruit, either on or off the tree, entered this critical phase and the climacteric rise was under way the ripening of the fruit was an irreversible process which could be slowed but not halted by the application of external factors. This climacteric rise in respiration was, at the time it was studied by Kidd and West, the first known event in this irreversible sequence and hence was a useful criterion of the transition from growth to senescence. As has been described elsewhere in this book (Chapter 16; Volume 2, Chapter 10) we now know more of the events which precede the respiratory rise. It has been established that in most fruits (see the review by Pratt and Goeschl, 1969) the establishment of physiologically active concentrations of the olefine gas, ethylene, in the intercellular spaces within the fruit, precedes the rise in respiration and that an exogenous supply of ethylene will both trigger off the climacteric in the unripe fruit and induce in them an autocatalytic process of ethylene synthesis. Ethylene may, therefore, be considered as the natural hormone of ripening, and the enhancement of ethylene biosynthesis to stimulatory concentrations, rather than the rise in respiration, is the event which marks the transition from the growth to the senescent phase of the fruit. This transition stage is important in that before it commences, exogenous ethylene will stimulate autonomous ethylene production and the attendant rise in respiration; when it has begun, applied ethylene is ineffective.

II. DEFINITION OF THE CLIMACTERIC

In view of the historical development of our knowledge of the subject, it is clear that in using the term climacteric, Kidd and West were referring specifically to a pattern of respiratory changes, and, indeed, in many later papers it is referred to as the "respiration climacteric". It is implicit in the results of modern work that the rise in respiration is a secondary event dependent on the available levels of ethylene; as discussed later, many other secondary events such as increase in RNA and protein synthesis, and changes in cell permeability occur during this period. It would seem to the author that the use of the term climacteric should be applied to the whole of this critical phase in the life of the fruit which is triggered off by ethylene and during which many changes are occurring (one of which, the respiration rise, is an easily measurable example). The use of respiration values of fruit is still a very useful means of assessing the physiological age of a fruit and of relating, chronologically, the other changes occurring in ripening. A very useful definition of the climacteric is that of Thomas (1956), namely that "the climacteric represents a state of autostimulation in which yellowing and enhanced respiration are two of the attendant effects". We should, in the light of recent research, widen this to include *all* the attendant ripening changes, apparent or underlying. The definition of the climacteric must also imply that it makes the transition from growth to senescence.

The climacteric may, therefore, be defined as a period in the ontogeny of certain fruits, during which a series of biochemical changes is initiated by the autocatalytic production of ethylene, marking the change from growth to senescence and involving an increase in respiration and leading to ripening.

III. PATTERN OF RESPIRATORY ACTIVITY IN VARIOUS FRUITS

Subsequent to Kidd and West's work on the apple, it was established that a similar pattern of respiration was associated with the ripening of many other fruits. For instance, the rise to a peak was shown for the tomato by Gustafson (1929), for the avocado by Wardlaw and Leonard (1935) and for the banana by Leonard (1941). It was soon clear that the majority of fruits show the climacteric pattern of development, and among these are the apple, apricot, avocado, banana, cherimoya, Cantaloupe melon, feijoa, mango, papaya, passion fruit, pawpaw, peach, pear, plum and tomato. In many fruits, the extent of the change in respiration at normal ripening temperatures is considerably greater than the 60–100% rise found in the apple. In the tomato and banana, the rise is three-fold; in the avocado it is four to five-fold. As with the apple, in the tomato the respiration rise occurs both in fruit detached from and attached to the vine (Clendenning, 1942) while the avocado only shows a climacteric rise in respiration after detachment from the tree (Biale, 1946). In many of the tropical and sub-tropical fruits described by Biale (1960b) the rise in respiration was rapid, and the stage of eating ripeness corresponded closely with the climacteric peak in fruits such as the avocado, the banana, the cherimoya and the mango. This differs from the apple (Hulme, 1958) and the tomato, where ripening is not complete until some time after the climacteric peak. Thus in tropical fruits, the various changes involved in the climacteric and ripening show a more complete overlap in time.

The view that all fruit exhibit a climacteric pattern of ripening was questioned by Biale (1960a) who classified fruit into climacteric and non-climacteric categories. In the non-climacteric category were placed the cherry, cucumber, fig, grape, grapefruit, lemon, melon, orange, pineapple and the strawberry. In these fruits, the respiratory pattern shows a slow drift downwards after detachment from the parent plant. In making the classification, Biale was clearly aware of the difficulties of placing these fruits in the non-climacteric category since the evidence on which the distinction was made was essentially negative. It was always possible that at a more appropriate physiological age, or under more appropriate storage conditions, the respiration pattern characteristic of the climacteric fruits might be displayed. In fact there are examples of fruits originally classified as non-climacteric (for example, the melon) which have in fact been shown to exhibit the typical climacteric pattern (Lyons et al., 1962; McGlasson and Pratt, 1964). When considering these two groups, the climacteric and non-climacteric, it is difficult to decide whether there is a distinct difference in the mechanism of ripening in the two types of fruit or whether events which occur slowly over a long period in the so-called non-climacteric types are merely telescoped in the climacteric fruits into a short dramatic period. Spencer (1966) speculated along these lines and it seems probable that the second is the more likely possibility. All fruits during ripening contain appreciable quantities of ethylene (although the quantities involved vary markedly, see Table I), but the behaviour of some fruits, for example, the citrus family, towards exogenous ethylene differs markedly from that exhibited for example by the apple.

An interesting case of a fruit in Biale's non-climacteric category is the pineapple, whose status is still a matter for dispute. This was studied by Bose et al. (1960) who concluded that it did show the climacteric pattern. More recently Dull et al. (1967) have reinvestigated the pattern of respiration in fruit picked at six stages and subsequently stored. Of the six stages, three were in the pre-maturation period and three were during the ripening phase on the tree. In the fruit picked at the most immature stage, there was a rapid fall in respiration to a minimum followed by a small rise and then a further rapid fall. In the next two specimens, the respiration showed a general drift downwards. However, as the fruit entered the ripening phase the initial fruits of subsequent pickings showed a rise in respiration which might be interpreted as a respiration climacteric "on the tree" (see a discussion of the criteria for establishing the occurrence of a respiration climacteric on the tree in Biale, 1950). The storage of such fruits is accompanied by a further rise in respiration but in no case was a peak reached. This was mainly because the experiments had to be terminated when fruit decay occurred. Treatment of the fruit with ethylene (100 p.p.m.) in the pre-maturation phase led to a stimulation of respiration but this was not associated with the visible signs of ripening. As the fruit on the tree entered the ripening phase, the effect of ethylene treatment

TABLE I. Range of internal C_2H_4 concentrations at different stages of development in various fruits

Fruit	Internal conc. of C_2H_4 p.p.m.
Apple	0·2 –1000
Avocado	0·5 – 500
Banana	0·2 – 50
Lemon	0·11– 0·17
Mango	0·04– 3·0
Orange	0·13– 0·32
Peach	0·9 – 21
Pear	0·1 – 300
Pineapple	0·16– 0·40
Plum	0·14– 0·23
Squash	0·04– 2·1
Tomato	0·8 – 30

was diminished. From the behaviour of these fruits, the authors conclude that they are not of the climacteric type but there seems at least strong grounds for suggesting that a climacteric occurs during the ripening of fruit on the tree. The finding that ethylene treatment of *immature* fruit leads to a stimulation of respiration without all the associated ripening changes occurring has parallels in the pome fruit (see Hulme, 1948). The interpretation of respiration data for a composite fruit such as the pineapple, composed as it is of fruitlets at different stages of development, is difficult and caution has to be applied in the conclusions, but it does seem that the status of the pineapple requires further study.

Among other fruit classified by Biale as non-climacteric are the citrus fruits and it is clear that they behave in many ways quite differently from other fruits. Even here, there is evidence that citrus fruits can show a climacteric respiration pattern (see Trout *et al.*, 1960; Aharoni, 1968), but the significance of this in relation to ripening is uncertain. When oranges, grapefruit or lemons are picked at the stage of horticultural maturity and subsequently stored- there is a general drift downwards in respiration. However, citrus fruits will respond to exogenously applied ethylene giving an increase in respiration, increased rate of chlorophyll loss and changes in the pectins of the peel but no change in the concentrations of reducing sugars, sucrose and acidity (see Volume 2, Chapter 3). If the ethylene is removed, then the rates of respiration and chlorophyll loss fall back to their original level. The application of levels of exogenous ethylene, up to about 100 p.p.m., leads to increased responses in respiration. This is quite unlike the situation in a fruit such as the apple where ethylene is merely acting as a trigger. Clearly, in citrus fruits, exogenous ethylene does not induce the formation of endogenous ethylene-producing capacity and thus, the effects of exogenous ethylene are reversible (Biale, 1960b). However, mature oranges do produce small amounts of ethylene of the order of 0·06 μlitre/kg/hour (Burg and Burg, 1962). This small production of ethylene can be stimulated by raising the O_2-tension of the atmosphere in which the fruit is stored (Biale, 1960b) above that of air, and, under these conditions (33, 64 or 99% O_2), lemons (Biale and Young, 1947) and oranges (Biale, 1961) give a climacteric pattern of respiration with associated enhanced ethylene production and rate of degreening (see Volume 2, Chapter 3).

Aharoni (1968) has obtained a climacteric pattern of respiration associated with the onset of ethylene production, colour changes and calyx abscission during the storage of immature grapefruits and oranges at 15 or 20°C. The fruits showing this pattern were very immature, only one-tenth to one-fifth of the weight of the mature fruit. Aharoni confirmed the earlier finding that the storage of commercially mature fruit under atmospheric O_2 tensions leads to a slow downward drift in respiration. He considers that the orange and grape- fruit should be considered as climacteric fruit (as do Trout et al., 1960) and that commercially mature fruit is in fact post-climacteric. In considering the case of citrus fruit, we must return to our definition of the climacteric as a period of enhanced metabolic activity occurring at the transition from the growth phase of the fruit to its senescence. It is difficult to see how changes occurring in such immature fruit can meet this definition. Another important difference is that mature citrus fruit, post-climacteric as described by Aharoni and Trout et al., still respond to exogenous ethylene, and this behaviour clearly delineates them from the true climacteric-type fruits. Although citrus fruits respond in this way to exogenous ethylene, this does not (at least at normal O_2-tensions) induce auto-stimulation of production of the gas.

It seems likely that there is no fundamental difference in the ripening mechanism of the climacteric and so-called non-climacteric fruits. No clear metabolic differences have yet been demonstrated. It is probable that in the non-climacteric types the ripening process proceeds more slowly without sudden changes in the demand for energy which is probably responsible, in climacteric fruits, for the climacteric outburst of respiration. It does seem possible that the citrus family stands somewhat apart from the other fruits and, especially, in relation to the mechanism of their responses to ethylene. They would repay further investigation in depth.

IV. BIOCHEMICAL CHANGES DURING THE CLIMACTERIC AND THEORIES OF ITS MECHANISM

In the second half of this chapter, attention will be given to the underlying metabolic changes occurring during the climacteric and to a consideration of the mechanism of the respiration rise and its significance in relation to the other processes occurring during ripening. Kidd and West (1930) put forward the tentative hypothesis that the climacteric was due to "a change in the state of the colloidal matrix of the protoplasm" and went on to consider two types of change; one leading to "greater amounts of effective enzymes" and the other leading to "a greater effective concentration of substrate either by elution or by increase in permeability of the surface of the protoplasm". Blackman and Parija (1928), who interpreted the respiratory changes associated with the senescence of the apple in terms of a "lowering of the organization resistance of the tissue" by which metabolic control was effected through membranes holding substrate and enzyme apart, stressed the importance of the second type of change. From these early studies, two different interpretations of the climacteric phase have developed. These are (i) that the climacteric is either a phase dominated by catabolic activity in which membrane permeability increases allowing substrates access to existing enzymes and subsequently to enhanced metabolism; or (ii) a phase of metabolic reorganization based on a change in the pattern of protein synthesis in which new enzymes are synthesized to catalyse the ripening process.

In recent years, fruit physiologists have expended much energy in an attempt to distinguish between these two possibilities. Sacher (1966) gave evidence that an increase in permeability of the cells of banana pulp precedes the onset of the rise in ethylene production and respiration. His results showed that, at the climacteric peak, the tissue was "essentially 100% free space to chloride, mannitol and sucrose". These findings have been challenged by Burg (1968) who showed that banana pulp cells at the respiration peak were capable of plasmolysis and the maximum estimate of free space was below 60%. Pratt and Goeschl (1969) challenged Sacher's findings that the increase in apparent free space occurred before the climacteric rise and claimed that if ethylene data is plotted in log form, it is possible to demonstrate that ethylene production could in fact precede the permeability changes. Various other workers have challenged the theory that the climacteric is caused by changes in membrane permeability (Brady *et al.*, 1969; Hulme *et al.*, 1968). Hulme *et al.* (1968), although ruling out any general permeability changes as causative effects, did suggest that small, selective changes in permeability especially of the tonoplast, may be involved in the early processes occurring during ripening. There is evidence that permeability changes are very early responses of Cantaloupe melons to treatment with ethylene (Pratt and Goeschl, 1969; Von Abrams and Pratt, 1967).

In recent years, a considerable body of evidence has built up suggesting that the climacteric period is one of developmental change involving both selective breakdown of some cellular systems and the redevelopment of others. It is a period of reorganization and redeployment. The initial finding of Hulme (1937, 1954) that there was an increase in protein nitrogen content of apples as they entered the climacteric phase, was the first pointer in this direction. Similar increases in protein nitrogen were observed in avocados and tomatoes by Rowan *et al.* (1958), but not in the banana (Sacher, 1966). This difference probably reflects the differences in the degree of reorganization occurring in the various fruits.

During the ripening of nearly all fruit, there is a disorganization of chloroplasts (see Bain and Mercer, 1967) which in some cases precedes their reorganization into organized chromoplasts (Spurr and Harris, 1968; Harris and Spurr, 1969). In the apple, the chloroplast lamellae break down and the constituents of the membranes, both lipids and proteins, are broken down and may be used as building materials as the new enzymic pattern develops (Rhodes and Wooltorton, 1967). The degree of new protein synthesis may have been considerably under-estimated in Hulme's early work. There is evidence from tracer studies that enhanced RNA and protein synthesis is associated with the climacteric in the apple (Hulme *et al.*, 1968), the avocado (Richmond and Biale, 1966, 1967) and the pear (Frenkel *et al.*, 1968). Studies with inhibitors of RNA and protein synthesis have shown that they inhibit processes associated with ripening such as development of ethylene-producing capacity (Galliard *et al.*, 1968), the breakdown of chlorophyll and the softening of the tissue (Frenkel *et al.*, 1968; Palmer and McGlasson, 1969). It has been shown that during the period of ripening there is a shift in the pattern of proteins within the tissue (see Chapter 7; Brady *et al.*, 1969) and that, during the period of enhanced amino acid incorporation in the pear, increased labelling of specific enzyme proteins is observed (Frenkel *et al.*, 1968) and in particular malic enzyme, known to be important in the ripening of pome fruits (Hulme and Wooltorton 1962; Dilley, 1962; Rhodes *et al.*, 1968), becomes labelled. These studies strongly suggest that the synthesis of new enzymic protein is the dominant feature of the rise in metabolic activity during the climacteric, and the permeability changes, where they occur, play a secondary regulatory role.

Further details of biochemical changes during the ripening of fruits will be found in Volume 2 in chapters dealing with individual fruits.

V. FACTORS AFFECTING THE RISE IN THE RESPIRATION DURING THE CLIMACTERIC

What are the factors controlling the rise in respiration and what is its relation to the general enhancement of metabolic activity occurring at this stage in the life of the fruit? The study of factors controlling the respiratory rise has lead to a study of the biochemistry of the cell particles, the mito-chondria, which are directly concerned with respiratory activity. Various groups of workers (Pearson and Robertson, 1954; Hulme *et al.*, 1963; Lance *et al.*, 1967) have shown an increase in activity of mitochondria isolated from various fruits at different stages of the respiratory rise. This increase can be interpreted as an increase in mitochondrial number, or an increased activity of a pre-existing mitochondrial system (see Volume 2, Chapter 10). At the present time, there is no clear evidence to distinguish between these two possibilities.

An early suggestion was that, as the fruit entered the climacteric phase and the respiration rose, the mitochondrial oxidation became progressively un-coupled from phosphorylative activity. Millerd *et al.* (1953) suggested that ripe fruit contains an uncoupling factor which enables the oxidation rate to rise without concomitant phosphorylation. More recent work has shown that mitochondria have high P/O ratios (Jones *et al.*, 1964) and retain high respiratory control ratios (Wiskich *et al.*, 1964; Lance *et al.*, 1965) until after the peak of fruit respiration, and Young and Biale (1967) have largely ruled out uncoupling as a controlling factor during the climacteric rise. Another possibility was that the increase in mitochondrial activity was due to an increased synthesis or availability of a co-factor involved in the respiratory pathways. The possibility of an increase in NAD during the climacteric in apples was ruled out by Rhodes and Wooltorton (1968). An increase in ATP in the avocado (Young *et al.*, 1962) and in the Cantaloupe melon (Rowan *et al.*, 1969) has been observed during ripening and the possibility that the rise in respiration is due to an increased availability of phosphorylation acceptors has been considered. However, it does not appear that there is a simple coupling between respiratory oxidations and protein synthesis at the adenosine pyrophosphate level, since Richmond and Biale (1967) showed that inhibitors of protein synthesis, such as puromycin, had no effect on the respiration of slices of avocados prepared from fruit at the respiratory peak.

A co-factor which is currently being closely studied as a factor controlling the respiratory rise is thiamine pyrophosphate (TPP). In both the avocado (Lance *et al.*, 1967) and the tomato (Hobson, 1969) the oxidation of malate by mitochondria prepared from fruit in the pre-climacteric phase is markedly stimulated by TPP. Once the fruit enters the climacteric phase, the response of mitochondria to TPP declines. The stimulatory effect of TPP on the mito-chondria of pre-climacteric fruit is thought to be related to the accumulation of the inhibitor, oxalacetate (OAA), in the mitochondria, and the role of TPP is to stimulate pyruvate oxidation and thus provide a pathway for the dissipa-tion of the OAA. It was suggested that TPP could thus play a regulatory role during the climacteric. Hulme *et al.* (1967) demonstrated for apple mito-chondria the development of a system for the removal of OAA but they thought the system involved transamination rather than TPP. This work and that of Biale's group indicates that qualitative as well as quantitative changes are occurring within the mitochondria during the climacteric rise.

The availability of substrate to the mitochondrial system is another possible controlling factor. In this case increased leakage of organic acid and sugar substrates from the vacuole would be important but at the present no clear evidence is available on this point. There is also no positive evidence that the rise is due to an increase in mitochondrial number, but in view of the fact that it has been shown that some other changes occurring in the ripening process are dependent on protein synthesis it is a possibility to be considered (see Volume 2, Chapter 10).

There is some rise in the Respiratory Quotient (RQ) and an increase in the activity of NADP-dependent malic enzyme and pyruvate decarboxylase in apples (and pears) over the climacteric (Hulme *et al.*, 1963). It would appear, therefore, that in these fruits, decarboxylation of malate to give acetaldehyde and ethanol may contribute to the climacteric rise in CO_2 production. This point is discussed in detail in Volume 2, Chapter 10. Increased activity of malic enzyme appears at present to be peculiar to the pome fruits; whether different soluble acid-metabolizing enzymes replace the malic enzyme system in other fruits is unknown.

The final point to be considered is the role of the respiratory rise in relation to the other processes of ripening. I think many would agree with Pratt and Goeschl (1969) who state that "the respiratory pattern only reflects the integrated energy requirements of the various more or less simultaneous, but separate, processes of ripening". There is evidence that the respiratory pro-cesses can be separated from the other changes of ripening. For instance, Dostal and Leopold (1967) showed that dipping unripe tomatoes in solutions of gibberellic acid has no effect on the climacteric rise in respiration but markedly retarded the colour changes associated with ripening. Frenkel *et al.* (1968), showed that by injecting the protein synthesis inhibitor, cyclohexi-mide, into the locule of unripe pears, many ripening phenomena such as colour and texture changes and ethylene production, were inhibited during the subsequent storage of the fruit but that the rise in respiration was not inhibited; it was, in fact, markedly stimulated. In this case, care must be taken in the interpretation of the respiration data in view of the known uncoupling properties of high concentrations of cycloheximide (Ellis and MacDonald, 1969). In no case has it been possible to promote the ripening changes in fruit having a clearly defined climacteric without also inducing the onset of the respiratory rise. Vendrell (1969) claims that senescence in slices of banana fruit may be "reversed" by treatment with 2:4D and IAA. His results could, however, be interpreted in terms of a delay in the development of the climacteric by an "artificial" return to a more "juvenile" balance between auxin and ethylene. This is not reversing senescence (in my view senescence in fruits does not commence until the onset of the climacteric), but it does provide indirect evidence (as yet there are no direct measurements available of auxin-ethylene balance in maturing fruits) that the onset of senescence, and the sensitivity of a fruit to stimulation into senescence by ethylene, is probably dependent on the auxin-ethylene balance as appears to be the case with other plant phenomena such as leaf abscission (see review by Mapson and Hulme, 1970). The approach of attempting to inhibit selectively parts of the ripening system may prove a very useful tool in the study of the interrelation of the individual processes of ripening.

VI. CONCLUSION

The significance of the climacteric phase of enhanced metabolic activity in the early stage of ripening of most fruits is that it marks the transition from the growth and maturation phases in the life of the fruit to the onset of senescence. It is the "beginning of the end" as Biale (1960a) put it. It is a period of enhanced ethylene, RNA and protein synthesis, of increased respiratory activity and of the selective breakdown of certain cellular structures and the reorganization of new ones. It is the period in which the fruit actively prepares for its senescence. It is this fact of the fruit actively preparing for senescence that fascinates fruit biochemists and it is the solution of this problem which could lead to a far better understanding of the senescence of plant organs in general. It is a historical coincidence that patterns of respiratory activity should play such an important part in our thinking on fruit ripening and in view of our present knowledge, the increase in respiration should be considered simply as one of many changes underlying the reorganization of metabolism which eventually leads to ripening. It is, however, still an interesting change and one which should warrant further study in the future.

REFERENCES

Aharoni, Y. (1968). *Pl. Physiol., Lancaster* **43**, 99.

Bain, J. M. and Mercer, F. V. (1964). *Aust. J. biol. Chem.* **17**, 78.

Biale, J. B. (1946). *Am. J. Bot.* **33**, 363.

Biale, J. B. (1950). *A. Rev. Pl. Physiol.* **1**, 183.

Biale, J. B. (1960a). "Handbuch der Pflanzenphysiologie" (W. Ruhland, ed.), **12**, (2), 536. Springer Verlag, Berlin.

Biale, J. B. (1960b). *Adv. Fd Res.* **10**, 293.

Biale, J. B. (1961). *In* "The Orange, its Physiology and Biochemistry" (W. B. Sinclair, ed.), p. 96. University of California Press, Berkeley.

Biale, J. B. and Young, R. E. (1947). *Am. J. Bot.* **34**, 301.

Blackman, F. F. and Parija, P. (1928). *Proc. Roy. Soc.* **B103**, 412.

Bose, A. N., Lodh, S. B. and De, S. (1960). *Proc. 1st Int. Cong. Fd Sci. and Technol.* **2**, 117.

Brady, C. J., O'Connell, P. B. H. and Palmer, J. K. (1969). *Phytochem.* In press.

Burg, S. P. (1968) *Pl. Physiol., Lancaster* **43**, 1503.

Burg, S. P. and Burg, E. A. (1962). *Pl. Physiol., Lancaster* **37**, 179.

Clendenning, K. A. (1941). *Can. J. Res. C.* **20**, 197.

Dilley, D. R. (1962). *Nature, Lond.* **196**, 387.

Dostal, H. C. and Leopold, A. C. (1967). *Science, N.Y.* **158**, 1579.

Dull, G. G., Young, R. E. and Biale, J. B. (1967). *Physiologia Pl.* **20**, 1059.

Ellis, R. J. and Macdonald, I. R. (1969). *Nature, Lond.* **222**, 791.

Frenkel, C., Klein, I. and Dilley, D. R. (1968). *Pl. Physiol., Lancaster* **43**, 1146.

Galliard, T., Rhodes, M. J. C., Wooltorton, L. S. C. and Hulme, A. C. (1968). *Phytochem.* **7**, 1465.

Gerber, C. (1897). *Annls. Sci. nat. Bot. Sec* VIII, t.IV, p. 1.

Gustafson, F. G. (1929). *Pl. Physiol., Lancaster* **4**, 349.

Harris, W. M. and Spurr, A. R. (1969). *Am. J. Bot.* **56**, 380.

Hobson, G. E. (1969). *Qualitas Pl. Mater. veg.* In press.

Hulme, A. C. (1937). *Rep. Fd Invest. Bd. for 1936*, p. 128.

Hulme, A. C. (1948). *Biochem. J.* **43**, 343.

Hulme, A. C. (1954). *J. exp. Bot.* **5**, 159.

Hulme, A. C. (1958). *Adv. Fd Res.* **8**, 297.

Hulme, A. C. and Wooltorton, L. S. C. (1962). *Nature, Lond.* **196**, 388.

Hulme, A. C., Jones, J. D. and Wooltorton, L. S. C. (1963). *Proc. Roy. Soc.* **B158**, 514.

Hulme, A. C., Rhodes, M. J. C. and Wooltorton, L. S. C. (1967). *Phytochem.* **6**, 1343.

Hulme, A. C., Rhodes, M. J. C., Galliard, T. and Wooltorton, L. S. C. (1968). *Pl. Physiol., Lancaster* **43**, 1154.

Jones, J. D., Wooltorton, L. S. C. and Hulme, A. C. (1964). *Phytochem.* **3**, 201.

Kidd, F. and West, C. (1922). *Rep. Fd Invest. Bd. for 1921*, 14.

Kidd, F. and West, C. (1923). *Rep. Fd Invest. Bd. for 1922*, 30.

Kidd, F. and West, C. (1924). *Rep. Fd Invest. Bd. for 1923*, 27.

Kidd, F. and West, C. (1930). *Proc. Roy. Soc.* **B106**, 93.

Kidd, F. and West, C. (1945). *Pl. Physiol., Lancaster*, **20**, 467.

Kidd, F., West, C., Griffiths, D. G. and Potter, N. A. (1951). *J. hort. Sci.* **26**, 169.

Lance, C., Hobson, G., E., Young, R. E. and Biale, J. B. (1965). *Pl. Physiol., Lancaster* **40**, 1116.

Lance, C., Hobson, G. E., Young, R. E. and Biale, J. B. (1967). *Pl. Physiol., Lancaster* **42**, 471.

Leonard, E. R. (1941). *Ann. Bot.* **5**, 89.

Lyons, J. M., McGlasson, W. B. and Pratt, H. K. (1962). *Pl. Physiol., Lancaster* **37**, 31.

McGlasson, W. B. and Pratt, H. K. (1964). *Pl. Physiol., Lancaster* **37**, 31.

Mapson, L. W. and Hulme, A. C. (1970). *Adv. Phytochem.* **2**. In press.

Millerd, A., Bonner, J. and Biale, J. B. (1953). *Pl. Physiol., Lancaster* **28**, 521.

Palmer, J. K. and McGlasson, W. B. (1969). *Aust. J. biol. Sci.* **22**, 87.

Pearson, J. A. and Robertson, R. N. (1954). *Aust. J. biol. Sci.* **7**, 1.

Pratt, H. K. and Goeschl, J. D. (1969). *A. Rev. Pl. Physiol.* **20**, 541.

Richmond, A. and Biale, J. B. (1966). *Archs Biochem. Biophys.* **115**, 211.

Richmond, A. and Biale, J. B. (1967). *Biochim. biophys. Acta* **138**, 625.

Rhodes, M. J. C. and Wooltorton, L. S. C. (1967). *Phytochem.* **6**, 1.

Rhodes, M. J. C. and Wooltorton, L. S. C. (1968). *Phytochem.* **7**, 337.

Rhodes, M. J. C., Wooltorton, L. S. C., Galliard, T. and Hulme, A. C. (1968). *Phytochem.* **7**, 1439.

Rowan, K. S., McGlasson, W. B. and Pratt, H. K. (1969). *J. exp. Bot.* **20**, 145.

Rowan, K. S., Pratt, H. K. and Robertson, R. N. (1958). *Aust. J. biol. Sci.* **11**, 329.

Sacher, J. A. (1966). *Pl. Physiol., Lancaster* **41**, 701.

Spencer, M. (1966). "Plant Biochemistry", (J. Bonner and J. Varner, eds), Chapter 30, p. 822. Academic Press, New York and London.

Spurr, A. R. and Harris, W. M. (1968). *Am. J. Bot.* **55**, 1210.

Thomas, M. (1956). "Plant Physiology", 4th Edn. pp. 291. J. and A. Churchill, London.

Trout, S. A., Huelin, F. E. and Tindall, G. C. (1960). C.S.I.R.O. (Aust.) Div. Fd Pres. Trans. Tech. Paper No. 14.

Vendrell, M. (1969). *Aust. J. biol. Sci.* **22**, 601.

Von Abrams, G. J. and Pratt, H. K. (1967). *Pl. Physiol., Lancaster* **42**, 299.

Wiskich, J. T., Young, R. E. and Biale, J. B. (1964). *Pl. Physiol., Lancaster* **39**, 312.

Wardlaw, C. W. and Leonard, E. R. (1935). *Res. St. Imp. Coll. Trop. Agric.*, Mem. No. 1.

Wyman, H. and Palmer, J. K. (1964). *Pl. Physiol., Lancaster,* **39**, 630.

Young, R. E. and Biale, J. B. (1967). *Pl. Physiol., Lancaster,* **42**, 1357.

Young, R. E., Popper, C. S. and Biale, J. B. (1962). *Pl. Physiol., Lancaster* **37**, (Suppl.) XXXIII.

Part IIIb

Physiological Disorders of Fruits

Chapter 18

Physiological Disorders of Fruit After Harvesting

East Malling Research Station, Maidstone, England

I. INTRODUCTION

When a fruit is harvested it is at maturity or capable of maturing. Thereafter, although in some cases further ripening may take place, the main process is that of senescence. It is the purpose of efficient transport and storage to control the ripening of the fruit and if possible to delay senescence.

Senescence is, nevertheless, a normal physiological process and only when abnormal non-parasitic manifestations appear do we identify physiological disorders. These may be present as abnormal appearance (external or internal), as abnormal flavour, or even as failure to ripen. Physiological disorders may be of two types—those which can be attributed to pre-harvest growing conditions, and those which owe their origin to imposed external conditions of transport and storage after the fruit has been picked.

Because of economic factors, much more attention has been paid to disorders of the important fruits of commerce than to disorders of lesser fruits, however physiologically interesting these abnormalities may be. Moreover much more effort has been directed towards minimizing commercial losses by the manipulation of storage and transport conditions than towards investigating the biochemical significance of abnormal metabolic changes.

It is unfortunate that the classification of disorders and the terminology employed is anything but uniform. Whereas the main classes of disorder can often be identified by experience, the numerous deviations, varietal differences and seasonal variations cause endless confusion and argument which would perhaps be unnecessary if more were known of the exact metabolic changes, and if the disordered tissues could be submitted to objective tests.

Physiological disorders of apples have been comprehensively classified and illustrated by Carne (1948). Another illustrated guide, which also includes disorders of pears is included in a booklet on storage by Padfield (1954). Citrus also exhibit many physiological disorders. These are described and illustrated by Fawcett and Klotz (1948) in a chapter which includes all citrus diseases. A bulletin by Rose *et al.* (1937) covers citrus and other sub-tropical fruits, and further United States Department of Agriculture bulletins deal with most of the commercially important groups.

In the following review it is proposed to consider some specific classes of physiological disorders rather than to seek out small deviations, and to concentrate on some of the major principles which have been established over the years. The illustrations will be concerned mainly with apples, partly because of the long history of storage technology on this major crop, and partly because of the author's specific interest.

After the fruit has been picked, attempts may be made to control its ripening by adjustment of temperature or by adjustment of the concentration of the gases in the surrounding atmosphere—usually carbon dioxide and oxygen. These represent the two main forms of fruit storage, "refrigeration in air" and "controlled atmosphere storage"; this latter is usually combined with some degree of refrigeration. Environmental control may bring its own problems in abnormal physiology, and some of these are considered below.

II. EFFECTS OF TEMPERATURE

It can be envisaged that during the normal ripening and senescence of a fruit a great many biochemical reactions associated with respiration are taking place simultaneously; for example, softening of cell walls, changes in cell permeability, development of flavour, etc. Some of these reactions are essential, some incidental and by-products of the mainstream reactions. All may have slightly different temperature coefficients. If the fruit ripens in its natural environment the chances are that whatever the fluctuations in external temperature, with consequent differential slowing-down or speeding-up of component reactions, the fruit will accept the resulting imbalances, and though the metabolism will alter there will be no obvious physiological stress, and the fruit will apparently mature and senesce normally.

If, however, the fruit is exposed to extremes of temperature (either high or low) then it can be envisaged that some reactions may be accelerated or retarded to excess, and the result will be that the general ripening pattern will be permanently disturbed—perhaps by the under-production of certain essentials, or by the over-production of substances which may be toxic. Then physiological disorders obvious to sight or taste might ensue.

This simplified picture merely makes the point that there is a safe range of temperatures for a particular fruit; exposure to temperatures outside this range for sufficient length of time will cause injury.

The group of disorders known as low temperature injuries occur at temperatures above the freezing point of the tissues and do not involve the formation of ice. Some fruits, such as pears, do not normally suffer from these disorders, but for most fruits there is a threshold temperature below which the fruit might be damaged, if subjected to prolonged exposure. The lower temperature limit at which fruits behave normally varies, as one might expect, with the region of origin. For instance, temperate fruits such as apples may tolerate from 0 to 4°C (there is considerable varietal variation) whilst the tropical banana behaves abnormally at temperatures below about 12°C. Sub-tropical fruits such as citrus, avocados and pineapples tend to have critical temperatures of down to 8°C.

Fidler (1968) has recently reviewed the subject of low temperature injury in fruits (and vegetables). He describes the types of injury (internal browning in apples, skin spotting in citrus, damage to vascular bundles in avocados, etc.) and then considers the direct effect of temperature and the interaction of other external factors, and finally the mechanism of low temperature injury.

It is not only low temperature as such which determines the extent of low temperature injury. The next most obvious factor is time of exposure. Recovery is known to take place from short exposures to potentially damaging temperatures, and it is probable that a minimum period of continuous exposure is required to cause injury. This would explain why interrupted exposures may be effective in reducing final damage—the metabolism recovers its normal pattern during the warming period. This interdependence of time and temperature has been elaborated on by Tomkins (1966) in a paper which considered the possible relationships between storage life and the controlled variables of temperature and gas concentrations; it explained why maximum storage life must vary with the chosen conditions of storage. Ulrich (1966) has also considered in detail the duration of fruit life in relation to temperature, with examples drawn from storage trials with apples, pears, oranges and other horticultural produce.

It was shown in storage experiments in South Africa that breakdown in

Japanese plums (held for relatively short periods) was greatest at about 3°C and was less at both higher and lower temperatures. Severe pitting of Marsh seedless grapefruit was also found to be negligible at 0 and 10°C and greatest at intermediate temperatures. Woolliness of peaches, another low temperature disorder, showed the same trend. These and similar studies led Van der Plank and Davies (1937) to make probably the most intensive analysis yet undertaken of progress curves of low temperature injury. To explain their results for certain fruits they postulated an "equilibrium factor" and a "kinetic factor". The equilibrium factor depends on the temperature; the kinetic factor depends on the fact that the actual chemical changes involved in low temperature injury are subject to retardation at the lower temperatures. The two factors are therefore in opposition. The temperature at which maximum injury occurs is modified by other factors such as the length of time of storage.

To account for progress curves of low temperature injury in Marsh seedless grapefruit stored for longer periods, Van der Plank and Davies postulated "primary susceptibility" and "secondary susceptibility". A characteristic of primary susceptibility is that certain fruits in the population remain undamaged however long the period of storage. The proportion remaining undamaged is lower as the temperature decreases. Secondary susceptibility is the result of changes occurring in the fruit after cooling. During further ripening the metabolic state may change towards a condition more sensitive to low temperatures. The observed effect on storage is that the proportion of damaged fruit will continue to rise with time. In bananas, for instance, all the fruits are eventually affected if kept for a sufficient length of time. Various fruits may show one or both types of susceptibility.

In apples, low temperature injury usually appears as a browning in the cortical region, with streaks of darker brown in the vascular tissues. The area of the cut surface which is seen to be discoloured varies from the barely visible to 100%, but the flesh may be quite badly affected before the injury appears as a darkening of the skin; in other words, the apples may appear to be sound unless they are cut for examination. The boundary between affected and sound tissue is diffuse, and the intensity of the browning may vary from season to season as though the chemical degradation is variable in degree. The tissue remains moist and does not dry out as in some other forms of flesh breakdown.

There are other forms of injury in apples attributed to low temperature, such as ribbon scald in the variety Ellison's Orange, and Jonathan scald.

Not much fundamental work has been done on the nature of low temperature injury, partly because recommended temperatures of storage are set higher than the danger level. Nevertheless, if more information was available it is possible that storage temperatures could be lowered slightly, with a consequent increase in storage life.

One fundamental biochemical study was made by Hulme et al. (1964). On the basis of previous work on keto-acid metabolism they investigated changes in pyruvic, oxaloacetic and α-oxoglutaric acids in Cox's Orange Pippin stored under conditions chosen to cause low temperature breakdown. They found that "low temperature breakdown is preceded by an accumulation of oxalo-acetic acid, and that both the oxaloacetic acid content and the subsequent intensity of low temperature breakdown can be considerably reduced by a short interim period at a higher temperature during the cold storage of the fruit". They pointed out that oxidation of succinate is inhibited by oxalo-acetic acid in small amounts, and that this would constitute an interruption in the Krebs cycle. Support for this suggestion is given by the fact that inhibi-tion of succinic dehydrogenase should cause α-oxoglutarate to accumulate, and that this does in fact happen in unwarmed fruit.

Just as abnormally low temperatures produce damaging effects so do abnormally high temperatures. For instance, bananas fail to ripen above 30°C; they remain green and the pulp becomes soft, and they are said to be "boiled" (Gane, 1936). Some varieties of plums show abnormal ripening at temperatures above 32°C (Uota, 1955). In avocados at 30°C, as at 5°C, the fruit does not ripen and the tissue darkens (Biale and Young, 1962). It is known that many fruits cease to produce ethylene between 35 and 40°C, and if ethylene is in fact a universal ripening hormone then its inhibition may be significant. However, it is interesting to note that normal temperatures in the tropics are often higher than those required to repress ethylene production. The fruit normally recovers from these occasional exposures to very high temperatures on the plant.

As with avocados, there is a superficial similarity between effects of low and high temperatures on apples. If portions of apple are heated to about 55°C for a few minutes and then exposed to air, enzymic browning occurs, and the location and appearance give the effect of low temperature breakdown. Presumably the enzymes have not been inactivated as they would be at a higher temperature, but the cell permeability seems to have been reduced, allowing the cell contents to intermix (as happens at a cut surface). It is possible that at low temperatures the permeability is again reduced without inactivation of en-zymes, and the characteristic browning of low temperature breakdown is seen.

Fidler (1968) has also speculated that the primary disturbance in low temperature injury might be physical rather than chemical—possibly an effect on viscosity or membrane permeability.

III. EFFECTS OF CONTROLLED ATMOSPHERES

A. General

The so-called "product generated" atmospheres of controlled atmosphere stores are the result of allowing accumulation of the carbon dioxide evolved during the respiration of the fruit. This may be permitted to stabilize at some desired level, or it may be removed by absorption with the object of lowering the oxygen level. Techniques in which "externally generated" atmospheres are injected into stores are gaining popularity and have advantages in some conditions and for certain applications.

Similar basic considerations to those governing the effects of temperature also apply to controlled atmospheres. In a natural environment the normal metabolism accepts fluctuations in "mass action" of the atmospheric components in the intercellular spaces. But when an artificial atmosphere is imposed the metabolic reactions may be forced into a state of imbalance and permanent injury may ensue.

B. Effects of Carbon Dioxide

The management of controlled atmosphere stores is now well understood, but in the early days of long-distance transport of fruit by sea the possible toxic effects of carbon dioxide were not realized. Damage to shipments of Australian apples to the United Kingdom from about 1911 onwards was not finally identified as carbon dioxide injury until the early twenties (Kidd and West, 1923), and a court ruling attributing the disorder to "inherent vice" in the fruit further delayed control measures. The fact that the injury was produced in shipments indicates that this injury could be produced by conditions created in an insufficiently ventilated ship's hold in the period of shipment (3 to 6 weeks).

The type of injury in shipments of apples, now referred to as brown heart, is an internal injury characterized by pockets of discoloured flesh in the cortex of the fruit which are moist and brown initially, but become cavities later in storage because of the collapse and drying out of the tissue. The areas may be quite small or may extend to almost the whole of the flesh, but do not usually extend to the peel and outer 2 or 3 mm of tissue. The apple may therefore appear sound to the eye, but has a characteristic spongy feel. The condition is non-progressive in that the damage does not extend further after the conditions of high carbon dioxide have been removed. A characteristic of the cut surface is that the boundaries between damaged and sound tissue are quite sharp, and in this respect the appearance is different from that of low temperature and senescent breakdown.

Pears are also subject to carbon dioxide injury, especially if picked a little late or allowed to ripen between picking and storage, and since pears will tolerate low temperatures (down to $-1 \cdot 7°C$ for some varieties) there is now a tendency to store pears in air at low temperature rather than risk carbon dioxide damage. However, since the recommended temperatures in air are close to the freezing point of the tissue, this method demands accurate control of temperature.

The use of enriched carbon dioxide atmospheres for the storage of citrus fruits has not met with much success (Miller, 1946, 1958). Skin damage or off-flavours were a recurring problem. For various reasons the controlled atmosphere storage of certain other prominent fruits (for example, bananas, apricots, peaches) has not been of commercial significance. Therefore, although carbon dioxide damage has been recorded in crops other than pome fruits, the effects have been something of a curiosity and little of fundamental importance has emerged.

Some fruits are not very susceptible to carbon dioxide injury, and high concentrations (15–30%) of carbon dioxide have been advocated for the short-term holding of certain fruits, for example, blackberry, blackcurrant, cherries, grapes, plums, raspberries, strawberries. The use of carbon dioxide in the transport and storage of fruits has been comprehensively reviewed by Smith (1963).

Under carbon dioxide injury, mention should also be made of core flush of apples, which in Cox's Orange Pippin apples grown in the United Kingdom is probably second only to fungal rotting as the principal source of commercial wastage. Core flush (referred to as brown core in some parts of the world) is a reddish-brown coloration originating in, and usually being confined to, the core region. In cross-section it is seen in the angles of the core locules. Core flush is believed to be partly senescent (because it only occurs late in storage) and partly a carbon dioxide injury. It may also be accentuated at low temperatures. Some evidence that core flush is a carbon dioxide injury has been given by Tomkins (1959) who found that core flush in Cox's Orange Pippin and Laxton's Fortune apples was directly related to the percentage of carbon dioxide in the storage atmosphere. Moreover, in seasons in which core flush occurs in 5% carbon dioxide with 3% oxygen it is considerably reduced in 0% carbon dioxide and 3% oxygen (Fidler and North, 1961).

Although core flush is often seen in small, dense apples which one usually associates with freedom from physiological disorders, the available evidence suggests that fruit size as such is not a factor influencing core flush. In a trial with about 800 Cox's Orange Pippin apples in 1966 (unpublished) which had been stored experimentally for six months in about 10% carbon dioxide, and which were size graded before examination, there was an equal amount of core flush in each size grade. The fruit was severely affected, and it is possible that a different result may have been obtained if the apples had been examined earlier; nevertheless it seems that core flush may differ from brown heart in the effect of fruit size, because all the evidence points to brown heart being more severe in large apples than in small (Smock and Van Doren, 1941).

There are conflicting reports about the effect of other factors on the extent of carbon dioxide injury. Here again it is necessary to interpret with caution storage results from data taken at pre-selected times, temperatures and concentrations. Detailed progress curves are really necessary before complete comparisons can be made. This theme has been amplified by Tomkins (1966), but the practical difficulties of doing the required number of trials are often great.

As regards temperature, Kidd and West (1923); Kidd *et al.* (1927), maintained that apples are more susceptible to brown heart at lower than at higher temperatures, and attributed this to the higher concentration of carbon dioxide in the fruit at the lower temperature because of the increased solubility. However, this observation has not always been confirmed and there are many reports of greater damage at higher temperatures than at lower. Blanpied and Smock (1961) found contradictory results in two successive seasons with McIntosh apples.

Results on the effect of oxygen concentration are also conflicting. Rasmussen (1961), storing Cox's Orange Pippin in up to 6% CO_2, recorded more damage in the presence of 9% O_2 than 3% O_2. Eaves *et al.* (1964), storing McIntosh at 5% CO_2, had more damage in oxygen concentrations above 2·5% than at the lower level. On the other hand, for pears, Hansen and Mellenthin (1962) recorded more injury at lower oxygen levels than at high. They used several carbon dioxide to oxygen ratios.

It is possible to demonstrate chemical changes associated with brown heart, but are any of them causally related? Thomas (1929) showed that alcohol and acetaldehyde accumulated in tissue damaged by carbon dioxide and concluded that these had proved toxic to the fruit. Bogdanski (1960) associated brown heart with the disappearance of ascorbic acid, and claimed that this was confirmed by the fact that the lowest levels of ascorbic acid in the fruit occur in those regions which first show signs of carbon dioxide injury. Hulme (1956) showed that carbon dioxide injury is accompanied by an increase in succinic acid in apple tissue, and suggested that this was toxic in the concentrations observed.

Much work has been done on skin porosity (of apples in particular) with a view to seeking an explanation of some physiological disorders in terms of gaseous exchange. The inability of internal carbon dioxide to escape, for instance, is an attractive theory for carbon dioxide damage. (The argument can also be used the other way to suggest that restriction of gaseous exchange gives "controlled atmosphere" conditions in the fruit—an elevated carbon dioxide level and hence longer storage life.) However, if the porosity of a population of apples from a single tree is examined it will be found that the large apples afford ready gas exchange whilst the small apples offer great resistance; yet large apples are commonly reported to be more prone to injury. Moreover, if a population of apples of the same variety, but from another tree, or from another orchard is examined, the same range of porosity may be found but the fruit may be quite different in its response to storage atmospheres. Therefore any explanation in terms of gaseous exchange alone would seem to be inadequate.

C. Effects of Oxygen

A certain minimum concentration of oxygen is necessary to support normal respiration during senescence. Below this level anaerobic respiration takes place and alcohol is produced. This can cause off-flavours and damage if the condition is prolonged (and if the alcohol reaches about 100 mg/100 g), but small amounts of alcohol disappear with aeration, and metabolism then proceeds normally (Fidler and North, 1961).

It is now common practice to store certain varieties of apples in 2·5% oxygen with as little as 1% carbon dioxide where core flush may be a problem. The control of the lower limit of oxygen is critical and requires accurate instrumentation (Fidler, 1965).

Fruits appear to tolerate oxygen concentrations of less than 5%, but the exact limit for normal ripening and senescence is variable. Lemons, for instance, are damaged in 3% oxygen (Rygg and Wells, 1962). It is reported that Cortland and McIntosh apples held at oxygen concentrations as low as 1% develop brown depressions in the skin, similar in appearance to soft scald (Smock and Neubert, 1950). The use of low oxygen tensions has been popular on the laboratory scale, but a distinction should perhaps be drawn between experimental effects and physiological disorders of commercial significance.

D. Effects of Humidity

The amount of water vapour in the immediate vicinity of the fruit has a considerable effect on its physiological behaviour. Atmospheres of near-saturation result in abnormal skin splitting (in apples and in plums, for instance), whereas storage in an atmosphere which is too dry ultimately leads to disfiguring shrivel. Between these extremes the humidity still exercises a modifying effect on the severity of disorders, especially flesh breakdowns in apples (Tiller, 1929) and skin pitting in citrus. Martin et al. (1967) have described storage experiments with Jonathan apples held at 0·6°C which showed a higher incidence of flesh breakdown associated with lower weight loss. Fidler (1968) found that low temperature breakdown in Cox's Orange Pippin apples held at 0°C for four months was much more severe in a sample which had lost 1·4% in weight than in another sample which had lost more than 3% in weight (see also Scott et al., 1964). It has recently been shown that water loss in the early stages of storage has a bigger effect than later evaporation on the severity of senescent breakdown in Cox's Orange Pippin apples stored at 3·3°C (Wilkinson, 1968a). It is suggested that since the permeability of the fruit skin to gaseous exchange decreases rapidly when evaporation takes place, the greater effect of early water loss may be a physical effect resulting in restricted ventilation of the intercellular spaces.

The incidence of soft scald of Ellison's Orange Pippin (which is also a low temperature injury) is affected by the extent of loss of water. This has been shown by Tomkins (1968) who did comparative trials in which fruit was stored in ventilated containers and in open trays.

In a variable temperature experiment, Van der Plank and Davies (1937) found that Marsh seedless grapefruit wrapped in waxed paper would withstand a temperature 3°C lower than the controls before showing low temperature injury, and they attributed this to the restriction of water loss.

Apples stored in atmospheres of very high humidity frequently split during ripening. This is sometimes referred to as "high humidity breakdown". A similar phenomenon occurs with plums kept under conditions of low evaporation. As an explanation of this, Tomkins, R. G. (private communication) suggested that the cells tend to round off as the cell adhesion becomes less, with a consequent increase in fruit volume. This follows because the cell volume would remain the same (they are full of incompressible fluid), but the cells would tend to occupy more space (since packed spheres are the least economical of total space). This explanation was supported by some experiments with apples which were kept in very high humidity conditions, and which were found to increase in volume by about 3% over a period of four weeks, without any corresponding change of weight (Wilkinson, 1965).

It would be interesting to determine what effect a change of cell shape would have on resistance to gas flow in the intercellular spaces, because the cells may not act as discrete spheres but may agglomerate and restrict ventilation, especially if the cell walls swell during softening.

Reverting to the reduction in physiological disorder which accompanies slight desiccation, it is difficult to see what chemical effect could be produced by a small water loss of the order of 1–2%. There will be a small concentration of constituents, but this is unlikely to have much effect. Little is known about how sharp is the border line between normal water relations and conditions of stress. It is possible that phenomena depending upon cell permeability might be affected, and conceivable that a slight loss of water might introduce a sluggishness into the metabolism. The respiration of apples in a dry atmosphere (as measured by oxygen absorption by the whole fruit) is lower than that of apples in wet atmospheres, but this may be another physical effect on skin porosity, resulting in restricted ventilation of the intercellular spaces.

IV. PRE-HARVEST FACTORS

A. General

In all biological systems the behaviour during maturity and senescence is to some extent conditioned by the environment during formation and development, and by the continuous history of nutrition. Many factors are involved, some controllable and some not. The complexity and variability of the biological end-product are some of the reasons for the great volume of contradictory information contained in reports of storage trials. This is not to say that the pre-harvest conditions are of overriding importance in determining storage behaviour, or that their effects will be greater than the effects of adjustment of storage environment. They do, however, modify behaviour to a greater or lesser extent, and the degree of biological variability of the experimental material, especially between seasons, is often overlooked, especially in short-term experiments. To be convincing, and to allow for the variation in material, storage experiments on the effects of growing conditions usually need to be on a scale involving large numbers of fruit spread over several seasons. Because of considerations of crop size, and even of expense, this is not always possible, but results from samples of small size can be misleading and fail entirely to allow for the variability in experimental material.

Of the pre-harvest factors over which a fruit grower has some measure of control the following may be mentioned: type of cultivation, irrigation, application of fertilizers, spray programme (nutrient, hormone and protective) and the date of harvest. He has little control, if any, over basic soil type and weather conditions, except that he makes the initial choice of site.

There are not many post-harvest physiological disorders which are directly attributable to pre-harvest factors, but notable among them are two important commercial disorders—bitter pit of apples (which will be described later), and endoxerosis (or internal decline) of lemons which was extensively studied by Bartholomew (1937). Both disorders appear to be associated with pre-harvest water stress.

B. Cultural Practice

Over the years, many attempts have been made to correlate storage behaviour with growing conditions for most commercially important fruits. Effects of soil, rootstocks, age, spacing, soil management, pruning and spraying have all come in for attention. For apples, Bunemann (1964) has made a comprehensive review of the literature regarding nutrition and its effect on quality.

There are many contradictory reports, and the same fruits do not necessarily react in the same way in different parts of the world. In general it can be said that of the major nutrients, the application of nitrogen (contrary to earlier opinion) has little direct effect on physiological disorders of apples— where there is an effect it is usually the result of increased growth and vigour, and effects on fruit size. Potassium is associated with either increased or decreased wastage depending upon the disorder being considered. For instance, it has been shown that, in certain circumstances, extra applied potash will reduce the severity of low temperature breakdown (Montgomery and Wilkinson, 1962), but it has frequently been found to aggravate bitter pit. Phosphorus appears to be generally beneficial if it can be utilized.

Cultural trials do not usually throw any light on the mechanism of physiological disorders.

C. Relationship to Mineral Composition

The partial control of bitter pit in apples is probably the outstanding example of the way in which orchard factors have been adjusted, in the past few years, to modify the incidence of a physiological storage disorder. It also serves as an example of the increasing awareness of the importance of the mineral composition of the fruit in influencing storage behaviour. On the other hand, bitter pit perhaps lent itself better than most to orchard control measures because it is essentially an orchard condition rather than one resulting from subsequent storage treatment.

Bitter pit is a condition in which the flesh of the apple is disfigured by small brown dry areas, perhaps a few millimetres in diameter. These "pits" are usually located in the outer flesh of the apple just below the skin, and may not be observed until the apple is cut or peeled. In severe cases the pits can be seen in the intact apple as dark depressions in the skin, and these are usually more prominent at the calyx end of the fruit. In some cases the trouble is limited to only one or two pits, but severely affected apples may be mottled throughout the tissue. Microscopic examination shows that the abnormal cells are collapsed and dead, but the cell walls are not different from those of healthy cells, and, despite their appearance, are not corky. The collapsed cells still contain starch grains, although late in storage starch has disappeared from the rest of the apple.

When Barker (1934) reviewed over 200 papers on the subject the only consistent features were that early picked fruit was more likely to develop bitter pit, and that fruit of large average size was also more susceptible. Bitter pit also seemed to be associated with certain weather conditions, notably periods of abnormal drought. The first advance in control came in Novia Scotia when De Long (1936) claimed that fruit affected by bitter pit contained less calcium than fruit not affected. This led to various attempts to increase the calcium level, but it was not until 20 years later that Garman and Mathis (1956) reported any success. This was in Connecticut with the variety Baldwin, and a programme of calcium nitrate sprays reduced the percentage of bitter pit from about 45% to 10%. This success was quickly followed by reports of partial control from various parts of the world.

Association of the disorder with chemical composition came slowly, partly because the average calcium level in the fruit is extremely low compared with that in leaves and stems, and accurate analysis and adequate sampling were necessary to establish the small differences involved. Moreover, the analysis of fruit tissue usually involves large initial samples to reduce errors, and methods of ashing and analysis have to be developed which take account of the fact that ratios of constituents in fruits are often different from those in other plant tissues and different interference problems arise.

It was shown that calcium was in the lowest concentration just below the skin, and at the nose end of the fruit—the two regions in which bitter pit is most commonly seen. The calcium concentration is also lower in large apples than in small, and since much of the calcium is assumed to be associated as pectate in the cell walls it has been suggested that the lower concentration in large apples is merely an indication of large cells, and hence of less cell wall material per unit weight.

In fact, calcium appears to be in near-critical amounts in apple fruits. An unexpected result of world-wide calcium spray trials was the demonstration that calcium sprays also reduce the amount of lenticel breakdown and senescent breakdown in stored apples. Lenticel breakdown, as the name suggests, is a flesh breakdown centred on the lenticels and giving rise to irregular brown sunken areas of 3 or 4 mm in diameter. The inability to isolate a fungus is taken to indicate that the disorder is physiological; it only occurs spasmodically, and little is known about it. Senescent breakdown is a flesh breakdown associated with over-ripeness and is variable in appearance. Typically, in Cox's Orange Pippin, it appears first as a diffuse browning of the skin associated with a small amount of discoloration of the tissue immediately below the skin, which spreads inwards with time. There may be mealiness, and the disorder frequently appears first at the nose end of the fruit. As mentioned above, this is now known to be a low calcium area. Senescent breakdown is progressive in that (unlike brown heart, for instance) it will develop further after the fruit has been removed from store. It is not uncommon to find individual apples of Cox's Orange Pippin exhibiting all three disorders (bitter pit, lenticel breakdown and senescent breakdown), and when this occurs the apple is found on analysis to be very low in calcium; the inference is that the crop as a whole is deficient in calcium.

Another disorder which appears to be linked with calcium is "water core breakdown". Sharples (1967) has given figures for calcium in fruits of Red

Miller and Miller's Seedling which indicate that those apples affected by breakdown had the lowest content of calcium.

The exact role of calcium, like that of all minerals, is still obscure, but it seems probable that it is of importance in the cell wall development, and its poverty may lead to a skeletal weakness. Doesburg (1957) found that the fraction of calcium which was insoluble in alcohol increased at the time that the pectin was becoming more soluble; that is, late in storage. He suggested that some of the calcium released during the breakdown of the cell walls was being precipitated by organic acids and that the process was controlled by the general pH change during ripening. The importance of calcium has led to renewed efforts to study the changes in the ratio of soluble to insoluble calcium during fruit development and senescence.

The movement of total calcium into the fruit has been followed by analysing apples at various stages of development, and it has been shown that most of the calcium moves into the fruit during the first few weeks of development (approximating to the period during which the cell walls are being formed). However, some calcium remains mobile in the later stages, and Martin (1967) has shown that ^{45}Ca applied to the fruit can be detected in the tree. Recently it has been deduced from seasonal studies of the calcium content of apples that during later development of the fruit as much as 1 mg may move out of the fruit in certain seasons, especially when the weather is dry (Wilkinson, 1968b). This may be of the same order of magnitude as that contributed by calcium sprays (as shown by fruit analysis). It is also after dry periods that bitter pit is most prevalent, and it is therefore tempting to speculate whether the actual manifestation of bitter pit (the brown, dry cells) may not be due to the movement of calcium out of these pockets of cells which are already in a critical state as regards calcium content.

Perhaps the importance of calcium has received so much attention because it has led to successful practical methods of control, but in fact there have been advances in the understanding of the importance of other mineral elements in the past decade, brought about to some extent by improvements in techniques of micro-analysis. The concentrations of potassium, phosphorus and magnesium have also been associated with storage disorders, and three papers by Perring (1968a, b, c) have presented some of the evidence on which these conclusions have been based. For instance, it has been found that low temperature breakdown is less likely in apples with high levels of potassium, phosphorus and magnesium than in apples with low concentrations of these elements.

Extensive storage trials with Cox's Orange Pippin apples have been described by Sharples (1968), using as many as 150 different orchards each season. Of the many fruit attributes which were measured, the mineral composition of the fruit was most closely linked with breakdown and bitter pit, and it was suggested that imbalance between potassium, magnesium and calcium might be responsible.

As an example of the interdependence of minerals Perring (1968b) found that whilst a Cox's Orange Pippin apple will be liable to senescent breakdown if the calcium level is less than 3 mg/100 g fresh weight, a phosphorus concentration of less than 8 mg/100 g fresh weight may have the same result even if the calcium level is high.

Although it is still not clear why an imbalance of minerals should predispose apples to certain post-harvest disorders, there are signs that modern methods of analysis will soon make possible the prediction of some disorders, and therefore the possibility of avoiding long storage of fruit likely to give trouble.

It has been found that the total nitrogen content of apples is of more significance in relation to fungal disorders than to physiological disorders. It is true that total nitrogen is related to protein nitrogen, and protein nitrogen to respiration, but so many exceptions have been found to the proposition that rate of respiration is related to subsequent development of storage disorders that such reports are now treated with caution.

Because the analysis of fruit requires special techniques (especially as regards initial sampling) attempts are now being made to relate the results of leaf analysis to storage disorders. Results obtained so far suggest that this may be possible for some elements. However, the further one departs from the composition of the fruit (where the disorder occurs) the more must be the caution in interpreting the results. For instance, the relationship between potassium and magnesium in the leaf is inverse, whereas in the fruit it is direct. This was first shown by Fudge (1939) for grapefruit, and later confirmed in apples. This may be because the fruit is acid, and the cations K and Mg are drawn to the fruit to maintain the buffer system. This is an example of the way in which the fundamental metabolic differences between fruits and leaves can be expected to lead to difficulties in applying the results of leaf analysis to the prediction of storage disorders.

D. Maturity

The stage at which a fruit is picked can have a profound effect upon the development of storage disorders. Obviously if the fruit is picked exceptionally early its development and nutrition are interrupted, and it may never develop its full flavour. Also obviously, a fruit which has become over-ripe on the plant can never have its maturity reversed by subsequent treatment. Between these extremes there are stages of development which seem to be associated with susceptibility to disorders. Kidd and West (1933) showed that when Bramley's Seedling apples were moved at different stages of maturity from moderate to low temperatures more low temperature break-down was found in apples which had been cooled when on the respiration climacteric. This has since been confirmed in Cox's Orange Pippin apples picked at successive stages of maturity. A similar effect has been shown for bananas. The state at which they are normally cut from the stems and distributed happens to be that at which they are most likely to be affected by low temperatures. This state coincides with the respiration climacteric. Bananas cut earlier or later are less susceptible to chilling (Furlong, 1962).

Many disorders do not show a maximum with time of picking, but the fruits become progressively more or less susceptible as date of harvesting is advanced. In apples, fruit picked early is more likely to develop scald (Fidler, 1959) and, possibly, core flush and bitter pit; when picked in an over-mature state it is more likely to develop senescent breakdown (Wilkinson and Sharples, 1967) and brown heart (Dewey, 1962). Earlier results on the deleterious effect of late picking (or of delayed storage) on the incidence of brown heart in pears have been confirmed by Tomkins (1959) and by Hansen and Mellenthin (1962).

The biochemical significance of effects of maturity on storage disorders are obscure. The fruit is continuously changing both physically and chemically and it is perhaps not surprising that abnormal temperatures and gas mixtures should vary in their effect depending upon the time at which they are applied.

E. Weather

Of all the pre-harvest factors affecting subsequent storage disorders, weather is probably the most important. It is also uncontrollable. In many temperate parts of the world (especially those subject to variable seasons) the climate may determine whether a particular disorder is an economic problem or not in any one year. For instance, in the United Kingdom bitter pit of apples is a negligible problem in certain seasons—usually those in which the summer has been wet and cold. Again, core flush may not be serious follow-ing warm summers, but may be a source of severe loss when the summer has been cold. Seasonal variation in the susceptibility of Bosc pears to brown heart was considered to be of major importance by Hansen and Mellenthin (1962).

The weather affects the nutrition of the fruit, and its water status when picked. It also affects the skin characteristics and physical properties con-trolling the "ventilation" of the fruit. From the point of view of chemical composition it has been shown that apples from a particular orchard may contain from 15–22% dry matter in successive seasons. (This represents a range of about 11–17% of sugars.) The total nitrogen content of these same apples has varied in certain seasons from 39–90 mg/100 g fresh weight—a difference far greater than can be shown in any one season by applying different levels of nitrogenous fertilizers. Potassium and phosphorus are also subject to seasonal variations, but not as great as nitrogen. Among organic constituents, ascorbic acid content is known to vary with summer temperatures, and the acidity and astringency also fluctuate.

In an effort to correlate weather and storage disorders in all manner of fruits the World Meteorological Organization (1963) sponsored a review of available literature. The result was somewhat confusing and difficult to apply. It is indeed the ambition of fruit storage technologists to be able to predict the severity of post-harvest disorders on the basis of preceding weather, but before this becomes possible it is likely that much more knowledge will be required of the biochemistry of the fruit. It will be evident from this review that much more is known about effects than about causes.

REFERENCES

Barker, J. (1934). *Occ. Pap. imp. Bur. Fruit Prod.* **3,** 28 pp.
Bartholomew, E. T. (1937). *Bull. Calif. agric. Exp. Stn* **605,** 42 pp.
Biale, J. B. and Young, R. E. (1962). *Endeavour* **21,** 164–74.
Blanpied, G. D. and Smock, R. M. (1961). *Proc. Am. Soc. hort. Sci.* **78,** 35–42.
Bogdanski, K. (1960). *Bull. Acad. pol. Sci.* **8,** 329–33.
Bunemann, G. (1964). *Gartenbauwissenschaft* **29,** 481–516.
Carne, W. M. (1948). *Bull. Coun. scient. ind. Res., Melb.* **238,** 83 pp.
De Long, W. A. (1936). *Pl. Physiol., Lancaster* **11,** 453–6.
Dewey, D. H. (1962). *Proc. XVIth Int. hort. Congr., Brussels* **1,** 452–9.
Doesburg, J. J. (1957). *J. Sci. Fd Agric.* **8,** 206 16.
Eaves, C. A., Forsyth, F. R., Leefe, J. S. and Lockhart, C. L. (1964). *Can. J. Pl. Sci.* **44,** 458–65.
Fawcett, H. S. and Klotz, L. J. (1948). *In* "The Citrus Industry" (L. D. Batchelor and H. J. Webber, eds), Vol. 2, pp. 495–596. University of California Press, Los Angeles.
Fidler, J. C. (1959). *Proc. Xth Int. Congr. Refrig., Copenhagen* **3,** 181–6.
Fidler, J. C. (1965). *J. Refrig.* **8,** 265–73.
Fidler, J. C. (1968). *In* "Recent Advances in Food Science", Vol. 4. Pergamon Press, Oxford.
Fidler, J. C. and North, C. J. (1961). *Annexe 1961–1 to Bull. int. Inst. Refrig.* 251–4.
Fudge, B. R. (1939). *Bull. Fla agric. Exp. Stn* **331,** 36 pp.
Furlong, C. R. (1962). *Annexe 1962–3 to Bull. int. Inst. Refrig.* 45–8.
Gane, R. (1936). *New Phytol.* **35,** 383–402.
Garman, P. and Mathis, W. T. (1956). *Bull. Conn. agric. Exp. Stn* **601,** 1–19.
Hansen, E. and Mellenthin, W. M. (1962). *Proc. Am. Soc. hort. Sci.* **80,** 146–53.
Hulme, A. C. (1956). *Nature, Lond.* **178,** 218–19.
Hulme, A. C., Smith, W. H. and Wooltorton, L. S. C. (1964). *J. Sci. Fd Agric.* **15,** 303–7.
Kidd, F. and West, C. (1923). *Spec. Rep. Fd Invest. Bd D.S.I.R.* **12,** 54 pp.
Kidd, F., West, C. and Kidd, M. N. (1927). *Spec. Rep. Fd Invest. Bd D.S.I.R.* **30,** 87 pp.

Kidd, F. and West, C. (1933). *Rep. Fd Invest. Bd D.S.I.R. for 1933*, 57–60.
Martin, D. (1967). *Fld Stn Rec. C.S.I.R.O. Div. Pl. Ind.* **6**, 49–54.
Martin, D., Lewis, T. L. and Cerny, J. (1967). *Aust. J. agric. Res.* **18**, 271–8.
Miller, E. V. (1946). *Bot. Rev.* **12**, 393–423.
Miller, E. V. (1958). *Bot. Rev.* **24**, 43–59.
Montgomery, H. B. S. and Wilkinson, B. G. (1962). *J. hort. Sci.* **37**, 150–60.
Padfield, C. A. S. (1954). *Bull. N.Z. Dep. scient. ind. Res.* **111**, 96 pp.
Perring, M. A. (1968a). *Rep. E. Malling Res. Stn for 1967*, 191–8.
Perring, M. A. (1968b). *J. Sci. Fd Agric.* **19**, 186–92.
Perring, M. A. (1968c). *J. Sci. Fd Agric.* **19**, 640–5.
Rasmussen, P. M. (1961). *Annexe 1961–1 to Bull. int. Inst. Refrig.*, 127–32.
Rose, D. H., Fisher, D. F., Brooks, C. and Bratley, C. O. (1937). *U.S. Dep. Agric. Misc. Publ.* **228**, 26 pp.
Rygg, C. L. and Wells, A. W. (1962). *U.S. Dep. Agric. AMS* **475**, 11 pp.
Scott, K. J., Hall, E. G., Roberts, E. A. and Wills, R. B. (1964). *Aust. J. exp. Agr. Animal Husbandry* **4**, 253.
Sharples, R. O. (1967). *Pl. Path.* **16**, 119–20.
Sharples, R. O. (1968). *Rep. E. Malling Res. Stn for 1967*, 185–9.
Smith, W. H. (1963). *Adv. Fd Res.* **12**, 96–146.
Smock, R. M. and Neubert, A. M. (1950). *In* "Apples and Apple Products", p. 237. Interscience, New York.
Smock, R. M. and Van Doren, A. (1941). *Bull. Cornell Univ. agric. Exp. Stn* **762**, 45 pp.
Thomas, M. (1929). *Ann. appl. Biol.* **16**, 444–57.
Tiller, L. W. (1929). *Bull. N.Z. Dep. Scient. ind. Res.* **16**, 23 pp.
Tomkins, R. G. (1959). *Proc. Xth Int. Congr. Refrig., Copenhagen* **3**, 189–92.
Tomkins, R. G. (1966). *Rep. E. Malling Res. Stn for 1965*, 60–76.
Tomkins, R. G. (1968). *Rep. Ditton Lab. for 1967–68*, 21.
Ulrich, R. (1966). *Proc. XVIIth Int. hort. Congr., Maryland, U.S.A.* **3**, 471–94.
Uota, M. (1955). *Proc. Am. Soc. hort. Sci.* **65**, 231–43.
Van der Plank, J. E. and Davies, R. (1937). *J. Pomol.* **15**, 226–47.
Wilkinson, B. G. (1965). *J. hort. Sci.* **40**, 58–65.
Wilkinson, B. G. (1968a). *Rep. Ditton Lab. for 1967–68*, 27–8.
Wilkinson, B. G. (1968b). *J. Sci. Fd Agric.* **19**, 646–7.
Wilkinson, B. G. and Sharples, R. O. (1967). *J. hort. Sci.* **42**, 67–82.
World Meteorological Organization (1963). *Tech. Note* **53**, 1–112.

Chapter 19

Apple Scald

D. F. MEIGH

A.R.C. Food Research Institute, Norwich, England

Certain varieties of apple are subject to a physiological disorder known as superficial scald, which develops if the fruit is stored for a sufficiently long period. Although the main bulk of a fruit remains sound, parts of the skin become brown. This makes it unattractive and reduces its resistance to rotting. Pears also suffer from a form of storage scald, but there is some doubt as to whether the two disorders are the same. Scald causes considerable wastage in the fruit growing industries of many countries. Some of the most widely grown varieties of apple, such as Bramley's Seedling and Granny Smith, are susceptible.

As early as 1903, Powell and Fulton had found ways of controlling the disorder and had investigated some of the factors which influence it. By 1919, Brooks *et al.* had showed that oiled tissue paper wraps reduced the severity of the damage, and had put forward the theory that the disorder was caused by accumulation of volatile products of the apple in the tissues of the fruit and the surrounding air, a theory which has since been widely accepted. In subsequent years, many of the cultural and storage factors which affect the incidence of the disorder were investigated, but the results of these experiments have often been a source of controversy, for apples grown in different surroundings appeared to behave differently. Today the biochemical causes still remain obscure and none of the methods of control, whether long established or of recent origin, have been completely success-ful.

At least three major obstacles have contributed to the apparent difficulties of the problem. Firstly, although the critical period for development of scald occurs during the first few weeks of storage, damage does not appear on the fruit until many weeks later. Secondly, the weather during the latter part of the summer can greatly influence the constitution of the fruit in relation to its susceptibility to scald. Experiments must therefore be planned with the knowledge that the fruits eventually removed from store may be found to be undamaged, or all scalded, or in some intermediate condition. Thirdly, the visible symptoms of the disorder, namely browning of the skin, can result from many other processes which kill the surface layers of cells. It is therefore difficult to distinguish symptoms of scald from those of other storage dis-orders or of physical or chemical damage.

In this account of superficial scald it seems appropriate first to describe the symptoms of the disease; then to summarize the various cultural factors, storage conditions and chemical treatments which are known to influence its severity; and finally to describe the results of the rather limited biochemical work that has recently been done. We shall not be concerned here with the details of cultural and storage practice, for extensive reviews have been com-piled on these aspects of scald control by Fidler (1959), Smock (1961) and Hardenburg (1965). These should be consulted for comprehensive biblio-graphies.

I. VISIBLE SYMPTOMS OF SCALD

Fidler (1956) has distinguished three main forms of scald in English apples and, essentially, these correspond to the forms recognized by Marcellin and Leblond (1957) in France.

(a) *Browning*: The skin becomes progressively browner in more or less well defined zones. Later the cells of the parenchyma begin to die, and at an advanced stage the symptoms may be mistaken for senescent breakdown. This form of the disorder is seen in the Newton Wonder apple.

(b) *Rugose scald*: A small circular zone round each lenticel remains uninjured. The injury, which is first visible as a faint bronzing of the green ground colour, becomes a deep brown but generally remains distinct in outline. The surface layers sink, leaving the lenticular zones as round green projections. The apples Edward VII and Belle de Boskoop provide good examples.

(c) *Lenticel scald*: This is the reverse of the rugose form, in that the injury is first visible at the lenticels, giving the apple a speckled appearance. This then spreads outwards.

Fidler and North (1965) have distinguished a further scald variant, termed "stem-end browning", in which the brown discoloration radiates from the stem cavity. This probably corresponds to the stalk cavity scald found in Sturmer Pippin apples by Padfield and Clark (1963).

The Australian workers Martin and Lewis (1961) have divided scald into two groups which they term "immaturity" and "senescent" types. The former develops when the fruit is still green, while the latter develops when the ground colour has changed predominantly from green to yellow. Among the senescent types these authors include lenticel scald, light induced scald, speckled senescent scald and senescent blotch. These are all held to be the result of attempting to store the apple beyond its potential life as a sound fruit, and strictly are not classified as superficial scald. Padfield (1958), in New Zealand, distinguished rugose scald from what he termed shadowy senescent scald, for the latter only appeared after the fruit was warmed and was not readily controlled by oiled wraps.

II. VISIBLE SYMPTOMS CONFUSED WITH SCALD

A. Senescence

It should be clear from the above description that it is not easy to distinguish between symptoms of browning or lenticel scald and the symptoms of ageing. Perhaps the strict criterion would be that scald develops on a green skin and can be controlled by wrapping in oiled tissue paper. Some of the chemical inhibitors of scald are known to reduce other forms of skin browning, though Padfield (1959) found that diphenylamine did not control senescent scald in New Zealand apples.

B. Harmful Chemicals

There are many compounds which, if applied to the skin of the apple in large enough amounts, will cause brown markings which can be confused with scald. Damage is sometimes caused by oiled paper wraps prepared with impure paper or unrefined oil (see for example, Fidler and North, 1966). Emulsifying agents and fungicides have also been implicated.

C. Other Storage Disorders

For a detailed account with illustrations, see Carne (1948), who described conditions found in Australia.

(a) *External CO_2 injury*, which is thought to be caused by low temperature conditions in conjunction with high CO_2 levels in controlled atmosphere storage, bears a resemblance to rugose scald but the lesions have sharper, more feathery edges.

(b) *Deep scald or ribbon scald*, which can occur in ribbon-shaped patches, extends 2 to 3 mm into the cortex of the fruit and is a form of low temperature injury (see Tomkins 1965b).

(c) *Jonathan spot* gives the fruit a speckled appearance. It has been found to occur in conjunction with a disorganization of organic acid metabolism, (Richmond *et al.*, 1964) and is found in red varieties of apple, notably Jonathan and Spitsbergen.

(d) *Handling injury.* The abrasion marks which develop on some varieties of apple and pear are related to the age and ripeness of the fruit when handled.

(e) *Light induced scald.* In hotter climates, local heating of the fruit on the tree can result in brown markings, and a similar injury is known to occur when apples are displayed after storage (Carne, 1948). Padfield and Smock (1960) found that this type of injury was not controlled by diphenylamine.

III. HISTOLOGICAL CHANGES

Fidler (1950) observed that in rugose scald in English apples the first stage, described as "bronzing", occurs when the epidermal cells and occasionally hypodermal cells become brown. In the "incipient" stage the epidermal cells and most of the layers of the hypodermis are brown. At the "severe" stage the epidermis and hypodermis are dead and have collapsed. Some cortical parenchyma is also dead.

Bain (1956) found that in Australian Granny Smith apples the cell contents of successive layers of hypodermal cells became brown with increasing severity of the disorder, starting at the outside. In severely scalded tissue the entire hypodermis was affected; the sunken surface was caused by collapse of the hypodermal cells and the underlying cells of the outer cortex. Contrary to Fidler's experience, the epidermis did not usually show any signs of injury. In cells of tissue which were known to have been damaged in storage but as yet showed no browning, no visible changes were found. However, the contents of the hypodermal cells stained more deeply with methylene blue and did not tear so easily on sectioning. Chloroplasts from slightly scalded tissue were apparently undamaged.

Bain and Mercer (1963) examined sections from scalded apples with an electron microscope. Two distinct types of disorganization were identified. In one, most obvious in the early stages of the disorder, vesicles were formed in the chloroplasts and throughout the cytoplasm. These changes closely resembled those occurring in ageing, non-scalded tissue and were probably the same. In the other type of disorganization, new electron-dense substances were formed, the protoplasts became "tanned" and collapsed. This type was considered to be characteristic of scald, and was superimposed on the other. Electron dense material, pitted in appearance, developed and increased in quantity in the vacuole and also became concentrated in the tonoplast as the severity of the disorder increased. An additional layer of material, solid in appearance, developed between the cell wall and the plasmalemma. In the final stages of the disorder the cytoplasm and vacuoles became increasingly electron dense, losing their identity as the cells collapsed. Bain and Mercer suggested that these changes were consistent with the breakdown of the control mechanism of the polyphenol system in the cell and that the electron dense materials were symptoms rather than the cause of scald. Similar changes were found to occur after apples were treated with chloroform or after freezing and thawing.

IV. BIOCHEMICAL CHANGES

Little is known of the chemical changes which precede the visible signs of disease. Metlitskii and Tsekhomskaya (1958a, b) found that varieties of apple susceptible to scald accumulated more alcohol and acetaldehyde during storage than those resistant to scald; this suggested that anaerobiosis was occurring. They found, on measuring the permeability of apple skin to gases, that in apples affected by scald skin permeability decreased more during storage than in apples unaffected. Dilley et al. (1963) found that they could stimulate scald on Rome and McIntosh apples by brief nitrogen treatments of 36–108 hours at 20°C and concluded that scald was induced under anaerobic conditions, followed by a period of aerobic development. This, however, is difficult to reconcile with the known inhibiting effect on scald of storage in atmospheres deficient in oxygen.

The respiration rate of scalded apple skin has been measured both by Siegelman and Schomer (1954) and by Metlitskii and Tsekhomskaya (1958a, b) and found to be lower than in a healthy tissue. This does little more than confirm that scalded tissue is dead.

Chemical aspects of the waxy skin coating and the volatile compounds produced by apples are discussed below in connection with the volatile theory of scald causation.

V. PERIOD OF SUSCEPTIBILITY TO SCALD

Having discovered that the oiled paper wrap protected the apple from scald, the early investigators used it in an attempt to determine the critical period during which the scald-producing agencies were most active. By leaving fruit unwrapped for various periods during storage Brooks *et al.* (1923) concluded that the development of the disease could be divided into the following four periods:

(i) 6 to 8 weeks: during this time it is possible to overcome scald by protecting the fruit with oiled wraps.

(ii) Next 5 to 8 weeks: preventative measures are now useless for long storage but apples will show no signs of damage if warmed during this period.

(iii) Remaining time in store: skin cells have been damaged but will only brown if exposed to warmth.

(iv) After removal from store: the affected skin becomes brown and dies.

Kidd and West (1935) tried to define the susceptible period with greater accuracy by dividing the storage time into three week periods. Each sample of apples was either wrapped for one period only or left unwrapped for one period only. They concluded from the scald produced that for normally harvested fruit the 4th to 6th weeks of storage were critical and for immature fruit the 7th to 12th weeks of storage. Padfield (1950) repeated this experiment with New Zealand fruit and found that irrespective of maturity the effectiveness of wrapping the fruit increased from the 1st to the 12th week of storage and then decreased again to the 24th week.

The development of diphenylamine as a scald preventing agent enabled Fidler and North (1965, 1966) to dip apples in an emulsion of diphenylamine at 0, 2, 4, 6, 8 and 10 weeks after the start of storage. In the first year's experiment, dipping was effective at any time up to the 10th week of storage; in the second year diphenylamine was effective when applied up to the 4th week of storage but it was progressively less effective thereafter.

VI. FACTORS AFFECTING THE INCIDENCE OF SCALD

A. Variety and Colour of Fruit

Some varieties of fruit, notably those with heavily pigmented skins, are resistant to the disorder. In susceptible varieties the scalded areas tend to occur in the green rather than the coloured or russetted parts. This is the general experience in many countries, but in France and Switzerland the reverse has been found on the Belle de Boskoop apple (Marcellin and Leblond, 1957). Huelin (1964), in experiments with flavonoids, obtained some reduction of scald by applying quercetin to the fruit before storage, but not with cyanidin. Both these compounds are known to be present in apple skin

(Sando, 1937). Shutak and Kitchin (1966) covered Cortland apples on the tree with muslin bags, about a month before harvest. Apples in black bags scalded more severely than those in white bags, which in turn scalded more than uncovered apples. There was the expected inverse correlation between the intensities of scald and skin coloration, but bagging might also have caused other changes in the fruit.

B. Cultural

(a) *Weather*. The incidence of scald varies greatly from year to year. A good example of this is seen in Fidler's (1956) work. Among Edward VII apples harvested annually from a single group of trees, in the years 1946 to 1955, from 0–94% of fruits were found to be affected by scald after storage. The percentage of the skin area of the apples that was affected by scald was correlated with the water deficit (evaporation minus rainfall); evaporation is influenced by duration of sunshine. There is evidence from several other countries that scald is severe when the last few weeks of the growing season are hot and dry, and mild when conditions are cold and wet. Uota (1952) found that if the temperature around the branches of McIntosh trees was controlled during the last three weeks before harvest, high night temperatures gave 100% scald and low temperatures 2% (see also Merritt *et al.*, 1961). In this case the incidence of scald bore an inverse relation to the extent of coloration of the skin, so an additional factor may have been at work.

(b) *Fruit size*. Large apples are more likely to scald than small ones. Since the mean size of fruit is often related to the size of the crop on the tree, this suggests that nutrition influences scald. Little work has been done in this field.

(c) *Maturity*. There is general agreement that if fruit is picked early in an immature condition, the incidence of scald is increased. On the other hand, according to Smock (1961) and Hardenburg and Siegelman (1957), if the fruit is over-ripe when picked, scald is again increased. Shutak and Kitchin (1966) picked Cortland apples at seven dates covering an unusually long period of almost three months. After storage the first and last picks were unaffected by scald. There was a progressive increase in scald incidence until the 4th pick, in which all the fruits were affected, and then a similar fall to the last pick. It is difficult to relate these results to others without knowing the physiological state of the fruit at picking time, namely the relationship between the time of picking and the time at which the climacteric rise began after keeping at a specified temperature.

C. Storage

(a) *Delay between picking and storage*. Pre-storage delay has generally been found to increase the incidence of scald. There are exceptions, however.

For example Ginsburg (1961) found that delay had little effect on South African Granny Smith apples.

(b) *Ventilation and air purification*. If scald is caused by a volatile product of the fruit, then purification of the air should prevent it. Carbon filters, air scrubbers and high speed ventilation have not given the same results in the hands of different investigators. This is further discussed in the following section on the volatile theory of scald causation.

(c) *Relative humidity*. It is not easy to distinguish the effects of high relative humidity from those of ventilation, for although a high R.H. has been found to favour scald development, this condition, if achieved by limiting ventilation, might stimulate scald by allowing a harmful volatile to accumulate. Kidd and West (1933, 1934) in experiments in which both low and high R.H. samples were ventilated at the same rate found that more scald developed at a high humidity. Meigh, D. F. (unpublished) found that in three out of four years in which comparisons were made, again at constant flow rate, apples in dryer conditions developed less scald.

(d) *Atmospheric composition*. The effect of high CO_2 concentrations on certain varieties of apple is to reduce the incidence of scald, by comparison with storage in air. On others, CO_2 has a scald-stimulating effect. Since high CO_2 concentrations are normally achieved by limiting ventilation, this additional factor may influence the result. There is more general agreement that reduction of oxygen tension to 3% or below reduces the incidence of scald (see for example Fidler and North, 1961), but some varieties of apple do not respond in this way (Tomkins, 1964, 1965a). Ulrich *et al.* (1961) found that storage in pure oxygen increased the severity of scald. There are a number of reports of the effect of polyethylene box liners on scald. The results of these experiments can be interpreted in terms of the concentrations of oxygen, CO_2 and water vapour that accumulate inside the liners as a result of the restricted ventilation imposed by the liner.

(e) *Temperature*. Although in some countries scald is found to be a low temperature disorder, Fidler's (1959) review shows that some workers record an opposite trend. Since at a higher temperature the fruit ages more rapidly it is possible that an opposing factor is at work. Kidd and West (1935) and Smith (1959) found that intermittent warming during storage reduced superficial scald. It has been argued that the treatment would encourage the evaporation of a harmful volatile from the fruit, but the effect is more probably due to action on enzyme systems. In this section it should be mentioned that a short pre-storage dip in warm water has been reported to reduce scald (Stoll, 1958). Some other workers confirmed this, but Fidler *et al.* (1965) did not find the treatment effective.

D. Chemical

(a) *Oiled wraps*. The protective effect of wraps is discussed in the following section.

(b) *Diphenylamine and related compounds*. Smock (1955) discovered the inhibiting action of diphenylamine on scald. Many papers on techniques of application have since been published, but no convincing theory of its action. Huelin (1964) found that the related compounds dibenzylamine, dicyclohexylamine and *N*-benzylaniline were almost as effective, but diphenylether, diphenylmethane, benzhydrol, benzophenone, benzanilide and benzylideneaniline were ineffective. Staden (1961) used as a working hypothesis the idea that a scald inhibitor would have the general formula

$$C_6H_5\text{—}X_n\text{—}C_6H_5$$
$$|$$
$$R$$

where X represents one of the elements S, O, N or C, *n* a number from 0 to 3 and R an element or radical. With the aid of this hypothesis it was found that *sym*-*N*,*N*-dimethyldiphenylurea had activity comparable to that of diphenylamine.

(c) *6-Ethoxy-1,2-dihydro-2,2,4-trimethylquinoline* (*Ethoxyquin*). Smock (1957) reported that ethoxyquin also had scald-reducing properties. Though it has usually been found that diphenylamine gives more complete control of scald, Hansen and Mellenthin (1967) found that ethoxyquin was more effective than diphenylamine in controlling pear scald.

(d) *Lecithin*. Staden (1966) found that egg or soya lecithin controlled scald in Belle de Boskoop apples, but since it formed a good substrate for moulds it was necessary to add an antibiotic, pimaricin, to the solution. This formulation also gave control of Jonathan spot, which diphenylamine did not.

VII. THE VOLATILE THEORY OF SCALD CAUSATION

Brooks *et al.* (1919) were probably the first to put forward the theory that scald was due to the accumulation of esters or similar products of the apple in the tissues of the fruit and in the surrounding air. They based this theory mainly on three observations: firstly, that loosely packed or well-ventilated apples developed less scald than tightly packed or unventilated ones; secondly, that wrappers impregnated with various fats and oils counteracted the disorder; and thirdly, that scald could be produced artificially by exposing apples to the vapours of aliphatic esters.

A. The Effects of Ventilation

Attempts to counteract scald by ventilation of the atmosphere or purification with carbon filters, permanganate scrubbers or water washers on a semi-industrial scale gave conflicting results in different countries; some attempts were successful and some not. Analysis of the ethylene and total odorous volatile compounds in the air of apple stores yielded no correlation of either of these with incidence of scald when wraps or carbon filters were used (Fidler, 1950). In an analysis of volatile alcohols, aldehydes, ketones and esters produced by apples, Meigh (1956, 1957) found no correlation between high rate of evolution of these compounds and a heavy incidence of scald (i) between varieties; (ii) between wrapped and unwrapped fruit; or (iii) between years of light and heavy incidence of scald. Huelin and Kennett (1958) confirmed that wraps did not reduce the concentration of these substances in the air surrounding the apples.

From time to time there have been attempts to show that volatiles evolved by one group of apples will cause an increase in scald development in another of the same or a different variety, when carried over them by the ventilating air stream. Stoll (1959) has described experiments in which volatiles from scald-susceptible varieties of apple caused a greater increase in severity of scald than volatiles from scald-resistant varieties. However, Staden (1961) in similar experiments, could detect no significant effects. Ulrich et al. (1961), using a single variety, Stayman Winesap, treated fruit internally and externally with air from a large container of apples. The treatment did not increase the incidence of scald.

The inconclusive nature of these investigations suggests that if a volatile is responsible for scald it must have a comparatively low volatility and constitute only a small fraction of those produced by the apple. Interesting evidence, however, was obtained from observations of single fruits. Shutak and Christopher (1960) found that if aluminium foil or clean apple cuticle were placed on an apple, the area of skin under the cover became scalded. Fidler (1950) had found that when apples had been wrapped with a leaf still attached to the fruit, the area of skin underlying the leaf was often scalded. On the other hand, when fruits became coated with activated carbon dust, there was no scald.

Marcellin and Mazliak (1965) placed small covers on the skin of William's pears and Stayman Winesap apples. If covers made of glass or polyamide perforated with a few tiny holes were used, scald developed underneath them while the surrounding skin was unharmed. Covers of polyethylene had no effect. The glass covers were impermeable to all vapours; the polyamide was permeable to oxygen and CO_2 but not to volatile organic compounds; the polyethylene was permeable to organic compounds but not to water vapour.

If the skin surrounding a glass cover was lightly oiled to reduce gaseous diffusion through the skin, CO_2 accumulated under the cover and the skin remained unscalded. If activated carbon was placed inside the glass cover scald was again prevented.

The cuticle of the apple has been examined as a possible barrier to diffusion of volatiles. It is known that at temperatures of 0-4°C the "oil fraction" of the waxy coating of the fruit, which contains unsaturated fatty acids, increases during storage and reaches a maximum after three or more months. If the fruit is removed to higher temperatures this accumulation is lost rapidly (Huelin and Gallop, 1951; Mazliak, 1963). Shutak *et al.* (1953) and Shutak and Christopher (1960) found that if wax was removed from the skin of the apples by solvents or scouring, before or during the early stages of storage, the treated areas were free of scald. If the skin was punctured the surrounding area of skin was also unharmed. Hilkenbaumer (1961) confirmed that removal of wax reduced scald but Padfield (1958) had not found this treatment to be effective. Since these treatments would increase the rate of water loss from the fruit the effects cannot be attributed definitely to escape of volatiles.

Meigh (1964, 1967) stored apples under a variety of conditions to give various degrees of scald severity. The waxy coating of the fruit was then fractionated. He concluded that neither the quantities of free or esterified fatty acids, nor of hydrocarbons of the wax were correlated with scald, but an unidentified long chain fatty aldehyde was found which was reduced in amount when fruit was covered with oiled wraps or treated with diphenylamine.

B. Oiled Paper Wraps

These were found to have a beneficial effect, which Brooks *et al.* (1919) attributed to the absorption of harmful volatiles. In subsequent years the use of oiled wraps to reduce scald became standard practice in the industry. The method only began to lose popularity with the increasing cost of labour and the development of chemical inhibitors. The chemical nature of the oil used in the wraps seems, within wide limits, to be of little significance. Even plain paper shavings or wood shavings (Metlitskii and Tsekhomskaya, 1958a) have some protective effect.

Apart from the possibility of volatile absorption, the physiological effects of wrappings are difficult to define. Oiled wraps do not obstruct gaseous exchange; they do not alter the rate of production of CO_2 by stored fruit or their respiratory quotient (Fidler, 1950), nor their production of volatile alcohols, aldehydes, ketones and esters (Meigh 1957; Huelin and Kennett, 1958). Transfer of oil from the wrap to the apple skin might alter the permeability of the skin. Kidd and West (1933) found that apples sprayed with oil scalded in the same way as untreated fruit, but Shutak and Christopher (1953) were able to reduce scald by dipping with a 3% oil emulsion. Direct treatment with oil was not as effective as oiled wraps for South African apples (Ginsburg, 1961). Since the use of oil has not become a practical alternative to control by oiled paper wraps it seems likely that effective scald prevention requires more than an alteration of skin permeability.

C. Treatment with Aliphatic Esters

Brooks *et al.* (1919) found that aliphatic esters caused scald-like damage on apples. They were, however, exposing the fruit to vapour concentrations far higher than would accumulate in a store. It is known that vapours of many volatile compounds will cause damage at a sufficiently high concentration, so that evidence of this sort has no significance unless the substances are added in amounts comparable with those produced by the apples themselves. Huelin and Kennett (1958) tested various carboxylic acids and their ethyl esters, and alcohols and carbonyl compounds known to be produced by apples, using low concentrations. They concluded that the causal substance was not a major component of the volatile substances found in the storage atmosphere.

VIII. α-FARNESENE, A POSSIBLE CAUSE OF SCALD

Murray *et al.* (1964) reported the presence of the sesquiterpene hydrocarbon β-farnesene in the natural waxy coating of Granny Smith apples, but a more detailed study enabled Huelin and Murray (1966) to identify the hydrocarbon unequivocally as the α-isomer, which differs from the β-isomer in the position of one of the four double bonds in the molecule. α-Farnesene was also found in the surface wax of Crofton and Delicious apples, Packham pears and quinces.

Huelin and Coggiola (1968) examined the effect of variety and maturity of apple, oiled wraps and treatment with diphenylamine on the concentration of α-farnesene in stored Australian apples. In general the farnesene content rose to a maximum and then declined again during a period of some 30 weeks of storage. More farnesene was found in earlier picked apples, which scald more severely and about twice as much in the scald-sensitive Granny Smith as in the scald-resistant Crofton variety. Where fruits were wrapped with oiled paper, farnesene moved from the fruit to the wraps until the wraps contained more than twice as much as the fruit. Though the total amount of farnesene in fruit and wrap was greater than in the unwrapped fruit, the wrapped fruit contained only 68% of that present in the unwrapped. Treatment with diphenylamine had little effect on the farnesene level of the first pick but reduced it in the second pick. It was found that diphenylamine inhibited the oxidation of farnesene.

Meigh and Filmer (1969) made a comparable study of English apples. They confirmed that during storage the farnesene level on the fruit rose to a maximum and then declined. There were indications that the rate of production of farnesene rose rapidly during the respiration climacteric. When concurrent measurements of production of CO_2, ethylene and farnesene were made at 12°C it was found that the farnesene content of the waxy coating increased rapidly from very low levels before the climacteric (about 0·1 $\mu g/cm^2$ skin surface) to reach a maximum in the Edward VII apple of about 34 $\mu g/cm^2$ skin surface and in the Cox's Orange Pippin of about 25 $\mu g/cm^2$ skin surface after 35 days of storage. This was of interest because Huelin and Murray (1966) had suggested that ursolic and oleanolic acids, which are major constituents of apple wax, owe their origin to a similar biosynthetic pathway from a farnesyl or nerolidyl intermediate. These pentacyclic triterpene acids are laid down in the apple wax at an earlier stage in the development of the fruit, however, and their concentration in the wax does not vary appreciably during the climacteric (Huelin and Gallop, 1951; Meigh et al., 1967).

Of the factors which control the incidence of scald, the variety of the apple being stored can override all others. Meigh and Filmer (1969) found, however, that at 12°C the Cox's Orange Pippin, which is scald-resistant, contained about two-thirds the amount of farnesene that was present in the Edward VII apple, which is liable to scald. It is possible that the difference might be greater at a lower temperature. In this experiment there was little difference between the amounts of farnesene produced by early and late picked apples, though early picking should result in more severe scald.

Meigh and Filmer (1969) stored Edward VII apples under a variety of conditions at 3°C and found, in agreement with the Australian workers, that when apples were wrapped, farnesene migrated from the skin to the wrap, but without any apparent change in production rate. In the English apples treatment with diphenylamine reduced the farnesene content. Storage in 8% CO_2 reduced both scald and farnesene content while delay between picking and storage increased both.

So far the circumstantial evidence suggests a more convincing correlation between farnesene content and scald severity than has been obtained for other components of the apple. It is interesting also that production of farnesene reaches a peak during the period in which the susceptibility of the apple to injury has been found to be high. If it could be shown that application of farnesene to apples during their period of susceptibility caused an increase of scald the correlation would be reinforced. To account for apparent discrepancies in the experimental evidence it might be necessary to elaborate the basic theory that a volatile substance induces scald. Scald resistant apples might, for example, possess some chemical defensive mechanism. The way in which injury arises might be far from simple. The Australian workers suggest that oxidative products of farnesene cause the disorder. This would be in keeping with the protection given by storage in atmospheres low in oxygen, and with the protective effect of diphenylamine and ethoxyquin, which are antioxidants. If more was known of the oxidative breakdown products of farnesene their effect on stored apples could be tested.

REFERENCES

Bain, J. M. (1956). *J. hort. Sci.* **31,** 234–8.
Bain, J. M. and Mercer, F. V. (1963). *Aust. J. biol. Sci.* **16,** 442–9.
Brooks, C., Cooley, J. S. and Fisher, D. F. (1919). *J. agric. Res.* **18,** 211–40.
Brooks, C., Cooley, J. S. and Fisher, D. F. (1923). *J. agric. Res.* **26,** 513–36.
Carne, W. M. (1948), *Bull. Counc. scient. ind. Res., Melb.* No. 238.
Dilley, D. R., Dedolph, R. R., MacLean, D. C. and Dewey, D. H. (1963). *Nature, Lond.* **200,** 1229–30.
Fidler, J. C. (1950). *J. hort. Sci.* **25,** 81–110.
Fidler, J. C. (1956). *Fd Sci. Abstr.* **28,** 545–54.
Fidler, J. C. (1959). *Proc. 10th int. Congr. Refrig., Copenhagen* **3,** 181–5.
Fidler, J. C. and North, C. J. (1961). *Bull. int. Inst. Refrig.* Annexe 1961–1, 175–8.
Fidler, J. C. and North, C. J. (1965). *Rep. Ditton Lab. for 1964–65,* 12–14.
Fidler, J. C. and North, C. J. (1966). *Rep. Ditton Lab. for 1965–66,* 10–11.
Fidler, J. C., North, C. J. and Edney, K. L. (1965). *Rep. Ditton Lab. for 1964–65,* 14–15.
Ginsburg, L. (1961). *Bull. int. Inst. Refrig.* Annexe 1961–1, 179–93.
Hansen, E. and Mellenthin, A. B. (1967). *Proc. Am. Soc. hort. Sci.* **91,** 860–2.
Hardenburg, R. E. (1965). *Review of literature on harvesting, handling, storage and transportation of apples,* ARS 51–4 U.S. Dept Agric., pp. 194–215.
Hardenburg, R. E. and Siegelman, H. W. (1957). *Proc. Am. Soc. hort. Sci.* **69,** 75–83.
Hilkenbaumer, F. (1961). *Bull int. Inst. Refrig.* Annexe 1961–1, 195–200.
Huelin, F. E. (1964). *J. Sci. Fd Agric.* **15,** 227–36.
Huelin, F. E. and Coggiola, I. M. (1968). *J. Sci. Fd Agric.* **19,** 297–301.
Huelin, F. E. and Gallop, R. A. (1951). *Aust. J. scient. Res.* **4B,** 526–43.
Huelin, F. E. and Kennett, B. H. (1958). *J. Sci. Fd Agric.* **9,** 657–66.
Huelin, F. E. and Murray, K. E. (1966). *Nature, Lond.* **210,** 1260–1.
Kidd, F. and West, C. (1933). *Rep. Fd Invest. Bd, Lond. for 1932,* 58–62.
Kidd, F. and West, C. (1934). *Rep. Fd Invest. Bd, Lond. for 1933,* 199–204.
Kidd, F. and West, C. (1935). *Rep. Fd Invest. Bd, Lond. for 1934,* 111–17.
Marcellin, P. and Leblond, C. (1957). *Fruits* **12,** 147–61.
Marcellin, P. and Mazliak, P. (1965). *Proc. 11th int. Congr. Refrig.* 1963, **2,** 851–6.
Martin, D. and Lewis, T. L. (1961). *Bull. int. Inst. Refrig.,* Annexe 1961–1, 201–6.
Mazliak, P. (1963). "La Cire Cuticulaire des Pommes". Doctorate Thesis, Paris.
Meigh, D. F. (1956). *J. Sci. Fd Agric.* **7,** 396–411.
Meigh, D. F. (1957). *J. Sci. Fd Agric.* **8,** 313–26.
Meigh, D. F. (1964). *J. Sci. Fd Agric.* **15,** 436–43.

Meigh, D. F. (1967). *J. Sci. Fd Agric.* **18**, 307–13.

Meigh, D. F. and Filmer, A. A. E. (1969). *J. Sci. Fd. Agric.* **20**, 139–43

Meigh, D. F., Jones, J. D. and Hulme, A. C. (1967). *Phytochem.* **6**, 1507–15.

Merritt, R. H., Stiles, W. C., Havens, A. V. and Mitterling, L. A. (1961). *Proc. Am. Soc. hort. Sci.* **78**, 24–34.

Metlitskii, L. V. and Tsekhomskaya, V. M. (1958a). *Biokhim. Plodov. Ovoshch.* (4), 42–50.

Metlitskii, L. V. and Tsekhomskaya, V. M. (1958b). *Dokl. Akad. Nauk SSSR* **122**, 863–66.

Murray, K. E., Huelin, F. E. and Davenport, J. B. (1964). *Nature, Lond.* **204**, 80.

Padfield, C. A. S. (1950). *N.Z. Jl Sci. Technol.* **32A**, (3), 45–8.

Padfield, C. A. S. (1958). *N.Z. Jl agric. Res.* **1**, 231–8.

Padfield, C. A. S. (1959). *N.Z. Jl agric. Res.* **2**, 953–70.

Padfield, C. A. S. and Clark, P. J. (1963). *N.Z. Jl agric. Res.*, **6**, 409–15.

Padfield, C. A. S. and Smock, R. M. (1960). *N.Z. Jl agric. Res.* **3**, 675–9.

Powell, G. H. and Fulton, S. H. (1903). *Bull. Bur. Pl. Ind. U.S. Dep. Agric.* No. 48.

Richmond, A. E., Dilley, D. R. and Dewey, D. H. (1964). *Pl. Physiol., Lancaster* **39**, 1056–60.

Sando, C. E. (1937). *J. biol. Chem.* **117**, 45.

Shutak, V. and Christopher, E. P. (1953). *Proc. Am. Soc. hort. Sci.* **61**, 233–6.

Shutak, V. and Christopher, E. P. (1960). *Proc. Am. Soc. hort. Sci.* **76**, 106–11.

Shutak, V. and Kitchin, J. T. (1966). *Proc. Am. Soc. hort. Sci.* **88**, 89–93.

Shutak, V., Christopher, E. P. and Pratt, L. C. (1953). *Proc. Am. Soc. hort. Sci.* **61**, 228–32.

Siegelman, H. W. and Schomer, H. A. (1954). *Pl. Physiol., Lancaster* **29**, 429–31.

Smith, W. H. (1959). *Nature, Lond.* **183**, 760.

Smock, R. M. (1955). *Am. Fruit Grow. Mag.* **75**, (11), 20.

Smock, R. M. (1957). *Proc. Am. Soc. hort. Sci.* **69**, 91–100.

Smock, R. M. (1961). *Bull. Cornell Univ. agric. Exp. Stn.* No. 970.

Staden, O. L. (1961). *Bull. int. Inst. Refrig.* Annexe 1961–1, 211–16.

Staden, O. L. (1966). *Rep. Sprenger Inst., Wageningen* 17–18.

Stoll, K. (1958). *Schweiz, Z. Obst- u. Weinb.* **67**, 621–5.

Stoll, K. (1959). *Z. Kaltetechnik* **11**, 400–3.

Tomkins, R. G. (1964). *Rep. Ditton Lab. for 1963–64*, 11–14.

Tomkins, R. G. (1965a). *Rep. Ditton Lab. for 1964–65*, 16–19.

Tomkins, R. G. (1965b). *Rep. Ditton Lab. for 1964–65*, 19–20.

Ulrich, R., Marcellin, P., Leblond, C. and Paulin, A. (1961). *Bull. int. Inst. Refrig.* Anexe 1961–1, 221–9.

Uota, M. (1952). *Proc. Am. Soc. hort. Sci.* **59**, 231–7.

Author Index

Numbers in *italics* refer to pages on which the full reference is given

A

Abbott, D. L., 417, *420*
Abdel-Gawad, H. A., *514*
Abdel-Kader, A. S., 506, 507, *514*
Abdul-Alim, M. A., 331, *358*
Abe, H., 436, *468*
Abe, Y., 290, *300*
Abeles, F. B., 202, *205*, 445, *464*, 486, 488, 490, 491, 493, 495, 502, 508, *514*, *516*
Aboulezs, A. F., 331, *358*
Abraham, R. J., 122, *144*
Abrams, G. von, 324, *358*
Adams, F., 416, *422*
Addicott, F. T., 430, 431, 444, 445, *464*, *469*, 500, *514*
Addoms, R. M., 393, *421*, 455, *464*
Aharoni, Y., 498, *514*, 525, 526, *532*
Ahmad, N., 324, 327, *366*
Ailhaud, G. P., 227, *238*
Akatsuka, M., 341, *361*
Akhtar, M., 351, *358*
Akinrefon, O. A., 300, *300*
Albach, R. F., 290, *300*
Alban, E. K., 142, *144*, 403, *421*
Alberding, G. E., 251, *268*
Albersheim, P., 26, *30*, 60, 69, 72, 73, 75, 78, 79, *80*, *82*, 84, 458, *464*
Alberts, A. W., 227, *238*
Albrigo, L. G., 396, *420*
Alcaide, A., 350, *358*
Al-Delaimy, K. A., 75, *80*
Aldrich, W. W., 390, *420*
Ali Hassan, 141, *146*
Allen, F. W., 192, *204*
Allentoff, N., 112, *115*, 198, *204*
Allmann, K., 105, 114, *116*
Al-Rawi, N., 140, *144*
Alvarez, B. M., 138, *144*
Amerine, M. A., 7, 12, *28*, 98, *115*, 125, *144*, 239, 254, *264*

Amezquita, R., 505, 506, 507, *517*
Amin, E. S., 336, *358*
Anderson, E. E., 240, 247, *265*
Anderson, J. D., 410, *420*
Anderson, J. T., 69, *83*
Anderson, J. W., 159, 160, *177*, 196, *204*, 479, *514*
Anderson, L., 10, *27*
Anderson, L., 377, *383*
Anderssen, F. G., 412, *420*
Andersson, J., 240, 247, 248, *264*, *267*
Andrews, P., 42, *51*, 410, *420*
Anet, E. F. L. J., 9, *27*
Anfinsen, C. B., 192, *204*
Angyal, S. J., 10, *27*
Anhder, L. D., 429, *469*
Anjou, K., 240, 248, 263, *264*, *267*
Ansell, G. B., 220, *237*
Ansell, M. F., 11, *29*
Antoszewski, R., 410, 417, *420*, *423*, 456, 457, 458, *464*, *467*
Anyas-Weiss, L., 79, *80*
Ap Rees, T., 505, *514*
Archer, T. E., 125, *144*
Argoud, S., 308, 326, *358*
Arigoni, D., 339, 350, 351, 352, *358*
Arima, K., 76, *87*
Arnon, D. I., 416, 418, *420*
Arnott, S. A., 339, *358*
Arthington, W., 35, *51*, 122, *145*
Asahira, T., 456, 458, 461, *465*, *469*
Asen, S., 277, 293, *300*, *302*
Ash, A. S. F., 6, 8, 9, 10, *27*
Ashley, T. E., 393, 398, 399, *423*
Askew, H. O., 391, 392, 404, 415, *421*
Aspinall, G. O., 33, 34, 41, 44, *51*, 57, 58, 72, *80*
Atal, C. K., 332, *358*
Atkins, C. D., 65, 66, 68, 70, 71, 75, *85*, 86, 251, *268*

C

G

H

K

Krauss, E. von, 308, *363*
Krauss, H., 60, *83*
Kreger, D. R., 215, *237*
Krehl, W. A., 10, *29*
Kreutzer, E., 323, *361*
Kribben, F. J., 428, *467*
Kriedemann, P. E., 399, 409, 416, 417, 419, *423*
Krinsky, N., 320, *363*
Krotkov, G., 12, *30*, 99, 103, *117*, 418, *422*
Ku, H. S., 187, *205*, *207*, 478, 490, 491, 493, *517*
Ku, Lily (Lim), 155, *157*
Kubota, T., 340, *363*

Kuendig, W., 72, *84*
Kugler, E., 250, *266*
Kuhn, R., 307, 308, 309, 310, 311, *363*
Kuksis, A., 214, *237*
Kulajewa, O., 418, *423*, 459, *468*
Kumamoto, J., 493, *516*
Kundu, A. B., 342, *360*
Kunishi, A., 489, 491, 492, 493, *517*
Kunishi, A. T., 193, *205*, 487, *517*
Kupchan, S. M., 344, *363*
Kurtz, E., Jr., 428, 460, *469*
Kusaki, T., 441, 443, 445, *467*
Kuusi, T., 246, *266*
Kuzmeski, J. W., 325, *362*
Kylin, H., 306, *363*

L

Labarca, C. C., 436, 440, *467*
Lachman, W. H., 325, *362*
Lafon, M., 256, *265*
Lafon-Lafourcade, S., 126, *145*
Laforge, F. B., 7, *29*
Laibach, F., 428, 432, *467*
Lal, G., 270, *303*
Lamberts, E., 77, *83*
La Motte, C. E., 452, *467*
Lance, C., 110, *117*, 529, 530, *532*, *533*
Land, D. G., 248, *267*
Lang, A., 459, *470*
Lang, R., 76, *84*
Langdon, R. G., 348, *363*
Lange, A. H., 428, 429, *467*
Lange, D., 64, *81*, *83*
Lankveld, J. M. G., 69, *83*
Lanz, E. M., 326, *363*
Lanza, M., 34, *51*
Lanzani, A., 332, *361*
Laporta, L., 229, *238*
Larrabee, A. R., 227, *238*
Larson, C. P., Jr., 509, *515*
Laskowski, M., 191, *206*
Lassen, S., 322, 326, *363*
Laties, G. G., 505, *516*
Launer, H. F., 72, *83*
Lavie, D., 341, 344, 345, 352, *361*, *363*, *364*
Law, J. H., 350, *362*
Lawrie, W., 332, *364*
Leblond, C., 556, 560, 562, 564, *568*, *569*
Lederberger, A., 68, *82*

Lederer, E., 310, 311, 350, *358*, *362*, *363*, *364*, *366*, *367*
Lee, A., 248, 249, 263, *267*
Lee, F. A., 90, 91, 97, *117*, 393, 394, 398, 399, *423*, *425*
Lee, K. H., 357, *364*
Lee, M. J., 75, *83*
Lee, T. C., 353, *364*
Lee, T. H., 494, 505, 506, 507, *516*
Leefe, J. S., 544, *553*
Lees, M., 210, *237*
Lehn, J. M., 344, *359*
Leland, H. V., 135, 136, 137, 138, *144*
Leloir, L. F., 23, 26, *28*, *29*, 47, 48, *51*, 59, *83*
Lenfant, M., 351, *364*
Leonard, E. R., 523, *533*
Leonard, S. J., *84*, 142, *146*
Leopold, A. C., 405, 418, *424*, 500, 501, *515*, *518*, 530, *532*
Le Rosen, A. L., 307, 309, 319, 325, *364*, *367*, *368*
Lesaint, C., 94, *115*
Lesley, J. W., 320, *368*
Letan, A., 291, 292, *302*
Letham, D. S., 407, *423*, 443, 444, 456, 457, *467*
Leuprecht, H., 75, 78, *83*
Levine, A. S., 76, 77, *82*, 184, *205*
Lew, F., 441, 442, *471*
Lew, J. Y., 195, *205*, *206*
Lewis, D., 460, *467*
Lewis, D. H., 9, 12, 16, 21, *29*

M

N

Pandey, I. C., 450, *471*
Pangborn, R. M., 239, 254, *264*
Panizo, F. M., 346, *362*
Panizzi, L., 12, *30*
Paquot, C., 225, *238*, 332, *365*
Parija, P., 509, *515*, 527, *532*
Parikh, V. N., 35, *52*
Parker, E. R., 461, *470*
Parr, C. W., 20, *30*
Parvez, M. A., 351, *358*
Pasich, B., 335, *359*
Pate, J. S., 412, *424*
Patel, D. S., 77, 79, *85*
Patel, J., 286, *304*
Pathak, G., 346, *365*
Patschke, L., 289, *303*
Patterson, M. E., 75, 77, *84*, 113, *118*, 156, *157*, 183, 188, 192, *205, 206*
Patton, S., 259, *267*
Paul, V., 330, *365*
Paulin, A., 562, 564, *569*
Pauling, I., 309, *368*
Pauling, L., 512, *518*
Pearson, H. M., 463, *469*
Pearson, Judith A., 156, *157*
Pearson, J. A., 108, *117*, 391, 393, *424*, 529, *533*
Peel, J. L., 260, *266*
Pemmier-Miard, J., 331, *364*
Peng, C. Y., 296, *303*
Perceval, E. G. V., 40, *51*
Percheron, F., 57, *82*
Pereira, R. L., 259, *268*
Peri, C., 270, *300*
Perkins, D. Y., 455, *469*
Perner, J., 283, 294, *304*
Perrin, D. R., 299, *301*
Perring, M. A., 550, 551, *554*
Persyn, A., 481, 482, *519*
Peterson, C. E., 429, *469*, 509, *515*
Peynaud, E., 9, *28*, 100, 106, *117*, 121, 125, 126, *145, 146*
Pfeffer, W., 430, *469*
Phaff, H. J., 73, 77, 78, 79, *81*, 84, *85*
Phan, C. T., 481, *518*
Phillips, W. R., 112, *115*, 198, *204*
Phinney, B. O., 441, *471*
Pickett-Heaps, 61, 70, *85*
Pieniazek, J., 445, *470*, 500, *518*
Pieniazek, N., 445, *470*, 500, *518*

BFP—X

Pieringer, A. P., 262, *264*
Pilnik, W., 61, 62, 63, 68, 77, 78, *83, 85*
Pinckard, J. C., 310, *368*
Pinochet, M. F., 246, 247, *266*
Pintauro, N. D., 72, *85*
Pippen, E. L., 72, *85*
Pithawala, H. R., 182, *206*
Pitts, L., 378, *384*
Pogosyan, E. A., 142, *145*
Poland, G. L., 8, *30*, 99, *116*
Polgar, A., 307, *368*
Pollard, A., 75, 76, *83, 85*, 183, *206*, 295, *303*
Pollard, J. K., 96, *116*, 138, 139, 140, *144, 145*
Pommier-Miard, J., 213, 234, *238*
Ponomarcora, N. P., 78, *85*
Ponsinet, G., 348, *365*
Ponting, J. D., 196, *206*
Pontis, H. G., 23, *28*
Pool, R. M., 450, *471*
Popjak, G., 348, *365*
Popovskii, V. G., 244, 245, *266*
Popper, C. S., 529, *533*
Porretta, A., 133, *146*
Porritt, S. W., 476, *518*
Porter, G. G., 22, *28*, 409, *421*
Porter, J. W., 319, 322, 353, 354, *362, 365*
Pose, J., 69, *81*
Possingham, J. V., 142, *146*, 412, *422*
Potgeiter, D. J. J., 353, *366*
Potter, E. F., 7, *31*
Potter, N. A., 10, 15, *29*, 521, *532*
Potter, R. S., 56, *85*
Poux, C., 127, *145*
Powder, F. B., 248, *266*, 344, *365*
Powell, D. B., 42, *51*
Powell, G. H., 555, *569*
Powell, L. E., Jr., 435, 436, 444, 463, *468, 469*
Pradham, S. K., 339, *359*
Pradhan, S. K., 339, 340, 351, 352, *358*
Prakash, R., 444, *468*
Pratt, C., 390, 395, 396, 397, 399, *424*, 436, 437, 444, 461, 462, 463, *469*
Pratt, H. K., 65, *81*, 148, 150, 156, *157*, 193, *205, 206, 207*, 226, *237*, 257, *266*, 324, *358*, 390, 396, *423*, 434, 435, 445, 459, *469*, 475, 476, 477, 478, 488, 490,

S

Swanson, C. A., 410, *425*, 451, *467*
Swardt, G. H. de, 283, *303*
Swenson, H. A., 56, 61, 72, *84*, *85*
Swift, L. J., 11, *30*, 331, *336*
Swindells, R., 129, *144*

Swisher, H. E., 2, 3, 4, 10, *30*
Sydow, E. von, 240, 247, 248, 263, *264*
Szabolcs, 309
Szinai, S., 344, *363*

T

Tabachnik, J., 260, *267*
Tager, J. M., 19, *30*, 113, *118*
Takahashi, N., 441, *470*, *471*, *472*
Takanashi, S., 428, *468*
Takeda, Y., 463, *465*
Takei, S., 240, 248, *267*
Takeo, T., 491, 493, 494, *518*
Talowsky, E., *383*
Tamayo, A. I., 230, *237*
Tamelen, E. E. van, 348, *367*
Tamura, S., 441, *470*, *471*, *472*
Tan, E. L., 331, *363*
Tang, C. S., 246, 259, *267*
Tanner, H., 93, *117*
Tanner, W., 27, *30*
Taper, C. D., 402, 410, 411, *425*
Tappel, H. L., 181, *206*
Tapper, B. A., 25, *28*
Tassel, M., 225, *238*, 332, *365*
Taufel, K., 64, *83*, 331, *359*
Tavakoli, M., 65, 72, 80, *86*, *87*
Taylor, B. K., 408, *425*
Taylor, R. J., 259, *264*
Taylor, W. C., 341, *359*
Teaotia, S. S., 450, *471*
Teijema, H. L., 353, *366*
Templeton,J.F.,339,340,351,352,*358*,*359*
Teranishi, R., 240, 243, 244, 245, 253, 258, *265*, *266*, *267*
Teranishi, T., 504, 505, 513, *516*
Tercelj, D., 121, 126, *146*
Terroine, E. F., 230, *238*
Teubner, F. G., 430, 432, 435, 436, 438, 453, *466*, *469*, *471*
Tewari, J. D., 332, *359*, *365*
Thakor, V. M., 331, *367*
Thaler, O., 123, 132, *146*
Thatcher, R. W., 179, *206*
Thibaudin, A., 223, 233, 234, *237*
Thimann, K. V., 90, 92, 97, *118*, 187, *204*, 432, 438, 459, *466*, *470*, *471*, 476, 478, 480, 481, 482, 483, 504, *515*
Thimaru, K. U., 286, *304*

Thomas, M., 523, *533*, 544, *554*
Thompson, A. E., 321, *367*
Thompson, J. E., 477, 488, 492, *518*
Thompson, P. A., 449, *471*
Thompson, W. W., 323, *367*
Thomson, C. L., 372, *383*
Thrower, S. L., 409, *425*
Tibenski, V., 71, *86*
Tikalsskia, V. V., 372, *383*
Tiller, L. W., 545, *554*
Tilney-Bassett, R. A. D., 320, *363*
Timberlake, C. F., 291, 292, *304*
Timmell, T. E., 58, *81*
Timofeeva, O. A., 244, 245, *266*
Tin, S., 307, 316, *367*
Tindall, G. C., 525, 526, *533*
Ting, S. V., 35, *52*, 136, *146*
Tinsley, I. J., 128, *146*
Tishel, M., 105, 111, *118*
Tobinaga, S., 339, 351, 352, *358*
Todd, G. W., 409, *421*, *425*
Toft, P., 352, *359*
Tokoroyama, T., 340, *363*, *367*
Tolbert, N. E., 181, 193, 194, *206*, 509, *515*
Tomes, M. L., 307, 318, 319, 320, 325, 326, 356, *358*, *362*, *365*, *367*
Tomimatsu, Y., 72, *83*
Tomkins, R. G., 102, *118*, 539, 543, 544, 546, 552, *554*, 558, 562, *569*
Torrey, J. G., 457, *471*
Toth, 2, 250, *266*
Townley, P. M., 154, *158*
Townsley, E. M., 134, *146*
Trebst, A., 295, *304*
Treharne, K. J., 353, *360*
Tremolieres, A., 223, *237*
Tressl, R., 242, 257, *264*, *265*
Tressler, D. K., 382, *383*
Trip, P., 12, *30*
Troescher, C. B., 148, *157*
Trogolo, C., 12, *30*
Tromp, J., 411, *425*

Z

Subject Index

ς